HF Antennas
for All Locations

SECOND EDITION

Les Moxon, BSc, CEng, MIEE, G6XN

Radio Society Of Great Britain

Published by the Radio Society of Great Britain
Cranborne Road, Potters Bar Herts EN6 3JE

First published 1982.
Second edition 1993, reprinted 1995, 2002.

Publisher's note

While the information presented is believed to be correct, the author, the publisher and their agents cannot accept responsibility for consequences arising from any inaccuracies or omissions

Cover: Annie McVicar
Illustrations: Derek Cole, Radio Society of Great Britain,
and Paul Edwards.
Production and typography: Ray Eckersley, Seven Stars Publishing.

Digitally Printed in Great Britain by Page Bros (Norwich) Ltd.

Contents

Preface to the second edition

The last 10 years have seen not only the advent of the new 10, 18 and 24MHz bands, bringing with it new problems and opportunities, but also ever-worsening interference levels as well as increasing demands for smaller, less visible, antennas typified by an upsurge of interest in small transmitting loops. Meanwhile the ever-increasing complexity of the HF antenna scene has made the need for a sound grasp of the relatively simple essentials even more important: these include recognition of ground-plane antennas as essentially dipoles, leading to a better understanding of ground losses and much smaller ground-plane systems.

Inevitably these circumstances provided an irresistible challenge for the author, with the range of available options extending in the case of beams to include more bands with fewer problems, no trap losses and better rejection of interference. This process has been assisted by a better understanding of the possibilities and limitations of resonant feeder systems and the emergence of new designs of small loop elements.

Apart from placing on record these and other developments in which the author has been personally involved, it has been a main aim in this second edition to leave fewer questions unanswered so that the experimenter is fully equipped for evaluating new ideas and dealing with whatever problems may come his way; nevertheless, to keep the subject matter within reasonable bounds the primary concern has been for the 'average' amateur whose need is to make the best use of limited resources. Hopefully those more fortunate will find much of interest, together with references to more specialised material such as large Yagi arrays and particularly their mechanical design to ensure survival under severe conditions.

A new chapter presents a comprehensive review of ways to make antennas smaller with particular emphasis on small transmitting loops, an important new growth area in which fact and fiction are already becoming somewhat entangled. Other areas in which progress can be recorded include 'invisible' antennas, vertical beams, and better ways of end-feeding dipoles.

The new edition owes much to suggestions, constructive criticism and encouragement from other sources. Apart from appropriate credits in the text, particular thanks are due to Dr O G Villard Jnr, W6QYT, Dr Yardley Beers, W0JF, and R van Straten, PA0UHF; also, for valued suggestions and careful checking of the new text, to Peter Swallow, G8EZE.

Les Moxon

Acknowledgements for the first edition

The author is indebted to numerous other amateurs for advising him of their queries, difficulties and experiences which have helped considerably in the choice and presentation of subject matter. He is grateful also to Pat Hawker, G3VA, John Piggot, G2PT, and others for some helpful criticisms leading to some revision of earlier chapters. Thanks also go to Robert Meadows for the cartoons.

Much use has been made of material from other sources as indicated by appropriate references.

Chapter 1

Taking a new look at HF antennas

Amateurs have been using HF antennas for 70 years or more so that some slowing down in the rate of progress might be expected. As evidence of this, some of the best antennas in use today were designed 30 or 40 years ago yet, impelled by strong incentives, the search for 'better' ones continues unabated. At times of slow progress it is not a bad idea to look at problems from new angles, and a possible first step is to erase from one's mind the picture of 'things as they are' and concentrate, for a few moments at least, on the way one would *like* them to be. Listing the reasons why they are not and challenging each in turn can be good fun; moreover, before accepting once again the status quo, one feels entitled to convincing evidence that there are no alternatives.

In the following pages the reader will find few such proofs but instead several challenges to existing beliefs and practices, 'proof of impossibility' being reserved mainly for the antenna gain figures frequently claimed by authors and advertisers.

The need for a new approach

Most amateurs are subject to more or less severe restrictions in the erection of HF antennas. Those able to erect beams at a height of 50ft (15m) can count themselves lucky, and any sense of frustration they may feel at not being able to double this will not be relieved by evidence reviewed in the next chapter pointing to the desirability of heights of 1000ft (300m) or so! The constraints by which amateurs are afflicted can be reckoned as ranging all the way from 'severe' to 'impossible', with each installation tending to be a special case. One has therefore the problem of selecting the antenna systems which provide the best 'match' to any given set of circumstances and, apart from possible improvements to antennas as such, the author believes there is an urgent need for better guidelines. This conviction arises from a study of the available literature, from his own personal experiences, and from numerous enquiries which in most cases cannot be dealt with adequately short of writing a book!

What then are the improvements needed, and how are they to be achieved? Perhaps the most urgent need and, as will be shown, one of the easiest to meet, is a substantial reduction in the size, weight and cost of beam antennas without compromising performance. There is also an urgent and increasing need for reduction in interfering signal levels, and the designer of a beam antenna is often faced with the dilemma of whether to maximise gain or minimise interference. There is, however, no mandate insisting that antenna characteristics have to remain unchanged when one switches from transmission to reception, so in principle this *should* be a non-issue; in practice, however, there is still a long way to go. In the case of a rotary beam the time required to change beam direction is a serious nuisance yet, with two or three elements, instantaneous beam reversal can be readily provided and combined with other advantages.

The contents of this book reflect the author's view that more often than not these objectives can best be achieved by the use of two elements which can be of any type provided that the currents are equal. The argument that one can do a lot better with loops or, in the case of dipoles, three elements, is disposed of by challenging the usual implicit assumption that dipoles have to be 'straight', thereby providing a good example of the critical approach suggested above.

On the basis of what used to be the only type of dipole array in normal use, the superiority of three elements can be demonstrated mathematically, but this conclusion has been invalidated by new forms of construction such as the VK2ABQ antenna. Pursuing the matter further, it turns out that by introducing different but equally realistic sets of practical constraints a case can be established either way.

What is possible?

Apart from the items already noted, perhaps the most insistent demands, given the possibility, would be for more gain or directivity. Although basically there is very little scope in this direction, much can be done to avoid wastage; for example, by avoiding unsound designs and in the case of multiband operation eliminating traps, the whole of each of the lower-frequency elements (or an equivalent length of element) being used at the higher frequencies. Better performance may also be achievable in those cases where a reduction of size and weight as mentioned above allows a substantial increase in height.

Possibilities appear to exist also for improvements in indoor antennas and other methods of achieving operation under difficult circumstances. Many amateurs are severely handicapped by height restrictions and, in this context, the author's investigations have pointed towards a much more important role for vertical beams, which at the time of writing appear to be almost non-existent for the higher frequencies. In this way it has been found possible to achieve reasonably competitive DX performance even when height is severely restricted, and to this end improved designs with simpler and more efficient methods of feed not requiring extensive ground systems have been worked out.

Reasons for the present situation

The fact that much scope still exists for improvements in amateur HF antennas can be attributed to widespread ignorance of a number of basic principles, leading to proliferation of unsound or inefficient designs. Textbooks have been geared mainly to the needs of students and professional engineers, and amateur handbooks have tended to be concerned more with the 'how' than the 'why', so that experimenters have for the most part lacked the insight which would enable them to challenge an observation by posing the all-important question: does it make sense? This is vital in any experimental work and especially in the case of HF antennas in view of the difficulty of making *reliable* gain measurements, as discussed in Chapter 18.

Towards a better understanding

In view of serious errors by some of the experts and the apparent complexity of the HF antenna scene, it is felt that the amateur can hardly be blamed for a situation which is somewhat less than satisfactory, or perhaps for thinking there is not much he can do about it. Nevertheless, most of the main essentials can be grasped intuitively. Thus most of what one needs to know about radiation from the simpler types of antenna can be deduced merely by observing the way in which the apparent length varies as one moves around, towards, or away from them as explained in Chapter 2. This point is elaborated in Chapter 3 to show that all such antennas behave in the same way regardless of shape or, up to a certain limit, size, so that a bewildering assortment of apparently different antennas can be seen as a single, quite simple device in various disguises. This constitutes a basic 'building brick', and beam antennas consist of two or more such sources of signal assembled in such a way that the radiated energy tends to be focussed in a particular direction rather than spread relatively thinly throughout the surrounding space.

Current misunderstandings are attributable largely to the failure to realise that there are two *completely different* methods for achieving this result, signals being arranged in the one case to *add* in the *wanted* direction and, in the other, to *subtract* in *unwanted* directions. In the additive case, elements have to be widely spaced otherwise the addition tends to be equally effective (or ineffective) in all directions, but with this proviso the gain obtainable is equal to *n*, the number of elements. For large gain one therefore needs a lot of elements and a lot of space so the first step is to invest in a lot of real estate – which puts it beyond the reach of the average amateur who must either settle for a small gain or hope for better luck using the subtractive method. In this case, close spacing of elements is not merely possible but essential, since wide spacing produces large phase differences and consequent addition in some direction or other.

Most amateur beams are in fact of this latter type, and so operate on the subtractive (or 'supergain') principle; unfortunately this appears to be little understood, thus accounting for numerous mistakes as well as failure to realise the full potential of close-spaced arrays.

Subtractive-gain arrays

Most of the difficulty stems from the fact that when elements are closely spaced they couple tightly together; it is the nature of this coupling and the way in which it is exploited that determines the behaviour of the antenna. Let us for the moment assume that in some way or other this has been optimised with a view to achieving as much gain as possible.

The first point to note is that, compared with additive arrays, the theoretical gain for a given number of elements is much greater, being equal to n^2 and independent of size provided only that this is *small* enough! Unfortunately, for reasons explained in Chapter 3, it is not possible to get very far along this particular road but, by way of a practical (or at least 'not impossible' example), consider the case of four elements. If these are arranged in an additive formation they would provide a gain of four times or 6dB, requiring for this purpose at 14MHz a space of about 80ft by 35ft (24m by 11m) or, in the case of a rotary beam, a turning-circle diameter of about 90ft (27m). The gain is roughly equivalent to that provided by the average linear amplifier; in contrast to this the n^2 formula predicts a gain of 16 times, equivalent to two linear amplifiers, *each* giving 6dB gain.

Unfortunately, as the reader may suspect, matters are not quite as simple in practice, as will be evident from the 'small print' in Chapter 5, but one design (p102) aimed at this objective succeeding in achieving a gain of 8.7dB with a turning circle diameter (when scaled for 14MHz) of 55ft (17m) only. The snag is that large 'subtractive' gains involve very large currents and a point is quickly reached where any increase in theoretical gain is offset in practice by increased loss in the form of heating of the antenna. There is also a small theoretical deduction to be made from the n^2 formula, ie 0.8dB for two elements, rising to 2.0dB for five and over. These effects lead to an upper gain limit in most practical cases of about 7–8dB for subtractive (or 'supergain') arrays, with the distinction between the two mechanisms tending to become somewhat blurred as the number of elements increases.

These complications need not worry the reader unduly since reasonably accurate guidelines based on data from a number of sources have been provided in Chapter 5. Furthermore, application of the n^2 formula, even without corrections, is often sufficient for assessing the credibility of claimed gain figures, which are quite often well in excess of n^2. Due to ignorance of the subtractive principle and its implications, such gains may be attributed to some unusual feature of the element shape or arrangement and there is an evident need to set the record straight, this being one of the tasks of Chapter 3.

For a given form of construction there is a practical lower size limit determined by losses as discussed in Chapter 3, and there is in all cases an upper spacing limit in the region of 0.2λ, above which 'supergain' decreases significantly as explained in Chapter 5, though wider spacings tend to provide a better compromise as the number of elements is increased.

Mutual coupling and its significance

At this point let us return to the question of the mutual coupling between elements, which differs from that between tuned circuits only to the extent that one has to consider mutual resistance as well as mutual reactance. This means that if two closely-spaced elements are connected to a transmitter, but the opposite way round, each *subtracts* resistance from the other, thus making possible the large currents which are needed to offset all the subtraction which is going on! It is important to note that *but for the mutual resistance there could be no gain*. The snag is that in the case of large gains or very small sizes of antenna the signal is the difference between two or more much larger quantities, and the practical consequences add up to severe losses, infinitesimal bandwidth and almost non-existent tolerances.

On the other hand, the role of mutual reactance is quite different and of particular importance in the case of two-element beams. In this case, one requires equal currents suitably phased so that cancellation can take place in unwanted directions but, when (as in the most usual case) one element is connected to the transmitter and the other energised from it via the mutual coupling, *current equality is impossible without mutual reactance.*

Attempts to resolve the problems of mutual coupling by calculation have tended to end up as algebraic equations of unmanageable proportions and most experimenters, observing that almost any assortment of closely-spaced elements can be made to work, have been disposed not to bother unduly with explanations. Unfortunately, although knowing 'how' has resulted in lots of antennas capable of producing big signals, lack of the *why* has led to absurdities such as the quad versus Yagi controversy which has been a prominent feature of the amateur HF antenna scene for more than two decades.

There has also been a consequent waste of much time, money and effort in the pursuit of better results by methods which either have no chance of success or lead to undesirable compromises of one sort or another; in addition it has ensured that virtually all such antenna designs have been in some degree (or in some respect) sub-optimum. For this reason particular importance attaches to Chapter 5 which shows that for two elements the problem can be reduced to simple dimensions merely by taking success for granted, ie one assumes the elements to have equal-amplitude currents which are correctly phased. In this case the answers emerge from a few lines of algebra, affording considerable insight into the basic processes and with the conditions for success spelt out in detail.

It may be objected at this point that existing beams do not have equal currents, that the obvious way to obtain equal currents is to drive both elements, but that such designs have enjoyed only brief periods of popularity. Reasons for this will be clear from the analysis in Chapter 5 which also indicates that, *except* in the case of some common types of driven array, current equality is not difficult to achieve. The currents are unequal because the coupling is insufficient but this only means that we need to *increase* it! In practice, in the case of a two-element Yagi with straight elements one need only bend them so that the ends are closer together. Alternatively one could merely reduce the spacing, but this does have some practical disadvantages (p93). A further alternative is to use loop elements which couple more tightly than dipole elements, and this is believed to be the main reason for the reputation of the quad. On the other hand, constructions such as the modified VK2ABQ and small delta-loop antennas described in Chapter 12 allow a free hand for adjustment of coupling besides providing smaller, lighter systems of equivalent performance. Adjustable coupling is an inherent feature of each of the smaller beams described in Chapter 12, with the exception of the small quad to which it can be added if necessary.

It is common practice to disregard the reactive component of mutual coupling, the resistance component being more important insofar as it determines the gain. However, Chapter 5 shows that the reactive component is also very important since without it in one form or another there can be no equalisation of currents; gain is reduced and directivity seriously affected. On the other hand, the provision of additional coupling reactance means that little or no detuning is required in the case of parasitic elements and the construction of efficient reversible beams is made much easier; radiation resistance is also increased, with advantages in respect of bandwidth.

In these and a number of other respects Chapter 5 breaks new ground. Extension of the analysis to three or four elements is much more difficult, but references appended to Chapter 5 between them cover the ground fairly fully, and attention is also drawn to a particularly important paper by Bloch, Medhurst and Pool describing in detail the four-element 'superdirective' array mentioned earlier in this chapter. The vector diagram for this, as plotted by the author from the theoretical design data given in the reference and compared with that for a typical two-element amateur beam (p102), demonstrates convincingly that amateur beams are members of the 'supergain' family. This fact, though pointed out on several occasions by the author and not challenged, has failed to attract general notice and might well be dismissed as 'academic' but for the importance of the n^2 rule and, for example, the prevalence of mistakes such as attributing additive-gain principles to close-spaced beams. Further to this, inspection of the diagrams may well suggest to the reader an intuitive approach to the task of obtaining maximum gain from more than two elements and the improbability of comparable gains being achieved along conventional lines.

Ideas to be avoided

The need for the 'why' extends not only to the best ways of doing things but also those which are best avoided. Hence Chapter 5 includes a detailed discussion of X-beams and Chapter 4 draws attention to the highly non-linear variation of phase along mismatched lines. This effectively rules out the use of non-resonant phasing lines for close-spaced driven arrays, although many such arrays have been described in the literature and can be expected to work after a fashion.

These examples highlight one of the main difficulties in seeking to simplify the HF antenna scene. Virtually all existing designs are open to criticism in one or more respects, not excluding some of the author's own earlier efforts such as phased arrays based on *resonant* lines. These are predictable and afford a foolproof method of achieving optimum performance *at a given frequency* but deteriorate when the frequency is changed, tending to become comparable with conventional parasitic arrays at the band edges unless readjusted. *Any departure from optimum usually results in simplifying assumptions having to be abandoned so that theoretical analysis becomes more difficult and in some cases virtually impossible.*

Often one can predict, for example, the impossibility of an antenna working in some intended manner but this does not necessarily preclude operation in some other mode. Thus in the case of the driven arrays mentioned above, the absence of power in the line going to the reflector should leave this free to operate as a parasitic element with the mutual reactance providing the necessary phase shift. However, it is equally likely that poor results will be obtained, in which case the user (unless equipped with better-than-average test facilities) may well be unaware of what he is losing. This pinpoints the desirability of avoiding the use of unpredictable systems and methods on the grounds that they are usually non-optimum.

The 'why' of correct design is the main concern of Part I and the 'how' that of Part II, though the author has tried throughout to maintain close links between theory and practice: in the case of feeding power to the antenna (Chapter 4) separation was felt to be neither feasible nor desirable.

Feeding the antenna

Chapter 4 aims at presenting the simplest possible explanation of transmission lines and draws attention to the value, for the solution of tuning and matching problems, of regarding the antenna itself as a 'transmission line'. Particular importance has been attached to ensuring that the feeder acts *only* as a feeder and not in competition with the radiating system; thus an inherent loss of up to 3dB has been deduced for the Windom antenna, considerable suspicion cast on most ground-plane systems, and stress placed on the need for symmetry, including where appropriate the use of baluns. The discussion of baluns concentrates on the essential simplicity and efficiency of these devices, particularly the ferrite-rod type with bifilar or trifilar windings. However, it would appear that here, as in so many other aspects of antenna design, failure to appreciate the main essentials has led to the production of a number of inefficient devices, thus tending to bring baluns as a whole into some degree of disrepute.

In view of the important role which the author foresees for vertical beams, particular attention has been given to problems of feeding, with the object of avoiding ground losses or losses by radiation from the feeder or radial systems. These are suspected reasons for the relatively poor performance of vertical antennas in general.

It is concluded that high efficiency can be achieved with *very short* radials or counterpoises, or by the use of dipole elements, and that it is best to avoid the use of $\lambda/4$ radials. Use of the Zepp feed without the G6CJ balancing stub is shown to be ill-advised for reasons which some might regard as obvious, the only puzzle being the persistence with which it has been featured in reference books, professional as well as amateur, although many years have elapsed since G6CJ drew attention to its defects and his case has been fully supported by the experiences of the author and a number of correspondents.

Multiband antennas

Methods for achieving multiband operation are the subject of Chapter 7. In this area also, inefficient methods which sacrifice bandwidth and potential gain, particularly at the higher frequencies, have hitherto been the order of the day. These seem unlikely to survive the impact of the newer frequency allocations, and methods based on remote tuning devices located in the antenna, though proposed by a number of writers (including the present author), have hitherto not been easy to implement. A viable alternative is to use resonant feeders as described in Chapters 4 and 7. The rival attractions of log-periodic antennas are offset by increased weight and windage, this type of antenna being discussed in Chapter 7 and explained in greater detail with practical examples in Chapter 14.

Other aspects of performance

Chapter 8 discusses the important topic of bandwidth, drawing attention to the several different meanings which this can have. Chapter 9 discusses the difference between transmitting and receiving requirements and suggests the separate optimisation of antennas in these respects as an important line for future development.

Effects of the environment

Differences in performance between amateur stations can be attributed very largely to differences in the environment and Chapter 10 attempts to put together as many as possible of the known facts. In addition it draws attention to the unknowns and indulges in considerable speculation. Particular attention is given to differences between horizontal and vertical polarisation, including the variation of signal strength with height and angle of radiation for various types of ground as calculated from handbook data. In conjunction with experimental evidence this suggests the desirability in many cases of experiments with both polarisations before making final decisions as to a permanent antenna system, an important factor being the ability of vertical antennas in many cases to work equally well or nearly as well at very low heights. Indoor and other unfavourable environments, together with the effects of obstructions, are also discussed.

Chordal-hop modes of propagation

Consideration of the environment is linked to the requirements of the ionosphere, since the environment in conjunction with antenna height and polarisation determines the angles of radiation which can be successfully achieved. Whereas high angles present few problems and are optimum for the shorter ranges, much confusion exists in regard to very long ranges. It is almost universally supposed that these involve multiple reflections between the ionosphere and the earth's surface, and that there are optimum angles of radiation which are greater at lower frequencies.

These beliefs have persisted and continued to form the basis of ionospheric propagation predictions, despite convincing evidence from a number of sources to the effect that (a) 'multihop' modes are abnormal, at least under those conditions of relatively low path loss which permit of amateur or other low-power communication, and (b) for optimum DX performance it is best to aim always for the lowest possible angles of radiation at all frequencies. This evidence, largely from professional sources, is reviewed in Chapter 2.

It is ironic that whereas chordal hop (tilt-mode) theories of propagation, which were first put forward by Albrecht in the early 'fifties, owed their origin to the experience of amateurs, the amateur literature has persistently followed the 'official line' whereby commercial services have for more than a quarter of a century denied themselves the advantages which accrue from exploitation of prevailing layer tilts. According to an investigation by the German broadcasting authority, official predictions have been found liable to errors of up to 25dB, this being accounted for by ionospheric focussing and the elimination of losses at ground reflections. The amateur has meanwhile been exploiting these modes very successfully, being denied only the true explanation of his consistent S9+ signal reports over distances in excess of 12,000 miles (19,000km).

Practical antenna design

The first chapter of Part II presents a comprehensive summary of types of single-element antenna, their respective merits or demerits and a detailed discussion of practical aspects. Chapter 12 recommends appropriate types of horizontal beam antenna (including miniature beams) for a wide variety of circumstances and suggests some methods of construction aimed at reducing visual impact and increasing effective height.

Chapter 13 consists of a detailed discussion of vertical beams with numerous examples. It has been necessary to evolve completely new designs based on bent or end-loaded dipole elements, or monopoles working against very short, inductively loaded radials or counterpoises. These can alternatively be regarded as an asymmetrical form of dipole which, though fed 'off-centre', appears none the worse for this. In regard to optimum groupings of vertical elements, considerable reliance has been placed on a computer study reported in *The ARRL Antenna Anthology*. However, like most of the literature, this assumes the use of direct low-resistance earth connections which are difficult to achieve, and undesirable insofar as they tie the antenna down to ground level.

Chapter 14 contains brief descriptions of various large arrays and also includes an explanation of the principles of log-periodic arrays, together with some performance details. For the average reader this is probably border country with which he is not directly concerned, but it is necessary for completion of the overall picture and hopefully of some general interest. It includes some space-saving ideas culled from various sources.

Chapter 15 comes down to earth again with the topic of 'invisible antennas'. This includes ideas from a number of sources as well as speculations by the author which, even if not directly applicable, may encourage those with a 'difficult problem' to treat it as a challenge rather than an obstacle.

Chapter 16 analyses the technical problems of mobile operation and provides suitable guidelines as well as some rather more speculative suggestions for the experimenter. It also puts at the disposal of the reader the author's fairly considerable experience of portable operation using carefully selected locations to achieve a low angle of radiation for DX communication with very low power and simple antennas.

Chapter 17 seeks to clarify the 'problem of making antennas as small as possible', correcting some misconceptions and comparing loops with dipoles. It includes design charts for small loops and suggestions for fitting dipoles into small spaces of various shapes and sizes.

Chapter 18 is concerned with providing simple and inexpensive ways of ensuring that the antenna is working correctly, and Chapter 19 tackles the problems of antenna construction and erection with a bias in the direction of making the most of limited resources.

Chapter 20 endeavours to provide practical guidelines for the choice of an optimum antenna or system of antennas to meet any given set of user requirements. It does this largely in terms of a random, but hopefully representative, set of scenarios and includes information in regard to UK planning requirements, a topic featured also in Chapters 15 and 19.

Opportunities for the experimenter

Part of the author's objective throughout the book has been, by the provision of suggestions and guidelines, to encourage

_..ater to tackle problems which have not yet been _.olved or may even involve some considerable degree projection into the future.

The design data for three-element arrays given on pp94, 95 is believed to be fairly reliable but the reader looking for a precise blueprint of some well-established design, guaranteed to work at the first attempt, must necessarily be disappointed. There is some doubt whether such guarantees are ever fully justified, a conclusion borne out by reports of manufactured antennas tested at the factory which have been found to be quite badly out of adjustment after erection, due probably to environmental differences.

On the other hand, though not yet tested on a sufficiently large scale, the exploitation of critical reactive coupling between a pair of close-spaced elements (as described in Chapter 5) implies a possible breakthrough in this respect. This is because it allows both elements to be adjusted to mid-band resonance before erection, with reasonable certainty that the beam will function correctly over at any rate most of the relevant frequency bands. The use of two feeders provides the added bonus of instantaneous beam reversal and an insurance against any likely degree of maladjustment. Such beams have the further advantage of relatively small size. Ease of adjustment is a further valuable feature of the vertical arrays described in Chapter 13 since, being at ground level, the elements are readily accessible.

In seeking to clarify the various aspects of HF antenna design, the author feels that more questions have perhaps been raised than answered. Be this as it may, there remains still a wide-open field for the experimenter who, it is hoped, will be able to set out from a firmer base. Anyone who feels that the subject is beyond their competence should take note of the bent-element example mentioned earlier in which the 'obvious', or rather the '*very* obvious', so successfully eluded all the experts (including the author). He may then have fewer qualms about his own abilities.

The importance of subjecting all findings to the test of 'does it make sense?' must, however, be stressed. Failures in this respect can be discerned as one of the main causes of the prevailing confusion and it has been the author's aim to convey to the amateur reader the kind of understanding needed for the application of this criterion, even at the risk of some sacrifice of scientific precision which in amateur work is usually not needed. Assumptions are not always stated if judged to be sufficiently obvious or implied, and students should perhaps beware of the absence of 'fine print' which has been included only where necessary in the amateur context.

It is regretted that in a few places it has been found necessary to dig into some of the deeper theoretical recesses and even engage in some elementary algebra. If difficulty is experienced, the reader may be content for the moment to note the conclusions since, when rightly nourished, understanding grows with experience.

Chapter 2

Waves and fields

The reader is assumed to have already some acquaintance with electricity, including a knowledge of Ohm's law, the difference between direct and alternating currents, the meaning of inductance and capacitance, and the idea of magnetic and electric fields. He will already be aware that when an alternating current flows in a wire it generates a similarly varying magnetic field which induces voltages in other wires within its sphere of influence and suitably oriented.

From this it is only a short step to grasping the idea of communication at a distance, except that if one is aware of the very limited range of electromagnetic induction effects it becomes necessary to suppose the existence of some other mechanism whereby the field surrounding a transmitting antenna is able to influence receiving antennas at great distances.

Most amateur antenna problems can in fact be tackled with no more knowledge of the structure of radio waves than the fact that they can be generated by the current in an antenna, travel at the speed of light, and are comprised (more often than not) of at least two components which need to be added or subtracted with due regard for phase. Nevertheless, somewhat deeper insight into the process of radio-wave propagation helps in the avoidance of pitfalls and may enable opportunities to be more fully grasped.

Just as the alternating current flowing in a loop of wire, Fig 2.1(a), can induce voltages and therefore currents in other loops, so an electric field between, say, two metal rods, Fig 2.1(b), can induce voltages between other similar objects in the vicinity and, as before, a current flows if the circuit is completed. From this point of view the end portions of an antenna wire can be thought of as the plates of a capacitor, the circuit being completed via the inductance of the wire between them. This may alternatively be regarded as a magnetic loop, the circuit of which is completed by capacitance between the ends.

An antenna can therefore be energised by either type of field, and conversely when it is energised both forms of energy can be identified by walking round it with current or voltage probes as is often done in the course of adjustments. The fields detected in this way, however, are known as 'induction fields' and decrease rapidly with distance, whereas an 'electromagnetic wave' can be visualised as a special relationship between an electric and a magnetic field as a result of which energy travels in the form of waves to great distances at the speed of light, as depicted in Fig 2.2.

The wave consists of an electric field (E) and a magnetic field (H) at right-angles to each other and to the direction of

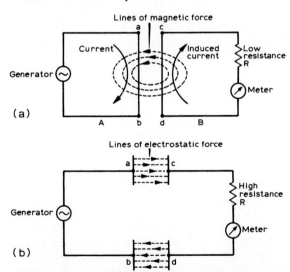

(a)

(b)

Fig 2.1. Induced currents. At (a) part of the magnetic field surrounding the conductor a-b also encircles c-d so that a current is induced as shown, and power is transferred from the generator to the resistance R. At (b), the voltage between a and b sets up an electric field which causes a voltage to appear between c and d via the capacitive coupling between the rods, and power is transferred as before. If the generator is powerful and the measuring device sufficiently sensitive the circuits may be moved a long way apart

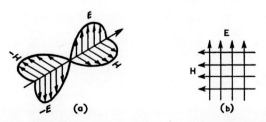

Fig 2.2. Instantaneous representation of an electromagnetic wave (a) along the path of travel and (b) as seen by an observer looking towards its source

propagation. The two fields are in phase, that is to say the
maxima occur at the same point of time and space in both
cases, the radiated energy being divided equally between the
electric and magnetic components regardless of whether the
source is electric or magnetic. Maxima and minima are
separated by a quarter of a wavelength in space and a quarter
of a cycle in time. The wave in effect provides the coupling
between transmitting and receiving antennas, the processes
of transmitting a wave and extracting signal energy from it
being closely related. Usually in amateur radio communication the same antenna serves for both purposes although, as
explained in Chapter 9, certain departures from this rule may
provide important advantages.

For an electromagnetic wave in free space, the ratio E/H is
a constant equal to 377Ω, and bears no relation whatsoever to
the ratio close to the antenna.

Wavelength and frequency

In Fig 2.3 the wavelength, that is to say the distance between
the crests of the waves, is denoted by the symbol λ in
accordance with usual practice. Since the velocity is 300×10^6
metres per second the number of crests passing the observer
in one second is $300 \times 10^6/\lambda$ if λ is measured in metres. This
is the frequency of the oscillations used to generate the wave
and also of the current induced in a receiving antenna; for
application to the HF band it is convenient to express f in
megacycles per second* in which case

$$f = 300/\lambda$$

Since the relationship between the electric and magnetic
fields is fixed, specifying either component automatically
determines the other. However, the usual procedure is to
specify field strength at the receiver in terms of the voltage ε
which would be induced in one metre of wire lying parallel
with the direction of the electric field, ε being dependent on
the radiated power and the attenuating properties of the path
between transmitting and receiving antennas.

Polarisation

An important property of the wave is its 'polarisation' which
means in practical terms that the transmitting and receiving
antennas should be 'the same way up', though this statement
will later be qualified.

One can perhaps liken the waves surrounding an antenna
to the ripples on the surface of a pond, inducing currents in
other antennas which they encircle momentarily as they
travel outwards, much as the ripples might cause a cork to bob
up and down. The wave is described as 'vertically polarised'
if the transmitting antenna is vertical, in which case the

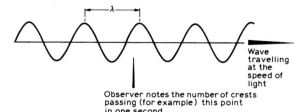

Fig 2.3. Magnetic or electric component of electromagnetic wave as
seen passing the observer. The frequency, defined as the number
of cycles per second (hertz) passing the observation point, is equal
to c/λ where c is the velocity of light

electric field is also vertical; similarly a horizontal antenna
radiates 'horizontally polarised' waves.

The plane of polarisation of an antenna may be inclined at
any angle. Inclined polarisation is often wrongly identified
with 'elliptical polarisation', which is completely different
since it involves rotation of the plane of polarisation cork-
screw fashion as the wave progresses and is produced by
radiating two waves, polarised at right-angles to each other
but with a phase difference of 90°. This means that a maximum of one wave coincides with a zero of the other, polarisation being momentarily horizontal at the instants when the
vertical component is zero and vice versa.

If both waves are of equal amplitude the polarisation is
described as 'circular' and rotates at a constant angular speed,
but in each case there is one complete revolution per cycle of
RF oscillation. Rotation can be left or right handed and must
be the same for reception as transmission. Reception with an
ordinary (ie plane polarised) antenna halves the signal power
since, in effect, only one of the two waves is received. At HF,
however, one is concerned mainly with signals reflected by
the ionosphere and these contain on average equal horizontal
and vertical components regardless of the polarisation of the
transmitted signal. The phase relation between these is random, which means there is no advantage in trying to combine
them in any simple manner, though use is sometimes made of
polarisation diversity techniques which exploit lack of correlation between the two components in order to reduce fading
in commercial systems.

Radiation from a conductor

The next step is to build up a picture of the radiation surrounding an antenna and the factors by which it is influenced. As a
convenient starting point consider a short length of wire, or
'doublet', carrying a radio-frequency current I. A receiver is
located at some distance d in the broadside direction and
experiences from the doublet a voltage V which is proportional to I and l. If now a second conductor is added as in Fig
2.4, having the same length l and carrying an identical current,
the voltage at the receiver is increased to $2V$. This must
obviously be true whether the conductors are separate, as
illustrated, or joined to form a single conductor of length $2l$.

Typically the antenna current varies along the length of the
conductor which can be pictured as divided up into lengths l_1,

---

* By international ruling the descriptive term 'cycle per second' has been
replaced by 'hertz', thereby commemorating the pioneer work of one of the
founders of modern communication by making it more difficult to explain. One
can but hope that readers have passed the stage where translation from
'cycles/sec' to 'hertz' requires a conscious mental effort.

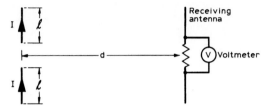

Fig 2.4. Method used for estimation of total field from wires having a non-uniform current distribution. A current *I* through the length *l* produces a signal voltage *V*. A second doublet carrying an identical current increases the signal to 2*V* but usually the doublets are portions of a single wire and *l* is variable, lengths being assigned so that they are just short enough to be regarded as having the same current throughout

l_2, l_3 etc, just short enough to be regarded as having the same current throughout, though they can be shorter and it may be more convenient to make them all the same. If the individual currents are I_1, I_2, I_3 etc, values $I_1 l_1$, $I_2 l_2$ etc can be assigned to each contribution; these can then be added and the sum divided for example by I_1 to obtain the length of antenna which would produce the same field if fed with a uniform current of this magnitude. Alternatively one could divide by the total length of conductor to obtain the average current, but the first procedure tends to be more useful since most calculations need to be referred to the feedpoint of the antenna where the current is most likely to be known.

The process just described is known as 'integration' and the mathematician has various shortcuts at his disposal. For the rest of us it is simpler, though admittedly more laborious, to draw out the current distribution on a piece of graph paper, count the squares under the curve, and divide by the length as illustrated in Fig 2.5. This diagram shows the sine-wave current distribution typical of $\lambda/2$ dipoles which form a basic building block for the majority of HF antenna systems. At this stage there is no need to be unduly concerned with how this current distribution comes about or the special significance of the half-wavelength which are topics for the next two chapters. However, since the circuit is completed via the capacitance between the two halves of the dipole and this capacitance is distributed along the wires, it follows that the current gradually decreases to zero as one moves outward from the centre.

It will be seen that for a sine wave the average current is 64% of the maximum or alternatively we can regard the maximum current as flowing through 64% of the length. It is interesting also to note that 71% of the field is produced by the middle half and only 29% by the end portions, so that if a shorter antenna is required it is better to sacrifice the ends rather than the middle. For the moment, however, the main essential is the direct relationship between field strength at the receiver and the product of length and current. For example, if it is found that reducing the length has no effect on field strength, this can only mean that the current has increased. This conclusion is subject to certain conditions since it requires elaboration for the case of large antennas or if there are phase reversals.

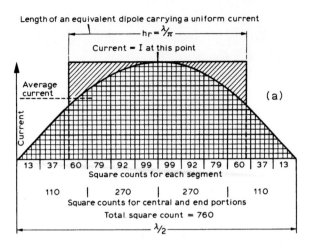

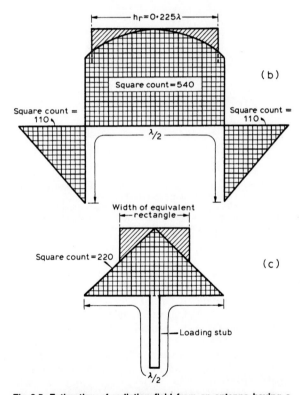

Fig 2.5. Estimation of radiation field from an antenna having a known current distribution by dividing it into elementary doublets. The example shows a $\lambda/2$ dipole and also the effects of reducing its length by bending over the ends (b) or folding in the centre as at (c). The figures indicate the relative areas of each segment. For short wires the radiation resistance (p25) is roughly equal to $80(S/160)^2$ ohms, where S is the appropriate 'square count'

Directional pattern

Next we have to consider the 'directional pattern' of the antenna, ie the effect of walking around it, or turning it round,

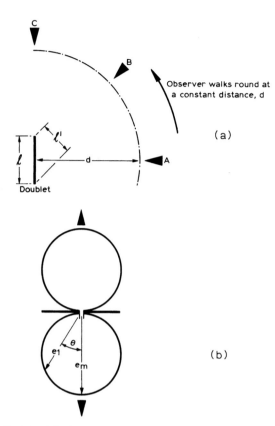

Fig 2.6. (a) Derivation of directional pattern. As observer walks round from A to B at constant distance the apparent length of the antenna shrinks from *l* to *l'*. At C, it disappears completely; *d* is assumed large compared with *l*. (b) Shows the directivity in polar coordinates of a λ/2 (or shorter) dipole: e_1 and e_m represent the relative field strengths in the directions indicated

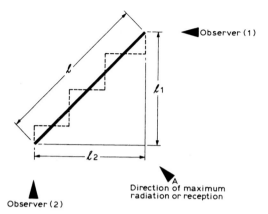

Fig 2.7. Resolution of a single dipole or doublet into an equivalent pair mutually at right-angles. The length *l* may be replaced by two sets of elementary doublets corresponding to the steps

as in Fig 2.6(a). In the end-on position it 'shrinks to a point' and becomes invisible. This applies equally to the radio signal, the electric field being no longer correctly aligned with the direction of propagation, and it is not surprising to find that for intermediate positions also the radio signal varies in exactly the same way as the apparent length of the antenna. The previous conclusion can now be expanded to read *for a transmitting antenna consisting of a single short straight conductor, field strength at a given point P is proportional to average current times the apparent length as seen from that direction*, ie the length *l'* in Fig 2.6(a). The ratio *l'/l* therefore describes the way in which signal strength varies with the direction relative to the line of the antenna; this is the 'polar diagram' of the antenna and is shown in Fig 2.6(b).

To obtain the radiation pattern for a more complicated shape of antenna it is often useful to resolve the radiation from a wire into two components at right-angles to each other. For this purpose each 'doublet' can be replaced by an equivalent pair at right-angles, thereby forming a 'staircase' as shown dotted in Fig 2.7 which shows two observers looking at the

same antenna from directions at right-angles to one another and seeing lengths l_1, l_2 respectively. Provided the wire still carries the same current the zigzag shape makes not the slightest difference to either observer, though the portions of antenna seen by one observer are now completely different from those seen by the other. The zigzag wire may now be further divided into straight portions, all these running in the same direction and being joined end to end, so that each observer now has his own personal antenna.

Throughout the proceedings, provided he stays in the same place, neither observer is aware of any change or the fact that he has not been looking at a dipole of length l_1 or l_2 oriented for his direction. Similarly an observer at A, the direction of maximum radiation, is also unaware of change; it might be argued that an observer at C, Fig 2.6(a), will now see something, but this is merely a matter of reducing the size of the steps! It follows that the two separate dipoles or doublets at right-angles are strictly equivalent so that the radiation from, for example, an inclined wire may be resolved into a horizontal and vertical component. Often two or more such wires may be combined so that one or other of these components is cancelled, leaving the user with, for example, some constructional advantage as in the case of the quad antenna which can be fitted into a much narrower space than a λ/2 dipole.

The trick of replacing any short piece of antenna wire by two equivalent wires at right-angles can be carried out for any direction of observation but is then valid for all observers, provided those who are able to see both parts of a step add or subtract the contributions according to the apparent lengths and whether the currents appear to be flowing in the same or opposite directions.

The argument thus far has assumed, implicitly, that all the wires are lying in the same plane but the principle can be applied to three dimensions by resolution into three 'orthogonal' (ie mutually at right-angles) components. The dimensions of each wire must be small enough for the radiation from all parts of it to be regarded as arriving simultaneously at the observer, with longer wires being subdivided, but they do not need to be very short. For example, two concentric λ/2 dipoles at right-angles carrying equal currents have the same radiation pattern as a single dipole lying in a direction half-way between them.

This result is of direct practical significance since it allows the directional pattern to be switched in 45° steps, thus obtaining better all-round coverage. The main point of the method, however, is to allow the directional pattern of any antenna to be estimated, however complicated its shape, provided the current distribution is known or can be measured. Having resolved each portion of the antenna into two components, it is a simple matter to add those seen by the observer while ignoring the others; the addition must, however, be carried out with due regard for any phase differences, as will now be explained.

Phase

In most practical cases there is not just one source of signal but at least two, since even if the antenna itself can be regarded as a single 'point source' of radiation there is a wave reflected from the ground as well as the direct wave from the antenna. It is convenient to regard the reflected wave as coming from the mirror image of the antenna in the ground, though in many cases this is an oversimplification and the topic is discussed at some length in later chapters. For the moment all we need to know is that there are two or more sources of signal which are going to have to be added, or maybe subtracted, in order to discover the *effective* signal in any given direction. This brings in the important question of 'phase' and an understanding of this is essential to further progress.

There are two kinds of phase relationships with which we need to be familiar, that between a voltage and the current producing it, Fig 2.8(a), and the phase relations between waves arriving from a number of different sources such as A and B in Fig 2.9.

To understand the difference in phase between current and voltage in Fig 2.8(a), consider the situation at (b) where the current flowing in the coil of wire (or inductance) generates a magnetic field which represents stored energy. After closing the switch it takes a little time for this store to be filled so that there is some delay before the current has risen to its steady value V/R in accordance with Ohm's law. Similarly the capacitance in Fig 2.8(c) takes time to charge up to the full voltage of the circuit, the current at the moment the switch is closed being equal to V/R. This falls to zero by the time the capacitor has been charged to the voltage V so that there is no longer any 'potential difference' across the resistor. In case (b) the current *lags* behind the voltage across L and in case (c) it *leads* the voltage across C.

In the case of AC or RF circuits the switching takes the form of reversals of polarity at the appropriate frequency with the current reversals leading, lagging, in phase, or in antiphase with the voltage reversals, except that usually one is not concerned with a switching process but the smooth transitions of a sine wave. Inductances and capacitances in AC or RF circuits 'impede' the passage of current by acting as stores for

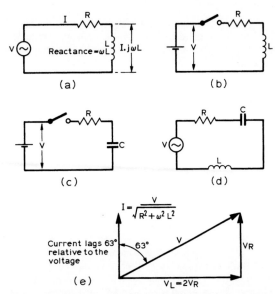

Fig 2.8. Explanation of phase. (a) Typical AC circuit. (b) Voltage across L drops to zero as current reaches its maximum value V/R (ie current lags behind voltage). (c) Current is initially V/R but falls to zero as soon as C is fully charged (ie current leads). (d) Resonant circuit: current phase lags if $\omega L > 1/\omega C$, leads if $1/\omega C > \omega L$, otherwise $I = V/R$. (e) Phase relations for circuit shown at (a), assuming $\omega L = 2R$

energy which is subsequently released, but they do not consume power. The impedances in ohms are equal in magnitude to ωL and $1/(\omega C)$ respectively, where ω is the 'angular frequency' in radians per second, L is in henrys and C in farads.

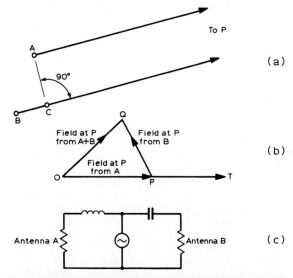

Fig 2.9. Combination of voltages subject to a phase difference: the device shown at (c) uses the principle of Fig 2.8(a) to apply a phase lag at A and lead at B so that fields at P from the two antennas A and B add in phase. Any number of voltages may be added in this way

These quantities are normally referred to as the 'reactance' (symbol X), the more general term 'impedance' (symbol Z) being applied to combinations of resistance and reactance so that Ohm's law for AC circuits becomes $V/I = Z = R \pm jX$ where j is used to indicate 'addition at right-angles' as explained on p74. The negative term denotes capacitive reactance and, if Z includes both inductance and capacitance as in Fig 2.8(d), we have $Z = R + j\omega L - j/\omega C$ so that the normal Ohm's law expression $V/I = R$ applies if $\omega L = 1/\omega C$.

This is the condition known as 'resonance' and is an important condition for the transfer of power from a transmitter to an antenna. The voltage across L, as we have seen, leads the current through it, whereas the resistance provides a simple example of Ohm's law, the voltage and current being in phase. In adding these two voltages it is necessary to allow for the fact that they are displaced in time by a quarter of a cycle and this may be done graphically as shown in Fig 2.8(e). This also shows the current which, because the circuit is inductive, lags behind the voltage. It is important to realise that, although Z determines the current, it is R alone that consumes power which is equal to I^2R just as in the case of a DC circuit.

In antenna work one is concerned largely with resonant systems but phase differences arise due to detuning and to the fact that the time of travel of a wave between different parts of an antenna system may represent a large fraction of a cycle, or even several cycles. This situation is illustrated in Fig 2.9 which demonstrates the way in which signals from A and B combine at a remote point such as P. Thus, if both signals start their travels in the same phase, that from B will have further to travel by an amount BC. Fig 2.9(b) has been drawn for the case where BC = $\lambda/3$ so that the phase difference is $1/3$ cycle or 120°. The field due to B is assumed to be only 70% of that from A, and the resultant field is 93% of that from Q alone. On the other hand, by using L and C as shown in Fig 2.9(c) it would be possible to give B a phase lead of 120° so that the fields at P add directly in phase to give a resultant OT which is 1.7 times that from A alone. Although this example has been chosen solely to demonstrate a principle, the design or evaluation of antenna systems consists very largely of operations of this kind.

Free space

It often simplifies antenna problems to divide the antenna into two or more parts, and as a rule the first step is to separate it from its environment. Thus we may first decide how an antenna would behave if it were in 'free space', that is to say far enough out in space for the presence of the Earth to be ignored, and then consider as a separate problem how this behaviour will be modified by the presence of the Earth or other surroundings. It then transpires as explained in Chapter 6 that *for a given height the effect of the Earth is the same for all antennas* provided that they are 'the same way up'.

Failure to simplify the problem in this way has led to many claims for this or that type of antenna based on a 'lowering of the angle of radiation' relative to its competitors. For the time

being therefore, unless otherwise indicated, all antennas under discussion are assumed to be in free space, the effect of the ground being explained in Chapter 6 after which the reader should be well placed for relating the basic characteristics of an antenna system to any given practical situation.

It will be recalled that, in general, signal strength is a maximum when both antennas are the same way up, ie have the same polarisation, and a similar rule is applicable to antennas in free space. To appreciate this, imagine trying to inject a signal from one wire into another one arranged symmetrically at right-angles. There is clearly nothing to tell the induced current which direction to flow so therefore there can be no induction, and similar reasoning can be applied to electrostatic couplings. If the polarisation is not identical at both ends, signal strength decreases with the angle of non-alignment in exactly the same way as it did with direction in the case of Fig 2.6(a), the analogy being obvious if one thinks, say, of a vertical receiving antenna as 'seeing' only the *vertical extent* of the transmitting antenna. This is also to be inferred from Fig 2.7.

Field strength versus distance

Referring again to Fig 2.6(a), the reader may be ready to accept that the apparent length l' can be used as a general indicator of relative field strength. If the distance is doubled l' subtends only half the angle at one's eye and thus looks only half as long, so one can infer that in free space signal voltage is inversely proportional to distance. Alternatively one could perhaps imagine oneself as a receiving antenna which is grabbing all the energy within its reach; at twice the range the energy is spread over four times the area so the fraction of it within reach is only a quarter of what it was before. This is known as the 'inverse square law', and 'the area within reach' is a loose description of the 'aperture' which is explained in more detail on p151.

These concepts provide two methods of obtaining the power available at the terminals of a receiving antenna. The first depends on the knowledge that the field strength produced at a distance d by a uniform current I amps flowing through a short wire of length l as in Fig 2.6(a) is given for the direction at right-angles to the wire by

$$\varepsilon = \frac{60\pi}{d\lambda} \, Il \quad \text{volts/metre}$$

The ratio of l' to l is a property of the angle θ, namely its cosine, so for other directions the expression can be written

$$\varepsilon = \frac{60\pi}{d\lambda} \, Il \cos \theta \quad \text{volts/metre}$$

In these expressions l, d and λ are all expressed in metres. Since in practice I is usually not uniform the product Il must be determined by the method of Fig 2.5. To find ε for any given direction, distance and wavelength, all that is then needed is the above formula plus a pocket calculator having a button labelled 'cos'. However, as a matter of practical convenience I is usually taken to be the current in the *centre* of the dipole and to make the sums 'come right' it is l instead of I that is multiplied by the appropriate factor.

The new value of l is usually known as the 'effective height' and designated by the symbol h for reasons which go back to the early days of radio before the advent of 'short waves', heights then being small compared with the wavelength and closely linked with efficiency. In deriving h from l it is usually accurate enough merely to multiply by 1, 0.64 or 0.5 depending on whether the current distribution most closely resembles the middle, the whole or the end portions of a sine wave.

The voltage induced in a receiving antenna having an effective height h_r metres by the field ε is by definition $h_r\varepsilon$ volts so that, knowing the radiation resistance R as defined in the next section, the signal power available at the receiver in the case of free-space propagation is given in watts by $(h_r\varepsilon)^2/4R$ or, for a $\lambda/2$ dipole, by $3.5\ \varepsilon^2\lambda^2 \times 10^{-4}$.

The alternative calculation is known as the 'Poynting vector method' and is based on the concept of the transmitter being located at the centre of a very large sphere representing the whole of space, the power flux at any point being given by $\varepsilon^2/377$ watts/sq metre. From Chapter 9 (p151) the aperture of a $\lambda/2$ dipole is $0.13\lambda^2$ and multiplication of these two figures leads to the same answer as before. The figure of 377Ω is often referred to as the 'impedance of free space'.

It will be noticed that the longer the wavelength, the greater the received power, since the receiving dipole occupies more space and therefore captures more of the radiated energy. The transmitting antenna, assuming this also to be a $\lambda/2$ dipole, is similarly increased in length but the directional pattern is unchanged and this means that the way in which the transmitted energy is distributed throughout the surrounding space is also unchanged. In other words, for a given power radiated the power flux or field strength at any given point in space is independent of frequency. In contrast the received signal power, by virtue of the greater capture area, is proportional to the square of the wavelength.

To illustrate the calculation of signal strength, consider the case of 100W radiated from a $\lambda/2$ dipole at 14MHz, and let us assume a similar antenna for reception. As explained in the next chapter the radiated power is accounted for by a resistance of 73Ω referred to the centre of the dipole so that, since power $= I^2R$, $I = \sqrt{(100/73)} = 1.17A$. To allow for the sine-wave distribution the actual dipole length must be multiplied by 0.64 as explained above, so the expression for ε becomes:

$$\varepsilon = \frac{60\pi}{d\lambda} \times I \times \frac{\lambda}{2} \times 0.64$$

$$= 60.3\ I/d \quad \text{volts/metre}$$

This is the 'free space field' and is only the first step in a calculation which must also take account of propagation factors such as those discussed in the next part of this chapter. Anticipating this discussion, it will make the example more interesting to assume a long antipodal path of 20,000km, ie $d = 20 \times 10^6$, and it will be more convenient to express ε in microvolts/metre so that

$$\varepsilon = \frac{60.3 \times 1.17 \times 10^6}{20 \times 10^6}$$

$$= 3.53\mu V/m$$

For the receiving antenna the value of h_r is $0.64\lambda/2$ or approximately 6.8m, and the open-circuit voltage at the terminals of a matched feeder connected to the centre of the antenna will be $6.8 \times 3.53 = 24\mu V$. The power available at the receiver is given by:

$$3.5 \times 3.53^2 \times 21.2^2 \times 10^{-4} \times 10^{-12}$$

$$= 1.96 \times 10^{-12}W$$

It is not possible to allow accurately for propagation losses but these may well be offset by ionospheric focussing as discussed on p16, so that the above figure stands as a possible value for the received signal power.

In case the reader is wondering what purpose is served by this type of calculation, it might well be asked for example whether the 100W is really necessary. For example, supposing there is no interference, how much signal power would be needed to produce a usable signal? The answer depends on the required signal/noise ratio, which in turn depends on whether the signal is CW or SSB and in the latter case, whether RF speech processing is used. There is a shortage of reliable figures but a signal equal to the noise level would probably be of interest, though somewhat marginal. The background noise in a quiet location will be mainly of cosmic origin and from handbook data is some 23dB up on the noise level of a resistance at room temperature. This is $10^{-17}W$ of available power for a bandwidth of 2kHz so that for the signal to be equal to the noise at 14MHz the received power must be at least $2 \times 10^{-15}W$.

In this example we have about 1000 times more power than this so that, if the noise level is reckoned as S1 and the author's unofficial estimate of 3.5dB to a typical average S-point (p271) is used, a signal report of S9 can be expected. Alternatively, marginal communication may be possible with a radiated power of 0.05W only. In practice allowance must also be made for gains or losses (a) in antenna systems, (b) due to ground reflections at both ends, and (c) focussing and attenuation in the ionosphere.

Ionospheric propagation

In designing an HF antenna or system of antennas, there are so many interesting and challenging problems to be faced that it is easy to lose sight of the main objective, namely to make the best possible use of the ionosphere. One can perhaps take refuge in the impossibility of defining 'best' since it depends on the particular interest of the individual user, but there are some aspects of ionospheric propagation which are relevant in the antenna context and need to be more widely known. To this end it is necessary to descend once again briefly from 'free' space into that which is bounded by two concentric spheres, the Earth and the ionosphere.

The characteristics of the ionosphere have been studied in great detail over the 70-odd years since it was first discovered but mainly in the context of relatively short ranges requiring only a single reflection from the ionosphere, communication over longer ranges being *assumed* to take place by multiple reflections between the Earth and the ionosphere. This has led to attempts to specify 'optimum' radiation angles and antenna heights, despite convincing evidence [1, 2] that the lower the angle that can be radiated, the better the average DX performance. Apart from this, evidence against multihop propagation as an important element in amateur radio communication over very long distances has been mounting steadily over the last 25 years or more [3, 4, 5, 6] and the reader may like the chance to judge this for himself.

At a more mundane level, most amateurs in planning their requirements are faced with the need for compromise and this may well become more acute as more HF amateur bands become available. A decision as to what band or bands are needed, for what purposes and in what order of priority is likely to be the first step in planning a new antenna or system of antennas. To this end it is important to know what waves can or cannot do after they leave the antenna and the ways in which this affects the selection of optimum frequencies of operation. It may then be necessary to decide whether to use several antennas or make a single antenna do several jobs, and what performance compromises, if any, can be accepted in order to simplify the installation. This in turn may react back on the initial requirements and, rather than try to achieve something which 'does everything all the time', it may be found best to use an adaptive approach whereby changes are made from time to time to suit the prevailing phase of the solar cycle.

Radiation from an HF antenna includes a 'surface wave' which is attenuated rather rapidly so that maximum ranges are typically of the order of no more than 50 miles (80km) or so, depending on antenna height, polarisation and the intervening terrain. It is often pointed out that vertical polarisation is 'necessary' for efficient communication by this means, though in practice (at least on the higher frequency bands) the author has found just the reverse, probably because most other stations use horizontal antennas and polarisation needs to be the same at both ends. Moreover, ground-wave ranges of 50 miles (80km) or more are often achieved even with horizontal antennas at modest heights whereas vertical antennas are too often inefficient.

The majority of amateur contacts in the HF bands, however, involve reflections from the ionosphere, and as a first approximation this can be regarded as a conducting 'shell' surrounding the Earth and acting as a reflecting mirror. Upper layers of the Earth's atmosphere become 'ionised' due to the bombardment of atoms by ultraviolet radiation from the Sun which sets free electrons, thereby leaving the parent nuclei positively charged. At night the bombardment ceases and

eventually the electrons (being negatively charged) get attracted to other nuclei so that the amount of ionisation decreases, but in the very rarified upper levels of the atmosphere this is a slow process.

A wave entering the ionosphere is bent (refracted) by encounter with the electrons, and if the bending is sufficient it is returned to Earth again. At the higher frequencies and vertical incidence the bending is very slight and the wave goes straight through into outer space. However, when the wave meets the ionosphere at an oblique angle, it has further to go before escaping and consequently experiences a lot more bending, so that it is returned back to Earth as illustrated in Fig 2.10. Due to optical analogies it is usual in this context to talk about rays rather than waves, and the bending just described is equivalent, as shown enlarged at (b), to reflection from a slightly greater height than that actually reached by the ray.

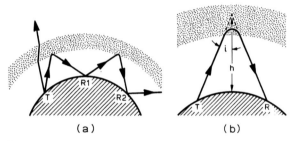

Fig 2.10. (a) Conventional picture of the ionosphere showing multiple reflection. (b) Actual path of wave corresponding to the virtual height *h*

The height thus defined is the 'virtual height' of the layer and there are several layers, the one of most importance for HF communication being known as the 'F2 layer' or, at night, merely as the 'F layer'. This is at a height of about 130 to 260 miles (210 to 420km), depending on the season, time of day, and the degree of ionisation. Therefore the reflecting properties are strongly influenced by the 11-year solar cycle, ie by the number of 'spots' on the Sun since these largely determine the amount of ultraviolet radiation.

The frequency at which a ray entering the ionosphere at vertical incidence just fails to escape and is reflected (or refracted) back to Earth is known as the 'critical frequency', f_c. At oblique angles much higher frequencies can be reflected up to and including the 'maximum usable frequency' (MUF) which is typically in the region of two to four times f_c. It is given by $f_c/\cos i$ where i is the angle of the incident ray to the vertical as shown in Fig 2.10.

The F2 layer is the highest layer, the lowest being the D layer which in daytime has an absorbing effect on rays passing through it. The D layer disappears at night because at this level the atmosphere is much more dense and ionisation does not persist after removal of the cause. The E layer is at a more or less constant height of 72 miles (116km) and, though useful for medium-range daytime communication, also disappears at night. Above this there is the F1 layer which exists only in daytime, is relatively weak and not of much practical importance.

Polarisation is 'lost' on reflection and this entails a 3dB loss in signal strength as mentioned earlier, but there are also losses by absorption; these vary greatly but are least just below the MUF so the optimum frequency band to use is generally the one nearest to the MUF but on the low side of it. Below this there is a gradual increase in absorption resulting in a lowest usable frequency (LUF), but this depends to a large extent on signal power and, unlike the MUF, is not sharply defined.

Apart from regular diurnal and seasonal variations dependent on the zenith angles of the Sun, both the MUF and the absorption indices (and hence the LUF) vary with the number and activity of sunspots. During the solar cycle of about 11 years the 'sunspot count', suitably averaged, varies from a low of three or four to a peak which over the last 150 years has varied between 60 and 200. There are however considerable day-to-day variations with a tendency for repetition at 27–28 day intervals, this being the period of rotation of the Sun. To get this in perspective a count of at least 50 is needed to provide consistent DX openings on 28MHz, although occasional contacts are possible over north-south paths even during sunspot minimum years.

The above picture of the ionosphere is much simplified and there are many anomalies, not all of them fully understood. Commercial and broadcasting services have an urgent need for up-to-date information on the best frequencies to use, including advance warning of when to make changes of frequency, and to this end ionospheric prediction services have been operating for many years. Predictions have hitherto been based on single-hop paths, making use of the latest sunspot numbers in conjunction with solar zenith angles and time of day etc. As mentioned earlier these have been universally applied to longer distances on the assumption of propagation by multiple reflections between the Earth and the ionosphere as illustrated by Fig 2.10(a).

This method of prediction has led to serious difficulties in the case of long-distance paths, eg between Europe and Australia, and its persistence has been difficult to reconcile with the discovery of chordal-hop propagation (Fig 2.11) by H J Albrecht in 1953 [3], the work of many other investigators, particularly Stein [4], and the experience of radio amateurs over more than half a century [5].

As far back as 1948 it seemed obvious to the author, as it must have been to anyone with experience of the long path to Australia over a sufficient period of time, that its behaviour was not consistent with the existence of intermediate ground reflections. However, Albrecht (who also based his conclusions on the observation of amateur signals between Europe and Australia) was the first to offer an explanation. The experiences of radio amateurs also provided encouragement for the more recent work on chordal hop [6] in which it was found that field strengths predicted by the International Radio Consultative Committee (CCIR) method were too low by no less than 25dB (equivalent to 300 times in power), this being

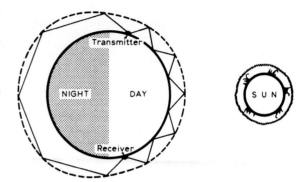

Fig 2.11. Showing how the change of effective layer height around dusk and dawn produces the layer tilts required for chordal-hop propagation between near-antipodal points, thus providing a night-time path with little absorption and the avoidance of ground-reflection losses

explained in terms of a focussing gain of 16dB plus a 9dB advantage due to the absence of ground-reflection losses!

An explanation of focussing gain follows from the fact that great circles passing through any point on a sphere also pass through the antipodal point. Waves transmitted from one point in whatever direction meet up again in phase at the antipode: if the ionosphere was a perfectly conducting shell 100W of transmitted power could be used to light a 100W bulb 12,000 miles away at full brilliance! The reason this does not happen is that the ionosphere is neither perfectly conducting nor a perfect sphere; moreover, the explanation has been oversimplified since it presupposes that the transmitter and receiver are in contact with the spherical surface which in this case is the underside of the ionosphere. Nevertheless, the gain of 16dB is quite impressive, more than compensating for an estimated absorption loss of 15dB and in line with the author's own earlier conclusion [5], arising from low-power portable operation on steep ground slopes, that focussing gain was at least comparable with the absorption whatever this might be.

It should be noted that focussing gain (a) applies only to chordal hop since otherwise it is neutralised by defocussing at the ground reflections in a manner very similar to the situation depicted in Fig 10.13, and (b) requires the angle of incidence at the ionosphere to be as small as possible. The dependence of focussing gain on range is shown in Fig 2.12 taken from reference [6], where it is stated that as the theoretical gain tends to infinity at the antipodal points it must be limited to an appropriate value such as 30dB for practical applications.

Referring to Fig 2.11 it will be seen that, because of the change in layer height between the light and dark sides of the Earth, there are regions of transition where the dotted line representing the ionosphere ceases to be parallel with the Earth's surface. These tilts result, as shown, in a chordal-hop mode of propagation via the dark side of the Earth. This is believed to be responsible for virtually all amateur communication over, for example, the long path between Europe and

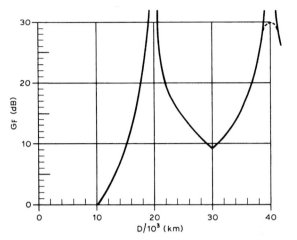

Fig 2.12. Antipodal focussing gain, showing variation of gain with distance for one complete circuit of the Earth. Maximum gain is theoretically infinite but for practical chordal-hop paths the curve should be rounded off as shown *(Telecommunication Journal)*

Australasia, but any transequatorial path tends to experience similar tilts over a large part of the day.

The various types of reflection at the ionosphere can be better understood by referring to Fig 2.13 which illustrates a typical situation in greater detail. The high-angle wave, after being bent slightly by its encounter with electrons, passes straight through into outer space. Meanwhile, a wave at a lower angle is bent sufficiently to cause its return to Earth as if reflected from the height indicated. Another wave at an even lower angle encounters a 'tilt' – not a tilt in the literal sense but its equivalent in the form of a varying refractive

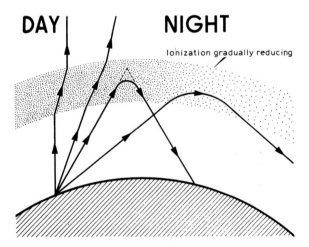

Fig 2.13. Chordal-hop conditions. High-angle ray passes through the ionosphere with little deviation, lower-angle ray is reflected in the usual way. At a still lower angle the wave finds itself in a region of gradually reducing ionisation so that the rate of bending becomes less and less until it emerges at a shallow angle; there is no return to Earth and the next reflection also takes place at the ionosphere (note: not to scale)

index. Thus at the angle shown, after the initial bending and before leaving the ionosphere, it finds itself in a region where the electrons are becoming fewer and the rate of bending is less, so that eventually it leaves the ionosphere as shown, only to travel round by successive chordal hops until it meets another tilt.

As well as large signal levels another marked characteristic of chordal-hop paths is an absence of slow fading, such as occurs due to interaction between different modes (eg two- and three-hop paths) when multihop propagation exists, as is usual for example across the North Atlantic. On this basis, as well as the usual absence of strong signals from intermediate ranges [5], the author is convinced that multihop propagation is unusual in amateur communication over very long distances, greater than, say, 5000 miles (8000km), and this finding would be consistent with those of Stein [4] based on back-scatter soundings of the ionosphere.

It may, however, be necessary to differentiate in this respect between amateur and commercial services, since the latter tend to be concerned with maintaining communication between specific points at all times, whereas amateurs are more interested in making the best use they can of whatever opportunities happen to exist at a given time. This obviously generates a bias towards the use of low-loss modes, irrespective of the destinations which they serve. As an instance, a British station wishing to communicate with Australia is usually content with the 2 or 3h time slot during which this is easy and, except perhaps in a contest, is not very interested in periods when hundreds of times more power is needed due to the absence of layer tilts.

The argument that there is no optimum radiation angle other than the lowest possible, though opposed to much accepted dogma, does not derive solely from theoretical requirements for maximum focussing gain but rests also on direct observations by Utlaut [1] over the North Atlantic path and by Epstein *et al* [2] over considerably longer paths, low angles being achieved by the use of very high sites (eg 1000ft or 300m) looking out to sea. In reference [2] much greater signal levels (typically 10dB) were consistently obtained from sites at 1000ft (300m) compared with sites at 150ft (45m) or so, though even the latter would qualify as exceptional by normal amateur standards, the advantage being greatest at the *lower* frequencies. This implies radiation angles less than 1° and, although it was sometimes found that high angles resulted in signals which were as good or better, average signal levels were increased and operating periods greatly extended by the inclusion of very low angles in the radiation pattern. On the available evidence, however, it would be unwise (even if it were possible) to exclude higher angles up to at least 10° or so.

For ranges less than 2000 miles (3200km) higher angles are required, as will be evident from Fig 2.14. Typical values of critical frequencies for summer and winter periods at the two extremes of a typical sunspot cycle [8] are shown in Fig 2.15. The values of MUF are obtainable by dividing this with the cosine of the angle of incidence *i* (Fig 2.10) of the wave entering the ionosphere. For very low angles of radiation we

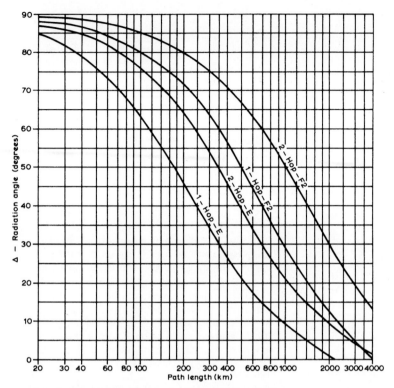

Fig 2.14. Radiation angle involved in one-hop and two-hop paths via E and F2 layers. (From NBS publication *Ionospheric Radio Propagation*, p191)

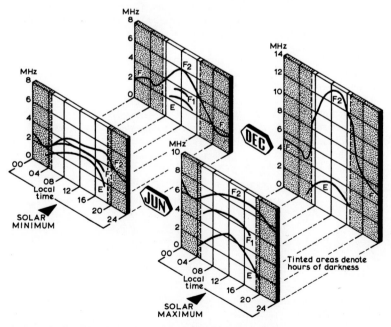

Fig 2.15. Typical diurnal variations of layer-critical frequencies for summer and winter at the extremes of the solar cycle *(Radio Communication Handbook)*

have sin $i \approx i$ (in radian where h is the layer heig... given in Table 2.1, figures for the F2 layer (daytime) being very approximate.

At typical angles of radiation i is slightly greater, being given approximately by $\sqrt{(h/1600)}$ for a 6° angle. Based on a radiation angle of 6° and temperate latitudes, Table 2.1 shows the highest and lowest of the amateur frequency bands needed for continuous DX communication at different periods based on the above data. In general, at least one band higher would be usable for north-south paths. It should also be noted that day-to-day variations are quite large and higher frequencies when usable will provide bigger signals.

The frequency pairs on the right of the table should result in a DX capability at nearly all times for some directions and apply also to single-hop ranges near the right-hand edge of Fig 2.14. Absorption is a maximum in daytime and the higher frequencies are needed for best propagation around midday, and in summer the greater part of the afternoon. Exceeding the lower frequencies may result in failure to communicate during most of the night and especially for an hour or so before dawn.

At intermediate times and intermediate portions of the solar cycle there may be considerable benefit from intermediate values of frequency, but an antenna system covering a range of one octave should meet most DX and medium-range requirements, excluding contest work at the solar maximum. Solar minimum conditions create a more difficult antenna problem due to the larger ratio of frequencies as well as the lower values although, if operation at night is dispensed with, the 10MHz band can be substituted for 7MHz.

From the f_c column it will be seen that for very short-range (zero-skip) skywave working the 1.8 or 3.5MHz bands are required at solar minimum but in addition the 7MHz or even the 10MHz bands may be usable at solar maximum. For ranges of the order of 600–1200 miles (950–1900km) the lower of the DX frequencies will be suitable for a large part of the time but one band lower may be needed, each of the bands being usable at times.

Table 2.1

Period and time		Height of F2 layer (miles)	(km)	f_c (MHz)	Average MUF (MHz)	Highest amateur band required for DX (MHz)	Lowest amateur band required for DX (MHz)
Solar min (summer)	day	260	420	4.5	18	18	7
	night	190	305	2.7	9.3		
Solar min (winter)	day	140	225	6.0	18		
	night	190	305	2.3	8		
Solar max (summer)	day	240	390	8.8	34	28	14
	night	190	305	7.0	24		
Solar max (winter)	day	140	225	13.6	40		
	night	190	305	4.9	17		

It would not be appropriate here to discuss the numerous anomalies and freak modes of propagation which can occur but it is useful to be aware of Dellinger fade-outs (SIDs) which occur very suddenly during periods of high solar activity, may last for several hours, can be total, and are accompanied by the disappearance of the cosmic noise levels which normally set a limit to the usable sensitivity of receivers. At such times increased sensitivity may allow communication to continue in some cases, or to be resumed at an earlier point in time, and some of the measures used for improving antenna and receiver performance under normal conditions in respect of interfering signals become counter-productive. These occurrences are, however, fairly infrequent and are virtually unknown during the minimum years.

Summary and conclusions

The aim in this chapter has been to provide the reader with simple ways of visualising the radiation from an antenna and its progress through space to the receiver. However complicated an antenna may appear, it can usually be understood by thinking of it as a number of simple components assembled in some logical manner as explained in later chapters. Unfortunately many antenna systems described in the amateur literature have been arrived at by trial and error without regard for the underlying principles. The result is sometimes successful but usually suffers from at least some minor deficiencies, and in the absence of the necessary logic the mode of operation may well prove incomprehensible.

References

[1] 'Effect of antenna radiation angles upon HF radio signals propagated over long distances', W F Utlaut, *Journal of Research of the National Bureau of Standards*, Vol 65D, No 2, March/April 1967, p167.

[2] 'A comparison of long-distance HF radio signal reception at high and low receiving sites', M R Epstein *et al*, *Radio Science*, Vol 1, 1966, pp751–762.

[3] 'Investigations on great-circle propagation between Eastern Australia and Western Europe', H J Albrecht, *Geophysica Pura e Applicata*, Vol 38, 1957, pp169–180; see also *Journal of the Wireless Institute of Australia*, Vol 21, No 5, 1953, and Vol 24, No 10, 1956.

[4] 'The role of layer tilts in ionospheric radio propagation', S Stein, *Journal of Geophysical Research*, Vol 68, p217.

[5] 'High-frequency antennae and propagation modes in relation to the amateur service', L A Moxon, *IEE Conference on Antennas and Propagation*, 28–30 November 1978.

[6] 'On the propagation of short waves over very long distances: predictions and observations', K J Hortenbach and F Rogler of Deutsche Welle (the German external broadcasting service), *Telecommunications Journal*, Vol 46 vI/1979, (ITU, Geneva), pp320–7.

[7] *Ionospheric Radio Propagation*, NBS Monograph 80, Washington, 1965.

[8] *Radio Communication Handbook*, Vol 2, 5th edn, RSGB, 1977, p11.17.

Chapter 3

Gains and losses

In judging the suitability of a transmitting antenna for its task there are many questions to be asked, of which the following (apart from their obvious importance) are the most basic.

(a) Does it radiate most of the power available, or is a substantial part wasted in the heating of wires, components, or surroundings?
(b) Does it, as far as possible, concentrate the radiated energy in wanted directions or is there wastage due to avoidable radiation in other directions?

Put briefly, the aim is to achieve negligible *losses* and as much *gain* as possible; this involves not only the antenna as such but the relationship between the antenna and its environment, which is the subject of a later chapter. We need, however, to proceed in two stages, first considering the antenna in isolation and ignoring for the moment some important aspects such as whether it continues to work when the frequency is shifted to another part of the band, how easy it is to make sure of correct operation, and whether it is likely to survive the first gale.

The aim of this chapter is to provide a clear outline without too much involvement in detail of the principles involved in maximising gain and minimising losses in the antenna itself, the problem of ensuring that all the available power finds its way to the antenna being the concern of the next chapter. Later chapters seek to interpret these principles in a practical context and Chapter 9 discusses a number of important differences between transmission and reception.

Gain and directivity

Referring back to Fig 2.6 it will be noticed that the radiated signal is stronger in some directions than others. If in a given direction the signal is stronger than the average the antenna can be said to have 'gain' in that direction, this being normally expressed in decibels. The decibel (dB) is the natural measure to use for this purpose since it denotes a 'power ratio' which is the kind of difference that the ear hears. Thus '3dB' means 'equivalent to a 2:1 difference in power' and each 3dB step indicates multiplication by two, or division if there is a minus sign in front of it.

The decibel is therefore a logarithmic unit, a power ratio of P_1/P_2 being expressed in decibels as $10 \log (P_1/P_2)$ or, in terms of the voltage ratio across any given value of resistance, by $20 \log (V_1/V_2)$. This is often more convenient to measure but it is essential to realise that *these are the same decibels,* the expressions being mathematically identical subject to the stated conditions. There is no such thing as a 'voltage decibel' though this point seems to have caused a lot of confusion.

Useful figures to remember include 1dB for a 25% increase in power and 10dB for a tenfold increase, with 1dB representing in most cases a just-appreciable difference in signal strength. Signal reports are based on the S-unit which has been frequently defined as a 6dB step but, since its inception and up to the time of writing, the average S-unit has been closer to 3-4dB which the author believes to be a much more realistic figure. Unfortunately, reliance by some experimenters on the official definition appears to have been the origin of some wildly inflated published figures for antenna gain.

If more energy is radiated in one direction, there is less available for others so that gain and directivity are closely linked. To have no gain in any direction, an antenna would have to radiate the same signal in all directions, in which case it is said to be 'isotropic'. The gain as defined above is therefore the *gain relative to an isotropic source* and, if two antennas have the same directivity, they must necessarily have the same gain. One disadvantage of isotropic antennas is that nobody has yet succeeded in making one, but this in no way detracts from their usefulness to mathematicians, an author trying to explain antenna gain, or an advertiser trying to make his gain figures look as good as possible without actually cheating!

On the other hand, the real interest for the amateur lies in the *relative* gain of various *practical* antenna systems and it is common practice to express gain in decibels relative to that of a λ/2 dipole (Fig 2.5). The latter's gain exceeds that of an isotropic antenna by 2.15dB so that use of an isotropic reference adds this amount to the gain figure. To avoid confusion it is normal for gain to be expressed in 'dBi' or 'dBd', depending on the chosen reference.

Antennas may consist of single wires, long or short, or numbers of separate wires or other conductors co-ordinated in such a way that there is a considerable concentration of energy in one direction. There is no precise definition of a beam antenna but any arrangement using two or more elements is normally classed as a beam. Further discussion of antenna gain is divided between single wires and beam arrays, leading to the conclusion that within each of these categories, assuming a given height and polarisation, there is a tendency for all antennas of interest in the amateur context to be equal. Thus it turns out to be remarkably difficult to influence appreciably the gain or directivity of a single piece of wire shorter than about 3λ/4, unless losses occur or unless at some point there is a reversal in the direction of current flow.

This is obvious in the case of a straight wire since the method of calculating the directional pattern described on p10 breaks down only if the various contributions to the field cannot be directly added. Such a breakdown occurs if, and only if, important contributions to the field are of opposite sign or come from points so far apart that the distances travelled to the receiver are widely different, thus resulting in a phase difference. This in its turn can only happen if the antenna is quite large but, to get this in perspective, it is useful to consider radiation in a nearly-endwise direction from the dipole of Fig 2.5. Contributions from near the ends will indeed be separated by nearly λ/2 so that they are out of phase but, after allowing for this, it turns out that the λ/2 dipole has a gain of only 0.4dB (5% in signal voltage) compared with the short doublet of Fig 2.4 and even a 50% increase in length yields no more than an extra 0.7dB.

It should be noted (p90) that in most cases these figures are not applicable to beams, so that shortening an element does not directly affect the gain in dBd. This means that the gain relative to a single element of the same type can be up to 0.4dB greater than the dBd. Failure to appreciate this point may account in part for the excessive gains commonly attributed to quad antennas.

It might be thought that a simple way to degrade the performance of an antenna would be to bend it, eg as in Fig 3.1(a) where one half of a dipole has been bent over at right-angles. Assuming optimum conditions to start with and maintaining the current constant, this will halve the field strength but, out of the total difference of 6dB, half is the result of reducing the effective length and half is due to tilting the plane of polarisation as explained in Chapter 2 (p12). Since, as already explained, gain is virtually independent of length, the current does not stay constant but increases to compensate for the reduction in length, whereas the polarisation is immaterial subject to conformity between the two ends of the link. To restore the field strength to its original value, more or less, it is therefore only necessary to rotate the bent dipole through 45° as in Fig 3.1(b). This is usually referred to as an 'inverted-V dipole', and is one of the most useful of all amateur HF antennas in view of the ease with which it can be supported, leading to numerous applications as described in later chapters. We have thus made no progress in the search for *worse* performance and, although by making the apex angle sufficiently acute, losses could be increased, it would probably be easier to fit an attenuator!

Another approach might be to try using not one but several bends, but it will be recalled that the worst that can be achieved even theoretically is an isotropic antenna which has

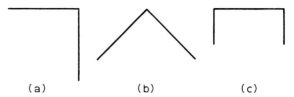

Fig 3.1. Bending of elements. In case (a) the effective field strength is halved for a given current if the receiving and transmitting antennas initially have the same polarisation, but current is increased by √2 so the loss is only 3dB. (b) Re-orienting (a) as shown restores field strength to its original value. (c) is equivalent to (b)

a loss of 2.15dB compared with a λ/2 dipole as discussed on p19, and it is difficult to get within even 1dB of this in practice. This tends to the conclusion that, subject to remaining in free space and avoiding extremes, *all single-element antennas have roughly equal gain,* thus leaving the designer free to concentrate on other aspects of performance or construction.

Unwanted modes of radiation

The close equivalence of different types of simple antenna discussed above is not generally realised and the author has heard, for example, strong criticisms of the inverted-V on the score of the power wasted due to 'radiation off the ends'. Such unwanted modes are a common feature of antenna patterns especially when elements are 'bent into odd shapes', and it may be necessary, if only for reassurance, to work out how much power is being wasted in them. They need also to be considered as potential sources of interference to reception.

The inverted-V provides a particularly important and instructive example. It is obvious from inspection that the endwise mode exists, and it can be readily analysed with the help of Fig 2.5, noting first that the U arrangement, Fig 3.1(c), though of less practical interest, produces the same field strength for a given current as the inverted-V, Fig 3.1(b). This follows from the 45° slope of the wires of the V which reduces the field from a given current by √2, whereas the loss of the ends in case (c) reduces the field by 30% (ie divides it by √2) as discussed in the last chapter.

The inverted-U, with its similar tendency to produce endwise radiation, has the advantage, important for the present purpose, of being much easier to analyse. From Fig 2.5 the ratio of field produced by each of the end pieces to the field in the wanted direction is 0.3/1.4 and although the 'ends' are out-of-phase there is enough phase shift in the endwise direction to prevent cancellation. Using the method of addition described on p12, the field strength ratio for the unwanted directions is given by (0.3 × √2)/1.4 = 0.30. To find the power ratios (assuming the same directional pattern for both modes) this has to be squared, ie the efficiency on this basis would be 1/1.09, a loss of 0.37dB only. However, the directional patterns are not the same since the ends (considered by themselves) resemble the W8JK antenna described on p22. This has a gain of 4dB so that less power has to be radiated to account for the observed field strength, thus bringing the loss down to only 0.15dB. The advantage of the U lies in the ease of calculation.

With such low losses there is no need to worry much about precision but a more accurate figure for the V obtained by graphical integration along the lines of Fig 2.5 comes to 0.23dB. Even this is much reduced when two elements are assembled as a beam or if the apex angle, which should be as large as possible and preferably not less than 90°, is increased to 120°. The effective mean height of the V is somewhat less than the apex height, and increased interference might be expected from a vertically polarised local station if there happens to be one within 20° or so of the end-on directions, though for high-angle (short-skip) signals there is little to choose between straight wires and bent ones. As will be evident from later chapters, the inverted-V has important practical advantages, particularly for 'invisible' antennas, and the above example should allay doubts which have probably caused many operators to opt for more expensive, larger and more visible antennas.

In the case of other types of antenna it is usually possible to deduce from the shape what unwanted modes of radiation are likely and arrive at a rough estimate of their magnitude along the lines of the above examples.

Small antennas

In Fig 2.6(b), following usual practice, the direction of the receiver relative to the best direction of transmission has been denoted by the Greek letter θ. Since field strength is proportional to l'/l, which is by definition the cosine of the angle θ, the radiation pattern shown in Fig 2.6(b) is commonly referred to as a 'cos θ' pattern. Its derivation here has involved no more than the use of a ruler, and references to cos θ here and subsequently should be regarded as a form of shorthand, not as an attempt to inflict advanced mathematics on the reader.

The important point is that cos θ provides a full description of the antenna directivity and therefore gain *without any reference to the dimensions which are therefore of no direct significance.* Later, when considering losses, it will be necessary to qualify this, but the primary fact is that most amateur antennas for the HF band other than beams and long wires can be regarded virtually as 'point sources' of radiation, and a point by definition has no size.

In practical terms 'point source' means that from all angles of view the distance to any part of the antenna is the same within some small fraction of a wavelength as the distance to all other parts, so that all contributions to the radiated field are in the same phase and can be lumped together. An antenna ceases to be a point source only if there are major current concentrations separated by distances of the order of at least λ/4 or if it includes antiphase sources, in which case small antennas can usually be represented by two such sources.

To obtain significant gain relative to a single source it is necessary to assemble two or more sources to form beam antennas in ways to be described later. Formulae describing the directivity then become more complicated but with closely

spaced elements, which is the case of most practical importance to amateurs, still contain only cos θ so that again there are no dimensions involved.

The explanation, as we shall see, is simple provided the number of elements is restricted to two or three, and thereafter ceases to be of much practical interest, though a number of mathematical studies have yielded conclusions bordering on science fiction. It has been shown that there is *no limit* to the gain theoretically obtainable from an antenna *provided only that there are enough elements packed together in a small enough space!* In particular Uzkov [1] has shown that the maximum gain theoretically possible, expressed as a power ratio relative to an isotropic source, is equal to n^2 where n *is* the number of elements; unfortunately with increasing gain and reducing size, the efficiency, bandwidth and allowable constructional tolerances decrease at an astronomical rate due to the requirement for much larger currents as explained below.

Antennas such as these are known as 'supergain antennas' and it has been shown [2] that the special characteristics just outlined are typical also of the operation of amateur close-spaced beams. This identity sets clearly defined limits on possible performance and explains rapid widening of the gap between theory and practice as the number of beam elements is increased. Its failure to attract much attention can perhaps be attributed to the fact that in practice it is possible to travel only a very short distance down the supergain road, so that typical amateur rotary monoband beams with three closely spaced elements represent, more or less, the upper limit of practical achievement for transmitting antennas based on supergain principles.

Large beams, typical of commercial installations and beyond the means of most amateurs, are based on a different set of principles, and in the next section the two modes of operation are examined and compared. Further discussion of the Uzkov limit and its implications for the design of amateur beams will be found near the end of Chapter 5.

Beam antennas

It is useful, particularly in the case of beam antennas, to think of the transmitter as being in the centre of a sphere, Fig 3.2, whose radius r represents the distance OA to the receiver. The surface area of a sphere is given by $4\pi r^2$, and an isotropic transmitting antenna would, by definition, illuminate the whole of the surface evenly, whereas the object of a beam is to concentrate all the available energy into a small area which includes the receiver.

If the beam is circular with a radius r_b at the surface of the sphere, the area which it illuminates is approximately equal to the cross-sectional area πr_b^2 provided r_b is not too large. The gain, being the ratio of the two areas, is given by $4r^2/r_b^2$ and, since $2r_b/r$ is equal to the width α of the beam in radians*, the gain is given by $16/\alpha^2$. If the beam is not circular but has widths of α_1, α_2 in planes at right-angles to each other, $\alpha_1\alpha_2$ may be substituted for α^2.

* To convert degrees to radians it is necessary to divide them by 57.3.

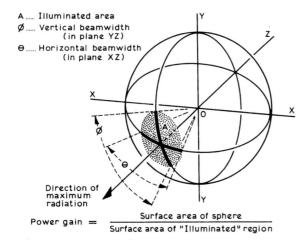

A ..... Illuminated area
∅ ..... Vertical beamwidth (in plane YZ)
θ ..... Horizontal beamwidth (in plane XZ)

$$\text{Power gain} = \frac{\text{Surface area of sphere}}{\text{Surface area of "Illuminated" region}}$$

Fig 3.2. Spherical representation of space surrounding an antenna. An isotropic radiator at the central point O provides uniform illumination of the sphere surrounding it. A directional antenna illuminates only a portion of the sphere, as shown by the shaded area. The terms 'horizontal' and 'vertical' are not applicable in free space but φ and θ can be identified with α_1 and α_2 in the text *(Radio Communication Handbook)*

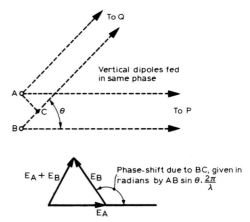

Fig 3.3. Additive gain. Two widely spaced, point-source elements fed in the same phase produce maximum field in direction P. To obtain relative field in any other direction Q, it is expressed in terms of the equivalent phase shift (AB sin θ × 2π/λ radians) and the fields produced by A and B added as shown at inset

To illustrate this, a circular beam with a width of 28.5° (α = 1/2) would have a gain of 16/(1/4), ie 64 times or 18dB. This formula is not strictly accurate for large beam angles since (a) the cross-sectional area of the beam is not quite the same as the corresponding area of spherical surface, (b) the angle has been used instead of its sine. These errors are, however, more or less self-compensating. In practice, beams always have sidelobes, ie they radiate some energy in unwanted directions and this reduces the gain slightly. The gain as defined above is relative to an isotropic source so that 2.15dB must be subtracted for comparison with a dipole.

As a more typical example, some published directivity patterns for a three-element Yagi array suggested vertical and horizontal free-space beamwidths (α_1, α_2) not exceeding 1.37 and 0.82 radians respectively, giving a gain of 16/(1.37 × 0.82) times or 11.5dB. Subtracting 2.15dB, one obtains a gain of 9.35dB relative to a dipole which is absurd, though not alas untypical of published figures. Suspecting the use of a square-law meter so that the quantity plotted was relative power, not field strength, a half-beamwidth of 45° was obtained for the vertical plane and, multiplying the vertical pattern by cos θ (as explained in Chapter 6) to obtain the horizontal pattern, the new values of α_1, α_2 came to 1.58 and 1.22 approximately. This brought the gain (relative to a dipole) down to 7.2dB, in line with the text of the article and within the possible theoretical limits, though still slightly improbable as a practical figure. This example is important insofar as it illustrates the only method, albeit an indirect one, open to the ordinary amateur for obtaining a meaningful figure for the measured gain of an HF antenna.

Appreciable errors arise (especially with low-gain arrays) from the fact that beam edges are not sharply defined, but the width between the half-power points provides a useful

approximation. This may be measured as described on p276 or obtained by plotting the directional pattern as explained below. This provides a simple method for obtaining a rough idea of gain whereas attempts at direct measurement in the HF bands with normal amateur resources can be highly misleading (p271). In all cases beams are formed by making use of phase differences so that signals transmitted from (or received by) different parts of the antenna add together in different ways depending on the direction.

Figs 3.3 and 3.4 illustrate the two methods using phase differences to favour preferred directions at the expense of other directions, and the inset is a reminder of the graphical method for adding two signals when there is a phase difference between them. In Fig 3.3 the elements A and B are fed in *the same phase,* causing the radiation to be additive in the direction P, whereas in the direction Q the contribution from B has further to travel and therefore lags in phase so that the

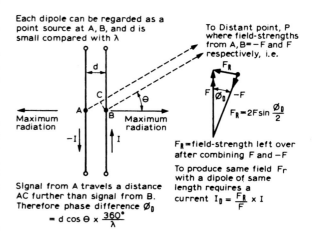

Fig 3.4. Mechanism of W8JK antenna

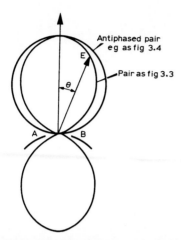

Fig 3.5. Polar diagram corresponding to Fig 3.3, assuming λ/2 spacing of co-phased elements fed with equal currents. This is the diagram for the horizontal plane assuming vertical elements, and requires multiplication by cos θ if these are replaced by horizontal elements aligned for the direction P. The pattern for similarly aligned but close-spaced elements fed in antiphase is shown for comparison; this is the cos² θ pattern from Fig 3.6

addition is less effective. In this way the width of the radiation pattern compared with that of a single element is reduced, thereby causing more energy to be radiated in the direction P. It is, however, important to note that for this effect to be appreciable A and B *must be widely separated,* since otherwise the phase difference is insufficient. The directivity of a simple array of this type is shown in Fig 3.5.

In the case of Fig 3.4, which illustrates the W8JK array, the mechanism is subtractive, the elements working against each other but less effectively for the wanted than the unwanted directions. This narrows the radiation pattern so that gain ensues, provided all the energy is radiated. Unfortunately gain implies large currents in the elements since the signal arises from the difference between two relatively large quantities, and losses may occur as described in the next section. Referring to Fig 3.4 it will be seen that along the line AB radiation from one element lags slightly behind that from the other because it has further to travel, the phase shift being 'equal to the spacing', eg one eighth of a cycle or 45° if the spacing is λ/8. In the direction P the field is reduced in proportion to the distance AC. The resulting directivity is shown by the solid lines in Fig 3.6.

It should be noted that in contrast to additive gain, which requires wide spacings, the subtractive principle comes into operation *only if A and B are closely spaced,* otherwise there will be some directions in which the fields are additive and the operative principle reverts to that of case (a). Due to their wide spacing, elements of an additive array can be regarded as more or less independent of each other, so that if two elements each receive half the total power the current in each is $I/\sqrt{2}$ where I is the current which would flow in a single element. However, due to in-phase addition this is equivalent to a single-element current $2I/\sqrt{2} = 1.414$, ie a gain of 3dB.

Extending the argument to n elements, the power gain becomes n times, but to satisfy spacing requirements the volume of space occupied by the array increases directly as the number of elements. High gain by this method therefore requires a large amount of real estate which puts it beyond the reach of most amateurs. The principle may, however, be applied to the combining of pairs of antennas; if these are equally good, adequately spaced and have the same polarisation, an extra 3dB gain is obtainable in this way. The effects of unequal performance or power sharing are described on p113.

Spacings between the elements of additive arrays normally need to be at least λ/2, although a row of elements may be backed by a row of reflectors spaced λ/4 and phase-shifted by 90°. In this case in-phase addition takes place in the forward direction and cancellation in the back direction.

Additive methods were the only ones generally recognised until the appearance of a classic paper by G H Brown [5] in 1937 which demonstrated the practical possibility of gains in excess of 5dB from pairs of closely-spaced elements. One of the sequels was the development of the W8JK array, to which reference has already been made, but, despite its deep roots in the history of amateur radio and the sanctity conferred by long and extensive use, it has to be said that the W8JK antenna has few practical merits.

This is because (a) achievement of gain despite close spacing and antiphase excitation implies large currents with consequent reduction in efficiency and bandwidth (pp28, 29) and (b) major improvements require only a small modification, in the course of which the W8JK antenna gets deprived

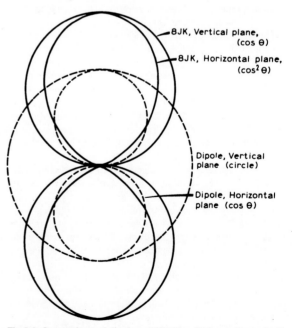

Fig 3.6. Comparison of dipole and W8JK radiation patterns (both antennas horizontal)

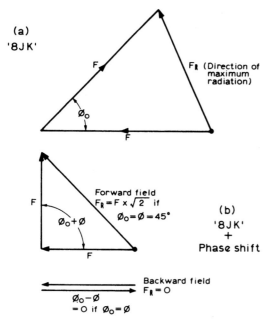

(a)

'8JK'

F_R (Direction of maximum radiation)

ϕ_0

Forward field
$F_R = F \times \sqrt{2}$ if
$\phi_0 = \phi = 45°$

(b)

'8JK'
+
Phase shift

$\phi_0 + \phi$

Backward field
$F_R = 0$

$\phi_0 - \phi$
$= 0$ if $\phi_0 = \phi$

Fig 3.7. Effect of phase shift. Vector diagrams are drawn to scale for the case of $\lambda/8$ spacing. Note that F_R is almost unchanged in going from $\phi = 0$ (the W8JK condition) to $\phi = \phi_0$ but the radiation is now unidirectional. Also F, and therefore the element current I, is much smaller. ϕ_0 is the phase shift ((d/λ) × 360°) corresponding to the spacing d

(perhaps rather unfairly) of its label. On the other hand, its virtues include extreme simplicity and the ease with which an understanding of its mode of operation can be extended to include all other small beams.

The directional pattern of the W8JK antenna is very easily calculated since, referring again to Fig 3.4, the distance BC varies with direction in exactly the same way as the variation in the apparent length of the individual elements, so that there are now two $\cos \theta$ patterns superimposed. The new $\cos \theta$ pattern applies equally to horizontal and vertical axes, so that to obtain the overall directional pattern of the antenna the pattern of the single element (which is $\cos \theta$ in one plane and omnidirectional in the other) is multiplied by $\cos \theta$ to give $\cos^2 \theta$ and $\cos \theta$ respectively. This is illustrated in Fig 3.6 where the patterns for this antenna are compared with those for a short dipole, reproduced from Fig 2.6(b). The corresponding half-power beamwidths are 66° and 90°, so that converting to radians and substituting for $\alpha_1 \alpha_2$ gives a gain of 6.36dB (4.2dB relative to a dipole) in excellent (though perhaps to some extent fortuitous) agreement with more accurate calculations described in Chapter 5 and featured in Fig 5.4.

The modification required to overcome the limitations of the W8JK beam is the introduction of a phase shift between the elements and if this is 'equal to the spacing', the net phase shift becomes zero for one direction and doubled for the other as shown in Fig 3.7. Zero phase difference implies cancellation of the signal so that the pattern becomes unidirectional as

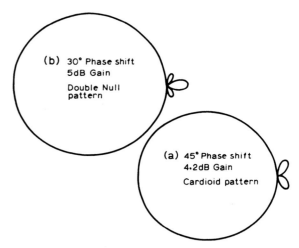

(b) 30° Phase shift
5dB Gain

Double Null
pattern

(a) 45° Phase shift
4.2dB Gain

Cardioid pattern

Fig 3.8. Radiation patterns (a) corresponding to Fig 3.7(b) and (b) showing the result of a 15° reduction in phase shift

shown in Fig 3.8 and a further advantage is that the field strength in the beam is almost doubled for a given current. Since the gain is about the same the current is halved, which reduces losses and leads to further practical advantages, including the possibility of making the antenna much smaller (p97). In addition, the SWR bandwidth (p144) tends to be increased in the same ratio. Instead of being given by $\cos^2 \theta$ the directional pattern in this case is $\cos \theta (1 + \cos \theta)$ as shown in Fig 3.9.

The energy no longer being radiated in the back direction is now being used to broaden the beam, thus providing increased angular coverage without alteration of beam direction. These patterns are for the horizontal plane, assuming the antenna to be horizontal, the vertical patterns being given by $\cos \theta$ and $(1 + \cos \theta)$ respectively. Since none of these patterns

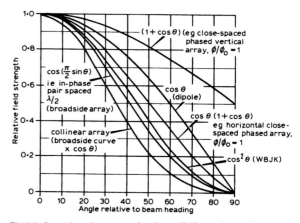

Fig 3.9. Cartesian plot comparing the radiation patterns of various types of two-element beam. In view of symmetry the plot is restricted to 90°. The unidirectional patterns are shown for the forward direction only. Patterns for the back direction (various values of (ϕ/ϕ_0) can be found in Chapter 5, p80. The pattern for a horizontal dipole is also included

contains any dimensions, the gain and directivity are not directly dependent on size, which is really stating the obvious since the way in which apparent length and apparent spacing vary with direction has nothing to do with the actual values of these quantities. It is assumed for this purpose that the ratio of phase shift to spacing is maintained constant, though the actual choice of phase shift is optional between fairly wide limits, 0.8dB of extra gain being obtainable with two thirds of the above phase shift. Fig 3.9 compares the $\cos \theta$, $\cos^2 \theta$, $(1 + \cos \theta)$ and $\cos (1 + \cos \theta)$ patterns in Cartesian form. The last two are for the forward direction only, back-direction curves for various values of phase shift being given in Fig 5.7.

This form of plot, though perhaps less familiar than a polar diagram, is more informative since it allows beamwidth and null angles (if any) to be read at a glance, and it can also be used for estimating (by the method demonstrated in Fig 2.5) the fraction of the total power which is radiated in the rear direction. It requires only a modest front/back ratio to reduce this to a small value, typically 6dB for less than 1dB of power wasted. For comparison Fig 3.9 also shows the patterns for additive gain arrays comprised of two elements spaced $\lambda/2$.

It will be seen from results presented in Chapter 5 that the assumptions start to break down at spacings approaching $\lambda/4$, at which point the additive principle becomes fully operative, so that spacings of $\lambda/4$ to $\lambda/5$ represent a region of transition from additive gain proportional to size to subtractive gain independent of size.

The modification to the W8JK antenna links it closely to the paper by G H Brown [5] which put an end to the belief, current until 1937, that spacings of $\lambda/4$ were mandatory, and showed how gains and directional patterns vary with spacing and phase shift when elements are closely spaced. Practical implementation can take various forms, of which the two-element driven array bears the closest resemblance to the original. There are, however, other and easier ways (p78) of avoiding the current inequalities which constitute a serious defect of many designs of close-spaced beam.

Beams with more than two close-spaced elements, though clearly members of the same family, are not amenable to simple theory. Their design is usually best tackled along experimental lines, bearing in mind the general principles which have emerged from study of two-element beams and making use of design charts such as those on pp94, 95. As stated earlier, the Uzkov formula predicts an upper limit of n^2 for the gain from n closely spaced isotropic elements. After applying small corrections for dipoles [6] the possible gain becomes 5.3dB for two and 8.4dB for three elements. In a separate study [7] a gain of 7.6dB was obtained for a three-element Yagi array using $\lambda/2$ dipole elements spaced 0.15λ.

Unfortunately the extra gain from the third element, except for about 1dB, is not realisable in practice. This is because the signal, however large it may be, is the difference between much larger quantities and the balance becomes rapidly more critical with increasing gain or reduced spacings. This is reflected in very tight constructional tolerances, narrow bandwidth (Chapter 8), and a very low value of radiation resistance which is less than 2Ω for the above-mentioned Yagi array.

The significance of this will be appreciated from the discussion which now follows.

Efficiency, radiation resistance and loss resistance

The proportion of power radiated depends on the ratio of radiation resistance and loss resistance, and there are also close links between radiation resistance and bandwidth as explained in Chapter 8. It has been shown for small antennas that directivity and therefore gain does not depend directly on antenna size, but if the length is halved the field strength can only remain unchanged if the average current is doubled. In accordance with basic principles, it must also meet the condition $P = I^2R$ where P represents the power radiated, and the resistance R needed to complete the relationship is defined as the 'radiation resistance'. This is not a resistance in the usual physical sense but a notion conjured up to account for energy travelling outwards from the antenna, much of it vanishing for ever into outer space. However, unlike some 'fictitious' resistances it is real enough to account for the measured values of antenna impedance, less any losses which may arise as discussed below.

The current I may be observed at *any* point in an antenna system and a value of R can be assigned to that point in such a way that the power relationship is satisfied, though unless otherwise specified the point of reference is usually taken to be the point of maximum current. It is often useful to remember that, barring losses, P must be the same at all points along an antenna element plus any associated feeder system, so that given for example relative values of I for two points in the system and the value of R for one of them, R for the other (which may be the radiation resistance at the feedpoint) can be readily determined.

It will be seen that as length is reduced R drops rapidly because of the increase in I, and power will be wasted if this becomes comparable with the loss resistance (R_L) which is possessed by all conductors at normal temperatures. This means that a fraction $R_L/(R + R_L)$ of the total power from the transmitter is wasted in heating the antenna wire. Alternatively the efficiency, defined as the ratio of power radiated/total power supplied by the transmitter, is given by $R/(R + R_L)$. Since RF current flows only on the surface of a conductor of normal dimensions, R_L for a given length of wire is inversely proportional to surface area.

Values of R_L can be obtained directly from Fig 3.10 which shows the variation of loss resistance with frequency for typical tubing and wire sizes, or Fig 3.11 which shows the dependence on wire gauge for several frequencies in the HF band. For comparison with the radiation resistance, the loss resistance of an antenna wire must be divided by two since the current along it is more or less sinusoidal, and the mean square current is therefore only half the value which it has at the usual feedpoint, ie the centre of a current loop. Approximately, for non-magnetic materials, the RF resistance varies as the square root of the resistivity and inversely as the surface area. Values obtained from the curves should be increased by about 25%

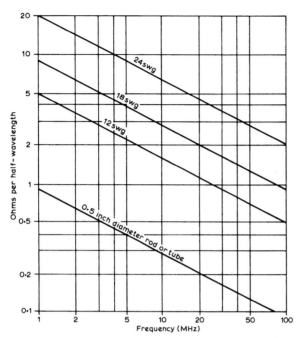

Fig 3.10. RF resistance of copper conductors. Resistance per unit length is proportional to the circumference of the conductor and the square root of the frequency. Uniform current distribution assumed

Table 3.1. Current distributions and multiplying factors for estimation of radiation resistance

Type of distribution	Factor
Uniform (ie rectangular)	2.46
Middle half of a sine wave	2.00
Sine wave	1.00
End half of a sine wave	0.69
Triangular	0.50

Example: If a dipole is halved in length by folding over the ends as in Fig 5.28(b), the second line of the table applies and $R = 73 \times 1/4 \times 2 = 36.5\Omega$.

for aluminium and rather more for aluminium alloy. For magnetic materials the losses are much higher.

The radiation resistance R is usually taken as 73Ω for a $\lambda/2$ dipole in free space, though it varies slightly with length/diameter ratio, mainly because of the slight effect this has on resonant length (p145). Values for other lengths and shapes can be readily deduced from this using the above principles, though allowance must be made for any differences in the way the current is distributed along the wire. This can be done by comparing areas under the curve as in Fig 2.5 but for rough estimates it is sufficient to assume one of the current distributions listed in Table 3.1, whichever seems most appropriate, and use the appropriate multiplying factor. This is in addition to multiplying R by the square of the length ratio.

The radiation resistance of dipoles shortened in various ways is shown in Fig 3.12 which is based on Fig 2.5. This shows clearly the enormous advantage of end-loading, but does not tell the full story which is even less favourable to centre-loading since the 'missing' section of the antenna has to be replaced either by a loading coil (which is a relatively inefficient device) or by a stub as in Fig 2.5(c). For comparison with the loss resistance of the wire the radiation resistance must be referred to the lower end of the stub, and for an antenna length of $\lambda/4$, assuming a sinusoidal current distribution throughout, it is necessary to divide by a further factor of two. Even this is not the end of it, since after reading Chapter 4 the reader will be rightly suspicious of the discontinuity at the feedpoint and, having mastered the use of the Smith chart,

will find himself (a) dividing by a further factor of two and (b) adding 8% to the loss resistance because the total wire length has to be increased by about this amount! This brings R down to about 1.4Ω only, compared with 36Ω for end-loading.

The large currents referred to in the context of the W8JK antenna, and the far larger currents experienced with three or more elements operating close to the Uzkov (gain = n^2) limit, imply correspondingly low values of R and, beyond certain modest gain levels, a reduction in efficiency. It is this fact, and this fact alone, which sets a limit to the possible reduction in size of antennas. Admittedly, long before this limit is reached the user may be complaining of narrow bandwidth (Chapter 8) which forces him always to operate near the same frequency, but this restriction was at one time commonplace, the best transmitters then being 'rock bound' (ie crystal-controlled) and some operators still have strong frequency preferences.

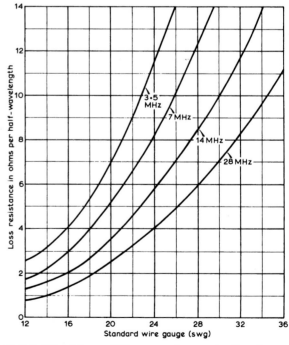

Fig 3.11. RF resistance of thin copper wires as a function of swg

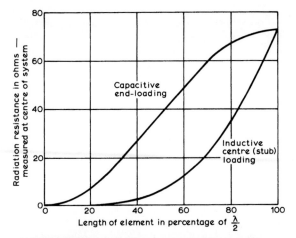

Fig 3.12. Radiation resistance of short dipoles with alternative methods of loading. For close-spaced beams the radiation resistance varies in the same way but values are reduced according to the rules given in Chapter 5, p79

A consequence of reducing the length of the antenna is the need for loading devices such as coils, stubs or 'capacitive hats' to maintain resonance, without which it is not possible to feed the antenna efficiently. The need for resonance can be demonstrated by considering the situation illustrated in Fig 3.13. This shows a 'generator' or RF source, of internal resistance R_G and open-circuit voltage V_G, feeding power into a load resistance R_L. From Ohm's law the current $I = V_G/(R_G + R_L)$ and the power in the load is $V_G^2 R_L/(R_L + R_G)^2$, provided the reactance is zero. This has a maximum value when $R_L = R_G$, and $V_G^2/4R_G$ is therefore defined as the available power of the generator. Any reactance X in series with the load reduces the load current in proportion to the increase in impedance, and if the reactance is not otherwise removable it must be tuned out by an equal reactance of opposite sign. Similarly, if the generator is reactive this requires a reactive load, the reactive components being equal and opposite in all cases. This condition is known as a 'conjugate match' and requires the generator and load to have equal resistances, any reactances being not only equal but of opposite sign, ie the load must be inductive if the generator is capacitive and vice versa.

A wire is resonant subject to a small correction for end effects when the length is a multiple of $\lambda/2$ or, if one end is grounded, any odd multiple of $\lambda/4$, but apart from convenience there is no special merit in such lengths. If a shorter antenna is required one way to achieve resonance is to take $\lambda/2$ of wire and merely fold it to fit the available space, in which case, as we have just seen, R varies greatly depending on the method of folding, whereas R_L (being determined almost entirely by the actual length and diameter of wire) tends to be more or less independent of how the folding is done. Some adjustment of length is usually needed if the shape is changed but this is not important for the rough estimation of efficiency.

The simplicity of this approach to the design of small antenna elements makes it easy to calculate the performance

and arrive at optimum designs as described in a later chapter (p97). Unfortunately, most existing designs of small antennas are based on the use of loading coils which add considerably to the effective value of R_L. Others use centre-loading but, due to the rapid escalation of losses, this allows only a very limited degree of size reduction.

Losses may occur also in the surroundings of an antenna since the electrostatic field associated with the voltages at the ends penetrates into adjacent dielectric material such as trees and brickwork etc which may have a high loss factor. These losses are not amenable to calculation since they involve dielectric constants, power factors and voltage gradients, none of which is likely to be known. However, being proportional to the square of the voltage, they vary with radiation resistance in the same way as the losses in the antenna wire, and it will be seen that the smaller the antenna or the lower its radiation resistance the more important it is to keep it well away from its surroundings. If, for example, an antenna has to be fitted into an attic or other confined space, it is difficult to imagine anything less suitable than the W8JK antenna since the antiphase connection ensures the lowest radiation resistance and highest end voltages that it is theoretically possible to achieve for a given design of element.

Earlier it was shown that gain and directivity are inseparable, but there is nevertheless an important distinction to be made between gain in this sense and the actual increase in level of transmitted signal, which in the case of close-spaced elements is obtainable only if there is a rise in the actual current flowing in the elements as discussed above. On the other hand, to establish a given directive pattern and obtain the corresponding 'directivity gain' it is only necessary to set up the correct current phases and *relative* amplitudes.

Losses, therefore, although they reduce the current and thus restrict the transmitting gain, need have no effect on directivity gain. In the HF band, noise levels are high so that in the case of reception, up to a certain point, losses have no effect on signal/noise ratios since both are reduced in the same ratio as discussed in Chapter 9. For reception it is therefore the directivity gain which is important, and losses can be largely ignored.

Summary

In terms of signal strength all single-element antennas have nearly the same effective performance for a given height and

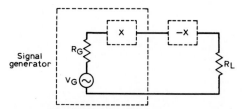

Fig 3.13. RF signal source supplies power to a load resistance R. For maximum power in load $R_L = R_G$ and any reactance X must be removed by suitable tuning such as the connection of a reactance $-X$ in series with the generator

polarisation unless there are losses or complications arising from large size or current reversals.

Gain and loss mechanisms have been explained and directional patterns provided for two-element arrays of various types. It has been shown that most amateur HF beams consist in effect of two or more closely-spaced point sources of radiation; the apparent magnitude (or 'brightness') and relative spacings vary with direction in a way which is independent of the size of the antenna, and this in turn means that the radiation pattern and gain are also fixed, subject to maintaining correct phase and amplitude ratios. For a given number of elements gain is inseparably linked with the directional pattern, subject to a limited range of options within which gain may be traded for better directivity as explained in Chapter 5.

Gain is theoretically unlimited provided an antenna is small enough, tolerances close enough, losses zero and bandwidth considerations ignored; unfortunately the gain obtainable is generally limited in practice to about 6dB. Larger directive gains are associated with very large currents and high losses unless antenna size is increased, in which case,

although the gain theoretically possible is reduced, more of it can be realised in practice.

References

[1] 'An approach to the problem of optimum directive antennae design', A I Uzkov, *Comptes Rendus de l'Academie des Sciences de l'URSS*, Vol 53, p35.

[2] 'Evaluating aerial performance', L A Moxon, *Wireless World* February and March 1959.

[3] 'Supergain aerials', L A Moxon, *Radio Communication* September 1972.

[4] 'Gains and losses in HF aerials', L A Moxon, *Radio Communication* December 1973 and January 1974.

[5] 'Directional antennas', G H Brown, *Proceedings of the IRE*, Vol 25, January 1937, p78.

[6] 'A new approach to the design of superdirective aerial arrays', Bloch, Medhurst and Pool, *Proceedings of the IEE*, Part III, September 1953.

[7] 'The gain of an idealised Yagi array', D G Reid, *Journal of the IEE*, Vol 93, Part IIIA, 1946, p546.

Chapter 4

Feeding the antenna

In the early days of radio, antennas often consisted of odd lengths of wire connected directly to the transmitter but this results in radiation of harmonics and other defects, making it unacceptable under modern conditions. These difficulties can be overcome and 'odd bits of wire' still have their uses but usually the antenna is located in some 'best possible' position which may be a long way from the transmitter, 50–100ft (15–30m) being typical and 200yd (180m) by no means exceptional.

Transmission lines, otherwise known as 'feeders', are used to carry power from the transmitter to the antenna and constitute an important part of the antenna system. They can take various forms but there are two main types, 'balanced lines' and 'coaxial lines', as illustrated in Fig 4.1.

In the case of the balanced line, the two wires carry currents in opposite directions, radiation being prevented because the fields generated are of opposite sign and the spacing is small enough to ensure that phase differences (such as those which form the basis of the W8JK antenna) are negligible. In the case of coaxial lines, the outer conductor is at ground potential and acts as a screen to prevent radiation from the inner

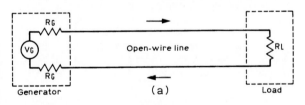

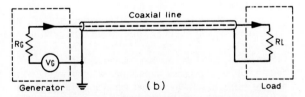

Fig 4.1. Generator connected to load via transmission line. V_G, R_G and R_L are as in Fig 3.13. In case (a) radiation is cancelled since the two wires, viewed from a distance, produce equal and opposite fields. In case (b) the outer conductor acts as an earthed screen to prevent radiation from the inner conductor. Transfer of power from generator to load is unaffected by the presence of the line, provided this is matched as explained later

conductor. The return current flows down the inside of the screen and is likewise prevented from radiating. Although a balanced line is assumed for the following explanation, the principles apply equally to all types of line.

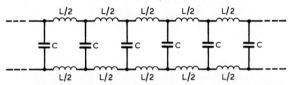

Fig 4.2. Equivalent circuit of balanced line. Velocity = $1/\sqrt{(LC)}$ metres/second and $Z_0 = \sqrt{(L/C)}$ ohms where L is in henrys per metre and C is in farads per metre

The wires have inductance and there is capacitance between them so that the line can be represented by the equivalent circuit, Fig 4.2. If a DC voltage is applied to the line, the current starts to build up in an inductance and as it does so the associated capacitor is gradually charged up to the applied voltage, this process being repeated all the way along the line. In terms of RF signals this translates into a wave propagating along the line with a velocity given by $1/\sqrt{(LC)}$, which for airspaced lines is virtually equal to the velocity of light.

If the line is filled with insulating material, this increases the capacitance per unit length, thus making it appear longer than it really is to a wave travelling along it, both the velocity and the wavelength in the line being decreased by $\sqrt{K}$ where K is the dielectric constant of the filling. Imagine now a transmitter connected to an infinitely long line in which there are no losses; energy leaving the transmitter will travel on for ever but the transmitter is aware only that 'something' is absorbing power from it and interprets this as a resistance. The value of this resistance is known as the 'characteristic impedance' of the line, and is usually denoted by the symbol Z_0.

The greater the value of the reactances which constitute the line as illustrated in Fig 4.2, the larger the value of Z_0 which is simply the geometric mean of these reactances, ie $Z_0 = \sqrt{L/C}$ and is therefore also inversely proportional to $\sqrt{K}$. Apart from the effect of K on C, both L and C are determined solely by the dimensions of the line and are given for two-wire open lines in convenient units by the formulae

$$L = 0.92 \log_{10} (2S/d) \text{ microhenrys per metre}$$

$$C = \frac{12.05K}{\log_{10} (2S/d)} \text{ picofarads per metre}$$

from which Z_0 (ohms) $= 276 \log_{10} (2S/d)$ for air-spaced lines ($K = 1$), S/d being the ratio of spacing to diameter of the conductors.

Similarly for concentric lines

$$L = 0.46 \log_{10} (D/d) \text{ microhenrys per metre}$$

$$C = 24.1K/\log_{10} (D/d) \text{ picofarads per metre}$$

$$Z_0 = 138/(\log_{10} (D/d)) \text{ ohms}$$

where (D/d) is the ratio of the diameter of the outer conductor to that of the inner conductor and the line is air spaced, but since concentric lines are usually filled with insulating material it is necessary to divide the value of Z_0 obtained from the formula by $\sqrt{K}$ as explained above. Design charts based on these formulae will be found on p36, methods of obtaining awkward values of impedance by the pairing of lines being also featured.

The next step is to imagine that at some distance from the transmitter the line is cut. What has been removed is still an infinitely long line which looks like a resistance Z_0, so that if it is replaced by a resistance of this value the transmitter is unaware of any change; all the power going into the line is absorbed in this 'terminating resistance' and the line is said to be 'matched'. If now the resistance is replaced by an efficient antenna designed to look like Z_0, all the power previously going into Z_0 will be radiated from the antenna.

At any point in the matched line the voltage and current are in phase, the ratio V/I of the RMS values is equal to Z_0 and the power flow is therefore given by VI, I^2Z_0 or V^2/Z_0. These expressions are identical, though sometimes one or the other may be more convenient.

If, on the other hand, the line is not accurately matched, some of the power reaching the termination is reflected back down the line. To understand this, it is helpful to start by considering a total mismatch, the line being either open-circuited as in Fig 4.3(a) or short-circuited as in Fig 4.3(b). On reaching the discontinuity, the wave finds itself with nowhere to go and, since it cannot just disappear, has to return back down the line, in which case it is said to be 'reflected'.

Considering first the open-circuit case, there is no current at the end of the line so that at this point the forward and reflected waves must be equal and opposite. Next let us stand back $\lambda/4$ from the end of the line and observe (a) the forward current wave, and (b) the reflected current wave, which left the transmitter two quarter-cycles earlier and is now on its way back. Due to phase reversal at the reflection there are two reversals in all, so the two waves are *always* in phase at this point and there is a current maximum. Another $\lambda/4$ back down the line the waves are again out of phase and the whole pattern repeats itself at $\lambda/2$ intervals.

In the short-circuited case, Fig 4.3(b), the *voltage* is zero at the point of reflection, the short-circuit being (as one might

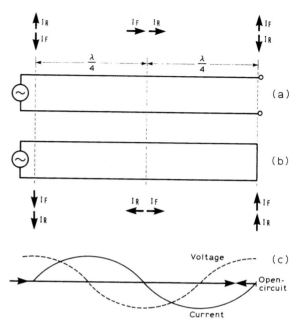

Fig 4.3. Lines with total reflection from the far end (a) open-circuit (b) short-circuit. I_F represents the amplitude and phase of the forward current wave and I_R that of the reflected current wave. Zero current at the end of the line means that the waves are in opposite phase at that point. Phases are indicated at $\lambda/4$ intervals moving back down the line towards the transmitter, using the convention of clockwise rotation to indicate advancing phase. Moving closer to the transmitter the forward wave arrives sooner and is phase advanced whereas the reflected wave has further to travel and is retarded. (c) shows the sinusoidal voltage and current distribution along one wavelength of open-circuited line

expect) a point of maximum current, so that the direct and reflected waves are in phase at this point. This is perhaps best appreciated by replacing the short-circuit with a low value of resistance which, in the absence of losses, absorbs all the available power (P). The usual formula $P = I^2R = V^2/R$ is applicable at all points in the line and this means that the smaller the value of R, the closer I gets to infinity. It follows also that a low value of I implies a large value of R and thus a large voltage, so that *voltage maxima coincide with current minima and vice versa*. Although in the short-circuit case there is no phase reversal on reflection, it is only necessary to move backwards down the line for a distance $\lambda/4$ to find the two waves out of phase, so that with 100% reflection $I = 0$ and the situation precisely duplicates that existing at the end of the line in case (a).

It may be noticed that consecutive maxima are opposite in phase, a matter of no great importance when working with lines but useful to remember later when applying the same ideas to antennas. It will now be evident that there is a pattern of current and voltage along the line with the maximum and minimum values of each not moving along the line but always occurring in the same positions. This is therefore described as a 'standing-wave pattern', the voltage and current waves being separated by $\lambda/4$ as in Fig 4.3(c).

Although this implies a phase difference of 90° between adjacent current and voltage maxima, it must not be confused with the much more important relationship between the current and voltage at any given fixed point on the line, which obeys the normal rules of AC circuits and can be worked out as explained below.

In the most usual cases, the line is neither perfectly matched nor completely mismatched, the load resistance being different from Z_0 and also having some reactance associated with it. On the face of it, this may seem a bit complicated but the difficulties can be resolved by proceeding in two stages, considering first a mismatch involving resistance only. It is then found that the effect of reactance can be translated quite easily into an alteration in the value of the resistance plus a shift in the positions of the maxima and minima. Still looking at Fig 4.3, let us suppose a resistive mismatch such that I_r is less than I_f, say $0.5I_f$. It will perhaps be obvious that maxima and minima occur as before and in the same positions, but now the maximum value is $1.5I_f$ and the minimum is $0.5I_f$.

The ratio of maximum to minimum, in this case 3.0, is defined as the 'standing wave ratio' (k) and I_r/I_f as the 'reflection coefficient' (r). Putting this into more general terms

$$k = \frac{1 + r}{1 - r}$$

This of course is always greater than 1 unless the matching is perfect, in which case $r = 0$ and $k = 1$. Sometimes, mainly in microwave work, the inverse expression is used so that k is always less than 1 but in such cases the need for inversion to comply with normal amateur usage will be obvious. Since the power flowing along the line must be the same whether it is observed at points of maximum or minimum voltage and the power is always equal to V^2/R, it follows that the resistance seen looking outwards at a voltage maximum must be k^2 times its value at the minimum.

This condition is met if

$$k = \frac{R_H}{Z_0} = \frac{Z_0}{R_L} \quad \text{ie } Z_0 = \sqrt{(R_H R_L)}$$

which is the geometric mean of the two resistance values, denoted here by R_H and R_L. This relationship is basic and may also be expressed in the form $R_H = Z_0^2/R_L$ which allows lines to be used as transformers as described on p33. Note that if the load resistance is greater than Z_0 there is a voltage maximum at the end of the line and, if less, a current maximum.

The foregoing theory predicts infinitely large currents and voltages if $R = 0$ and there are no line losses. In practice there is always some loss as explained below but very large currents and voltages can be experienced under fault conditions, and a short- or open-circuit can result in damage to feeders, meters, transmitters and other components. There can even be a fire hazard, as the author found on one occasion when a short-circuit developed in an open-wire feeder, causing high voltage to appear at the lead-in which consisted of

plastic-insulated mains cable pushed through holes in a window frame! The insulation broke down at this point, resulting in fairly impressive fireworks and thus emphasising the need for adequate insulation of lead-in or indoor wiring if there is a chance of high voltages developing under fault conditions.

Similar considerations apply to 'resonant lines', this being a description commonly applied to any line operating with a large mismatch. Such lines are often used (as explained later) to allow the use of a non-resonant antenna, in which case tuning of the antenna plus its feeder is carried out at the transmitter and relatively large currents and voltages exist in the line.

The current in a resistance must by definition be in phase with the voltage, and this condition exists at all points along a matched line, at a resistive load in the case of a mismatched line and, moving back towards the transmitter, at intervals of $\lambda/4$ from a resistive load. At any given intermediate point there will be some other fixed phase relationship between forward and reflected waves, depending on the relative distances travelled. This causes both amplitude and phase to vary along the line as shown in Figs 4.4 and 4.5.

It will be noticed that phase shift along the line is highly non-linear, and at the intermediate points there are substantial phase differences between the voltage and current waves. These differences, which increase with the reflection coefficient, make nonsense of the widely-used assumption that phase shift is directly proportional to line length, although this has often been employed in the design of two-element driven arrays. In these systems both elements are connected to the transmitter and it is usually assumed that a difference in feeder length of $\lambda/8$ produces a phase shift of $360/8 = 45°$ or *pro rata*. This is despite the fact that it is difficult and often impossible to guarantee accurate matching of both elements, one of which (as explained in Chapter 5) can have a value of R which is zero or even negative!

The standing wave pattern with a moderate mismatch is shown in Fig 4.5(a), the ripple being nearly sinusoidal in shape, whereas with a greater degree of mismatch it takes on the appearance of Fig 4.5(b) which closely resembles a plot of the amplitude of a sine wave.

It is important to note that the voltage pattern, though similar in other respects to the current distribution, is displaced from it by $\lambda/4$ so that voltage maxima coincide with current minima and vice versa. This follows from the facts that voltage must be zero at a short-circuit where the current is a maximum, and current must be zero at an open-circuit. The voltage standing waves are shown in Fig 4.5 by dotted lines.

From Fig 4.3 or Fig 4.5 it will be seen that the same relative phases exist at any two points along the line separated by half a cycle, which means that maxima and minima occur twice per wavelength along the line. It follows that as the incident wave moves along the line at the velocity of propagation, the reflected wave vector rotates relative to it at twice the signal frequency.

Fortunately this harmonic frequency does not exist as

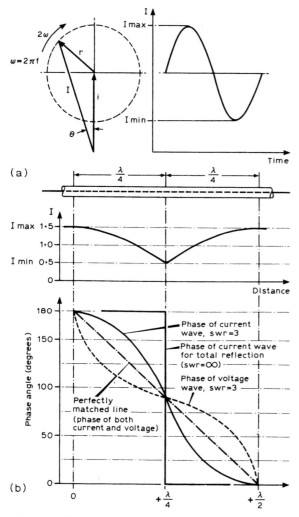

(a)

(b)

Fig 4.4. (a) Development of the standing wave pattern due to interaction of the incident and reflected current vectors. Variation of line current with distance is derived directly from the variation with time of the two vectors. At any given point on the line the relative phase of the vectors is fixed, but as the incident wave travels along the line the relative phase changes with time at the rate of $2\omega t$. (b) Variation of phase along the line corresponding to the current wave in (a). The dotted line shows the phase variation for the voltage wave. Phase variation is also shown for a perfectly matched line and a completely mismatched line

such, the situation being analogous to that of two trains approaching each other at 50mph (80km/h) and passing therefore at a *relative* velocity of 100mph (160km/h). In the same way the incident wave travelling outwards along the line 'sees' the reflected wave rushing back past it at what appears to be twice its own velocity. In most cases there is no need to think in terms of reflection coefficient since SWR meters are readily available or easily constructed, and SWR is related to the load impedance R by the simple formula $k = Z_0/R$ or R/Z_0, whichever is larger.

It is important to appreciate that power reflected is *not lost*. The process of 'matching' the transmitter to the antenna system ensures that in the absence of feeder losses all the available power goes into the antenna, if only because it has nowhere else to go!

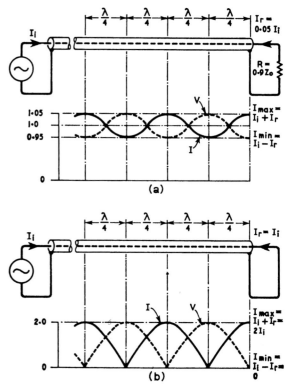

(a)

(b)

Fig 4.5. Standing-wave pattern corresponding to Fig 4.4(a) shown over a full wavelength for two cases: (a) a nearly matched line, (b) a short-circuited line. Note that there are *two maxima* and *two minima* in each wavelength

Matching of the transmitter to a mismatched line is achieved as described on p27 and can be regarded as a kind of deliberate and carefully organised mismatch which ensures that the reflected power is re-reflected and thus sent back to the antenna, the process being repeated until all the power has been radiated. This is fortunately not a procedure which has to be carried out consciously by the operator but a description of what actually happens when 'knobs are twiddled for best results'.

On the other hand, if a transmitter is adjusted to work into a matched line *and a subsequent mismatch is not corrected by re-adjustments at the transmitting end* there will be a mismatch loss given as a power ratio by $4r/(1 + r)^2$ as plotted in Fig 4.6. Misinterpretation of this formula may be responsible for the prevailing tendency to overemphasise the importance of low SWR, though changes in SWR due to variation with frequency of antenna impedance can make it impossible to

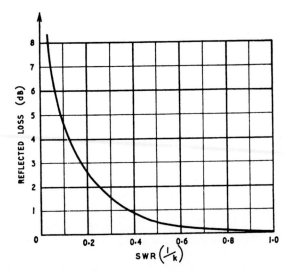

Fig 4.6. Curve showing loss due to mismatch when this is not compensated at the input end of the line

tune over the band without the complication of having to rematch. In general, values of SWR up to 2 or 3 have little ill effect, although very high values may produce the side-effect just described or an unacceptable amount of additional loss in accordance with Fig 4.9. It is true that some transmitters are not designed to cope with impedance variations but these can be corrected by the use of an external tuning unit (p60).

Reactive load

As mentioned earlier the line termination is likely to include some reactance. For example, if an antenna is tuned and matched at ground level and then raised into its operating position there will almost certainly be some change. If this proves unacceptable it is important to know how to correct it. This presents no great difficulty since there is always some point P along the line, within $\lambda/4$ of the antenna, where the reactive component of the antenna impedance resonates with the reactance of the line which therefore behaves as if it were terminated by some value of resistance R_p at the point P. This will be a position of maximum voltage or current, and in the case of high-impedance lines can easily be located using any convenient RF indicator such as the current probe described on p279.

If matching cannot be achieved at the antenna itself, the connection of a transformer at P or appropriate matching stubs can be used as explained on p39 to achieve a low value of SWR in the feeder between P and the transmitter. If P is not accessible, a point $\lambda/2$ closer to the transmitter can be substituted. The actual value of R_p may be obtained from the SWR since $k = R_p/Z_0$ or Z_0/R_p. Conversely, having determined P and k or R_p, the value Z_a of the antenna impedance may be read from a Smith chart and this knowledge used to achieve better matching at the antenna as explained on p70.

In the case of low-impedance lines the determination of P or Z_a is more difficult because there is no access to the centre conductor but, given a measurement of impedance at the transmitting end of the line, Z_a can be read from the Smith chart in this case also. A bridge for impedance measurement is described on p283.

Despite a somewhat fearsome appearance the Smith chart is basically simple and has so many applications that a little time devoted to its mastery with the help of pp65–75 is well spent. In the meantime it will be sufficient to note the characteristic behaviour of lines with different reactive terminations as illustrated in Fig 4.7.

Line losses

There is always some loss in a transmission line due to the ohmic loss of the conductors and losses in insulating materials, these being proportional to the square of the current and voltage respectively. Since increased SWR means that parts of the line experience higher currents and voltages, any losses are correspondingly increased, though if small enough to start with they may still be negligible.

The effect of line losses is illustrated in Fig 4.8 which shows how losses cause the reflected wave to be weaker at the transmitter where the forward wave is strongest. Thus the SWR measurement at the transmitter may be much less than the SWR at the antenna. Measurement of a low SWR at the transmitter therefore does *not* necessarily indicate a good match since it could also be due to a large line loss. The author has found that such a loss can occur due to radiation from the line in the absence of a balun, even though the measured loss in the line when this is disconnected from the antenna may be negligible.

Such effects can be highly elusive and an arrangement which works well in one set of circumstances may fail badly in another. To insure against this, careful note should be taken of the precautions listed on pp52–56. Additional line loss caused by a high SWR is directly related to matched-line loss, and can be obtained from Fig 4.9. Fig 4.10 shows the reduction due to line losses of the SWR observed at the transmitting end of the line. Short lengths of line have many uses as transformers, resonators (eg in lieu of tuned circuits), capacitances, inductances and matching stubs, some of which are described below.

Lines as transformers

It has been shown that if a line is terminated by a resistance R, this appears as a resistance Z_0^2/R when viewed from a distance of $\lambda/4$ down the line. It follows that to transform a resistance R_1 to some new value R_2, all that is required is $\lambda/4$ of line having Z_0 equal to $\sqrt{(R_1 R_2)}$. For example, to match a $\lambda/2$ dipole having a radiation resistance of 73Ω into a 300Ω feeder

$$Z_0 = \sqrt{(300 \times 73)} = 148\Omega$$

Line of this impedance is not readily available but can be

contrived by using two lengths of 75Ω line as explained on p36.

Approximations to other likely impedance values can be similarly achieved using pairs of lines available on the market or readily constructed. If necessary, several sections of line having characteristic impedances Z_{01}, Z_{02}, Z_{03} etc can be used to obtain a required transformation in several stages. Thus an antenna resistance of 37.5Ω could be matched to 150Ω by using a λ/4 section of 75Ω impedance, and this in turn to 600Ω by using a λ/4 section of 300Ω line. Unfortunately, these methods are not easy to adapt for operation on more than one frequency band.

The explanation has been simplified by considering resistive impedances only, but the transformation is equally valid for reactances and can be expressed in the more general form

$$Z^2 = Z_0^2/Z_1$$

This involves quite complicated algebra, except that once again the Smith chart comes to the rescue by providing answers at a glance.

There is a very close analogy between the action of lines and that of tuned circuits. Thus, referring to Fig 4.11, the resistance R in series with the coil is equivalent to a resistance X^2/R in parallel, and the Q of the coil (which is equal to the voltage step-up ratio) is X/R compared with Z_0/R for the line. A short-circuited line, often referred to as a 'stub', can be used in lieu of a tuned circuit or, if this is not convenient, a shorter

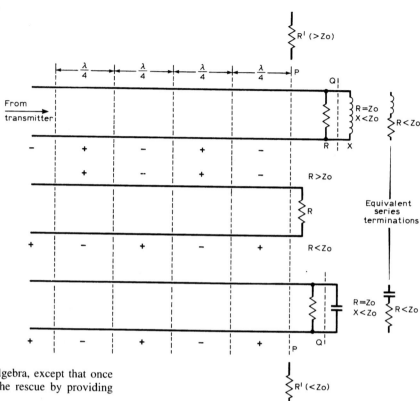

Fig 4.7. Behaviour of lines with typical resistance and reactive terminations. The figure shows the sign of the reactance seen looking outwards along the line from positions indicated. When the termination is partly reactive there is always some line length PQ, less than λ/4, which results in the equivalent of a resistive termination R'. If R' (or R) exceeds Z_0 the sign of the reactance varies along the line as shown by the top figure; if lower, by the lower figure. With large SWR the line presents a reactive impedance equal to Z_0 in the centre of each λ/4 interval; this can be assumed as an approximation (error less than 10%) if the SWR is less than 3. Series/parallel equivalents and length of the line PQ can be obtained from the Smith chart. This figure may also be applied to centre-fed antennas by regarding them as opened-out lines (p69)

line may be used with additional capacitance to bring it to resonance. The advantage takes the form of higher Q (ie lower losses) since usually a larger diameter of conductor can be used and the 'proximity effect' between adjacent coil turns is avoided.

Lines as reactances

Reactances making use of short lengths of transmission line have many uses, one of which has just been described, and the physical resemblance of very short lines to single-turn coils (if the line is short-circuited) or small capacitances (if the line is open-circuited) is fairly obvious. Somewhat less obvious (but equally useful) is the fact that in the case of a resonant line as in Fig 4.11(b) any change in frequency is equivalent to inserting a short length of line where previously there was a

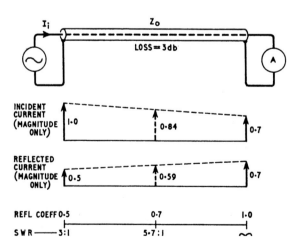

Fig 4.8. Effect of line attenuation on incident and reflected currents shown for the extreme case of a short-circuit

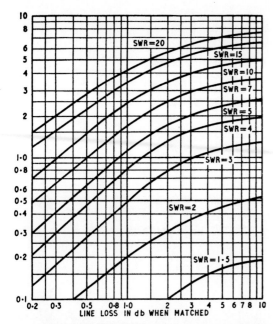

Fig 4.9. Additional line loss due to the indicated values of SWR, for any given matched-line loss. The SWR is the value *measured at the load*, SWR at the transmitter being reduced in line with Fig 4.10. These losses are due to extra heating of the line with increased voltages and currents, and will be incurred in addition to the matched line loss regardless of whether or not the generator matches the line

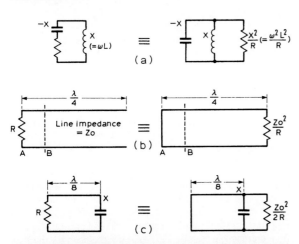

Fig 4.11. Comparison between lines and tuned circuits. Left-hand figures contain series resistances ($R \ll Z_0$ or ωL), right-hand side shows equivalent parallel resistances. At (c), half the line has been replaced by a capacitor having the value $X = Z_0$, but any line length less than $\lambda/4$ can be used subject to appropriate choice of capacitance. As the line length is reduced below $\lambda/8$ it resembles a lumped inductance more and more closely so that the distinction between (a) and (c) rapidly disappears. At (b), AB illustrates the effective contraction in line length due to a reduction Δf in frequency, the ratio of AB to $\lambda/4$ being equal to $\Delta f/f$. The lowest possible value of R is the self-resistance R_0 of the coil or line but any of the arrangements shown may be used for transforming larger values of R up to the values indicated on the right

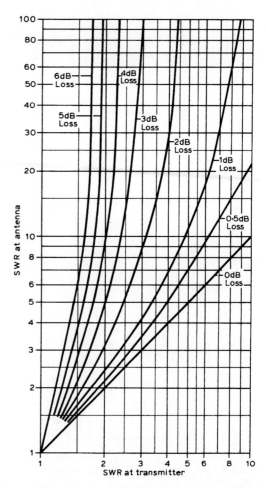

Fig 4.10. SWR at input end of transmission line versus SWR at load for various values of matched line loss *(ARRL Antenna Book)*

short-circuit. In the case of Fig 4.11(b) a decrease in frequency of 5% would move the short-circuit from A to B, and the portion of line AB would present at A the inductive reactance appropriate to a line whose length is 5% of *l*. Similarly, a decrease in frequency of 5% would result in a capacitive (ie negative) reactance of the same amount which is given for both cases approximately by

$$\pm X = 2\pi Z_0 \cdot \frac{\Delta l}{\lambda}$$

'Δ' indicates that the quantity of interest (Δl) is not the line length *l* itself but a small change in *l*, so that starting for example with a resonant line of length $\lambda/4$ and subjecting it to 1% change of frequency, $\Delta l/\lambda$ becomes 1/400.

For lines, Z_0 is obtainable from Fig 4.12, and for antennas from Fig 4.13. A particularly interesting aspect of this example is its application to $\lambda/2$ dipoles, which can be regarded as $\lambda/4$ lines opened out, thus decreasing the capacitance and increasing Z_0 in typical cases to about 1000Ω. For this

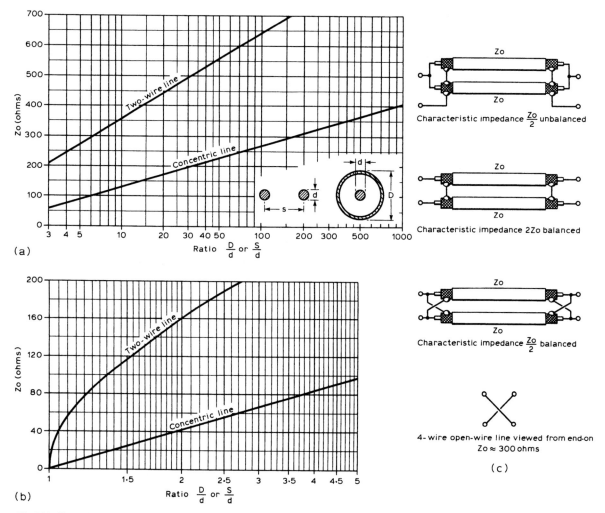

Fig 4.12. Chart giving characteristic impedance of concentric and two-wire lines in terms of their dimensional ratios. Air insulation is assumed so that the values of Z_0 must be divided by the square root of the dielectric constant, ie by the velocity factor which is usually about 0.67 for coaxial lines. Even for open-wire lines it is slightly less than 1.0 due to spacers and end effects, and can be as low as 0.9. Methods of obtaining awkward values of Z_0 by using lines in pairs are shown at (c)

example X comes to 15.7Ω and for equality with the radiation resistance of 73Ω it has to be multiplied by 4.65. This corresponds to 4.65% of detuning which is the half-bandwidth of the antenna as explained in Chapter 7. It is also the condition for an SWR of 2.0, assuming the line to be matched at resonance. The formula can also be used for finding the reactance of a short length of line which is short-circuited at one end, in which case the actual length l is substituted for Δl.

The formula is accurate within 10% provided $\Delta l/\lambda$ is less than $\lambda/12$, but for greater accuracy at larger values of Δl the exact formula should be used, ie

$$X = Z_0 \tan 2\pi \frac{\Delta l}{\lambda}$$

Assuming access to a pocket calculator this may be just as

convenient but the simpler formula can be taken as 16Ω for each per cent of detuning per 1000Ω of Z_0, and has proved invaluable while doing odd jobs on the antenna farm or working out some new idea in the bath! If it is supplemented by remembering that $X = Z_0$ if $\Delta l = \lambda/8$, the need for the 'tan' rarely arises.

For an open-ended line the following exact formula is applicable

$$X = \frac{-Z_0}{\tan(2\pi\Delta l/\lambda)}$$

Again the 'tan' can be omitted if $\Delta l/\lambda$ is less than $\lambda/12$ but the main use is for calculations of capacitance and for short lines it can be rewritten in the form

$$C \approx \frac{33}{Z_0} \cdot \frac{l}{v}$$

where C is in picofarads, l in centimetres, and v is the velocity factor of the feeder, ie 1.0 for air-spaced lines and approximately 0.66 for coaxial cable.

Antennas as transmission lines

The idea of taking a resonant $\lambda/4$ line and opening it out to form a $\lambda/2$ dipole can be extended to any type of antenna, which can then be regarded as a balanced line if fed symmetrically or, if fed at one end, as an unbalanced line with the ground providing the return path. Although Z_0 is increased and radiation resistance is acquired, all transmission-line rules are still applicable, with the radiation resistance providing the termination. It will be recalled, however, that R is usually defined with respect to a current maximum and therefore appears as a large resistance Z_0^2/R at the end of the line, assuming this to be open-circuited as in the case of a dipole. The larger the value of Z_0 or the smaller the value of R, the larger the end voltages and the greater any losses due to the close proximity of trees and brickwork. This effect may, however, be partly offset due to the reduction in capacitance resulting from increased Z_0. Unfortunately, in this respect few guidelines are available.

It is possible to terminate antenna wires in their characteristic impedance so that no standing-wave pattern appears and the bandwidth is increased, but in the case of very short wires most of the energy is then absorbed in the termination instead of being radiated. However, a more interesting situation arises with long wires, since the energy absorbed is that which would otherwise have been radiated in the back direction (p109), and an amateur fortunate enough to have a few acres of ground at his disposal can use a number of such wires to form V and rhombic arrays providing high gain in a small number of fixed directions.

By regarding antennas as transmission lines, many mistakes can be avoided and anomalies explained. Thus many of the antennas described in later chapters have been folded to reduce their overall length, a procedure which nearly always results in a bad mismatch unless it is realised that the usual length formulae are no longer applicable. For example, if the antenna is shortened by folding in the centre to form a stub, reactance is removed at high Z_0 and replaced at low Z_0 so that the length of the stub must be increased in proportion to the difference in the values of Z_0.

Let us suppose, for example, a reduction in length of 2m in the case of a $\lambda/2$ dipole for 14MHz ($\lambda = 21$m). Remembering to picture the antenna as a line which has been opened out, this amounts to a reduction in line length of 1m so that, assuming a typical value of 1000Ω for Z_0, a reactance $2\pi(1000/21)\Omega$ has been removed. Since Z_0 for the stub is only about 600Ω this must be increased in length by 1000/600 or 1.67m to compensate for the reduction in antenna length. This means a nett increase of 1.34m in the total length of wire in the antenna system, and it follows that resonances will no longer be in strict harmonic ratio.

Matching the antenna to the line

Usually the antenna is arranged to be resonant, with the help if necessary of tuning devices such as the stub in the previous example, which is strictly speaking not part of the antenna since it does not contribute to the radiation. In most cases the feeder is matched to the antenna at a point of maximum current, mainly because of the low impedance of available transmission lines, although it also helps to reduce losses by keeping points of high voltage away from supporting structures.

Many antennas have a radiation resistance which matches the impedance of available types of transmission line so that a simple series connection can be made as in Fig 4.14(a). In other cases a parallel connection as in (b), (c) or (d) may be necessary. Often, however, there is a case for the use of so-called 'resonant' lines, ie lines operating with a high value of SWR as a result of transferring the tuning and matching process from the antenna to the transmitter or, more usually, to an external antenna tuning unit (ATU or 'transmatch'). The latter converts whatever impedance happens to exist at the lower end of the feeder into the value required for correct loading of the transmitter.

For frequencies up to 30MHz any length of antenna from about $\lambda/2$ upwards may be centre-fed with up to 100ft (30m) or so of open-wire resonant line as in Fig 4.14(e) without incurring significant losses, all adjustments being carried out in the shack. Such an arrangement has the advantage of being 'multiband' since it allows a 3.5MHz dipole to be used at any of the higher frequencies, although with a long feedline the adjustments in the shack may be extremely frequency sensitive. The SWR is 8.0 in the case of a $\lambda/2$ dipole, dropping to 4.0 or less when the same dipole is used at the higher frequencies.

Losses (if any) are predictable in accordance with Figs 3.10 or 3.11 in conjunction with Fig 4.9. By way of example, 140ft (43m) of 600Ω line made from 16swg (1.6mm) copper

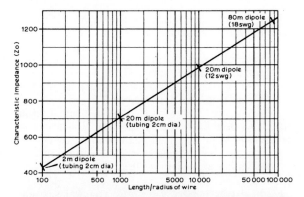

Fig 4.13. Characteristic impedance of straight antenna wires (based on data in reference [20]). Points marked on the curve are typical examples. (Note that the addition of 120Ω gives the Z_0 of parallel wires spaced by the length of the antenna; this is useful as a rough approximation in calculations involving antennas with bent ends)

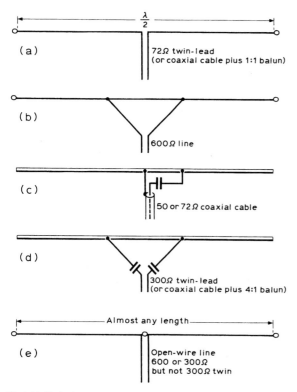

Fig 4.14. Methods for centre-feeding antennas: at (a) and (e) a series connection is used and at (b) to (d) the antenna is shunt (or parallel) fed

has an RF resistance at 28MHz of 30Ω, corresponding to a loss ratio of 630/600 or 0.22dB under matched conditions, the additional loss for an SWR of 8 being 0.5dB. The total loss, 0.72dB, is less than the typical loss of 1.5dB for the same antenna fed with a matched high-grade coaxial line as in Fig 4.14(a). Though expensive and less efficient, the coaxial line is usually considered to be more convenient, and in the case of a dipole works also on the third harmonic. For example, a 7MHz dipole operates also on 21MHz although (as explained in Chapter 6) the radiation pattern will be different. Some types of multiband dipole (pp130, 132) may also be fed in this way but it is important in the case of an unbalanced feeder to use a balance-to-unbalance transformer (or 'balun' for short, pp58–60) at the antenna. These devices, as described later in this chapter, are extremely efficient as well as simple to construct.

In the case of parallel-feed systems such as Fig 4.14(d), it has been found convenient to match the antenna to a 200 or 300Ω impedance, in which case it may be fed with 50 or 72Ω coaxial line plus a 4:1 balun. Alternatively, it may be fed with 300Ω line or with an even number of half-wavelengths of 600Ω line, open-wire line being more efficient even with an SWR of 2 or 3. In these cases the balun is still required for presenting the transmitter with a 50 or 72Ω impedance, but can in many cases be located in the shack so that it does not

need weatherproofing, the author's personal preference being for a combination of methods.

Thus if 600Ω line is used in lengths which are multiples of λ/2 at 7MHz (about 62–65ft (19–20m) physical length) it will be similarly resonant at 14, 21 and 28MHz. Any length deficit is made up by the use of coaxial line (<62ft) plus balun. With a 4:1 impedance ratio balance-to-balance transformer at the top end, this arrangement can also be substituted for the low-impedance twin lead of Fig 4.14(a), the losses in the pair of transformers usually being less than the extra losses in the twin lead or coaxial line which it replaces. Alternatively, if an ATU (or 'transmatch') is used in the shack, the 600Ω line may be of any length, and this would seem to be the simplest course if the antenna is required to operate on the 10, 18 and 24MHz bands as well as those just listed.

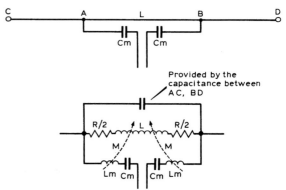

Fig 4.15. Equivalent circuit for shunt-fed antenna. This is drawn for the case of a T-match or balanced version of Fig 4.14(c), but the principles apply to all shunt-fed systems. *L* represents the inductance of AB, and the radiation resistance (though in fact distributed along the whole antenna) can be represented by an equivalent resistance *R* in series with *L* which is tuned to resonance by AC, BD so that a resistive impedance $\omega^2 L^2/R$ appears across AB; in the case of a T-match this result is modified to take account of L_m, C_m, and the coupling between L_m and L

In the case of beam antennas or short dipoles, *R* may be much less than 50Ω and other methods of matching may be required. The gamma match, Fig 4.14(c), though popular, is not a balanced system and does not necessarily overcome the problem of radiation from the feeder. Use of the delta match, Fig 4.14(b), or its close relative the T-match, Fig 4.15, is preferable and with some types of antenna may well be found essential. Any feeder impedance can be used with the delta match but with 600Ω line the capacitors can be omitted. With the help of the Smith chart, matching networks can be devised using inductance and capacitance to match any impedance to any other impedance but are usually restricted to single-band operation.

Fig 4.15 has been included to provide a further insight into the operation of shunt-fed systems. This can function in one or more of several ways, for example as indicated in the caption which provides a good method of matching to a high-impedance feeder. Alternatively if C_m is short-circuited, such that $M = 0$ and $2L_m = L$, then half the current flows through the matching circuit and the feeder sees an impedance $4R$, but it has been found that this can lead to reduced bandwidth.

It is evident that due to the large number of variables there can be more than one solution, and that solutions are not all of equal merit. Difficulties arise mainly in matching to low-impedance lines but there is no problem whatsoever in the direct delta match to 600Ω line, Fig 4.14(b). The delta can in fact be regarded merely as an extension of the 600Ω line, the slight change in Z_0 over quite a small length being immaterial.

It is unfortunate that the delta match, though ideal for its purpose, has had a 'bad press' owing to a number of misconceptions. The case against it rests mainly on the belief that radiation takes place from the delta; moreover the shape of the delta is said to be critical, though values have been published (and are in most of the handbooks) for a single dipole.

There is no foundation for these beliefs. Consider first the radiation from the delta, of which there are two components, the only significant one being aligned with the antenna radiation and part of it! The other is the 'wide-spaced line' effect for which the formula given later in this chapter (p55) predicts a loss of only 0.25dB for a line with a spacing of $\lambda/10$ (ie 7ft (2.1m) at 14MHz) and a length of at least 5λ [1]. A delta match with typical dimensions of 3 by 4ft (0.9 by 1.2m) can be expected to produce a *few hundred times less* than this amount of radiation loss though there will be some increase if the line is mismatched.

As for the shape of the delta, one is assured that this still works after experiencing such severe distortion that it turns into a T-match, so obviously there can be no need to worry about minor shape differences! For a fixed antenna the author prefers to drop the two wires straight down so that they only come together at ground level, thus obviating the need for spacers. This has been found to work perfectly, possibly helped by the fact that, calculating the dimensions in accordance with the caption to Fig 4.15, the delta spacing is very much smaller than the figures usually quoted: typically about 44in (112cm) for a two-element beam with $\lambda/8$ spacing at 14MHz. In the case of a rotary beam, it has been found convenient to bring the sides of the delta in to a point on the mast just above the beam rotator, which can be bypassed mechanically by splicing in a short length of 300Ω twin line.

Having thus, it is hoped, finally vindicated the delta match for high-impedance feedlines, it only remains to point out that its advantages apply also to use in conjunction with a 4:1 balun for feeding an antenna from low-impedance lines. As for other alternatives, the gamma match has already been discussed to its disadvantage, though this does not necessarily mean that it will produce large amounts of line radiation in all (or even most) circumstances. If existing results are entirely satisfactory and there are no obvious signs of feeder radiation (such as a skewed radiation pattern when observed using a field-strength meter sensitive to horizontal and vertical fields) it might be best to leave well alone*.

* Reference [17] reports on a severe case of TVI cured by changing from coaxial line to 75Ω or 600Ω balanced line and reference [18] analyses in greater detail the deficiencies of the gamma match.

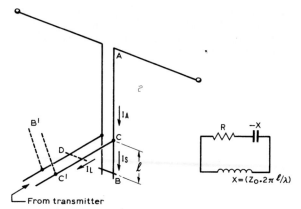

Fig 4.16. Stub matching of open-wire line. The antenna plus the line AB is resonant and matching is correct when

$$l/\lambda = \frac{1}{2\pi}\sqrt{\frac{R}{Z_0}}$$

where R is the radiation resistance; instead of the shorted stub BC the open-circuited stub B'C' may be used though this is much more likely to disturb the line balance

Another method of obtaining an impedance transformation is the folded dipole: Figs 5.17(b) or 11.1(b). This is mechanically awkward in the case of tubing elements but can be a useful alternative to use of a transformer in the case of wire elements. By use of multiple wires or unequal diameters a wide range of transformation ratios becomes possible [2], though this restricts operation to a single band. The delta match has been found more generally useful in these cases also. Methods which require the cutting of tubing elements in the centre without some good reason should be avoided because it weakens the elements and complicates the structure. It is better to use 'plumber's delight' construction in which beam elements are electrically bonded to the supporting boom. Apart from the mechanical advantage, this construction may reduce the risk of lightning strikes or static discharges but requires careful attention to symmetry to avoid currents in the boom which waste power and 'skew' the radiation pattern.

Use of matching stubs

Stubs may be connected at suitable points on a transmission line to eliminate standing waves between these points and the transmitter, though the SWR on the antenna side of the stub remains unaffected. Sometimes this can be done at or close to the antenna, but it often happens that a feeder is brought down to a point near the base of a mast where it is accessible, though there may still be a long run of feeder from there to the shack. A stub at this point can be used to improve the average SWR even though the antenna itself may not be accessible, and Fig 4.16 shows how this can be used to improve the 'resonant line' feeder system described above. For multiband operation a different stub may be used for each band.

If the half-length of the antenna plus the distance AB is an odd number of quarter-wavelengths the radiation resistance R

appears at B in the absence of the stub. Moving towards the antenna by a short distance l to the point C, a capacitive reactance equal to $Z_0 2\pi l/\lambda$ appears in series with R, and this is shunted by the inductive reactance of BC which, since the system is resonant, must also have the value $Z_0 2\pi l/\lambda$. This leads to the equivalent circuit in Fig 4.16 and, since the voltage across L is X/R times that across R, the impedance R_p seen looking across the line at C is given by X^2/R where $X = Z_0 2\pi l/\lambda$. For matching R to Z_0 in the case of a $\lambda/2$ dipole we require

$$X = \sqrt{(RZ_0)} = \sqrt{(73 \times 600)} = 209\Omega$$

so that

$$l/\lambda = 209/6.28 \times 600) = 0.055$$

which is a stub length of 3.8ft (1.1m) at 14MHz.

Provided the SWR is not *too* low (in which case a stub is hardly necessary) it is easy with BC disconnected to determine approximately the points of minimum voltage or current with suitable probes such as that shown in Fig 18.12 (or in the case of voltage, a neon lamp), the voltage nodes being separated by exactly $\lambda/4$ from the current nodes. Having located point D in this way and calculated the length BC, the stub is attached to the line ACD so that DC = BC.

For greater precision I_S and I_A should now be compared; if I_S is less than I_A it means that the reactance of the stub is greater than that of the antenna and therefore AB is too long. Moving the shorting strap at B until the currents are equal results in the correct length for AB, and if necessary C may now be moved to restore BC to the correct length. If the correct stub length is one of the unknowns then, having located B, it is necessary to observe the current at a point along the line exactly $\lambda/4$ from C. If greater than the current at C, it means that the line is terminated in too high an impedance and so must be tapped further down onto the stub, and vice versa.

It is possible in theory, and with sufficient care even in practice, to use an open-circuited stub as shown dotted, the distance DC' being equal to DC and DB' to $\lambda/4$. The problem with this is line unbalance which occurs unless the stub wires are exactly equal in length and symmetrical also with respect to any surrounding objects, so that in the absence of some overriding necessity it is much better to use the shorted stub CD.

It should be noted that, having gone through this procedure at ground level where everything is accessible, the stub may be moved nearer to the antenna by $\lambda/2$ or (in appropriate cases) any multiple of this. Charts are available in many handbooks [2, 3] for determining the position and length of stubs when the SWR and the positions of voltage minima are known. However, the author has found the above procedure to be particularly simple and relatively foolproof, the only rider to this being the desirability of making sure that I_L is less than I_A, thus guarding against the remote possibility of getting one's lengths so badly out that BC finds itself connected to C' instead of C, which has been known to happen. Instead of an inductance resonating with a capacitance one then has two

equal inductances in parallel! The most obvious way to determine the resonant length would be by means of a GDO and this is a convenient method with a simple dipole. However, in the case of a beam the resonant length is affected by the presence of the other element or elements, there can be more than one 'peak' and the method is unreliable.

In the case of coaxial lines the inner conductor is not accessible and a somewhat different procedure is needed based on measurement of impedance, SWR and use of the Smith chart as explained in Chapter 18, though the principles involved are similar.

Asymmetrical feed

A generator of RF may in principle be inserted at any point in a resonant wire, eg as shown in Fig 4.17(a). It then 'sees' the capacitive reactance of the left-hand wire in series with the inductance of the right-hand wire and some appropriate value of radiation resistance to which it can be matched so that all is well. What is not admissible is the hanging on of odd bits of wire at points where there is appreciable RF voltage as shown in Fig 4.17(b).

Although the absurdity of this is obvious in the case of the left-hand sketch the equivalent arrangement on the right is sometimes advocated. There are now in effect two antennas AC and BD, plus a tuning error, which can be resolved by means of an ATU or transmatch (p61) at the transmitter so that power will still be radiated, though the system bears little resemblance to Fig 4.17(a). The pattern may be difficult to predict and efficiency is likely to be poor, particularly if there is a long feeder run at low height.

There is a way out of this problem as shown in Fig 4.17(c). Here the left-hand side of the dipole is tuned to resonance with a series inductance and the right-hand side with capacitance, thereby presenting the feeder with a resistance load equal to the radiation resistance referred to that point in the antenna system. This is simply the usual value (which is referred to the centre of a $\lambda/2$ dipole) multiplied by the square of the current ratio, eg $73 \times 2 = 146\Omega$ for a dipole fed at $\lambda/8$ from one end. Due to the series resonance the voltage distribution is now as shown dotted, the voltage to ground at the end of the feeder being approximately zero as in the centre of the element.

There is, however, still one pitfall, since the length BD could be $\lambda/4$ or some odd multiple of this. In other words it could present an alternative low-impedance path at B so that the current would again be shared between the branches. Similarly any voltage induced in the feeder, say from BC, could result in the situation shown at (d); these effects are both avoided by exercising care in the choice of feeder lengths. For example, if BD is equal to $\lambda/2$ it looks like a dipole with one end short-circuited so that it 'doesn't work', and the unwanted response is thereby eliminated. This problem is not confined to off-centre feed but can arise with any system that is not inherently balanced, and will be encountered again in the general discussion of feeder radiation on p53.

For the extreme case of 'off-centre feed' we should perhaps come down from free space to the earth's surface and

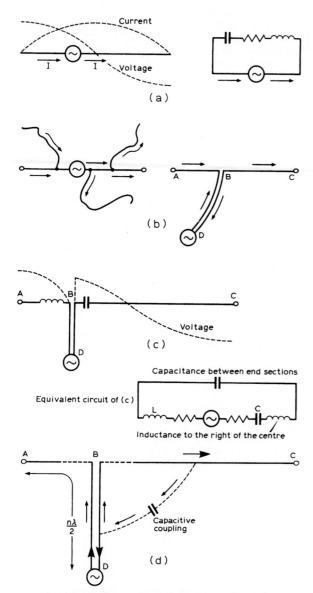

Fig 4.17. Off-centre feed. (a) Small self-contained transmitter, off centre, produces normal current and voltage distribution. (b) Hanging things onto the antenna wire produces chaos; this includes the off-centre feed DB shown on the right. (c) Correct method of off-centre feed, the antenna being resonant as viewed in each direction from the feedpoint. Voltage distribution is virtually the same as at (a) but, turned on end, this can be regarded either as a dipole or as a vertical monopole with a short counterpoise earth. (d) Difficulty arising if BD is an odd multiple of λ/4; voltage induced in BD from BC can result in unsymmetrical current distribution and feeder radiation. The effect is probably negligible unless ABD is resonant

consider the Marconi antenna, Fig 6.26. Here the earth has replaced one half of the dipole and a large proportion of the available power is usually wasted in the resistance of the earth connection. To overcome this, an extensive system of ground

radials is usually recommended, advice which if followed to the letter would usually involve digging up not only the whole of one's own garden but those of several neighbours as well.

This topic recurs in Chapter 10, but it is interesting to observe in passing that if the arrangement of Fig 4.17(c) is rotated anticlockwise into a vertical position the left-hand half can be regarded as the 'earth connection'. As such it can be further improved by using two or more short radial wires in place of AB, the effective 'earth resistance' amounting to no more than the small ohmic loss in the loading coil.

Such an arrangement is often described as a 'counterpoise', a term which applies in general to any grouping of wires insulated from earth and acting in lieu of an earth connection; such groupings are normally arranged so that the wires generate opposing fields, as a result of which little or no radiation takes place from the counterpoise.

This discussion thus far has failed to take account of losses due to currents induced in the ground adjacent to the antenna; these exist even in the case of dipoles and may well be increased if advantage is taken of the shortening of AB in order to erect the antenna at the lowest possible height. Dipoles can, however, also be reduced in height by the use of end-loading (p183), and it is concluded that for most purposes the distinction between 'dipole' and 'monopole' has little relevance apart from such incidental differences in height. A height of only 1 or 2m should be sufficient for reducing losses due to earth currents to an acceptable level [6].

A number of practical situations involving off-centre feed will next be considered.*

Feeding the 'odd bit of wire'

The random length of wire, end-fed, was one of the commonest antennas in the early days of amateur radio and can still be very useful as discussed in Chapter 15. Fig 4.18 shows the method of feeding such antennas and this can also be applied to vertical antennas which are often much easier to feed at their lower ends than in their centres.

In Fig 4.18(a) the impedance Z_a to earth at the end of the antenna wire is in series with the impedance Z_c of the counterpoise, and it is desired to match the transmitter into the impedance $(Z_a + Z_c)$. If the length of the antenna is anywhere near a multiple of λ/2, Z_a will be high and it is easy to make Z_c small compared with Z_a so that it has little effect on the matching process. Typically, at resonance Z_a may be about 8000Ω and a capacitance of a few picofarads to ground will suffice for Z_c. At 14MHz this can be provided by about 3ft (1m) of wire clipped onto the picture rail but at lower frequencies or as one departs from resonance it becomes necessary to increase the size of the counterpoise. However, no real difficulty arises until the antenna approaches the λ/4 resonance or an odd multiple of this, in which case Fig 4.18(b) should be used.

Matching can usually be achieved with one or other of the

* Long-wire resonant antennas containing two or more half-wavelengths can be fed in the centre of any current loops. Such feeds are asymmetrical only in the physical sense and not appropriate to the present discussion.

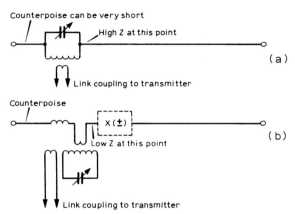

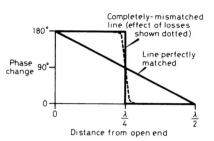

Fig 4.20. Variation of phase along matched and mismatched lines. The dotted lines illustrate the effects of losses

Fig 4.18. Methods of feeding 'odd lengths of wire'. Provided the impedance is fairly high, method (a) can be used with only a very short counterpoise. Sometimes the counterpoise has been omitted, relying solely on the stray capacitance of the coil but this is not recommended. (b) is recommended for low impedances, X tunes out the reactance (if any) of the antenna. Longer counterpoises, ideally about λ/8 and resonated by series inductance, are needed in the case of low impedance. Depending on antenna length positive or negative X may be required as shown, this arrangement being very similar to Fig 4.17(c)

arrangements shown, with the matching circuit providing extra selectivity for the rejection of harmonics etc. It is advisable that there should be no direct connection to the transmitter since this can result in currents 'wandering vaguely' to earth via mains wiring etc.

Ground-plane antennas

These usually consist of λ/4 vertical antennas grounded by means of a set of radial wires insulated from earth as in Fig 4.19. A single λ/4 radial can be used but in this case it forms a considerable part of the radiating system and seriously distorts the pattern.

At least two radials are normally advised, three or four

being more usual, and the antenna is usually fed with low-impedance coaxial line despite the considerable risk of radiation from the feeder as discussed on p53. There is a fundamental fallacy in the use of resonant radials since the theory rests on the premise that the currents in the radials are equal, in which case the fields they produce are self-cancelling with virtually all the radiation coming from the vertical element. Unfortunately for this idea, the phase reversal of the current-wave at resonance (illustrated in Fig 4.4) means that since length tolerances are always finite it is impossible to maintain current equality whilst tuning through resonance, except by virtue of unspecified losses [25]. This is shown more clearly by Fig 4.20, illustrating the following important principle:

If loss-free resonant conductors connected in parallel are required to carry equal currents they must not be connected solely at a point of maximum current.

This is axiomatic and will be encountered in various forms but, applying it to the present problem, let us consider any pair of radials such as Fig 4.21(a) and suppose that initially both were tuned with extreme precision to 14,250kHz but a small change of garden layout has caused one of the resonances to drop by 0.7% to 14,150kHz. In between these frequencies one radial is now inductive, the other capacitive, so that at 14,200kHz they form a parallel-tuned circuit: Fig 4.21(b). For typical wire radials the reactance will be about 6Ω and for

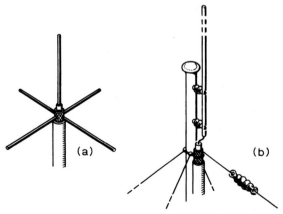

Fig 4.19. Ground-plane antenna. (a) Basic system: any number of radials can be used but preferably at least two. (b) Typical installation with guy wires acting as radials. Radials are usually λ/4 but see recommendations in text

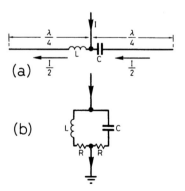

Fig 4.21. Unequal radials. Inequalities simulated by L and C. R represents losses (including radiation). For example in text, $\omega L = 1/\omega C$ and $Z = \omega^2 L^2/2$. If one radial is slightly too long and the other short, they form the parallel-tuned circuit shown at (b)

the pair, from Fig 3.11, the loss resistance (12swg) would be 0.6Ω, giving a *Q* of 10 and a resistance to ground of 60Ω. If this were to happen, the radials, because of the phase reversal, would constitute a dipole effectively in series with the monopole, and since they are now broadband the currents would be equalised, the 'dipole' would disappear, and we would be back with the same problem!

Faced with this kind of situation even a computer goes berserk, the equalising of currents through several imped-ances all equal to zero being outside its terms of reference. It is clearly unsatisfactory to have a system dependent on unspecified losses for its correct functioning. This is not the only problem, since with λ/4 radials difficulty has been found in equalising currents owing to coupling between the radials and a feeder trailing along the ground underneath them, as in Fig 4.23. The situation is clearly one of extreme complexity, much at odds with the usual simple picture of ground-plane antennas and, being easily avoidable, this would seem to be the sensible course.

Having thus established that the resonant length λ/4, far from being mandatory, is the one to be avoided, it follows that the radials must be detuned sufficiently to ensure that the currents are in the same phase and of comparable amplitude. With sufficient detuning the equalisation of radial lengths ceases to be critical but it remains essential to comply with the rules for asymmetrical feeder systems formulated earlier in this chapter; these demand resonance on each side of the feedpoint so that *after being connected in parallel the radials must be tuned to resonance by means of a single reactance common to all of them.*

At this point it is important to be clear about the purpose of the radials: what they can do and what they cannot do. It is helpful to start by removing the ground-plane antenna to free space where it works just as well in spite of the fact that 'ground' no longer exists, and it becomes more clearly recognisable as an 'asymmetrical dipole', one pole of which has been prevented from radiating by using more wires and (for example) arranging them in opposing pairs; it will be clear from the discussion on pp9, 10 that it has the same radiation pattern and therefore the same gain as any other short dipole. Since it is only half the length, its radiation resistance must be only a quarter that of a λ/2 dipole apart from a small correction (p90) which brings it up to 20Ω, this figure being independent of anything done to the radials since these are non-radiating. This means that they can be short-ened to any desired extent without affecting the value of *R*, and without affecting the efficiency either so long as the resistance of the loading coil remains small compared with 20Ω.

At this point the reader is doubtless becoming impatient, wondering why, in free space where we now are, one should bother with radials. Surely it would be much easier to settle for a dipole with the transmitter in the middle of it, in which case (having got rid of the feeder as well) this would cease to be a fit topic for the present chapter?

These are good questions but, before descending from the calm of outer space into the storm of controversy now

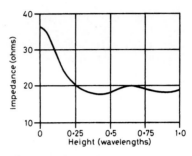

Fig 4.22. Base feed impedance of λ/4 antenna as function of height of radials above the ground

awaiting us at ground level, there is one further question to be asked: what are the radials for, anyway? They do in fact serve three purposes: (a) acting as one pole of a dipole so as to provide a return path for the current flowing into the other pole, (b) reducing the current on a coaxial feeder so as to prevent it radiating, and (c) the primary function of allowing the 'dipole' to be brought right down to ground level without having to dig a deep hole for the lower half.

Shortly before 'hitting the ground' it starts to undergo a metamorphosis, losing its dipole identity and becoming a monopole; its radiation resistance rises to 36Ω because of mutual impedance between the antenna and its image in the ground, the vertical-plane radiation pattern broadens to one half that of a dipole (one can in fact arrive at the 36Ω figure by thinking of the antenna plus image as a dipole with its radiation confined to one half of a sphere) and losses are incurred because of currents flowing in the ground.

One thing the radials do *not* do is act in any way as a reflecting plane nor, since the fields from them very nearly cancel in all directions, can they contribute in any way to angles of radiation. Replacement of the radials by a perfect reflecting plane would of course confer 'monopole' status on the ground-plane antenna, resulting in a feedpoint impedance of 36Ω regardless of height, and this figure has hitherto been the one most widely accepted. The 20Ω figure first came to the author's attention as a measured result in an old issue of a professional journal. Although endorsement has come from a number of other quarters it remains highly controversial, a number of leading authorities having apparently fallen into the trap of regarding the radials as an actual 'ground-plane' even though, since it consists of discrete wires, it is under the necessity of compliance with the rules set out on pp9, 10 for the derivation of antenna patterns.

The variation of feedpoint (or radiation) resistance with height can be derived by treating the antenna and its image as a collinear pair separated by the distance between the 'centres of gravity' of the current distributions, yielding results virtu-ally identical with Fig 4.22 which was the outcome of a rigorous mathematical analysis [23] by VK2BBF.

It has been confirmed experimentally that, provided the inductance of the loading coil is suitably increased and its loss resistance remains small compared with 20Ω, the radials can be as short as desired, except that below about λ/12 the decrease in bandwidth starts to becomes significant and a practical lower limit of about $\lambda/20$ tends to be set by the difficulty of preventing feeder radiation (a main cause of TVI) rather than by increasing losses or associated increases of noise level during reception. Even so, single pairs of $\lambda/20$ radials have been used successfully with losses (calculated and also confirmed by field strength measurements) of less than 0.4dB, which is comparable with the loss by radiation from a pair of $\lambda/4$ radials. Radiation from radials can be readily assessed by the method set out on p9, and shown to drop rapidly from an initial low value to virtually zero (even for a single radial) as the length is reduced below $\lambda/4$.

In the past the large amount of space occupied by $\lambda/4$ radial systems and the difficulty of using them for beams have been serious limitations. Short radials are widely and wrongly regarded as compromises, due possibly to the alleged poor quality of some commercial products, though hardly a matter for surprise in view of the report [21] that the inventor of the ground-plane antenna was forced into specifying extra radials because nobody would believe that two were adequate! In like vein it seems that some readers find it difficult to believe that short radials can be as good or better than longer ones, and to clear the matter up beyond reasonable doubt it was felt necessary to 'tidy up some loose ends'. This escalated into a major programme with answers generating a lot more questions and some 'sticky moments' as well as surprises, though most of this material is more appropriate to later chapters.

The effect of shortening the radials can be understood in terms of the equivalent circuit (Figs 4.2, 4.33) since the reduction in C, which is obvious, translates into an increase of Z_0, ie the effect is basically the same as reducing the wire diameter (though it may be much greater).

Other findings can be summarised as follows. Existing ground-plane installations are likely, in the main, to be satisfactory but if possible (particularly if performance is suspect) should be checked for current equality; this should be done at two frequencies (eg both ends of a band) since equality at one frequency does not rule out the possibility of a phase reversal. Attention has been focussed sharply on problems of feeder radiation and the importance of measures to reduce it, making it important to avoid situations like the one illustrated in Fig 4.23 which shows how, in the case of a four-radial ground plane at low height, symmetry can be upset by coupling between the feeder and the radials; the solution in this case is to increase the base height, bury the feeder, or decrease the length of the radials. In practice difficulty was experienced with a height of 4ft at 14MHz, but there were no noticeable current differences with a height of 8ft, or with two radials if the feeder was brought away at right-angles. There was no difficulty in the case of short radials either, and the observed field strengths were independent of the radial systems.

The 'tolerance notch' described earlier was not observable and would almost certainly have been masked by ground losses at the heights available. The effect is difficult to isolate and its physical reality remains speculative, but it is clearly a hazard to be avoided, unless there is good reason to the

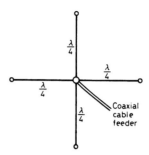

Fig 4.23. Bird's eye view of four-radial ground plane. How does one achieve symmetry?

contrary such as not wanting to disturb an existing system that appears to be working well! It is also to be observed that from the point of view of gain the equalisation of radial currents is not particularly important. Consider for example the case of a single radial; this deprives the vertical radiator of half the transmitter power so there is a loss of 3dB. However, if a second radial is added, even if it carries only half the current of the other radial, the field strength in the unwanted mode is reduced to a third of that in the wanted mode and the power lost is only 0.45dB if there is no radiation from the feeder, though this will be a major hazard because of the lack of symmetry. This can be readily checked by means of a current probe (assuming the radials to be accessible), noting that the check should be made at the two ends of a band to exclude the possibility of a phase reversal, ie currents apparently equal but opposite in phase, which is a possibility though only at one frequency.

Fig 4.24 shows an experiment [25] using very short $\lambda/20$ radials which proved particularly instructive; initially matters appeared to go badly wrong, with the change from $\lambda/4$ radials resulting in a marked decrease in field strength although the antenna current was unchanged. After failing to find any

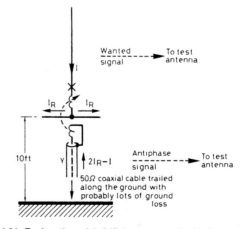

Fig 4.24. Explanation of 2–3dB loss caused by feeder radiation. Inter-winding capacitance provides path for out-of-balance currents. Results similar with feeder connected directly to X. Loss in both cases cured by linear trap at Y; see Fig 4.40. Length of radials is $\lambda/20$

current on the outer of the coaxial cable (an error later traced to insufficient probe sensitivity) there was thought to be only one possibility, a non-sinusoidal current distribution in the radiator.

A first attempt to check this was inconclusive because too much of the element was out of reach, but later the sine-wave distribution was confirmed by means of an equivalent 'asymmetrical dipole' laid out in the horizontal plane. This was an interesting antenna in its own right, paving the way for a new breed of end-fed horizontal antennas to be featured in later chapters. However, a suspicion that the current in the radials was more than it ought to be supplied the missing clue in accordance with Fig 4.24, which serves also as a graphic illustration of the perils of allowing current to flow on the outer of the coaxial cable. The problem was easily resolved by means of the trap illustrated on p55 and the field strengths were then identical for the two radial lengths. In another test the author obtained identical antenna currents and signal reports at 14MHz when comparing four λ/4 radials with a set of four 40in (100cm) radials or two 60in (150cm) radials, using in each of the latter cases a common loading inductance of approximately 3µH.

A loading inductance of 3µH can consist of a six-turn coil of 3in (7.6cm) diameter and 1in (2.5cm) long, in which case a good match at 14MHz can be obtained by overwinding with a single-turn coupling coil spaced about ¼in (6mm) from the main winding. Due to inter-winding and other stray capacitances, the absence of a direct connection to the radiator is no guarantee of freedom from feeder radiation, though usually sufficient with longer (>λ/10) radials at low heights provided resonant lengths of feeder are avoided. Sometimes direct connection may be found better, in which case linear loading (eg as in Fig 11.19) offers the advantages of lower losses and no need for weather protection.

The use of direct connection is subject to two rules: first, the point of connection must be the true electrical centre of the antenna system and, second, any current flowing, say, in the outer of the coaxial cable due to unbalanced coupling from the antenna must not be able to find its way to the inner conductor. The electrical centre can be checked by first exciting the driven element with radiation from another antenna which should be spaced at least λ/4. Using a current probe (p239) the position of minimum voltage can be located by touch, ie one should be able to touch it without affecting the antenna current. This should be the lower end of the radiator.

A recommended form of counterpoise, designed to minimise coupling into the feeder and make the best use of space, is shown in Fig 4.25.

Feeding long-wire antennas

V- and rhombic antennas are high-impedance balanced systems which can be fed with open-wire lines, but single-wire systems present a more difficult problem unless one end can be brought into the shack as described earlier. Such wires may be terminated in their characteristic impedance as shown in

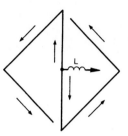

Fig 4.25. Compact two-radial ground plane (plan view); the loading inductance *L* allows the size to be further reduced and ensures that both radials are capacitive, thus avoiding any risk of imbalance due to phase differences. Current distribution in the radials is marked by arrows

Fig 4.26 and this is also the impedance presented at the feedpoint.

Typical values range from about 500Ω for a continuous thin wire to about 150Ω for a capacitively stretched wire (p239). A suitable counterpoise for 14MHz might have a capacitance of 6pF (2000Ω) to ground tuned by a coil having a loss resistance of 10Ω. The loss would be less than 0.3dB and with 3% detuning the reactance of the counterpoise would be only 120Ω, ie less than Z_0, so that SWR should remain acceptable over the width of any band likely to be required. Because of the inherent asymmetry, balanced feeders present problems but use of coaxial line with its outer conductor earthed by the counterpoise is feasible, provided the line length is such that it does not also provide a low impedance to ground.

Single-wire feeders (The 'Windom' antenna)

A single wire of any length may be used as a transmission line with the ground providing the return path. Such a line may be matched by connecting it to the correct point on an antenna system, eg at a distance of about 0.067λ from the centre of a λ/2 dipole which is thereby energised as in Fig 4.27(a).

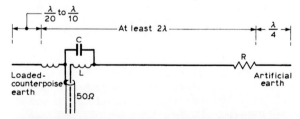

Fig 4.26. Feeding of terminated long-wire antennas. The principle is similar to that of Fig 4.17(c) but the antenna can be any length, though preferably at least 2λ, and no tuning is needed. The counterpoise can be replaced by a λ/4 'single radial'. The optimum value of *R* is about 500Ω; this absorbs the back radiation, resulting in a unidirectional pattern as explained in Chapter 6. For multiband operation 'fans' of 'artificial earths' or counterpoises may be used, having wires cut to length or inductively loaded as in Fig 11.14(c) for each frequency. The tuned circuit LC provides a 10:1 step-up in impedance, suitable values for 14MHz being *L* = 1.86µH, *C* = 68pF

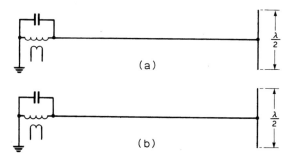

Fig 4.27. (a) Single-wire feed to λ/2 dipole. (b) Long wire antenna identical with Fig 4.26 except that a λ/2 dipole is used as the terminating resistance, and the earth is conventional. The feed is displaced from the centres of the dipoles by 0.067λ

Thin wire can be used for the feeder and advantages include low visual impact and the possibility of second-harmonic operation. Disadvantages are high levels of feeder radiation, losses in the ground return path, and better ways of doing the same job, so that the single-wire feeder in this form is now obsolescent. A new variant of this system has now emerged [21] as a possible solution to a number of problems but, before proceeding further, it may be of interest to digress for a moment and look again at the case of the long antenna wire terminated in its characteristic impedance. As with a transmission line this removes standing waves but, as explained in Chapter 6, the resistance absorbs the power which would otherwise be radiated in the back direction. This leaves the gain in the forward direction of the wave unaffected, and if the wire is long enough a large gain is possible. The terminating resistance can take the form of the right point on a λ/2 dipole, Fig 4.27(b), in which case the power in the termination is radiated instead of being converted into heat. However, as the radiation from the dipole is distributed over a wide angle, the high-gain undirectional pattern of a long wire is not greatly affected.

By this time the reader may be puzzling over the similarity between (a) and (b). There *is* in fact no difference, and the argument clearly implies a feeder loss of 3dB in the case of the Windom, a figure in good agreement with the author's experience, though some allowance should also be made for losses in the earth connection. The loss will be reduced if the feeder is very short and for a feeder length of λ/2 it can be roughly estimated from the impedance ratio 73/500. This comes to 0.6dB, and as an 'educated guess' something rather less than this might be expected for the ground-return loss, assuming a short loaded counterpoise wire for the 'ground' at the transmitter.

What has now emerged [25] is an end-fed version according to which one can take any random wire and convert it into the equivalent of a Windom antenna by inserting a small capacitor in the right place as illustrated in Fig 4.28, the manner of operation being as follows. Consider a typical resonant conductor insulated at both ends as illustrated and refer to the Smith chart, p70; it needs only a short movement Δl inwards along the wire to find a resistance of 500 or 600Ω

Z_0 of the wire, and this has in series with it a large inductive reactance which is easily tuned out by means of a small capacitor C. At its shack end the feeder encounters the counterpoise and a transformer for matching it to the 50Ω required by the transmitter. Values of Δl and C can be obtained from Fig 4.29 which can be used also for the matching of balanced feeders by means of series capacitance.

As thus far described, this system has the same basic limitations as the older version but derives practical merit by filling the need for a method of end-feeding antennas in the absence of good alternatives. This, however, is not the end of the road, where two very useful new options reveal themselves [24] as illustrated in Fig 4.30. First there is the 'zero length option' whereby the single-wire feeder is shortened so that, in effect, the transformer and counterpoise get dragged up all the way to the antenna, coaxial feeder from the shack being paid out as necessary. The single-wire feeder has now disappeared, leaving us with an antenna end-fed with coaxial cable and no losses; not only has the single-wire line shrunk to zero length but by inference from the experiments with ground-plane antennas, p119, the close proximity between antenna and ground-plane means that, except at very low heights, current passes directly between them instead of via the ground. In fact, lengthening the radiator of a ground-plane antenna, with appropriate tuning adjustments, provides a simpler route to the same goal.

Next, there is the 'nearly-zero length option' which can be used to push points of high RF voltage away from places where they are being a nuisance, thereby keeping RF out of the shack or solving the difficult switching problem presented by the beam described on p227. In this case there was a further bonus in the form of wide bandwidth, a valuable property of this type of antenna which had originally been masked by the inherent narrow bandwidth of the 'improved' version of the Zepp feed; though still seen as a useful option for the beam illustrated in Fig 13.14, this is probably also heading for

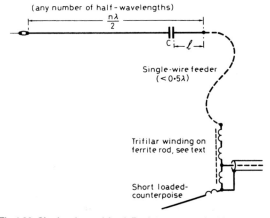

Fig 4.28. Single-wire end-feed. Resistance seen looking outwards from the wire from C equals the Z_0 of the wire. The series reactance is tuned out by C. The values of C and *l* depend upon the radiation resistance and are given by Fig 4.29. Can also be used to feed an inverted ground plane (p185)

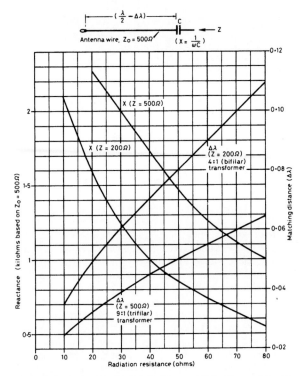

Fig 4.29. Matching data for single wires end-fed with coaxial cable (ARRL)

obsolescence. An important feature of the new options has been the development of transformers for 500Ω impedances as described on p58.

Zepp feed or 'J-match' – standard version

There is an urgent need for the end-feeding of some types of antenna, particularly vertical dipoles or inverted ground-planes which are often difficult for mechanical reasons to feed anywhere other than at their base. End-feeding of reso-nant horizontal antennas is also desirable in many cases and, although the method shown in Fig 4.18 offers one solution, there may be problems in housing the components.

The 'obvious' answer in these cases is the Zepp feed which has deep roots in the history of radio and an honoured place in most of the standard textbooks. It is a pity therefore that in its recognised form it "does not work" [5].

To appreciate this, consider Fig 4.31(a) which shows replacement of the tuned circuit of Fig 4.18(a) by a λ/4 resonant stub, the antenna being made slightly longer than λ/2 so that it looks like a capacitive reactance in shunt with a considerably larger value of resistance. The counterpoise is made equal in length to the extra length of the antenna so that it has the same capacitance to ground, and the system is balanced as illustrated by the equivalent circuit, Fig 4.31(b). It will be seen that if the length of the antenna is reduced to

λ/2, balance requires a counterpoise length of zero as in Fig 4.31(b), which means that the circuit is not completed and the antenna is no longer energised.

With an LC type tuner, balance is not required so there is no need to get into this predicament, but suppose that as shown in the lower figures the tuner circuit is replaced by λ/4 of resonant line. This has basically the same properties as the tuned circuit except that to prevent radiation from this line it is necessary to ensure balance and this is a further reason why the arrangement shown at (b) *ought not to work*. This is the traditional 'Zepp feed'.

This problem was first pointed out by G6CJ in the *RSGB Bulletin* for December 1955, just as the author was in the process of clocking up yet another addition to a long list of antenna failures, most of which have since been attributed to use of the Zepp feed. To overcome this problem G6CJ proposed the addition of a λ/4 stub as shown in Fig 4.32. Starting from the end of the antenna, note that there are two current paths but, because current flowing into the new stub has λ/2 further to travel, there is a phase reversal so that the voltage across the stub is balanced relative to earth.

It can be deduced from Fig 4.31(c) that if at the end of the antenna there is a voltage V across the impedance R_e the Zepp feed will see a voltage $2V$ across $4R_e$, ie Z_0^2/R which is typically $1000^2/70 = 17,000\Omega$, giving an SWR in 600Ω of 29 compared with 8 for the same dipole centre-fed. Hence the SWR tends to be rather large with consequent reduction in bandwidth and possible increase in losses, so that it is unwise to exceed a resonant feeder length of λ/4 or to use for this any type of line other than 600Ω open-wire. At the low-imped-ance end of this line any of the usual methods may be employed for matching into the remainder of the feeder system.

The reader may well be wondering how it is that if the Zepp feed does not work it managed to avoid suspicion of its bona-fides for so many years, being ousted from popularity mainly

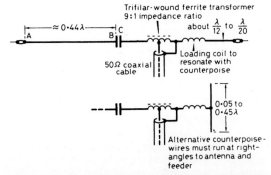

Fig 4.30. Dipole end-fed with coaxial cable or single-wire feeder. C (pF) ≈ 160/f. Length AB depends on R and Z_0 (see Fig 4.29). With the 9:1 ratio, options include single-wire feed between C and the transformer or merely reducing the SWF length to zero, obtaining a dipole end-fed with coaxial cable; in this case a 4:1 ratio can be substituted, with AB reduced to 0.405λ. Short lengths of SWF can still be used to distance the high voltages at C from the balun and coaxial cable without changing the feed system character (ARRL)

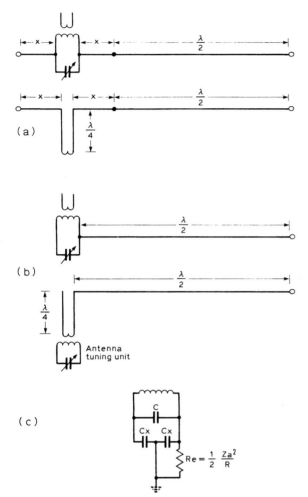

Fig 4.31. Voltage-fed antenna. (a) is very similar to 4.18(a) and lengths are not important if a tuned circuit is used. If this is replaced by a stub the lengths x, x must be equal or the line will be unbalanced; x must not be too short, ie the reactance of C_x in the equivalent circuit shown at (c) must be small compared with R_e or again there will be unbalance. The arrangement at (b) ought not to work but may do so after a fashion as a result of stray capacitances; this is the basis of the Zepp feed or J-match. At (c) note that R_e is equivalent to a resistance $4R_e$ across C. R is the current-loop radiation resistance and Z_a the characteristic impedance of the antenna

by the swing of fashion which currently favours low-impedance coaxial lines. The reason is believed to be in part that antenna current used to be regarded as a good indication of antenna efficiency, and plenty of current flows in the tuned circuit of Fig 4.31(c), likewise in the tuned feeders of Fig 4.31(b).

This of course is not a sufficient reason in itself since no amount of amperage would be convincing without some radiation but, though not normally a good method of obtaining radiation, Fig 4.31(b) is not a good method of preventing it either and under certain conditions it can even work efficiently. This happens if, in addition to the capacitance

between the wires, there is also capacitance to earth from each wire separately, thus recreating the situation shown in Fig 4.31(a) despite the absence of the counterpoise.

Attempts have been made to explain the functioning of Fig 4.31(b), despite the connection of only one terminal, on the grounds that if electromagnetic fields take long enough to reach the load only one terminal of this needs to be connected to the generator, the antenna itself being quoted as an example of an "open circuit in which large currents can flow" [22]. Against this the author can only offer the historical note recorded above and many years of experience during which, whatever their faults, antennas have always behaved in strict accordance with circuit or transmission-line rules and, as explained earlier, the antenna and feeder can always in principle be represented by equivalent circuits such as Fig 4.2.

If, for example, such a line is cut in half, the right-hand side can be replaced at any given frequency by a single reactance and resistance without affecting anything on the left; it is true that if more than one section (or additional frequencies) are involved it may be difficult to derive suitable equivalences without invoking such extra resources as the Smith chart (p85), and circuit theory is not always the best way of dealing with problems, but its rules must always be treated with respect and no current can flow out of a generator without the completion of a circuit between its terminals. In proof of this, consider a source of power and a resistive load, each hidden in the proverbial 'black box with two terminals'; unless allowed access to both there is clearly no way of deciding whether or not either of the boxes contains also a delay network. It is in any case important to realise that, apart from its radiating properties which can be adequately represented by an equivalent resistance (R), the antenna is essentially a transmission line and can therefore be simulated by discrete LC components as in Fig 4.2.

A single section as shown, together with its derivation, in Fig 4.33 is usually sufficient in the case of simple antennas. In no circumstances do such lines, or line sections, bear the slightest resemblance to an open-circuit; as with any other AC circuit there are electric or magnetic fields associated with these components but, as explained in Chapter 2, there is no

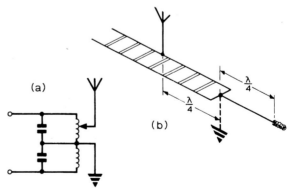

Fig 4.32. Unbalanced antenna – balanced line

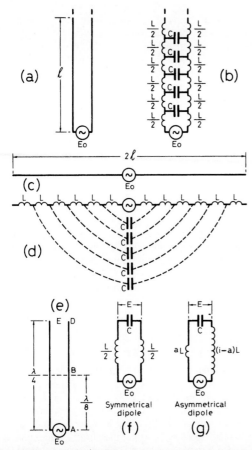

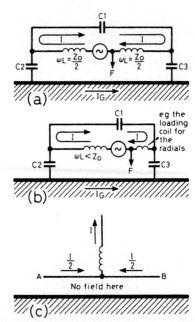

Fig 4.34. Equivalent circuits for dipoles close to ground: (a) symmetrical and (b) asymmetrical. The feeder (at F) will radiate unless maintained close to ground potential. (c) shows why the ground current I_G might reasonably be expected to disappear in the case of a ground-plane antenna (ARRL)

$$Z_0 = 276 \log (2l/a) - 120 \qquad (1)$$

This applies to cylindrical conductors of length $2l$ and radius a, and gives an average value of Z_0, which varies somewhat along the line.

Some values for multiple wires and helices will be found in Table 7.1.

Such data is essential for application of the Smith chart or equivalent circuits such as Fig 4.34. At low heights the dipole can be identified with a pair of single-wire lines at a height h above ground and connected in series, for which the formula to use is:

$$Z_0 = 276 \log (2h/a) \qquad (2)$$

Although with the help of these and other simple formulae most feeder problems can be resolved by the application of normal AC circuit and transmission-line principles, 'fault' situations, particularly those involving imbalance such as the Zepp feed in its traditional form, are not amenable to calculation.

Just to remind the reader, we are still in 'free space', having been left there in Chapter 3 in order to simplify matters, and by definition the earth does not exist. If on the other hand we come down to earth, one might intuitively expect the Zepp feed to work after all, provided the wires are far enough apart and close enough to the ground to ensure that currents induced in the ground by one wire are not all cancelled by equal and opposite currents induced from the other.

Fig 4.33. Derivation of equivalent circuits of antennas. A typical line is shown at (a) and (b) shows the conventional representation of such a line in terms of lumped constant. (c) Shows the same line opened out to form a dipole. (d) Its equivalent circuit which differs from (b) only to the extent that L and Z_0 are larger, C smaller, and radiation resistance (not shown) has been acquired. (e), (f) and (g) illustrate simpler versions of the equivalent circuit for the special case of $\lambda/4$, the inner half of the line being replaced by a single inductance for which $\omega L = 1/\omega C = Z_0$, the voltage ratio E/E_0 being given in all cases by Z_0/R or $\omega L/R$ where R is the internal impedance of the generator or, in the case of an antenna, the radiation resistance (ARRL)

'electromagnetic' wave present until after the separate fields generated by the conductors constituting the antenna have travelled far enough from it to 'get their act together'.

For antenna tuning and matching calculations involving departures from resonance it is usually necessary to know the Z_0 of the antenna and Fig 4.13 is an attempt to remedy the prevailing scarcity of data. This is based on the following formula [20] and, though not strictly applicable to bent wires, has proved useful as a rough guide even when dealing with complex shapes including loops, though it can be expected in such cases to give values which are somewhat too large. It will be noticed that there is no height dependence and, referring to Fig 4.34, this links it to the condition C2 and C3 = 0, ie heights above about $\lambda/6$.

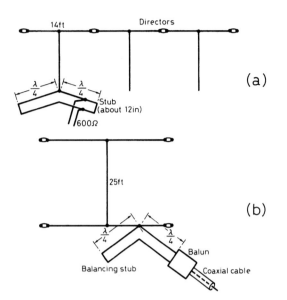

Fig 4.35. Zepp-fed vertical arrays. (a) Three-element using Zepp-fed inverted ground-plane elements. (b) Alternative method of feeding the beam illustrated in Fig 13.14

It has in fact been found by the author in two cases that the balancing stub, Fig 4.32, was not essential but in each of these cases the wires were spaced about 7in (18cm) and only some 2–3ft (0.6–0.9m) from the ground. Even so the system did seem to be less critical, particularly in respect of balance in the main feeder, when the stub was in use.

The tuned-line version of Fig 4.31(a) suffers from narrow bandwidth because (due to the greater length) the impedance on the right-hand side of the line changes with frequency more rapidly than that on the left, thus upsetting the balance.

Fig 4.35 illustrates two different applications of the balanced Zepp feed, somewhat freely adapted from actual cases

to demonstrate some of the possibilities and limitations of a Zepp feed with the added balancing stub.

In case (a), a (current point) R of 20Ω would have appeared as about $75k\Omega$ across the top of the 600Ω line, giving a Q of 125, ie 5Ω at the bottom end. The required length of matching stub, as remembered, was about a foot, and apart from the narrow bandwidth (less than 1%) the performance was satisfactory. In contrast, a rough estimate for the coaxial end-feed system described earlier (the SWF 'Zero-length option') suggests that, had it then been available, it would have yielded a bandwidth of about 3%, as well as being a lot more convenient.

Case (b) is rather different, having eventually emerged as one of the preferred methods of feeding the beam described on p231, Fig 13.14. A particularly interesting feature of this was the discovery that with the balancing stub in place the feedpoint could be moved inwards to a point of lower impedance without affecting the balance; this implies removal of the bandwidth constriction, though at the time in question bandwidth was not an issue and remained unchecked. In this case the balanced Zepp presented no problems, though it is basically cumbersome and in most cases the coaxial alternative is likely to be more suitable.

What type of feeder?

Coaxial feeder is well ahead of the field in popularity due in part to the mistaken idea that it does not radiate, but it is also the most convenient since it can be 'run anywhere', even underground, with no special precautions except to make sure that water cannot get into any joins or terminations. The disadvantages are high cost and high losses, ranging between about 0.8dB and 2.4dB per 100ft (30m) at 30MHz, and roughly proportional to the square root of frequency. Many of the older cables also have a limited life.

The best low-impedance flat twin (eg type 214-023) is comparable with the best coaxial cable but it is advisable to

Table 4.1. UK UR series coaxial cables

UR No	Nominal impedance Z_0 (Ω)	Overall diameter (in)	Inner conductor (in)	Capacitance (pF/ft)	Maximum operating voltage (RMS)	Approximate attenuation (dB per 100ft)				Approx RG equivalent
						10MHz	100MHz	300MHz	1000MHz	
43	52	0.195	0.032	29	2750	1.3	4.3	8.7	18.1	58/U
57	75	0.405	0.044	20.6	5000	0.6	1.9	3.5	7.1	11A/U
63*	75	0.853	0.175	14	4400	0.15	0.5	0.9	1.7	
67	50	0.405	7/0.029	30	4800	0.6	2.0	3.7	7.5	213/U
74	51	0.870	0.188	30.7	15,000	0.3	1.0	1.9	4.2	218/U
76	51	0.195	19/0.0066	29	1800	1.6	5.3	9.6	22.0	58C/U
77	75	0.870	0.104	20.5	12,500	0.3	1.0	1.9	4.2	164/U
79*	50	0.855	0.265	21	6000	0.16	0.5	0.9	1.8	
83*	50	0.555	0.168	21	2600	0.25	0.8	1.5	2.8	
85*	75	0.555	0.109	14	2600	0.2	0.7	1.3	2.5	
90	75	0.242	0.022	0	2500	1.1	3.5	6.3	12.3	59B/U

All the above cables have solid dielectric with a velocity factor of 0.66 with the exception of those marked with an asterisk which are helical membrane and have a velocity factor of 0.96. This table is compiled from information kindly supplied by Aerialite Ltd and BICC Ltd, and includes data extracted from Defence Specification DEF-14-A (HMSO).

Table 4.2. USA RG series coaxial cables

Cable no.	Nominal impedance Z_0 (ohms)	Cable outside diameter (in)	Velocity factor	Approximate attenuation (dB per 100ft)					Capacitance (pF/ft)	Maximum operating voltage (RMS)
				1MHz	10MHz	100MHz	1000MHz	3000MHz		
RG-5/U	52.5	0.332	0.659	0.21	0.77	2.9	11.5	22.0	28.5	3000
RG-5B/U	50.0	0.332	0.659	0.16	0.66	2.4	8.8	16.7	29.5	3000
RG-6A/U	75.0	0.332	0.659	0.21	0.78	2.9	11.2	21.0	20.0	2700
RG-8A/U	50.0	0.405	0.659	0.16	0.55	2.0	8.0	16.5	30.5	4000
RG-9/U	51.0	0.420	0.659	0.16	0.57	2.0	7.3	15.5	30.0	4000
RG-9B/U	50.0	0.425	0.659	0.175	0.61	2.1	9.0	18.0	30.5	4000
RG-10A/U	50.0	0.475	0.659	0.16	0.55	2.0	8.0	16.5	30.5	4000
RG-11A/U	75.0	0.405	0.66	0.18	0.7	2.3	7.8	16.5	20.5	5000
RG-12A/U	75.0	0.475	0.659	0.18	0.66	2.3	8.0	16.5	20.5	4000
RG-13A/U	75.0	0.425	0.659	0.18	0.66	2.3	8.0	16.5	20.5	4000
RG-14A/U	50.0	0.545	0.659	0.12	0.41	1.4	5.5	12.0	30.0	5500
RG-16A/U	52.0	0.630	0.670	0.1	0.4	1.2	6.7	16.0	29.5	6000
RG-17A/U	50.0	0.870	0.659	0.066	0.225	0.80	3.4	8.5	30.0	11,000
RG-18A/U	50.0	0.945	0.659	0.066	0.225	0.80	3.4	8.5	30.5	11,000
RG-19A/U	50.0	1.120	0.659	0.04	0.17	0.68	3.5	7.7	30.5	14,000
RG-20A/U	50.0	1.195	0.659	0.04	0.17	0.68	3.5	7.7	30.5	14,000
RG-21A/U	50.0	0.332	0.659	1.4	4.4	13.0	43.0	85.0	30.0	2700
RG-29/U	53.5	0.184	0.659	0.33	1.2	4.4	16.0	30.0	28.5	1900
RG-34A/U	75.0	0.630	0.659	0.065	0.29	1.3	6.0	12.5	20.5	5200
RG-34B/U	75	0.630	0.66		0.3	1.4	5.8		21.5	6500
RG-35A/U	75.0	0.945	0.659	0.07	0.235	0.85	3.5	8.60	20.5	10,000
RG-54A/U	58.0	0.250	0.659	0.18	0.74	3.1	11.5	21.5	26.5	3000
RG-55B/U	53.5	0.206	0.659	0.36	1.3	4.8	17.0	32.0	28.5	1900
RG-55A/U	50.0	0.216	0.659	0.36	1.3	4.8	17.0	32.0	29.5	1900
RG-58A/U	53.5	0.195	0.659	0.33	1.25	4.65	17.5	37.5	28.5	1900
RG-58C/U	50.0	0.195	0.659	0.42	1.4	4.9	24.0	45.0	30.0	1900
RG-59A/U	75.0	0.242	0.659	0.34	1.10	3.40	12.0	26.0	20.5	2300
RG-59B/U	75	0.242	0.66		1.1	3.4	12		21	2300
RG-62A/U	93.0	0.242	0.84	0.25	0.85	2.70	8.6	18.5	13.5	700
RG-74A/U	50.0	0.615	0.659	0.10	0.38	1.5	6.0	11.5	30.0	5500
RG-83/U	35.0	0.405	0.66	0.23	0.80	2.8	9.6	24.0	44.0	2000
RG-133A	95	0.405	0.66						16.2	4000
RG-213/U*	50	0.405	0.66	0.16	0.6	1.9	8.0		29.5	5000
RG-218/U**	50	0.870	0.66	0.066	0.2	1.0	4.4		29.5	11,000
RG-220/U***	50	1.120	0.66	0.04	0.2	0.7	3.6		29.5	14,000

* Formerly RG8A/U   ** Formerly RG17A/U   *** Formerly RG19A/U

space it out from any supporting structures. The velocity factor of most types of flat twin is greatly affected by moisture, making it unsuitable for outdoor use where phase stability is required.

The types of 300Ω twin ribbon most widely available at the time of writing in the UK, though often recommended as an alternative to open-wire line, are extremely sensitive to moisture. The velocity factor of older types can change by up to 20% and in the case of the semi-transparent plastic types severe deterioration has been found after a short period of use, resulting in a weather-dependent loss of several decibels per 100ft (30m).

Heavier-duty 300Ω line with slotted insulation is now sometimes obtainable and very much better; at 14MHz a 70ft length operating into a 50Ω load (ie at an SWR of 6.0) was tested under wet and dry conditions using an ATU in the shack to establish an SWR of 1.0 at the transmitter. In both cases the loss was difficult to measure, being well under 0.5dB in both cases, but the change from wet to dry caused the SWR to rise to 5 or 6 prior to re-adjustment of the ATU, consistent with a measured change of 5% in the velocity-factor. It can be inferred that either a reduction of feeder length to 30ft or an increase in load resistance to about 120Ω would have sufficed to keep changes in SWR below 2.5 or 3 and thus (for example) within the range of an automatic ATU (p64).

Open-wire 300Ω line is quite easy to construct if heavy-gauge copper wire can be stretched tightly between two points (p293). It was found that by using flexible line only where this was essential, feeder losses of less than 1dB per half-wavelength could be achieved at an SWR of 15 without undue inconvenience from weather changes.

An even better alternative would appear to be the TV-type 300 or 450Ω open-wire line, though at the time of writing this would have to be obtained from sources in the USA.

Although open-wire line has to be rated lowest in terms of convenience, there are usually no major problems except for long indoor runs and the mechanical bypassing of beam rotators, a problem which can be overcome without detriment to performance by the use of *short* 300Ω line inserts, and which hardly arises anyway in the case of the reversible beams described in later chapters.

It is much the cheapest and most efficient type of feeder and *there is no foundation for the belief that it is any more liable to produce radiation than other types of feeder*. This can be easily checked by means of the formula on p53, but in effect the radiation from a long line is as if from a dipole having a length equal to the spacing and carrying the line current which, in view of the high Z_0, is in any case low if the line is matched.

Radiation can of course result from imbalance but, assuming reasonable care in this respect, the more likely causes of radiation are those which tend to affect all types of feeder equally as discussed in the next section. Attenuation using 14swg (2mm) conductors [1] is of the order of 5dB *per mile* (3dB/km) or 0.1dB per 100ft (30m) at 30MHz and this can be reduced by using thicker conductors, the attenuation being inversely proportional to the surface area of the copper so that each time the attenuation is halved the weight and approximate cost is multiplied by four. For losses comparable with coaxial feeder the wire size could be reduced to 36swg (0.2mm), and for runs of up to 100m there seems little point in going to anything thicker than 18 or 19swg (1.2mm).

It is evident that if the shack is a long way from the antenna there is no alternative to the use of open-wire line. By way of illustration, the author used to have a shack on the 'antenna farm' and a more convenient one in the house linked by 150yd (137m) of line made from odd bits of wire with several changes of gauge, averaging about 1mm diameter and incorporating two 4:1 baluns which provided 50Ω terminations. The line operated at a nominal SWR of 3.0, and with the further addition of an ATU the overall loss was only 1.6dB at 14MHz. This included estimated losses as follows:

Matched line loss	0.6dB
Extra loss due to mismatch	0.3dB
Two baluns	0.2dB

This makes no allowance for bends which are an additional source of losses and probably account for the residual 0.5dB loss. After much experiment with high-ratio transformers, additional ATUs and the like, the above arrangement was found to be best for convenience and efficiency, and can be recommended to anyone with a similar 'long-line' requirement. Obviously the losses could be much reduced by the use of, say, 14swg (2mm) wire and the avoidance of sharp bends. This would bring the estimated loss down to less than 1dB.

Radiation from feeders

Feeder radiation, though it may result in the occasional 'unlikely' contact, is more commonly associated with EMC problems, additional feeder loss (which can be large), and increased noise or interference in reception. Radiation from feeders can arise in several different ways [8].

Fig 4.36 illustrates a typical antenna fed at the centre with a feeder which may be of any type, and it is assumed for the moment that the system is energised by inductive coupling into an ATU with no earthing at the transmitter. If the feeder has an effective electrical length l as defined by Fig 4.36(a) which (allowing for top loading by the dipole) is an even number of quarter-wavelengths, it will resonate as an antenna and can be used as such. In fact a 14MHz dipole with about 44ft (13.4m) of vertical feeder, voltage fed at the lower end, performs well as a low-angle radiator for 7MHz DX. On the other hand, a length of 17 or 51ft (5.2 or 15.5m) would enable it to radiate efficiently on 14MHz, though probably in an unwanted direction or at an unsuitable angle of elevation.

This problem can be highly elusive, being dependent on a large number of variables so that its occurrence tends to be unpredictable and remedies that are successful in one case are useless in another. The best way of avoiding it is to ensure symmetry throughout the antenna and feeder systems, not overlooking the balance-unbalance transformation usually required at the transmitter; this is often difficult, as vertical

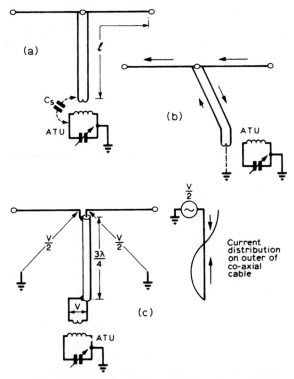

Fig 4.36. (a) If *l* is an even multiple of λ/4 the feeder is energised as a vertical radiator via the stray capacitance C_s. (b) If not brought away at right-angles the feeder is energised by unequal inductive or capacitive coupling as indicated by arrows. (c) Excitation of standing waves in coaxial feeder if current distribution is symmetrical. Even if feeder is at earth potential excitation can take place as at (a) or (b)

antennas are inherently unsymmetrical relative to the ground. In the case of horizontal transmitting antennas, losses due to imbalance tend to be negligible subject to feeding in the centre, keeping balanced lines away from other objects by distances of a few times their spacing, the use of baluns in the case of coaxial cable, and in all cases ensuring that feeders leave the antenna at right-angles for a distance of at least λ/2.

Even when all these conditions appear to be met, however, there is no guarantee of freedom from EMC and noise problems; other antennas or electrical conductors may upset balance either directly or through disturbance of the electromagnetic field pattern. Otherwise, trouble is usually attributable to the feeder constituting or forming part of an alternative radiating system capable of excitation either directly or by coupling from the main system, and if the asymmetry cannot be rectified the most likely cure lies in detuning the feeder by alteration of length or by the application of traps.

Baluns, though easy to check for efficiency, are subject to finite tolerances in respect of balance and may also have design failings as discussed in the next section.

The problems of pick-up from local noise sources and of TVI, though basically the same as the prevention of power

loss caused by feeder radiation, are much more difficult. These demand a correspondingly higher standard of suppression as the following example illustrates: 6dB suppression of an unwanted mode relative to a wanted mode means that only a fifth of the power is being lost, whereas the corresponding 6dB reduction of a 20dB noise level still leaves a lot of noise.

In going from horizontal to vertical polarisation matters take a further turn for the worse, though it should still not be too difficult to ensure radiation of most of the available power in the right mode and, if favoured with a quiet environment, pick-up of noise on the feeder is unlikely to be of consequence. If less fortunate it will be necessary to take a closer look at the problem, with Fig 4.36 as a convenient starting point; this shows how an unwanted mode can be excited by capacitive coupling at the transmitter unless the coupling coil is balanced to earth and shielded. The two halves of the dipole can also induce currents in the vertical feeder (the outer in the case of a coaxial line) but, given perfect symmetry, these are equal and opposite and therefore cancel. On the other hand, any asymmetry due to failure to bring the feeder away from the dipole at right-angles, or not connecting it to the exact centre of the dipole, or proximity of one half of the dipole to a tree or building, will lead to a net current in the down lead and hence to radiation in an unwanted and probably lossy mode with considerable potential for EMC problems.

Earthing the feeder at the transmitter alters the length required for resonance, and leads to a rather less predictable situation as the earth resistance and effective length of the earth connection are introduced into the problem. The safest course is probably to avoid earthing, keeping the electrical length of the system as far from resonance as possible. If necessary the resonance can be shifted by altering the feeder length or by connecting an earth or short counterpoise to the centre point of the coupling coil as shown dotted. Avoiding resonance minimises but does not necessarily eliminate the unwanted radiation at the fundamental frequency and the problem (though basically similar) may prove much more intractable at harmonic frequencies responsible for some of the EMC problems.

In the case of balanced lines the unwanted current is induced in the same direction in both conductors, subtracting from the transmission line current in one conductor, adding in the other, and displacing the SWR pattern in one relative to the other. This makes it impossible to obtain reliable measurements of SWR and a similar problem arises when current flows on the outer conductor of a coaxial line.

If a dipole fed with coaxial line is symmetrical with respect to earth, half the terminal voltage of the antenna can be expected to appear between the outer of the coaxial line at its top end and earth, Fig 4.36(c). The feeder must then appear like an 'inverted ground plane' antenna, for which the radiation resistance at resonance is about 20Ω and the power radiated in the unwanted mode will be

$$\frac{V^2}{4 \times 20} \text{ watts}$$

ie as much power is radiated from the feeder as from the

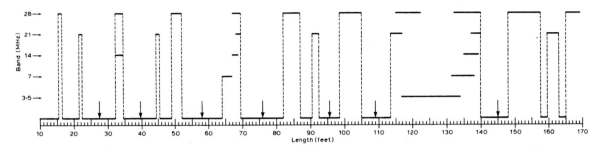

Fig 4.37. Lengths shown by solid lines along the horizontal axis avoid exact resonance in the 3.5, 7, 14, 21 or 28MHz amateur bands in systems where the coupling apparatus is isolated from ground. Best operating lengths corresponding to *l* in Fig 4.36(a) are at the centres of the wider ranges as shown by the arrows. To include 10, 18 and 24MHz while avoiding undue proximity to band edges it will be necessary to make some provision for alteration of *l* when the waveband is changed. The diagram needs some modification for the longer lengths if not all bands are required, since not every resonance is shown; eg if 28MHz is not needed 85ft could be used but, owing to a resonance at 14MHz, not 100ft *(ARRL Antenna Book)*

antenna. More likely, symmetry will not be achieved and feeder radiation will take place as previously described. As before, the situation can be more or less rectified for the fundamental frequency by avoiding resonance but this is unlikely to prevent radiation of harmonics unless these are effectively filtered.

A long line will have many resonances which may be fairly broad, and it is impossible to avoid all of them if the antenna is required to operate on all bands including 10, 18 and 24MHz. However, if only a few frequencies are involved *l* may be chosen with the help of charts such as Fig 4.37. Careful attention to symmetry will go a long way towards avoiding problems, the use of a balun being mandatory in the case of coaxial lines. It remains important, however, to suppress at the source any harmonics, which by radiation from the feeder could cause TVI, since baluns have a finite bandwidth and are likely to be ineffective at the higher harmonic frequencies.

By the provision of one or more counterpoise wires, it is possible to alter the effective value of *l*, Fig 4.36(a) as required. The precise length usually has to be found by experiment since it depends on stray capacitance, impedance discontinuities and, if the antenna is joined to the case of the transmitter, a number of indeterminate paths to earth which may even include the mains wiring.

As explained above, particular difficulty attaches to vertical and end-fed antennas since in these cases perfect symmetry is unobtainable, but use of non-resonant lengths in conjunction with loose couplings as described on p53 or the 'balanced' Zepp feed described earlier (p48) may provide a satisfactory solution.

Fig 4.38 illustrates a number of procedures which (used together if necessary) are believed to offer the best chance of success. It shows a conventional ground-plane antenna with its feeder taken straight down to an ATU which, as a first step towards tackling the problem, has been designed to ensure that any current on the outer of the coaxial feeder flows directly to ground instead of pursuing an uncertain course via the 'rig' and maybe the house wiring. Note that in the absence of the counterpoise, if ABC = λ/2 it becomes a top-loaded

vertical antenna in its own right, and as such will be energised efficiently by mutual coupling from BD so that AD becomes a dipole with BC now redundant. This may well be a useful trick to 'have up one's sleeve' and serves at least to demonstrate vividly the pitfalls of the problem; note also that with ineffective grounding on the 'rig' side of the ATU, RF can still find its way into the mains via the interwinding capacitance of the transformer.

The role of the counterpoise is therefore crucial, but if inconvenient a good external ground (possibly with series tuning of the lead inductance) may be the solution. An alternative course, which may also be used in addition, is to lengthen the feeder sufficiently to destroy the resonance, the extra length being accommodated if necessary by coiling it up

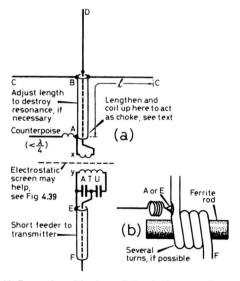

Fig 4.38. Prevention of feeder radiation in the case of a ground-plane antenna. There should be no feeder radiation if point A is securely grounded by the counterpoise and the length *l* is non-resonant. Joining x, y is equivalent to making the usual direct connection to the transmitter, in which case winding EF onto a ferrite rod or ring as shown at (b) may be effective

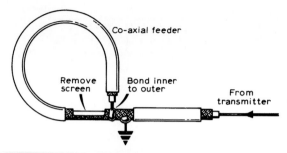

Fig 4.39. Screened coupling loop. Outer is sometimes partly removed to reduce current flow on outside of sheath

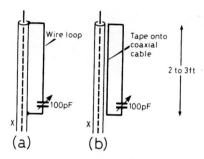

Fig 4.40. Traps for eliminating antenna current on outers of coaxial lines. Values and dimensions are for 14MHz but are not critical

to act as a choke at point B. This could improve matters further and, in the case of a 'trapped vertical', prevent trouble occurring on the higher frequency bands but, though frequently recommended, it is not a cure-all and could even make matters worse by causing a resonance to occur in another band.

It is perhaps worth making here the general point that chokes make little impact on the situation if located near a current-zero of the mode one is trying to suppress. Hence it is a good idea to try and locate any point of maximum current existing on the outer of the coaxial feeder and treat this as a preferred location for the choke, whilst making sure that it does not merely shift the position of the maximum. It is advisable at an early stage in the procedings to 'get one's bearings' with the help of a GDO, avoiding if possible ends of conductors or other 'high-voltage' points where readings, if obtainable, may be affected by body capacitance. If a resonance is located in the middle of a wanted band it may be possible to shift it by altering the length of the ground radial shown in Fig 4.38 or moving it to a different point on the downlead. Other ways of altering feeder resonances include the use of loose coupling as in Fig 4.24, and in some cases the use of a balun has been found effective.

Faced with problems of feeder radiation the use of an RF probe is strongly recommended as an aid to diagnosis though the simplest form of probe, Fig 18.13, may not be sufficiently sensitive for this task, and in any case the use of RF amplification as in Fig 18.16 is advisable to permit working with the lowest possible radiated powers and thus minimise 'spectrum pollution'. It is important if at all possible to have access to point B, so that the radials can be fine-tuned to minimise current on the coaxial cable outer at this point. This task is much easier with short radials since it requires only a single minor adjustment of the common loading coil, whereas with Fig 4.19(a), as explained earlier, equalisation is critical as well as essential.

For this adjustment the probe should be held or taped in place sufficiently far below B to ensure that there is no direct pick-up on it from the antenna itself. If B is not accessible, observations at a lower level can be used either to give the system a clean bill of health or as a basis for further experiments with detuning. To this end, the linear trap, Fig 4.40, is a particularly useful tool and, of all the available measures,

comes closest to being a certain cure, though care is needed since as well as being a trap it can also become a means of altering the tuning in an unfavourable as well as a favourable direction. The best place for it is close to B, and it should be found when correctly tuned that the current if any at D falls to zero coinciding, more or less, with a maximum in the loop. The loop current may in fact seem rather large, but this merely indicates that it is 'doing its job'.

The above procedures are readily adaptable to other asymmetrical dipoles and also to balanced feeders; in this case a current probe with the plane of its loop aligned with the feeders and moved round them as in Fig 4.41 should indicate a minimum in the position shown, and maxima decreasing rapidly with increase of distance/spacing if the line is well-balanced. With wide-spaced, open-wire lines it is best to look for a centrally placed minimum.

Fig 4.41. Use of current probe to check feeder balance. Probe should give symmetrical indications when moved round line as shown. (Unless carried out near a voltage minimum the indications may be affected by body capacitance)

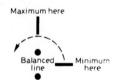

Unscreened lines are in themselves potential radiators but, subject to accurate balancing, this should be negligible for frequencies in the HF band. The power radiated for an RMS line current of I amps and a spacing D is given by:

$$P_r = 160 \left(\frac{\pi D}{\lambda} \right)^2 I^2 \quad \text{watts}$$

D and λ being measured in the same units so that D/λ is the line spacing measured in wavelengths. This is the same power as would be radiated from the same current in a short dipole of length equal to the line spacing [1].

For 600Ω line with 6in (15cm) spacing and a current of 1A (ie 600W) the line radiation at 14MHz is therefore

$$160 \left(\frac{\pi}{134} \right)^2 = 0.09W$$

The proportion of any harmonic power radiated by the line increases as the square of the harmonic number, but seems

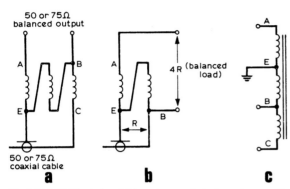

Fig 4.42. (a) Trifilar balun, 1:1 impedance ratio but can also provide 1:9 ratio (balanced or unbalanced) or 4:9 unbalanced on both sides. (b) Bifilar balun, 4:1 ratio. (c) Trifilar balun redrawn as auto-transformer to illustrate the principle of operation. The three (or two) windings are wound as one, with the least possible spacing between wires, though individual turns may be spaced out along the core as shown in Fig 4.43

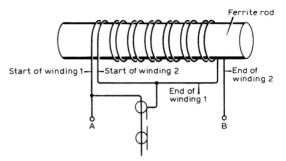

Fig 4.43. Construction of bifilar (4:1) balun. Although the wires must be bound tightly together spacing between turns is not critical unless impedances are very low, in which case leads must be as short as possible. Terminals AB provide a balanced output

likely to remain insignificant. The figures given by the above formula must be multiplied by four to account for radiation from the terminal connections, but even so for a 75Ω line with 0.08in (2mm) spacing only about one millionth of the incident power is radiated, as compared with the possibility of up to one-half as previously discussed for an unbalanced line.

This is still not the full story. A major advantage of coaxial line is that it can be laid anywhere, even buried underground. In contrast to this, low-impedance twin line generates a field which can be detected externally and, though it spreads only a short distance, makes it advisable to keep the line clear of trees and buildings etc, at least to the extent of mounting it on stand-off insulators. It is a minor disadvantage of open-wire lines that the balance is easily disturbed and the presence of objects near the line can cause asymmetry and hence radiation. The use of open-circuited matching stubs should where possible be avoided, since line balance is particularly sensitive to the proximity of the open ends of such stubs to surrounding objects.

Baluns

Most transmitters have an unbalanced output connection intended for use with a coaxial cable, whereas the majority of antennas are balanced, so that conversion from an unbalanced to a balanced system has to take place at one end or the other of the feedline. There are many ways of carrying out this process but, ignoring such commonly-used devices as the gamma match which is inherently unbalanced and a lot of other arrangements of less general interest, one is left with the trifilar and bifilar wound auto-transformers shown in Fig 4.42, of which there are a number of variants.

These devices, contrary to much that has been written about them, are highly efficient as well as extremely simple both in theory and practice. All one needs to do is take two or three lengths of enamelled copper wire about 10in (25cm) long, twist or bind them *very tightly* together (this is the vital

part of the process), wind them onto any odd bit of *ferrite rod* (Fig 4.43) that happens to be lying around, and connect them as shown. For a 3–30MHz balun, the theory states merely that the inductance must be large enough not to shunt the line significantly at 3MHz and the 'leakage reactance', which appears in series with the output, must be negligible at 30MHz. This is a very small amount and failure to realise the crucial nature of this requirement may be responsible for some of the difficulties which have been reported.

Another possible explanation is the prevalence of balun designs which are claimed to involve 'transmission line' principles. The leakage requirement also rules out the tapping of baluns which has frequently been recommended for obtaining impedance ratios other than the usual 1:1 or 4:1, although this is feasible for spot frequencies subject to some re-tuning of the antenna.

For further insight into the principles, reference may be made to Fig 4.44 which shows at (a) two wires of identical length laid alongside each other, so that if the spacing is small enough all the lines of magnetic force resulting from a current

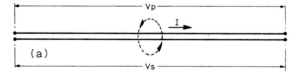

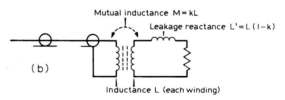

Fig 4.44. (a) Unity-coupled transformer formed by laying two straight wires close together. The alternating current *I* produces a voltage V_p as shown. The voltage V_s is virtually equal to V_p because almost all the magnetic lines of force surrounding the top wire also encircle the lower wire. (b) Equivalent circuit of transformer, leakage reactance = $L(1 - k)$ where *k* is the coupling coefficient. *k* is very close to unity in mains transformers and in RF transformers based on the principle of (a) above

flowing in one wire also surround the other wire, and there is no leakage. Separate the wires, allow them to be unequal in length, or attach long leads to their ends, and the above condition is no longer satisfied. The auto-transformer connection further reduces the leakage since a large part of the winding is common to input and output sides of the transformer.

Fig 4.44(b) shows the principle of operation; assuming a 50Ω load and a shunt reactance of 200Ω at 3MHz, a glance at the Smith chart (p70) gives an SWR of 1.25. At 30MHz the shunt reactance is 2000Ω and a leakage reactance of 12.5Ω causes the SWR to rise to 1.25. This is a leakage coefficient of only 0.625% but can nevertheless be realised easily enough if the above instructions are carefully followed.

It is important to realise that the core has no role other than to enable the required specification to be met at 3MHz while using the smallest possible length of wire so that the leakage is minimised. Any additional coupling provided by the core is trivial as may be proved by removing it, in which event the balun becomes useless on the lower-frequency bands but is barely affected at 28MHz. Frequency-independent compensation for the leakage reactance (so long as it does not exceed about 25Ω) is possible by means of a parallel capacitor connected on the output side. It will be evident from this explanation that the tighter the coupling, the greater the frequency range that can be covered.

Readers familiar with the large amount of recent literature on this topic may find it hard to believe that it can be simplified to this extent. Nevertheless, using these rules the author has constructed large numbers of baluns of many shapes and sizes. In one test no less than six ill-assorted small and large baluns in pairs, back-to-back, were inserted between a 400W PEP transmitter and the antenna with an overall loss of only about 0.5dB and no untoward effects, except that one very small one got too hot to touch!

Many other baluns have been constructed and the procedure outlined seems to be virtually foolproof provided impedances are restricted to the range of about 25–300Ω and the sole concern is to ensure efficient operation of the antenna.

Moreover, similar devices of comparable performance are available from a number of manufacturers. Baluns of this type *do not* require any special care in matching, adjustment of the antenna being apparently neither more nor less critical as a result of their use, and oft-repeated assertions that baluns cannot be used with mismatched loads are also incorrect; in proof of this, Table 4.3 was compiled from the calculated and measured values of SWR at 14MHz for a 200Ω load fed through a 4:1 balun, various degrees of mismatch being arranged by connecting reactances in series. A few loss measurements were also made, using a second identical balun to provide the overall 1:1 impedance ratio required for conforming with the needs of the power meter. The agreement is seen to be excellent, and in view of the inclusion of two baluns in the signal path the low losses were very encouraging.

Despite the fact that baluns have been fraught with many problems caused by lack of understanding, it is important to realise their limitations, such as the fact that if the balun is

Table 4.3. Performance of baluns when mismatched

L or C	SWR (theoretical)	SWR (measured)
22pF	8	7
47pF	3	2.7
67pF	2.27	1.95
110pF	1.64	1.6
220pF	1.29	1.24
1μH	1.54	1.6
1.7μH	2.53	2.6
3μH	4.55	4

Measured losses at 14MHz: 0.2dB at SWR = 4; and at 21MHz: 1.4dB at SWR = 4 and 0.3dB at SWR = 2

located at the antenna it will not help with imbalance caused by unequal coupling from the two halves of the antenna into a coaxial feedline; in this case [19] a choke may be required instead or in addition. The author's personal preference is for balanced feeders, in which case the balun can be located in the shack and there are other ways of achieving the same object. Other problems with baluns tend to arise when working with very low or high impedances.

There are some further limitations. At impedance levels around 12Ω, for example, leakage reactance can be a problem, requiring particular care with connecting leads, the lowest possible value of inductance, and possibly the use of capacitive compensation as described above. Another problem, particularly evident with low impedances, takes the form of imbalance which can be severe and is attributable to phase shifts occurring in the transformer windings, a conclusion which emerged from tests inspired by reference [19], where attention is drawn to a similar effect due to mismatches arising from 'transmission line' behaviour of the same windings.

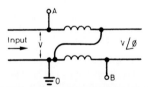

Fig 4.45. Imbalance due to phase shift. 'Balanced' output appears across AB, but one half is phase-shifted by the angle φ which may be derived either from the inductance of the 'transmission line' OB or the time delay along it

In search of further insight, a typical nine-turn bifilar balun winding was made up and found to have a Z_0 of 45Ω in line with the reference, the electrical length at 14MHz being 0.03λ. Referring to Fig 4.45, it can be seen that one half of the output voltage is phase-shifted by 11°. Alternatively, from p35 the reactance of the short line is 8.5Ω and this reactance in conjunction with a 45Ω load also gives an angle of 11°, supporting the view that at HF the balun line lengths are normally much too short to demand treatment as such. This is clearly matter of personal choice, the difference becoming important only if the line is long enough for voltage and

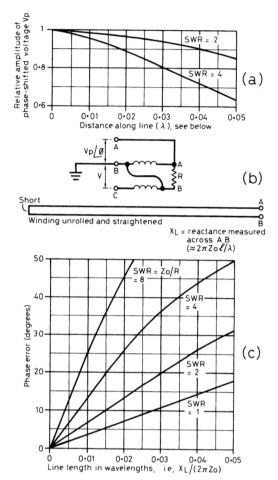

Table 4.4. Bifilar transformers

Type of core	Shunt inductance (µH)	Lowest useful frequency (SWR = 1.4) (MHz)
Ferrite rods, various, CSA = 0.8–1.2cm²	5–7	3.4
Ferrite ring, CSA = 0.36cm², OD 3.6cm	2.5	0.8
Iron dust toroid, 2in diam (TMP T200)	1.3	23.5
Air-cored, 1.6in diam, 0.8in length	1.6	19

Examples are based on bifilar line length of 40cm (actual), 70cm (electrical). Line impedance is approx 50Ω. Series reactance X_L (see Fig 4.46) is approx 0.13µH. Imbalance at 28MHz with line matched is approx 20%.
Notes. (a) The lowest useful frequency is arbitrarily based on shunt reactance of three times the line impedance. As a design target this should be doubled. (b) This example can be adapted to fit most other situations. For a 50Ω input at 28MHz it would be desirable to reduce X_L by a factor of two or three.

that, if R is reduced to 12.5Ω, one half of the output voltage at 14MHz is phase-shifted by 37° and also reduced in amplitude by 20%. It is interesting to note that Fig 4.46, though derived by circuit theory, is in fact the enlarged central portion of Fig 4.4(b).

Faced with the problems of high impedances, the author's efforts initially met with little success, and requirements for matching into and out of 600Ω lines between low impedances were met by using 4:1 baluns into and out of the 600Ω line, which was allowed to operate with an SWR of 2 or 3. This arrangement proved highly efficient and much more convenient than alternatives based on the use of pi-couplers or ATUs as described in the next section.

The suspected cause of the problem, self-capacitance of the windings, has since been confirmed and, with the added incentive supplied by the new forms of single-wire feed, tackled successfully for monoband operation. Three different trifilar unbalance-to-unbalance transformers were constructed for matching coaxial feeder into the Z_0 of antenna wires as described on p47, and in each case it proved an easy matter to achieve correct matching and efficient operation by tuning the transformer for resonance with its own self-capacitance. This was achieved by adjusting the position of the ferrite rod either for minimum SWR or externally using a GDO, both methods giving identical results.

Table 4.4 gives relative inductance values for the same bifilar pair wound on various cores, and it can be inferred that if low impedances or a large frequency range are involved there could be a substantial advantage in the use of ferrite rings, but only if core saturation is avoided. Also to be noted is the relatively poor performance of toroid dust cores. For most applications the relative simplicity and freedom from saturation leads to a preference for *ferrite rods*. Powder-type toroid rings have also been used successfully despite the increased leakage inductance; those tested were supplied as a kit and from the instructions it seemed that the core was

Fig 4.46. SWR and phase error in bifilar baluns. Note: the figures on the curves are equal to 50/R and therefore equal to the SWR in the line formed by the bifilar pair. The phase-shifted voltage across R is in series with the line input voltage V

current differences between the two ends to be attributable to time of travel instead of merely the equivalent component values.

A particularly interesting example of this is provided by the loaded radials discussed earlier, the lumped circuit approach being useful (as a crude approximation) for lengths down to about λ/8 after which it is time to dig out the Smith chart! Returning to the balun, this example implies an out-of-balance voltage of about 10%, even though perfect balance may have been indicated by the usual voltage tests. Wound on typical ferrite rods, this bifilar pair provided an inductance of 15µH which would have been adequate only down to about 6MHz. Whether or not the corresponding 20% imbalance at 28MHz is acceptable depends on the tasks demanded of the balun, as discussed earlier.

As the load resistance is reduced matters get rapidly worse, as illustrated by Fig 4.46. This shows for the current example

being relied on for ensuring adequate coupling, but in this respect it was found to contribute very little, and SWR at 28MHz was in excess of 2.0. After evolving the procedure outlined earlier, this was reduced to 1.4 for a 1:1 balun and around 1.2 for a 4:1 balun. The reason for worse leakage in the case of the powder core is linked to the need for more turns which follows from the lower permeability of the material.

Ferrite rings are less convenient than rods and there is a possibility of cross-modulation at high power levels due to saturation of the core [9]. The risk of this should be much less with rods, due to the greater reluctance of the magnetic circuit which is mostly 'air gap'. On the other hand, reduced leakage as a result of the shorter winding length could in many cases be an important 'plus' feature for rings; in line with this a coupling factor of 0.5 was observed between short coils on opposite sides of the ring (4cm OD) mentioned above, whereas with the much larger iron-dust toroid the coils had to be nearly touching to achieve an equally good result.

Balun transformers are so efficient that rods of less than 0.5in (13mm) diameter and a length of 2in (51mm) or less can be used for powers up to the legal limit (400W PEP) in the UK. A 1:1 balun using 17 turns on a powder core 0.69in (18mm) diameter (Amidon toroid type T-68-6) had measured losses averaging less than 0.1dB, an SWR better than 1.35 over the range 3.5–28.5MHz without compensation, and handled a power of 20W CW with only a modest temperature rise.

It is important to note with all types, however, that under some conditions of severe mismatch high temperatures can develop, and even for normal operation some means of escape for heat should be provided. Failure was experienced in the case of a balun encapsulated in Araldite for weather protection, and attributed to a combination of several factors: the Araldite, a bad mismatch and operation for too long under key-down conditions. Other failures have been attributed to the use of enamelled wire from an old mains transformer, the enamel having a tendency to chip off. Cotton covering, though perhaps obviously unsuitable, was once used in an emergency, thereby creating a further emergency!

Construction

Twisting of the wires is satisfactory, avoiding the extremes of too tight a spiral or enough slack for daylight to be visible between the wires. It is probably better, however, to use straight wires side by side and bind them together as tightly as possible with insulating tape. The wire diameter should ideally be as large as will conveniently fit on to the core, but it is not critical. Some commercial baluns use a single-layer trifilar winding but, though reasonably satisfactory, this results in a slightly worse specification.

Starting from scratch with a ferrite core of unknown properties, six or seven turns (which need not be closely spaced) provide a good starting point, the completed balun being tested at low power on all necessary bands with an SWR meter and a dummy load consisting of, say, two 5W 100Ω carbon resistors in parallel. If the inductance is just right there will be a just-perceptible increase in SWR at the lowest frequency. If the balun is to be used, say, for a triband beam covering 14–28MHz the SWR may be allowed to rise from a typical value of 1–1.15 at 14MHz to 1.3–1.4 at 7MHz.

A good test procedure is to construct two identical baluns, connect them back to back, and insert them in the feeder, first on one and then on the other side of the SWR meter. On the antenna side they should have little effect on the SWR reading except on the lowest band, whereas placing them on the transmitting side of the meter provides an indication of the total insertion loss (if any) for the two baluns.

For weather protection many types of plastic container may be pressed into service, using for example ordinary screw-type terminals with appropriate washers to ensure an adequate seal. Immersion of a completely unprotected transformer with twisted windings in a bucket of water produced an immediate loss of several decibels, some of which persisted after removal, but a 'temporary' arrangement with taped windings and no other protection was used for several months in all weathers with little or no variation in relative signal reports. Nevertheless, adequate protection is essential if the transformer is to be used in an inaccessible position.

Applications

A 1:1 balun is needed for the centre feeding of dipoles and some beams with low-impedance coaxial line; this includes the arrays based on multiband dipoles described on p198. It can also be used for conventional designs of quad antennas.

The 4:1 balun is required in conjunction with T and delta matches, eg Figs 4.14 and 12.1, and is suitable for feeding into and out of 'mismatched' 600Ω lines as recommended earlier. Similar devices can be used and are often required as impedance transformers in balance-balance or unbalance-unbalance situations (pp37–39). Despite some increase in leakage reactance, the trifilar construction can be used as a double-wound transformer (balanced on both sides), giving a 4:1 impedance ratio as required for example when feeding dipole arrays with 300 or 600Ω line.

An alternative to this is to combine a 1:1 balun with a 4:1 balun to obtain a 4:1 balance-to-balance transformation. Two such transformer pairs have been tested back-to-back as described above with satisfactory results, though the trifilar arrangement is simpler and appeared to be equally good. A rather complicated split-winding version of this was evolved to provide symmetry in respect of stray capacitances, but these do not appear to be a problem when working at the 200Ω impedance level.

A trifilar winding can also be used to provide 9:1 or 9:4 unbalance-unbalance or 9:1 balance-balance transformation and on occasion these ratios have been found useful.

Nothing has yet been said about transmission-line transformers, to which there have been many references in the literature, and the reader may well be expecting enlightenment. The two wires of Fig 4.44(a) may be regarded as a transmission line so that if a voltage is applied to one end an equal voltage appears at the other if the line is properly matched.

This in itself does not get us far, but if the line is coiled onto a ferrite core it then acts as a choke for in-phase currents so

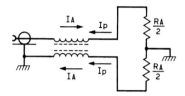

Fig 4.47. Transmission-line balun. The winding acts as a transmission line in respect of the current I_A but the two wires act together as a choke in respect of an in-phase current I_p such as may be induced due to lack of symmetry in the antenna system. The load impedance R_A, representing the antenna system, is normally balanced with respect to earth. This type of balun is not recommended: see text

that only equal and opposite currents can flow in the line. If one side of the input and the centre of the output load is earthed, the necessary balance may be established as shown in Fig 4.47. By using two such lines with their inputs in parallel and outputs in series, a 4:1 ratio is obtainable as before.

There are difficult problems in the matching of the line and reference [10] points out that "design is complicated because there is mutual coupling between turns, which modifies the characteristic impedance. However, suitable units are available commercially". The reference also points out that matching is critical so that it is "essential that the antenna match the 300Ω twin line at all frequencies at which the balun assembly will be used".

Problems with 'transmission-line baluns' are discussed in reference [11], leading by an entirely different chain of reasoning to a design very similar to Fig 4.42. This article also stresses the connection between low leakage reactance and wide frequency range which, though it appears to be ignored in much of the literature, was pointed out also in reference [12] and has been well known for a long time to at least some designers of commercial baluns.

It is feared that some readers, particularly those familiar with the earlier edition, may feel that the humble transformer-type balun, so easy and cheap to build yet highly efficient, has lost its erstwhile simplicity. All that has really happened is that more is now known about them and the reader can still have every confidence in designs based on Figs 4.42 and 4.43, particularly if the low-frequency coverage is restricted to bands actually required, and there is an awareness of the phase imbalance which may occur if one tries to work into very low impedances. If despite this any problems arise, a wider selection of guidelines is now at his disposal.

Antenna tuning unit (ATU)

In principle, the use of an ATU allows any antenna system to be connected to any transmitter. Some designs are intended to cope with any situation, however extreme, and others are suitable only for correcting a typical mismatch in a coaxial line. Most valve transmitters can be adjusted to compensate for an SWR up to at least 2.0 but some solid-state ones require an SWR of 1.0, and in this case the use of some form of ATU is essential because most antennas show some variation in SWR over a frequency band. Typically, a three-band trapped

beam which is peaked for the centre of a phone band may have an SWR rising to three or more in the CW band, although it is still capable of radiating a good signal and can be used if an ATU is available. It may even be possible in this way to use it on a completely different band, as the author can testify after hearing an excellent DX signal on 18MHz from just such a 21MHz antenna, though it would not of course have been working as a beam, and a balun or even the coaxial feeder might well have been put at risk of breakdown.

A 'universal' unit must be able to cope not only with this type of situation but also such diverse requirements as the end-fed antenna of Fig 4.18 and short dipoles fed with resonant open-wire lines. This adds up to a complex set of design problems requiring some degree of compromise, and it is difficult to guarantee loss-free performance under all circumstances. Designs are available in various handbooks [12, 13] and commercial units are available at prices which are perhaps an indication of the size of the problem. The author prefers to recommend a more 'piecemeal' approach on the following lines.

1. For end-fed antennas (including odd bits of wire) use tuning units which are an integral part of the antenna system, eg as in Fig 4.18. Coupling may be adjusted to provide a good match to low-impedance line.

2. With 600Ω feeder operating at an SWR of less than three, connect a balun plus low-impedance line at a point of low impedance, in or as near as possible to the shack. This should be acceptable except in some cases of multiband operation with resonant lines.

3. In cases of very high SWR, consider the use of a tuner on the lines of Fig 4.48, with the help of Fig 4.49 for determining whether the series or parallel configuration

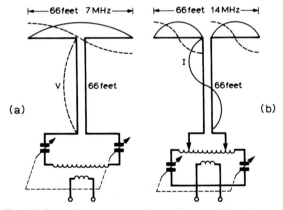

(a)   (b)

Fig 4.48. Centre-fed antennas with tuned feeders. The antenna to the left is $\lambda/2$ long and has a low input impedance; the feeder is also $\lambda/2$ long and thus repeats the low impedance so that series tuning should be used. On the right is a similar antenna operating at twice the frequency so that high RF voltage exists at both ends of the feeder, and parallel tuning is best. The effect of feeder length is illustrated in Fig 4.39. The tuning capacitor sections should each be 50pF maximum for 14MHz and higher frequencies, proportionately larger values being needed for lower frequencies. The voltage ratings of the capacitors should be comparable with those required for the transmitter tank circuit

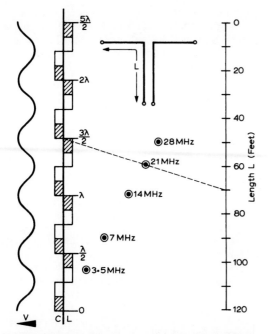

Fig 4.49. Standing-wave chart for tuned feeders. A line through the length *L* of feeder plus half-antenna and the appropriate frequency shows, at its intersection with the wavelength scale, the nature of the input impedance. Rectangles to the left of the line indicate capacitive impedance, those to the right being inductive. The shaded areas indicate high impedance, the blank areas low impedance. This diagram is suitable for use with dipole antennas fed with open-wire lines. It may be applied to a bi-square loop by measuring *L* from the open-circuited top, and to quad or delta loops by measuring *L* from points λ/4 out from the top centre

should be used [15]. Avoiding extremes, an ATU such as Fig 4.51 may provide a simpler alternative, and may also be used in conjunction with Fig 4.53 which was devised specifically for the feeding of multiband beam antennas based on resonant feeders as described on pp211–217.

4. With matched 300Ω line use a 4:1 balun.

5. Having thus obtained a low impedance, use an elementary form of ATU based on a 'simple' pi- or L-network such as Fig 4.50(a) or (b) to correct any residual mismatch.

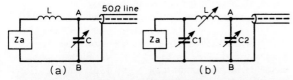

Fig 4.50. L and pi matching networks for 50Ω lines are shown at (a) and (b) respectively. The antenna impedance Z_a may be expressed in the form $R_a + jX_a$, and X_a, if capacitive, tuned out by part of the reactance *X*. If R_a is less than 50Ω it can be made to appear as 50Ω across AB by increasing the value of *X*, the inductive reactance resulting from this being tuned out by *C*. If R_a exceeds 50Ω the input and output terminals may be reversed. If X_a is inductive it can be tuned to resonance by the left-hand capacitor of the pi-circuit, (b), and over a limited range the additional control in the case of the pi-circuit can obviate the need for a variable inductance

Despite the simple appearance, a full analysis of these circuits is very complicated and it is frequently possible to obtain a match with two completely different component settings, at least one of which involves a substantial loss. The theory is simple enough, assuming a small value of *L*, in which case after allowing for the tuning out of any antenna reactance there is an impedance transformation given by the inverse square of the capacitance ratio. On paper this method of design is demonstrably foolproof, but it is disconcerting when (as happened to the author) the unit falls apart in the middle of a contact due to the solder melting. The connections, incidentally, were not the author's usual 'haywire' but could fairly have been described as 'heavy duty' and the power was well under the legal limit.

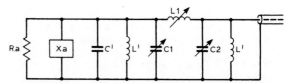

Fig 4.51. Practical pi-network for use with 50Ω line. For 14MHz L1 = 0.4µH, L' = 0.6µH, C1 = C2 = 450pF maximum. Note that in this case X_a is the equivalent parallel reactance component of the antenna impedance and C', which is required for resonating X_a if this happens to be inductive, can be provided by C1. L1 may be switched, about three positions per octave being recommended

A recommended design of pi-network ATU is shown in Fig 4.51. There are two cases to be considered, depending on whether the antenna impedance is less or more than Z_0, but since the network can be turned round it is only necessary to consider the low case as in the figure, where the tuned circuit L'C' is used to remove the antenna reactance X_d which may be positive or negative. Reference to the Smith chart shows that for an SWR of 2.0, X_d will be not less than 63Ω, and a value slightly lower than this should be chosen for the reactance of L'. The lowest value of capacitive reactance provided by C' should be half this since it may have not merely to tune out the reactance of L' but provide an equal reactance of opposite sign. For any value of SWR less than 2 the antenna reactance can now be removed, leaving a resistance R_a.

There remains now the more difficult task of choosing the components on the right of the diagram so that a pure resistance of 50Ω appears at the output terminals. In principle C1 is not needed, the L-network formed by L1 and C2 being sufficient. The combination of L1 and R_a results in a resistance

$$R_a \left(1 + \frac{\omega^2 L_1^2}{R_a^2} \right)$$

which can be arranged to have any value at the output terminals. and this is shunted by an inductive reactance

$$\omega L_1 \left(1 + \frac{R_a^2}{\omega^2 L_1^2} \right)$$

which is tuned out by C2. This means that L1 must be variable from zero upwards and, although suitable components exist, they are relatively inconvenient to use since they employ a slider which travels the entire length of the coil, making some 40 turns in all. All of this range of adjustment may be required when changing frequency within the 3.5MHz band!

Design charts are available for pi-networks [16] and, although the procedure is still quite involved, the values shown have been obtained for 14MHz. C1 incorporates C′ and these values can be scaled as necessary for coverage of other bands, the appropriate network being selected by a two-pole switch. Variable capacitors similar to those used in old valve-type broadcast receivers are suitable for powers up to 400W PEP, though unless three- or four-gang specimens can be obtained it may be necessary to switch in additional fixed capacitors on 3.5MHz. The range may be extended by switching in a trifilar-balun-type transformer, the connections being rearranged to give a 2:3 voltage ratio, ie an impedance step-up or step-down of 4:9. This circuit will correct most mismatches up to at least 3 to 1, or at worst bring them within the range that can be corrected by adjustment of the transmitter.

With C1 or C2 and L′ tuned to resonance and L1 variable, Fig 4.51 takes on some resemblance to the transmatch described in reference [14] which is designed to match any random-length antenna. Perhaps one should, however, add a note of warning from [16], which points out that losses in an L-network increase with increasing transformation ratio and can be large.

Resonant feeders

Resonant feeders have long been a preferred method for achieving multiband operation, the G5RV antenna being the best-known example, and Chapter 7 draws attention to their advantages for the construction of beam antennas providing coverage of the relatively new 10, 18 and 24MHz bands in addition to the older DX bands. Important features of this method include the simplicity of the basic concept and a range of recommended options, extending from small 'invisible' arrays to three-element 'monsters' providing gains at the higher frequencies substantially in excess of conventional monobanders. In the case of beam elements, however, there can be problems in the shack where, in addition to the tuning and matching of driven elements, there must be provision for the tuning of parasitic elements, interchange of elements for beam reversal, and in some cases the adjustment of coupling between elements for the achievement of deep nulls and maximum gain. This section describes what is believed to be a new approach aimed at making it easier to handle the problems in the shack inherent in high values of SWR and lots of bands. Though difficult to implement at the longer wavelengths, there are likely in this case to be better alternatives.

Open-wire lines with a Z_0 of 300 to 600Ω are capable of operating efficiently at very high values of SWR, which means that apart from their more familiar uses they can be used as the basis for multiband beam elements virtually free from the losses and some of the frequency limitations by which conventional beams are afflicted.

The usual price paid for this is the need for each element to have its own separate feeder all the way from the shack where the operator has work to do instead of having it all done for him at the antenna. In effect all tuning of the antenna has to be done in the shack but, once the initial adjustments for each band have been determined, this usually involves only the use of a single knob having as its primary function the nulling-out of interference. With the availability of deep nulls, instantaneous reversal of beam direction, and two elements often doing a better job than the usual three, this looks like an attractive package. However, to take full advantage of the multiband feature with each band conceivably needing different treatment, it can be an unnerving proceedure for those who like a tidy shack or whose patience is limited.

One recommended solution requires each element to be resonated by plugging in suitable 300Ω extension lines coiled up inside the shack. This might appear in its early stages to be a prescription for making matters worse but has the merits of being basically straightforward with good 'tidying-up' potential. The use of well-balanced 300Ω line rather than 600Ω extensions is advised, not only for convenience but in order to keep RF fields inside the shack down to a low level, though short lengths of the narrow-gauge 600Ω line recommended by the author (p292) have also been used without running into any 'RF in the shack' or imbalance problems.

As a starting point, the open-wire line or possible alternative (see below) should be ended just inside (or outside) the shack; take four or five assorted lengths of 300Ω line adding up to about 3/8λ and preferably fitted with plugs and sockets. Using a GDO, determine the length of 300Ω line needed to bring either of the elements to resonance (they should be identical, but check). Do this for each band. If out of luck one or two additional short lengths may be needed and, worse than this, one may end up faced with the prospect of having to dispose of possibly up to 10 long lengths of 300Ω line inside the shack; however, with one or two tricks at our disposal there is no need to despair. Moreover, pausing to look on the bright side, the driven element thus terminated has a low feedpoint resistance, usually between 20 and 300Ω, into which matching is no problem, and RF voltages are correspondingly low so that any matching, switching, or fine tuning arrangements which may be needed can be based on inexpensive and readily available components. Not only this, but in order to obtain deep nulls the coupling between beam elements can if necessary be adjusted by overlapping and taping together the lower ends of the lines.

This procedure has been applied to three very different designs of beam and feeder system (Figs 12.23, 12.25 and 12.29), and in each case five-band operation was achieved by ringing the changes on four lengths of extension line per element with a maximum total length of 15ft hanging in loops from hooks in a low ceiling. No problems were encountered from occasional crossing wires though, on principle, spacings between lines equal to several times the spacing of the feeder wires should be maintained except in the context of coupling adjustment.

Although such a system may be acceptable in, say, an outside shack, this is less likely in the case of a living room, and to continue the tidying-up process it is useful to return to

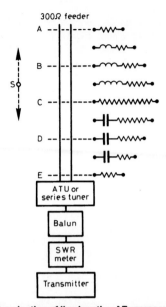

Fig 4.52. Determination of line lengths. AE represents λ/2 of 300Ω line adjacent to the transmitter, though we are concerned only with the existence of SE, of which the length must be determined separately for each band to provide a resistive (low) impedance at E. The line is divided into eight sections for which the nature and magnitudes of impedances seen looking outwards are denoted by symbols. S, the point of entry of the feeder into the shack, can in principle be anywhere on AE but use of series/shunt capacitors (see text) restricts SE to less than λ/4

first principles in the form of Fig 4.52, which depicts the different impedances which could be seen looking outwards from any point on the half-wavelength of feeder nearest to the transmitter. S is the point of entry of the feeder into the shack, its position on the line, as well as the SWR, being determined by the characteristics of the antenna and feeder system including, as already envisaged, a possible change from, say, 600 to 300Ω line at S, though (as suggested later) this might not be the best place to make it. The required extension line in the shack is represented by ES, and except for 'being there if required' SA can be ignored, any discontinuity having been taken into account by determining the position of S and measurement of SWR.

The symbols alongside the line illustrate pictorially the nature and magnitude of the impedance looking outwards along the feeder from its lower end. If S falls anywhere between A and roughly half way from B to C, the inductance can be tuned out by series capacitance to yield a resistance of 300Ω or less and no extension line is needed for matching, though if needed for other reasons its inductance can be tuned out by the same capacitor. If S falls closer to C or within about the same distance below it, parallel capacitance can be substituted for the same section of line. Below this, in principle, the capacitance of the line can be tuned out by series inductance, though this is not recommended in view of possible losses and other side effects. Worst cases based on one of the simpler versions of the SDL array described on

p211 could include an SWR of 20 in a 600Ω line which, in the best case, would become an SWR of 10 in the 300Ω line; in the worst case (an odd number of quarter-wavelengths) the SWR would be increased to 40, and though not a 'hopeless case' there would be some adverse effect on performance so that if possible the impedance transition should be moved λ/4 closer to the antenna. This could well make matters worse on another band, but usually there is (at worst) only one band in need of such drastic action.

This method has been applied to systems involving 'worst case' SWR values ranging from 6 to 30, and it has been found easy to implement using plug-in extension lines. A fully switched system would be feasible but, although inexpensive low-voltage components can be used at the lower end of the lines, any switching or tuning which involves the central portion BD of the line (Fig 4.52) and high values of SWR will have to withstand voltages similar to those in PA tank circuits and need to be of comparable quality.

Due to narrow bandwidth on the lowest frequency bands and possible wet-weather effects in antennas and lines, some provision for fine tuning is needed, and this can take the form of lengthening the line somewhat and using series tuning as in Fig 4.53; this avoids the need for an ATU but requires a ganged pair of separate capacitors. Though not available as a standard commercial item, such a pair can be readily devised using single capacitors as shown in the figure. The feedpoint resistance (R) is obtainable from the SWR and use of the nearest available balun ratio will usually bring it within the adjustment range of typical valve output stages. If necessary R can be increased by lengthening the line and using a smaller value of capacitance, though if carried too far (beyond a factor of 1.5 or 2) this could lead to voltage breakdown of the capacitor. Alternatively, the ATU illustrated in Fig 4.51 is more versatile and careful checks have shown its performance to be identical.

Also of interest is the variable-length line, Fig 4.53(c), though it is difficult to meet all requirements with a single device because of the wide range of impedances and the need for unused line ends to be short so that there is no capacitive shunting of the impedance.

As an alternative to 300–600Ω line, the possibility in some cases of using resonant feeders based on twin lengths of 95Ω coaxial feeder arranged as in Fig 4.12 is not excluded, though it would rule out some of the simpler types of element. By selecting a best option in accordance with Figs 7.4 and 7.5 it should be possible to keep SWR below 5 or 6 on all or most bands, estimated total losses being less than those of most conventional multiband beams. Referring to Table 4.2, RG-133A should be suitable for this purpose or, for low power only, RG-62A/U.

Hitherto, resonant feeders have been recommended for use with beam antennas in only a few instances. They tend to impose extra demands on the operator and, though one can 'learn to live with them' as the author has been doing for many years, it has required the allocation of additional bands with relatively close spacing for them to emerge as the sole solution (and a very good one) to an important problem. Even

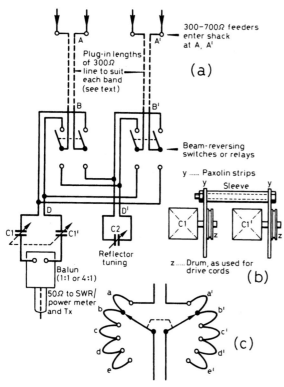

Fig 4.53. (a) Shows the tuning and matching system used with the Claw and Miniclaw (p217), feeder impedances being 600Ω and 300Ω respectively. With 600Ω feeder its length should if possible be arranged to avoid high RF voltage at AA' on the lowest frequency band. Extension line lengths in excess of about 0.3λ can be avoided by series capacitance at A, A'. Plug-in baluns were used but could be switched. An ATU can be substituted for C1 and may be preferred for solid-state amplifiers if carefully checked for losses, but in general parallel capacitors should NOT be used. For components below the B-B' line, 250V ratings (500V for C2) should be adequate. This applies also to any switches used as a replacement for plugs at B, B'. **(b)** Method of ganging C1, C1' if only standard single-ended capacitors available. **(c)** Line stretchers: aa', bb' etc are 4 to 6in lengths of 300Ω line. They may be inserted at B, B' or, with some modification of AB, A'B', used instead of C1, C2. Note: full power must not be applied with the wrong extension lines in place

so, they have to be used with discretion, accepting limitations as to the type of element and the length of feedlines.

In the search for better ways of using resonant lines for multibanding a fundamental limitation has been identified; this stems from the existence of at least one impedance discontinuity, ie at the junction between the feeder and the antenna. This may assist matching at one or more frequencies but makes matters worse at others, SWR being multiplied by a factor which often approaches the square of the impedance ratio. In fact, with bands closely spaced (as they now are between 14 and 28MHz), this is virtually certain to happen in one case at least.

Since the 'worst' has to be good enough, this is clearly a serious restriction, and the only way round it is to *eliminate*

the discontinuity. This can be done by using two or three wires in parallel, or heavy-gauge tubing, for the antenna whilst keeping the feeder impedance as high as possible. There is a further bonus from this since another important effect of the discontinuity is to destroy the simple harmonic ratio of the resonances, and by bringing the 14, 21 and 28MHz resonances more into line, interesting new matching possibilities are created. These ideas are featured in more detail in later chapters.

Automatic antenna tuning units

These are available but expensive. Apart from the added convenience they make it possible to move between any frequencies within a band in the space of two or three seconds provided they are not required to correct an SWR in excess of about 2.5 or 3, so that in some cases of operation with tuned feeders they might have to be supplemented by a manual coarse adjustment. On the other hand, use of an automatic SWR meter allows an ATU to be adjusted, usually within a few seconds, at a low power level such as 2W or less, these devices being much less expensive.

The need for such devices is dictated largely by the critical demands of solid-state amplifiers, and these can be a problem if it is desired to make full use of the excellent 'deep-nulling' features of the two-element arrays described in the next chapter. An automatic ATU should be able to take care of impedance changes caused by nulling, but another option is to switch to a separate tuner for reception, not forgetting to use the transmit mode for checking channel occupancy.

Protective multiple earthing (PME)

PME has been widely used for domestic electricity installations in the UK since the mid-'seventies. The essential feature is connection of the main earthing terminal of the supply to neutral, all other conductors within the building being bonded to it. Under rare fault conditions the neutral can become live, but with everything bonded together there should still be no dangerous potentials around. All very good in theory, but the situation could change dramatically, with fatal consequences, if external antenna or earth wires are brought into the shack. One solution is to use an ATU such as Fig 4.48, 4.18, 4.31 or 4.36. These can be readily adapted for low-impedance lines, the essential requirement being adequate insulation between primary and secondary as well as of any antenna or associated ground wires entering the shack or capable of being touched by anyone inside.

Alternatives rely on the use of a separate safety earth for the radio equipment in conjunction with an RCD (residual current device) which compares the currents at the live and neutral terminals and disconnects the supply in the event of any difference. A problem here is to ensure that there is no possibility of simultaneously touching the rig or antenna system and any other mains-operated electrical appliance or in-house metalwork. Before proceeding on these lines, advice should be sought from other RSGB publications or the electricity supply authorities.

The Smith chart

As the author has tried to show, most antenna problems with which the amateur is faced can be tackled without much knowledge of mathematics. Most of us can visualise a wave travelling through space and are ready to accept, for example, that field strength at a distance is proportional to current multiplied by the length of antenna wire through which it flows, without needing to master the intricacies of Maxwell's equations; usually all that is needed is knowledge of a few such basic principles, common sense and access to the appropriate data.

Transmission lines are another story, and for a long time the author – having an impressive record of failures in mathematics examinations – was content to leave them to the experts. They usually seemed to work, after a fashion anyway, and the antenna was the interesting part! In fact, although feeder matching can usually be achieved by trial and error, use of the Smith chart is straightforward, saves time and reduces the risk of mistakes. The delightful simplicity of the chart is, alas, belied by a somewhat fearsome appearance, and the aim is to penetrate the disguise and provide sufficient insight into the principles and methods of use for the chart to take its rightful place in the armoury of readers faced with problems of antenna design and feeder matching.

Nevertheless, the potential of the chart for some rather complex manoeuvres poses a problem since it is felt that a description covering all the important uses would not be the best way of explaining it to everyone who might benefit, bearing in mind that many amateur transmission-line calculations are of a simple type such as discovering the impedance of an antenna from measurements at the lower end of the feeder. In an effort to get round this problem, the chart is presented in Chapter 18 as a 'piece of test equipment' complete with a set of instructions. It is hoped that readers who have persevered thus far will now read on, but if they find it sends them to sleep they should turn at once to p284 where the subject is presented in lighter vein.

Among the topics not covered in Chapter 18, the application to antennas, as distinct from feeder systems, has been largely overlooked and is of particular interest as it provides an insight into many peculiar aspects of antenna behaviour and often saves a lot of arithmetic. Moreover, it has particular relevance for amateur applications since it reveals at a glance how to tune any odd bit of wire to resonance even when, for example, the wire has to be bent to fit it into a confined space. For this application the antenna has to be regarded as a transmission line with the appropriate value, or values, of characteristic impedance assigned to it. Unfortunately this information, although given in professional textbooks, is not readily available to the average amateur. It would in any case be impossible to present accurate data covering all possible ways of bending an antenna wire, but with the aid of intelligent guesswork the data presented here should be adequate for most amateur purposes.

It is necessary at this point to say a little about 'j notation' if only to assure readers who have survived their first glance at the chart that they are not going to be asked to master yet another new concept. Nevertheless, j does appear on the charts produced commercially and it is felt that most readers, after working through a few examples using the charts, will find it useful as shorthand since it is much easier to write '50 + 35j' than '50Ω of resistance and 35Ω of inductive reactance'. This is the general form in which the chart produces answers to questions, and at first glance it may look like an unfinished sum requiring an understanding of j for its completion. In fact, the 50 and the 35 are 'different kinds of ohms' and tend to be of more interest when they are separated than after they have been added.

Typically the 50Ω represents the radiation resistance of an antenna or some other load into which one wishes to deliver power, and the 35Ω is a reactance which needs to be removed by tuning, ie by connecting an equal and opposite reactance in series. Conventionally a negative sign is used to denote capacitance, and in this case the chart indicates the use of 35Ω of capacitance so that the complete answer to the problem becomes $50 + 35j - 35j = 50\Omega$ which provides a good match to standard low-impedance cable. For the present purpose this is all the reader needs to know about j, although a further acquaintance with it gives added flexibility in the use of the chart and is essential to a proper understanding of many aspects of electrical and radio technique. An attempt to provide a simple explanation of j has been included as an appendix to this chapter.

Here the chart is presented initially as an impedance diagram since impedance is a familiar concept to most readers and, as the examples prove, this approach is adequate for a wide variety of applications. Nevertheless, as we shall see, an understanding of admittance enables the chart to be used as an admittance diagram and as a simple calculator for making impedance-to-admittance conversions, which greatly extends its usefulness.

In many cases the chart requires an input which can only be derived by direct measurement of impedance or admittance at whatever points happen to be accessible in an antenna or feeder system. However, it will be shown that good use can be made of the charts, even if the reader is equipped with nothing more than an understanding of the difference between resistance and reactance, some simple form of SWR indicator or RF voltage probe, and a few odd lengths of cable. If open-wire feeders are used, the only instrument needed consists of a small pick-up loop, rectifier and meter. Holding the pick-up loop at a roughly constant distance from the feeder, it can be moved along the line to determine the SWR and the positions of the current minima with sufficient accuracy for most purposes.

Properties of lines

As explained earlier, if, for example, a 50Ω resistance is connected to one end of a 50Ω line, the impedance observed at the other end will also be 50Ω, and this holds true for any length of line. For any other termination, the observed impedance varies with line length; for example, Fig 4.54 shows what happens when the 50Ω resistance is replaced by one of

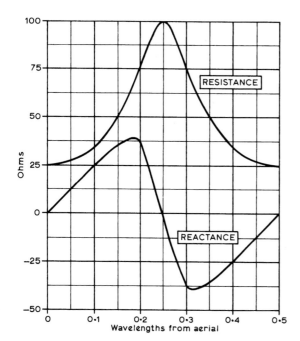

Fig 4.54. Variations of resistance and reactance along a 50Ω feeder when connected to a resonant antenna having a feedpoint resistance of 25Ω (SWR = 2.0)

25Ω, corresponding to a standing-wave ratio of 2.0. These are the curves which would be traced out by walking backwards down the line towards the transmitter, observing the apparent value of the 'load impedance' as seen from each point on the line. In the absence of line losses, the pattern repeats itself every half-wavelength, and a given resistance always has the same value of associated reactance, although the sign of this changes from positive to negative at intervals of λ/4.

Reactance can therefore be plotted against resistance, as shown in Fig 4.55. The fact that this particular plot happens to be a circle need not unduly concern the reader, who is asked

to note only that a pattern has been traced out which repeats itself at λ/2 intervals. A distance (measured in wavelengths) scale can be marked off (as illustrated) round it so that, given any point on this pattern, the impedance at any other point on the line can be obtained merely by moving the correct distance round the pattern. All points on the line, including the antenna itself, must fit on to this pattern so that if the antenna impedance and line length are known, the impedance at the transmitting end can be read directly from Fig 4.55.

It is then a simple matter to devise, for example, a matching network such that the antenna is presented to the transmitter as a matched load. Alternatively, from measurements at the transmitter the antenna impedance can be read from the chart and used to determine whether, in order to improve the SWR, the antenna need be lengthened or shortened, or some other adjustment made.

The circle diagram

So far only one value of SWR has been considered, though obviously a family of circles could be drawn covering a fairly wide range of values. Useful though this might be, the diagram in this form leaves much to be desired: the scales are too cramped at their lower end and cover too small a range of impedances; different sets of curves are needed for each value of feeder impedance; and the non-linear nature of the distance scale makes it rather inconvenient to use.

To overcome these problems the obvious first step is to make the resistance and reactance scales non-linear, expanding the lower ends and compressing the upper ends. In this way any desired range of values, even extending all the way from zero to infinity, can be accommodated. The next step, rather less obvious, has been aptly described [6] as 'bending the graph paper'. In effect, the reactance scales are bent round so that they form a complete circle with their ends, now scale-marked infinity, meeting at infinity on the resistance axis as shown in Fig 4.56, which is the basis of the Smith chart.

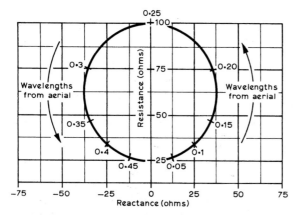

Fig 4.55. Similar to Fig 4.54 except that reactance is plotted against resistance

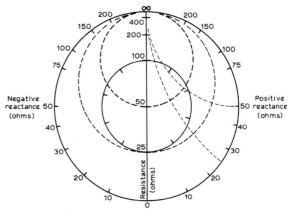

Fig 4.56. The circle diagram or Smith chart. This is similar to Fig 4.55 except for 'bending the graph paper', the centre line being the resistance scale. Two lines of constant resistance and two of constant reactance have been shown dotted. The inner circle is drawn for an SWR of 2 and the markings on it are steps of 0.05λ

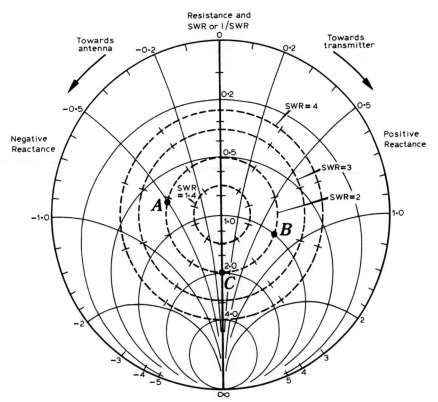

Fig 4.57. Simplified Smith chart. Each circle represents a constant value of SWR and meets the resistance scale at points corresponding to the value of the terminating resistance and its reciprocal, the SWR being equal to the higher of the two figures. Note that the reciprocal of any point on any circle is the opposite point on the same circle. The markings on the circles are steps of 0.05λ. The points marked A, B and C correspond to the example in the text

Fig 4.56 is identical to Fig 4.55 except for the distortion and bending of the scales, which has been done in such a way that the impedance plot remains circular although the wavelength scale marked round it is now linear. In other words, movement round the circle of any given number of degrees always corresponds to the same fraction of a wavelength whatever the starting point. A further advantage of the new diagram is that the circles of constant SWR now share a common centre and make use of the same wavelength scale, which is usually marked around the outer circumference of the chart.

To make Fig 4.56 into a useful tool one further step is necessary – the addition of suitable scale lines as in Fig 4.57 (which shows a simplified version of the chart) or Fig 4.58 (which is typical of charts available from commercial sources). In the case of Figs 4.55 and 4.56 the reader could easily fill these lines in for himself since the originals were plotted on ordinary squared paper, ruled with sets of equally spaced parallel lines at right angles. Unfortunately, when the graph paper is 'bent' these lines get bent with it and, since by definition parallel lines meet at infinity, the scale markings appropriate to Fig 4.55 all converge on the point marked '∞' when transferred to the Smith chart. To avoid undue congestion at this point, therefore, most of the lines have to stop short, and the curious pattern results from this convergence plus the obvious practical need to maintain a reasonably uniform density of scale lines throughout the diagram.

Despite omission of most of the lines shown in Fig 4.58, Fig 4.57 would be adequate for amateur use since usually no great accuracy is either needed or possible and it has important advantages. Unlike Fig 4.58 it cannot be accused of the 'fearsome appearance' which seems to have had a considerable deterrent effect on would-be users, and it includes SWR circles enabling it to be used without the addition of a cursor or having to keep a pair of compasses handy. Nevertheless, after working through a few examples the user will appreciate the convenience of having more scale divisions as in Fig 4.58 as well as the SWR circles of Fig 4.57. Unfortunately their addition in monochrome to Fig 4.58 merely increases its resemblance to a spider's web but this problem is easily resolved by the use of red ink for the circles.

The bending of the scale lines should cause no difficulty if it is appreciated that lines of constant resistance are circles or parts of circles which touch at infinity but also pass through the appropriate point on the resistance scale (ie the vertical line in the centre of the diagram), and lines of constant reactance are arcs of circles centred off the diagram but also meeting at infinity as explained earlier.

Another important respect in which Fig 4.57 differs from Fig 4.56 is the scaling, which suggests that it has been drawn for a rather improbable line impedance of 1Ω. In fact, this is another bit of clever trickery and overcomes the remaining defect of Fig 4.55 which, as readers may recall, was the need to prepare different charts for different values of line

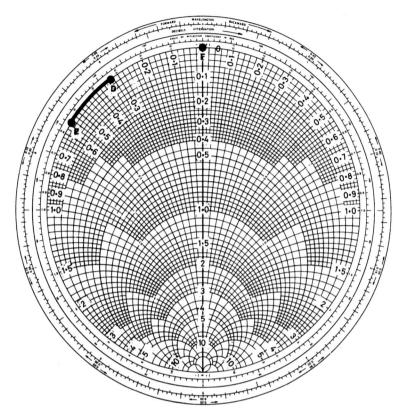

Fig 4.58. Typical Smith chart. The additional lines make for greater accuracy and convenience despite the adverse effect on appearances. SWR circles need to be added for most calculations. Points D, E illustrate the application of the chart to finding the new value of resonant length which results from folding part of an antenna wire, as discussed in the text. Subtraction of a length DF at a Z_0 of 1000Ω can be compensated by adding a length EF at a Z_0 of 600Ω

impedance. The method is known as 'normalisation' and is a simple standard conversion process of the kind with which anyone who travels abroad is familiar – the difference being that instead of converting pounds into francs or miles into kilometres, when entering on to a Smith chart ohms have to be converted into 'zednoughts', Z_0 being the symbol used to represent the line impedance. For example, if the line impedance is 50Ω, then 50Ω is one Z_0, and if the line is used to connect a transmitter operating at 14MHz to a load consisting of 100Ω of resistance plus a reactance of 85Ω (ie an inductance of 1μH), the chart is entered at the point corresponding to 100/50 (ie 2 zednoughts) on the resistance scale and 85/50 = +1.7 on the reactance scale. Putting this into j notation, the impedance is $(100 + 85j)\Omega$ and becomes $(2.0 + 1.7j)$ after normalising to 50Ω. In the latter case there is no need to fill in the unit of impedance since a Z_0 is the only one recognised by the chart.

The charts illustrated in Fig 4.58 are available in graph-paper form. They can be used as graph paper for the permanent recording of such experimental results as the variation of antenna impedance and SWR across a band of frequencies, but for the present purpose the chart is of more interest as a calculating device. For this purpose one method is to glue it onto a hard surface and employ a rotating cursor of transparent material with marks corresponding to the points on the resistance scale (greater than one) over which they pass. As the cursor is rotated, the points marked 1.5, 2 etc describe

circles representing these values of SWR. Nevertheless, the red ink method is simple, labour saving, and adequate unless hard use is anticipated. If any other marks required are made in pencil and rubbed out when no longer required, a single chart marked up with red SWR circles can be re-used many tImes.

The simpler types of calculation are those confined to a single circle on the chart, such as points A, B and C in Fig 4.57. For this example it is assumed that one wishes to know the impedance of the antenna, given that a measured value of $(35 - 25j)\Omega$ has been obtained at the 'shack' end of a 50Ω line. Dividing by 50 this is plotted as the point A, ie $(0.7 - 0.5j)$ on the chart. Given that the feeder length is an odd number of quarter wavelengths, we arrive at point B where the antenna impedance is read off as $(1.0 + 0.7j)Z_0$, ie $(50 + 35j)\Omega$. This was the value cited earlier as 'the sort of answer the chart might give' so we already know what to do about it, ie connect a capacitive reactance of 35Ω in series with the antenna.

There are, however, various alternatives; note that had we stopped short of point B by 0.15λ, ie at point C, the answer would have been 100Ω with no reactance so that a feeder system consisting of 0.15λ of 50Ω line adjacent to the antenna plus any length of 100Ω line would be perfectly matched except for the short length of 50Ω line. Feeder which is close to 100Ω impedance is unobtainable but the nearest popular value would be 75Ω, giving an SWR of 1.33 which is quite good enough. Note that had we used 75Ω feeder 'all the way' the normalised antenna impedance would have been (0.47 + 0.33j) which sits on an SWR = 2.4 circle, an even worse result than in the case of the 50Ω feeder cable.

Application to antennas

It is common practice to make a clear distinction between 'antennas' and 'transmission lines'. This attitude appears to be reflected in the prevailing usage of the Smith chart which is of course quite correctly regarded as a 'transmission-line calculator'. Nevertheless, as mentioned earlier, the antenna can also be regarded as a transmission line, and from the point of view of tuning and matching there are important advantages in so doing. The alleged 'bandwidth' of an antenna is usually not that of the antenna but some combination of antenna and feeder system, and in dealing with such a combination the Smith chart can be particularly useful.

In treating the antenna as a transmission line, it is essential to think of it as a line which has been unfolded so that, for example, a λ/4 line turns into a λ/2 dipole. This unfolding must of course lead to an increase in the characteristic impedance (Z_0) since it reduces the capacitance, and the load resistance (being identifiable with the radiation resistance) is usually small compared with Z_0, so that the SWR is high. As well as being an antenna, the wire remains basically a transmission line whose length is half that of the antenna, and if Z_0 and the radiation resistance are known, the Smith chart can be used to discover the impedance at the centre or ends of the wire. The wire may be bent into any shape, in which case different parts of it may have different values of Z_0, and in dealing with these cases the performance of the Smith chart is particularly impressive since each change of impedance along the antenna and feeder system can be regarded merely as a frontier at which we have to change currency, ie normalise to the new impedance.

The main difficulty so far has been lack of impedance data; this is readily available for transmission lines, but access to professional textbooks is usually needed in the case of antenna wires. Fig 4.13 rectifies this omission to the extent that it should cover most cases of importance for amateur applications. Data on radiation resistance is widely available but usually relates to positions of current maxima; given this information, however, the radiation resistance referred to the antenna terminals, when the antenna wire is not a resonant length, may be roughly determined with the help of the chart. However, from this point of view values of R tend to be rather on the low side, and if the distribution is known they may be derived more accurately by using the usual I^2R formula, I being the current and R the radiation resistance at any point in the system, and I^2R the same for all points. This has been done for single wires with lengths up to 3λ/4 in Fig 4.59, which also includes the case of elements which have been physically shortened by bending back the ends of the wires.

In the case of full-wave dipoles the terminal resistance is best obtained from the current loop radiation resistance (180Ω) by regarding the antenna as a λ/4 transformer, obtaining Z_0 from Fig 4.13 and evaluating $Z_0^2/180$. In principle the

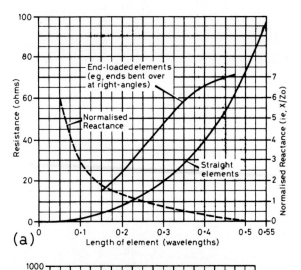

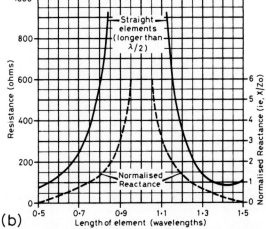

Fig 4.59. Variation of impedance with length at the centre of dipole elements. These are the figures required when working with the chart in its impedance form as described here. Radiation resistance is expressed as an equivalent series resistance at the centre of the element. Unlike the equivalent parallel resistances they are independent of wire diameter. For two-element beams the resistances and the multiplying factors given on p85 are applicable. The reactances are in normalised form suitable for direct entry into the chart, but can be converted into ohms by using them as multipliers for the appropriate Z_0 values, obtainable from Fig 4.13. The resistance figures, based on a computer program, were supplied by W0JF

chart can be used for this purpose by entering it at the point $180/Z_0$, and proceeding round it for a distance λ/4. This procedure, incidentally, demonstrates the inversion of impedances whereby they turn into admittances, a particularly important feature of the chart as explained later.

Note that if $Z_0 = 900Ω$, $Z_0/180 = 5$ and use of the chart produces the answer in the form $5Z_0$, ie $5 \times 900 = 4500Ω$ which, as some readers may be quick to point out, could have been obtained with much less trouble by simple arithmetic. The situation is very different, however, if even a small

Transmission loss
(1dB steps)

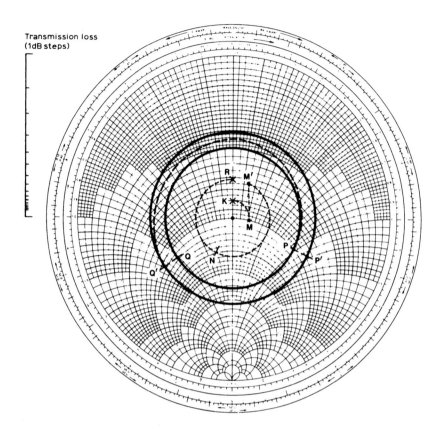

Fig 4.60. Application of Smith chart to typical problems. Points K, M, M', N, R illustrate the effect of a discontinuity in the line impedance. The effect of a typical line loss is illustrated by the spiral transition from the inner circle at P to the outer circle at Q'

amount of reactance is introduced, ie if the antenna is no longer exactly resonant, as in the following example.

Suppose it is desired to erect a $\lambda/2$ wire dipole for 7MHz but there is only room for a length of 0.4λ. Having read elsewhere that the middle 0.1λ can be folded into an open-wire stub this is tried, but the SWR is very poor since the reference followed the usual practice of omitting to state that the required total length of wire is no longer $\lambda/2$. The questions are, what *should* be the length of the stub and what will be the radiation resistance 'seen' by a feeder connected to its lower end?

The antenna is treated as a 0.2λ line having a typical Z_0 of 1000Ω and, since the SWR in this 'line' is rather large, one is restricted to operations on or very close to the outer edge of the chart. Starting from the far end of the line (the bottom of Fig 4.58) we may proceed clockwise round the edge for a distance 0.2λ, arriving at point D; this is a reactance $-0.33j$, ie it is required to add 330Ω of inductance in series. Since Z_0 for the stub is 600Ω, the normalised value of X is 330/600, ie 0.55, which comes opposite the 0.08λ mark (point E) on the wavelength scale marked round the edge of the chart. However, had we taken $\lambda/2$ of wire and merely put a fold in the middle to take up the slack, this would have resulted in a stub length of 0.05λ only. The stub must therefore be lengthened by 0.03λ or 4.2ft (1.28m), ie a total wire length of 8.4ft (2.56m)!

To obtain the feedpoint resistance, a value of 40Ω is given by Fig 4.59 but this is the value at the antenna end of the stub, not that seen by the feeder. In principle we could have entered the chart at the point (0.04 $\mp$ 0 55j) and, proceeding clockwise by 0.05λ, arrived at the point 0.036 or 36Ω. However, this part of the scale is so cramped that, although one can just about see that the reduction in R is not enough to matter, it is much easier to work out R from the basic power relationship as suggested above. Thus we note that the antenna is only 18 electrical degrees from the end of the stub, which is a point of maximum current, and cos 18° is 0.95 so the increase in current at the feedpoint compared with that at the antenna is 5% only.

Since I^2R must be the same at all points, R at the feeder terminals is 10% less than 40Ω, ie 36Ω which, though a bit low, is still a reasonable match to 50Ω feeder. Had the dipole length been a full $\lambda/2$ it would have been better of course to use 75Ω feeder.

Multiple changes of impedance

In an antenna system there may be several changes of impedance. The chart makes light work of this situation as illustrated by the following example which is plotted as points K, M, M', N and R in Fig 4.60.

A 14MHz antenna is assumed to have an impedance of 40Ω providing an acceptable match to 50Ω cable. The required feeder length is 106ft (32.3m) but unfortunately there is only 95ft (29m) available and at current prices we cannot afford any more. In the junk box, however, there is plenty of 75Ω cable, and a velocity factor of 0.67 is assumed for both cables. The required overall length could be obtained by splicing in λ/4 of 75Ω cable, and the question is where should we put it? Next to the antenna, next to the transmitter or somewhere in between?

The electrical length of the 50Ω feeder is 2.125λ, which takes us from the antenna, point K, to a point M on the chart, an impedance of 0.97 + 0.22j. Adding on the λ/4 of 75Ω cable, this value must be normalised for the new impedance, multiplying by 50 and dividing by 75, ie multiplying by two-thirds to give an impedance of 0.65 + 0.15j. This is point M′ and fits on to a SWR circle of 1.6 which is the value applicable to the 75Ω line. If it is desired to know the impedance at the transmitting end of the line, this can be found by proceeding λ/4 round the 1.6 SWR circle to the point N.

Next suppose the extra length is placed at the antenna end of the line. The starting point is now 40/75 but is inverted by the λ/4 line to become 75/40 at the start of the 50Ω cable. Normalising to 50Ω involves a multiplying factor of 1.5, bringing the resistance and therefore the SWR up to 2.74 which is much higher than before and applies to most of the feeder run, whereas the previous highest value 1.6 applied only to the last 11ft.

Much time can be spent in trying to improve on the first result, since the chart allows experimentation on paper with a wide range of cable lengths and positions, but the following is a good solution. Proceeding from the antenna at 50Ω for λ/8 and then changing to 75Ω again gives point M′. After a distance of 0.476λ the point R is reached. This is a resistance of 0.63, ie 47.5Ω, and re-normalising to 50Ω this becomes 0.95, providing an SWR of 1.05 in the 50Ω cable which may be used for the remainder of the feeder system.

In the examples above it has been assumed that the SWR is constant along each section of line, though it should be noted that losses in a transmission line cause the SWR to vary along the line. In effect, looking into the lower end of a lossy line, it appears to a large extent to be matched by its own losses, whereas at the antenna end the SWR is determined only by the relationship between Z_0 and the load impedance. The relation between line loss and the SWR at its ends is illustrated in Fig 4.10, and this information is also incorporated in the transmission loss scales on the left of the chart.

The method of allowing for line loss is illustrated in Fig 4.60. The point P represents an impedance measurement at the transmitter with its SWR circle drawn in, and the outer circle corresponds to the SWR at the antenna. The distance between the two circles depends on the line loss, and if the loss is known (eg from data tables) the SWR at the antenna can be obtained from Fig 4.10 or more conveniently by using the scale at the left of the chart which is marked in steps of 1dB, a loss of 1dB being assumed for the present example. Horizontal lines may be drawn from this scale so as to transfer the decibel step to the centre line of the chart, the outer circle then being drawn so that the distance between the circles corresponds to the appropriate portion of the transmission

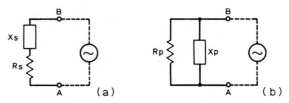

Fig 4.61. Equivalent impedance circuits. For every series arrangement of resistance and reactance as shown at (a) there is an equivalent parallel circuit (b) such that measurement of impedance across the terminals AB is identical in both cases

loss scale. It is convenient to set a protractor to the radius of the inner circle and then place it against the loss scale, enlarging the radius by the appropriate amount. This is then used for drawing the outer circle.

The distance from P to Q corresponds to the line length but, in moving from the transmitter to the antenna, the track is now a spiral as shown dotted, so that instead of ending up at Q we find ourselves at Q′ which gives the impedance of the antenna. Conversely if Q′ is known we can find P, and in this case the 1dB line loss has changed the impedance 'in the shack' from (0.88 − 1.14j) to (1.0 − 0.9j).

This brings us to another important aspect of the Smith chart, namely its use for the inversion of impedances so that they turn into admittances. This allows parallel combinations of resistance and reactance to be substituted for the equivalent series networks and vice versa. In many cases it is much more convenient to use the parallel approach and, once familiar with the chart, the reader will find [6] that it is a highly flexible device allowing him to wander at will through impedance, admittance and transmission line territory uninhibited, not merely by changes of Z_0 as explained above, but also such obstacles as the cumbersome formulae previously needed for making series-parallel substitutions.

It will be recalled (p34) that a λ/4 line can be used for impedance inversion whereby an impedance Z is changed to Z_0^2/Z and, since the Smith chart is based on a 'zednought' of one, it follows that moving halfway round it (ie a distance of λ/4) is equivalent to converting Z into 1/Z so that the impedance $R_s + jX_s$ illustrated in Fig 4.61(a) becomes

$$\frac{1}{R_s + jX_s}$$

The equivalent parallel circuit is shown at Fig 4.61(b) and, following the normal rules for impedances in parallel, we have

$$\frac{1}{Z} = \frac{1}{R_p} + \frac{1}{jX_p}$$

These quantities are defined respectively as the admittance Y, conductance G and susceptance jB, so that

$$Y = G + jB = \frac{1}{R_p} + \frac{1}{jX_p} = \frac{1}{R_s + jX_s}$$

From this equation it is possible to derive the following identities:

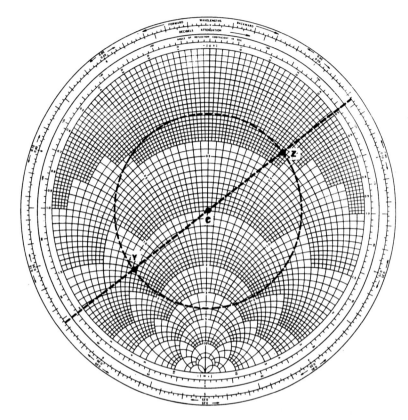

Fig 4.62. Illustration of impedance inversion and conversion of impedance into admittance or vice versa by use of the Smith chart. Z, Y are equidistant from C which means that each is the reciprocal of the other

$$R_p = R_s \left(1 + \frac{X_s^2}{R_s^2} \right)$$

$$X_p = X_s \left(1 + \frac{R_s^2}{X_s^2} \right)$$

Referring to Fig 4.62, the point Z represents a normalised impedance $0.31 + 0.45j$, and to find its reciprocal one need only proceed round the circle to the opposite point Y where the admittance can be read off as $1.03 - 1.5j$. These figures are respectively the conductance and susceptance in admittance units, ie 'Y-noughts' which are reciprocals of zednoughts so that if $Z_0 = 50\Omega$ then $Y_0 = 1/50$mho, a susceptance of 1.5 'Y-noughts' being therefore equal to 1.5/50mho. The change in sign which accompanies the inversion is discussed later, but for the moment is best ignored.

For better or worse, most of us are used to thinking in terms of impedance rather than admittance and ohms rather than 'zednoughts', and to obtain the required component values in ohms, ie R_p and X_p, the admittance terms have to be inverted to give $50/1.03 = 48.5$ and $50/1.5j = -j33\Omega$ respectively. The step of converting the figures read from the chart into admittances and then back into ohms can be skipped as soon as the user is familiar with the principles, the 1.03 and 1.5 being *divided into* Z_0 to obtain R_p and X_p, whereas the initial figures, 0.31 and 0.45, were *multipliers* so that going through

the reverse process we have $R_s + jX_s = (0.31 + 0.45j)Z_0 = (16.5 + 22.5j)\Omega$.

Thus we find ourselves back at the starting point from which indeed we have never moved, the half-circuit of the chart being no more than a paper exercise for carrying out the series-parallel conversion without resort to the rather cumbersome algebraic formulae quoted above.

The importance of this procedure may be seen by supposing that the $(16.5 + 22.5j)\Omega$ is a measured value of the impedance of an antenna which it is required to match to a 50Ω feeder. If the chart is treated solely as an impedance chart the best we can do is tune out the inductance with a series capacitor, reducing the SWR to 3.0 from 4.0, but the parallel conversion indicates an almost perfect match subject only to getting rid of the *equivalent parallel reactance* of j33Ω. This requires the simple addition of a parallel capacitor having a reactance of $-j33\Omega$, ie 345pF for a frequency of 14MHz.

Had the series reactive term been missing at the start of the exercise we should have been less fortunate, and for a more general solution of the matching problem reference may be made to Fig 4.63 taken from reference [7] where the solution is obtained from the formulae. The top diagram illustrates the problem and as a first step the reactance is tuned out at (b), leaving a 5:1 resistive mismatch. By manipulation of formulae it is found that a series reactance $+30j$ results in a value of 75Ω for R_p. The addition of a capacitor to tune out X_p results in an impedance match and the final solution is shown at (e).

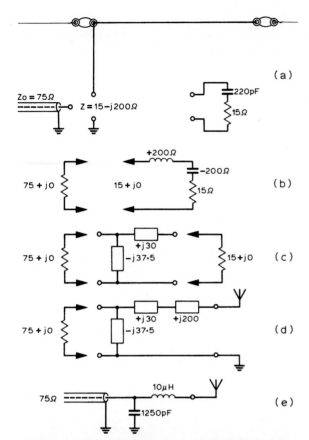

Fig 4.63. Example to illustrate the matching of two arbitrary impedances. Tuning out the reactance of the antenna results in a 5:1 resistance mismatch. Detuning slightly, to the extent of ±j30Ω, matches the resistances but results in a reactive mismatch which is removed by a reactance ∓j37Ω. The practical solution of the problem is shown at (e) for 3.5MHz

Being thus conversant with the essential logic, the procedure can be greatly simplified by using the Smith chart along the lines of the previous example. A straight-edge is placed across the centre of the chart and rotated so that the intercepts with the $R = R_s$ and $R = Z_0$ scale lines are equidistant from the centre. The intercept points (which are similar to Z, Y in Fig 4.62) correspond respectively to X_s and X_p but, whereas X_p is the actual value of the component required, X_s includes the reactance of the antenna which must be added or subtracted depending on the respective signs. In the case of Fig 4.63 we have $Z_0 = 75\Omega$ and $R_s = 15\Omega$. There is a series reactance of $-j200\Omega$ which as a first step is tuned out, being later replaced by the correct value, ±30Ω in conjunction with the required value of ∓37.5Ω for X_p, as shown in Fig 4.63(d). The plotting of this example on the chart is an exercise the reader may like to try for himself, particularly if he has experience already of the algebraic method.

In the case of the previous example, use of an admittance bridge (Fig 18.21) would have given the values of $G + jB$ directly, and hence the required value of X_p (ie $1/B$), without reference to the chart. However, in another instance the value of G might be just as unsuitable as the value of R_s in the first example, so that the above procedure would need to be applied in reverse.

An alternative method of solving the matching problem is to proceed down the line from the antenna to the point at which R_p is equal to Z_0 or, re-phrasing this in 'admittance language', $G = Y_0$. After determining the corresponding value of X_p, connection of a parallel reactance $-X_p$ will establish correct matching, though the portion of line between this point and the antenna continues to operate at a high SWR.

In general we can use either procedure and have a choice of two quite different solutions to the problem, one of which is often much more convenient than the other. On a point of mathematical detail, equating $1/jX_p$ to jB means that $1/X_p = j^2B = -B$, so that if X_p is positive B is negative and vice versa. In other words a capacitor, though its reactance X is negative, is regarded as having a positive susceptance (B). Similarly an inductor has a negative susceptance. This should not confuse the reader since the sign is a matter of convention, the change being a formality needed for 'keeping the record straight'. In the same vein it may be noticed that j is shown as negative on one side of the chart and positive on the other, so that inverting jX one obtains a susceptance $-jB$, meaning that X and B are both inductive.

Recommendations

The correct choice of feeder system depends on the type of antenna and the layout of the station. Coaxial feeder is usually the most convenient but is inefficient and very expensive. In contrast, open-wire line can be quickly constructed from inexpensive materials and more often than not can be used either on its own or in conjunction with relatively short lengths of coaxial cable, in which case the length of the open-wire line should preferably be a multiple of λ/2.

Due to a large decrease in velocity factor when wet, the older type of plastic twin-line (75 or 300Ω) must be avoided, though it may be used in short lengths such as might be required for insertion in a 600Ω line to bypass the beam rotator. Slotted 300Ω line is about four times better but with high SWR can still be troublesome when getting wet or drying out.

Baluns, preferably of the auto-transformer type wound on ferrite rods, should always be used when going from a balanced to an unbalanced system or vice versa. These devices are broadband, inexpensive to construct, and highly efficient, but there are restrictions on their use and pp56–60 should be consulted. An ATU can also operate as a balun but experience has led to a preference for separate baluns in conjunction with an unbalanced ATU for feedline impedances less than 300Ω, or a balanced ATU if the impedance is high, eg a high-voltage point on an open-wire line. An ATU can usually be designed for a specific task using inexpensive components such as can be found in any well-stocked junk box, but universal units are more difficult to design, expensive to buy, and not recommended.

For the feeding of vertical antennas there is no need for the extensive buried-earth systems usually recommended, and advice apparently requiring one to buy up several neighbouring properties in which to bury several miles of expensive copper wire should be ignored. Moreover, in the case of above-ground radial systems the length usually recommended (λ/4) is the one above all others to be avoided for reasons explained on p42, and existing systems should be checked for lack of symmetry as well as feeder radiation by the methods described.

'Monopole' vertical elements should be 'earthed' to short inductively-loaded counterpoises and fed with due regard for the advice given on pp42–45. Symmetrical (dipole) vertical elements should be centre-fed if the feeder can be brought away at right-angles and without coupling into other elements. Usually it is, however, more convenient to use a 'Zepp' feed at the lower end, although the Zepp feed can be very inefficient in its conventional form; it must be terminated at the antenna end by a λ/4 open-wire stub closed at its far end, as first pointed out by G6CJ.

Appendix – use of j

Most readers will be familiar with the fact that when 10Ω of resistance is added to 10Ω of reactance, the impedance offered to the passage of an electric current is not 20Ω but something less. To avoid doing the sum, the impedance in this case would usually be written down in the form 10 + 10j, the j being merely a form of shorthand to indicate that the answer (if needed) may be obtained by adding the two quantities 'at right-angles'. For example, if we represent them by drawing two lines at right-angles using a scale of 1cm to an ohm and then make this into a complete right-angled triangle, the length of the line which completes the triangle is 14cm, and 14Ω is the answer to the problem. Suppose, however, that before adding the two lengths, the second one is turned through a right-angle not once, but twice. It is now going in the opposite direction and the sum of the two quantities is zero, ie it is the answer to the sum '10 minus 10'.

Turning the second quantity through two right-angles has, in effect, multiplied it by (−1) and with this picture in mind the reader will probably have little difficulty in identifying −1 with $j \times j$ or j^2, so that j can be considered as shorthand for $\sqrt{-1}$. This is not a 'real' number since, however useful it may be to the mathematician, there is no such thing in nature, hence the usual description of the 10j as the 'unreal' part of the impedance. It is also unreal in another sense – when a current flows through the circuit, power is consumed only in the resistance. If the j term is positive, it represents an inductance, in which case energy is stored in a magnetic field and then released.

When a voltage is applied to an inductance the power going into the magnetic field constitutes a load on the source and the flow of current is impeded until the field has built up to a value corresponding to whatever maximum current the circuit is capable of supporting. In other words, the current is

said to lag behind the voltage, and in AC circuits this lag is a quarter of a cycle, or one right-angle, hence the j. Conversely the current going into a capacitor is initially large but drops to zero when it is fully charged, so the current is ahead of the voltage and the j is of opposite sign, ie negative, though the '+' and '−' are dictated only by convention.

Although the reactive part of an impedance does not consume power, it limits the flow of current and prevents a generator from delivering all the power of which it is capable. Fortunately it can usually be neutralised by a reactance of opposite sign – the process known as 'tuning'. Reactance is therefore the basis of selectivity, and performs other useful functions, so it should not be regarded merely as something to be got rid of – even though this is what one is usually trying to do when using the Smith chart for the solution of an antenna or feeder problem.

It is important to realise that when working with complex impedances, ie those containing both resistance R and reactance X, the two parts play quite different roles. In general it is more useful to know the separate constituents of an impedance than its absolute magnitude which can of course easily be worked out from them, being given by $\sqrt{(R^2 + X^2)}$ or by graphical methods as described earlier. When, therefore, an impedance is given in the form $R + jX$, this is not an unfinished sum but a particularly informative bit of shorthand.

Moreover, since j can be handled like any other algebraic symbol, it enables those whose knowledge of mathematics extends no further than simple algebra to tackle quite elaborate calculations involving complex numbers, such as coupled circuits, antennas (including close-spaced beam elements), phase-shift networks, and the series/parallel conversions mentioned earlier; expressions for the latter are to be found on p71, but the manipulations can be very cumbersome and those with experience of using them will be the first to appreciate the delightful simplicity of the Smith chart for this purpose.

Since expressions containing j carry implications of direction or phase, the associated calculations are known as 'vector' algebra but in its simpler forms this differs from ordinary algebra only to the extent of substituting a 'minus' for j^2, as explained earlier.

References

[1] *Radio Engineers Handbook,* F E Terman, McGraw-Hill, 1943, p193.
[2] *Radio Communication Handbook,* Vol 2, 5th edn, RSGB, 1977, p12.34.
[3] *The ARRL Antenna Book,* 12th edn, ARRL, 1970, p117. See also reference [1], p189.
[4] 'Aerial reflection', F Charman, BEM, G6CJ, *RSGB Bulletin* December 1955.
[5] 'The Smith chart', L A Moxon, *Radio Communication* January 1977.
[6] 'More on the Smith chart', G Garside, *Radio Communication* December 1977.

[7] *Radio Communication Handbook,* Vol 2, 5th edn, RSGB, 1977, p12.40.

[8] *Radio Communication Handbook,* Vol 2, 5th edn, RSGB, 1977, p12.31.

[9] 'New class of coaxial line transformers', G Badger, W6TC, *Ham Radio* March 1980.

[10] *The ARRL Antenna Book,* 12th edn, ARRL, 1970, p98.

[11] 'High performance broadband balun', J J Nagle, K4KJ, *Ham Radio* February 1980.

[12] *Radio Communication Handbook,* Vol 2, 5th edn, p12.51.

[13] *The ARRL Antenna Book,* 13th edn, 1974, p181.

[14] *The ARRL Antenna Anthology,* 1978, p92.

[15] *Radio Communication Handbook,* Vol 2, 5th edn, RSGB, 1977, p12.45.

[16] *Radio Engineers Handbook,* F E Terman, McGraw-Hill, 1943, p212.

[17] 'A 14Mc/s coax fed dipole and 7 G3OGR, *RSGB Bulletin* March 196

[18] 'Why coax', E M Wagner, G3BID, 7

[19] 'Balance to unbalance transformers', Ian White, G3SEK, *Radio Communication* December 1989.

[20] *Radio Engineers Handbook,* F E Terman, McGraw-Hill, 1943, p864.

[21] 'Technical Topics', *Radio Communication* February 1989.

[22] *The ARRL Antenna Book*, 15th edn, 1988, p26-4.

[23] 'The feed impedance of an elevated vertical antenna', Guy Fletcher, VK2BBF, *Amateur Radio* (Australia) Aug–Oct 1984.

[24] 'Technical Topics', *Radio Communication* May 1991.

[25] 'Ground planes, radial systems and asymmetric dipoles', *ARRL Antenna Compendium*, Vol 3, ARRL, 1993.

Chapter 5

Close-spaced beams

More often than not a frequency band is either 'dead' or capable of supporting communication even with low powers and simple antennas, a point underlined by experiences recorded in Chapter 10, so why, it might be argued, go to the extra trouble and expense of a beam? It is thought that the main benefit accrues from the reduction of interference during reception, though the 4 to 6dB gain provided by typical amateur beams is an important bonus and probably the reason which carries most weight with the majority of amateurs. For these reasons, and because of the need for beams which can be erected in a limited space and pointed in any direction, the close-spaced beam with two or three dipole or loop elements provides the mainstay of amateur long-distance communication on the higher-frequency bands. Such beams are widely available from commercial sources but many have been constructed from published data, and new designs are a common feature of amateur journals.

The need for a multiplicity of antenna designs might be questioned in view of the close equivalence between different antenna systems which was demonstrated in Chapter 3, but this was primarily in respect of gain; important differences arise when account is taken of other aspects in conjunction with local circumstances, individual interests and abilities, and the cost factor. In consequence there is a need for many different types of beam, affording plenty of scope for ingenuity. Many important innovations owe more to patience and common sense than technical expertise but questions often arise for which there is 'no answer in the books' and experimenters frequently complain of lack of expert guidance. This is reflected in a tendency to attribute good results to impossible causes such as 'lowering the angle of radiation' (p115), proliferation of designs open to more or less serious criticisms, improbable claims for some systems and waste of time and money in the search for better results by methods which have no chance of success.

Extensive browsing through the literature has unearthed gain figures for two-element beams ranging all the way from 3dB in some professional journals to 14dB for the Swiss quad [7], yet theory is quite specific as to what the gain ought to be, and for the cases in question admits of nothing outside the limits of 4 to 5.7dB relative to a dipole. Lower figures are difficult to explain, except in some cases on the basis of excessive phase shift or built-in losses, whereas higher figures

may be due to failure to realise the difficulties of measurement (pp271–278) plus the enthusiasm normally engendered by optimistic results.

To avoid such errors the reader need only select the most appropriate curves from Fig 3.9 and insert the 3dB beamwidths in the ($16/\alpha_1\alpha_2$) formula, p22, not forgetting that 2.15dB must be deducted to obtain the gain relative to a dipole. Even this tends to give slightly optimistic results, the task of Chapter 2 being to establish basic principles without involving the reader in too much detail. Nevertheless, attention was drawn to sources of error and these can add up to about 1dB.

An understanding of coupled circuits is a first step towards acquiring insight into the mechanism of two-element beams, including recognition of the need to increase the capacitive coupling between dipole elements by bending the ends inwards. This greatly improves the front/back ratio of two-element arrays, paving the way for highly efficient reversible beams which can be remotely tuned.

Mutual impedance

When two circuits tuned to the same frequency, Fig 5.1, are placed near each other, there is usually some degree of coupling between them, that is to say a current I_1 flowing in *one* circuit induces a voltage V_2 in the *other*. By close analogy with Ohm's law the ratio V_2/I_1 is defined as the 'mutual impedance' Z_m. It is the same with antennas except that by meekly accepting such conventional constraints as the use of straight elements the antenna designer usually denies himself any control over the coupling. Furthermore, whereas normal coupling between tuned circuits can be represented by a 'mutual reactance', that between antennas can be reactive, resistive or complex which means that it includes both resistance and reactance. The tendency to ignore the reactive component has unfortunately led (as we shall see) to unsolved problems and missed opportunities.

Critical coupling ($k = 1$) exists between identical resonant circuits when $I_2 = I_1$, the ratio I_2/I_1 being equal to the coupling factor k. A similar situation exists in the case of antennas, though it is necessary to distinguish between 'driven' operation in which each element is connected to the transmitter through some network or arrangement of feeders intended to enforce correct phasing and power sharing, and 'parasitic' operation

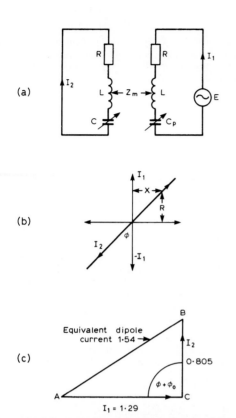

Fig 5.1. (a) Coupled circuits. The current I_1 flowing in the primary induces a voltage I_1Z_m in the secondary, resulting in a current $I_2 = I_1Z_m/(R + jX)$ where $X = 0$ at resonance (ie ($\omega L = 1/\omega C$). For tuned circuits as shown $Z_m = j\omega M$ where M is the mutual inductance. For closely spaced antenna elements, Z_m is in general a complex impedance, ie it has the form $(R_m + jX_m)$, though X_m can be zero. (b) shows phase shift φ due to X for the case of $X_m = 0$ but is equally applicable to the case of $X = 0$ if R, X are replaced by the appropriate values of R_m, X_m. (c) shows calculation of gain for a parasitic array with $\lambda/8$ spacing and $\varphi = 45°$; obtaining I_1, I_2 and φ (see p84) the triangle is drawn and the gain, expressed as a voltage ratio, is measured off to scale. The generator perceives the secondary as an impedance $Z_m{}^2/(R + jX)$ in series with its own circuit. Equalisation of I_1 and I_2 requires $X_m = bR$ (see p83)

which is closely analogous to the action of coupled circuits as just described. In this latter case one element only is connected to the transmitter, the other element or elements being energised via the mutual coupling. It will be seen that this in fact plays an equally important role in both cases and there is a close relationship between the two types of operation, amounting to virtual identity when both are designed correctly.

Mutual coupling and gain are closely linked and without mutual *resistance* there can be no gain. This applies to all close-spaced beams and can be readily understood by taking yet another close look at the W8JK system. The way in which this achieves directivity and therefore gain was explained on p23, and it was shown to depend on values of R which are much lower than those for the elements in isolation. It follows that ohms are being subtracted from each element as a result of the presence of the other, and these subtracted ohms are the

'mutual resistance' (R_m), the subtraction sign being due to the antiphase connection which is a feature of the W8JK system and its derivatives. On the other hand, with in-phase connection and close enough spacing, two elements become indistinguishable from a single element except that each takes half the current. In this case the ohms are added, giving a total of $R_m + R \approx 2R$ for each element, this being equivalent to R for the two in parallel which therefore behave as one.

The role of mutual reactance is rather different from that of resistance since it makes no direct contribution to gain but without it the equalisation of currents is impossible. Fortunately, unlike resistance, it can be brought fully under the control of the antenna designer.

Two-element close-spaced beams

These may consist of a pair of 'driven' elements as in Fig 3.7 or a driven element having a second or 'parasitic' element energised from it by mutual coupling in a manner similar to the operation of pairs of coupled circuits. Depending on the degree of coupling, the current in the parasitic element may be greater or less than that in the driven element. In seeking a better understanding of small beams, two-element arrays such as these are the obvious starting point; not only this, but approached from the right angle they provide a simple introduction to a topic which can all too easily expand into areas of extreme complexity and little benefit.

Readers are invited to recall the explanation of beam formation in the case of pairs of closely spaced elements given on p23, where it was shown that with the simple figure-of-eight pattern of the W8JK antenna as a starting point unidirectional patterns could be formed by introducing a phase shift, and that such patterns (which follow from simple geometry) depend *solely* on the ratio of phase shift to spacing. This means that, for a given power radiated and the same φ/φ_0 ratio, all such beams have the same gain and radiation pattern so that in identical circumstances they provide the same signal strength at any given point in space. It was also shown that with equal currents gain is extremely simple to calculate. Main features of such antennas include very deep nulls for the rejection of interference, accurate correspondence between gain and null directions which can be placed under the control of the operator and, with correct design, relatively non-critical adjustments. None of this is apparent from the standard reference books, where difficult calculations depict the gain and directivity of parasitic arrays as a function of element spacing and tuning with no clear relationship to the desired end product, nulls being non-existent and discrimination against interference from back directions extremely poor. Fig 5.2 explains why straight elements minimise coupling, and the practical consequences of this can be inferred from the current-ratio curve in Fig 5.3 for $X_m = 0$, which corresponds to a spacing of just over $\lambda/8$, and is typical of two-element Yagi arrays.

Prior to the advent of computers, these calculations were not merely difficult but extremely time-consuming, as the author can attest from many hours wasted in arriving by an

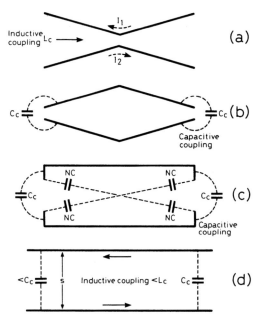

Fig 5.2. Inductive and capacitive coupling of two elements. (a) Elements bent inwards at their centres couple inductively. (b, c) Ends bent inwards couple capacitively. (d) Excessive coupling may be neutralised by capacitors as shown in (c). In (d), the two couplings cancel each other if $S = \lambda/8$, leaving only the resistive coupling R. Straight elements minimise coupling. Reflectors need capacitive coupling; directors need inductive coupling which is usually less easy to provide (Ham Radio)

extremely devious route at several of the curves presented in this chapter. Later it came as a relief (also a surprise) to have them confirmed by almost 'at a glance' results obtained by doing the right calculations instead of the wrong ones.

As the author has pointed out elsewhere [25], 'conventional wisdom' is seriously flawed by starting from the implicit assumption that elements have to be straight instead of from the desired end product which requires the currents to be equal, a condition which can be readily met and goes hand-in-hand with easier methods of construction. In contrast, as demonstrated by Fig 5.2 (and further explained below), the use of straight elements minimises coupling and ensures that equalisation of current is impossible with realistic values of spacing, accentuating differences and making them the worst possible choice. Apart from serious degradation of front-to-back ratio due to the unequal currents, the necessity to take account of current ratios influenced by a number of random factors drags an additional variable, a particularly nasty one, into the calculations and fully accounts for the difference of viewpoint indicated above.

It also adds up to the fact that two-element beams [25] have been "deprived of their rightful status" due to "an imperfect grasp of essentials which has turned an inherently simple situation into one of needless complexity". It is true that the desirability of equal currents has been widely recognised but some, in an attempt to equalise them, have invited worse trouble by using phasing lines. As explained in the last

chapter, these only work correctly when matched, a condition not easy to achieve when working with tightly coupled elements, one of which (as explained later) may have a zero or negative value of input resistance! On the other hand, there are relatively few problems if, for example, one starts by taking a pair of self-resonant dipoles having their ends bent inwards, in which case either can be used as a reflector for the other. The additional capacitive coupling due to having the ends closer together not only equalises the currents but provides a suitable phase shift so that detuning of the reflector is not necessary. Also open to criticism is the usual practice of specifying front-to-back ratio in terms of the reciprocal of the beam heading, although all back directions are equally important.

Resolving the problems of driven arrays by means of Fig 5.21, which can also be used as a tuner for parasitic elements, the parasitic mode was found much easier to use, as later explained by the curves for large X_m in Fig 5.3 which demonstrate the possibility of single-knob adjustment over a relatively wide range with little change in current ratio.

With correct design, two-element arrays can often be superior to bigger beams in DX performance because small size, allied to relatively low weight and windage, allows them to be erected at a greater height, thus offsetting the fairly small amount of additional gain obtainable by using three or four

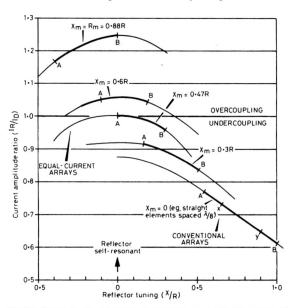

Fig 5.3. Current ratio for pairs of elements spaced $\lambda/8$ in terms of reflector tuning as X_m is varied. AB is an advisory working range in conformity with Figs 5.4 and 5.7. At A, $\varphi/\varphi_0 = 0.6$, nulls at $\pm128°$. At B, $\varphi/\varphi_0 = 1.0$, null at $180°$ relative to beam heading. R is the radiation resistance of a single element, and reflectors require negative values of X_m or positive values of X; the reverse applies in the case of directors. Coupling depends on element shape and spacing, but lengths are not critical. To assist perspective, points x, y on the lower curve correspond roughly to 5% detuning of tubular and wire dipoles respectively. Variation of reflector tuning allows nulls to be moved in either direction from the mean position which is determined by the ratio of X_m to R_m

elements. In contrast to their larger relatives, nearly all the 'theoretical' gain is realisable in practice; in addition, very deep steerable nulls can be achieved in the case of interfering signals coming from the rear directions. Even more important for some of us are the possibilities of fitting them into relatively small spaces or concealing their existence in various ways. Other advantages include the possibility of instantaneous reversal of beam direction and the ease with which multiband operation can be achieved by using a pair of resonant feeders.

Realisation of these advantages is helped by a proper understanding of the method of beam formation but, as indicated above, this is greatly simplified by starting from the assumption of equal currents in the elements. This is because a particularly awkward variable is thereby removed from the equations, leaving the gain and radiation pattern uniquely determined by the ratio of the phase difference between the currents to the spacing of the elements. As with other forms of coupled circuit, equalisation of current is dependent on establishing the right amount of reactive coupling (X_m), a condition which tends to occur naturally with some types of element, though in general some degree of assistance is likely to be needed.

The differences between equal-current arrays and the majority of two-element beams in current use, as set out above, are sufficiently fundamental to justify treating them as two different kinds of antenna, which can be defined as follows.

(a) Equal-current systems, having their gain determined solely by the spacing/phase shift ratio. These include the quad, some examples of driven arrays, and beams constructed in ways which enhance the amount of reactive coupling between elements, eg by bending the ends in towards each other as described above. Within wide limits of shape and size the gain of all such arrays is virtually identical, depending solely on the spacing/phase shift ratio.

(b) Arrays with straight elements, having a gain determined in substantial part by the physical dimensions; these conform to historical precedent, current equality being impossible unless the spacing is too close for the achievement of acceptable efficiency and bandwidth.

Apart from physical differences, the introduction of current ratio as an extra variable escalates the 'theory' from a few lines of algebra to as many pages; methods of calculation are explained below and yield the performance figures summarised in Figs 5.4 to 5.10 and Fig 5.16 which, in conjunction with Fig 5.3, demonstrates for a typical case the adverse effects on performance of unequal currents. Note that with $\lambda/2$ elements spaced $\lambda/8$ the drop in gain is less than 0.5dB, but this assumes there are no resistive losses (which would accentuate the difference), and the adverse effect on F/B ratio is catastrophic.

Fig 5.4 relates gain, radiation resistance (R), and front/back ratio to the phase-shift ratio, and explains why, when using a reflector, the SWR tends to rise steeply towards the

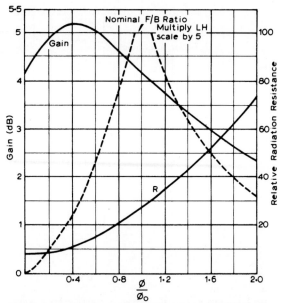

Fig 5.4. Variation of gain, radiation resistance and front/back ratio with φ/φ_0, where φ_0 is the phase shift corresponding to the distances between the elements and φ is the electrical phase shift relative to the antiphase condition. Resistance scale is correct in ohms for each of a pair of dipoles spaced $\lambda/8$ and carrying equal currents

low end of the band, an effect which is accentuated by moving the nulls away from the reciprocal of the beam heading. They also illustrate the effect on performance of opting for an easier life by settling for a phase-shift ratio of 1.0 or greater. Fig 5.5 relates null direction to phase-angle ratio, thereby establishing a rigorous link between gain and null direction. This is the only method known to the author whereby an amateur can reasonably expect to obtain a precise figure for the gain of an HF antenna, but is of course restricted to specific types of antenna and the assumption of negligible losses.

Fig 5.3 explains a long-standing mystery whereby the performance of reversible parasitic arrays was found in practice to vary between providing deep nulls, but on a few stations only, to achieving them on most stations. This is now seen to be due to the change from slight under- to slight overcoupling, and accounts also for the fact that in moving around the band or altering the null directions the null depths tend to remain constant, even if the antenna is narrow band to the extent of requiring frequent adjustment of the ATU. These are outstanding features of the SDL arrays (p89) which have been a main concern of the author in recent years, but should apply equally to other loop shapes or dipoles fed with resonant lines. It can be inferred from Fig 5.3 that, with slight overcoupling, the allowable variation in X_m is of the order of ±20% for greater than 20dB F/B ratio. Fig 5.8 shows from various sources the rate at which gain decreases as recommended limits of spacing are exceeded, this being nearly independent of the design or number of elements. These curves are for the maximum gain condition, $\varphi/\varphi_0 = 0.3$ to 0.4, and Figs 5.9 and 5.10 show that the decrease is roughly doubled by the common

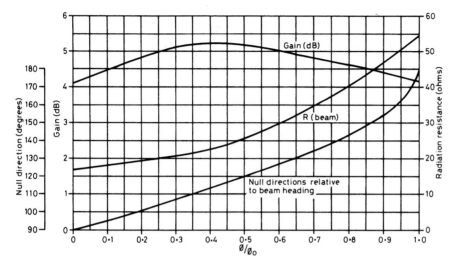

Fig 5.5. Relationship between phase angle, gain, null directions, and radiation resistance for all close-spaced, two-element beams with equal current drive. Note: losses not included; gain figures valid within 0.3dB for null depths greater than 10dB (approx). Radiation resistance (in ohms) for half-wave elements spaced λ/8 (see text for other beams) (Ham Radio)

practice of placing nulls on the reciprocal of the beam heading.

An important aim of this chapter is to show how features of equal-current arrays which are unique to this type of antenna can be exploited to maximum advantage. However, this is only part of the story, much of which is more appropriate to later chapters where it is set in the context of multiband beams providing efficient coverage of five or six bands by the use of resonant feeders and 'impedance-transforming loops' (pp124–128), 'invisible' arrays (p247) and, since these beams are lightweight and reversible, reducing the need for towers and beam rotators. Despite the virtues of two-element, equal-current arrays, the conventional Yagi with three or more elements remains an important option for those able to erect large structures, though the further escalation in the number

of variables demands an entirely different approach, to which we shall be addressing ourselves in due course.

Calculating the gain of close-spaced, equal-current arrays (two-element)

It can now be seen that the properties of close-spaced beams as described in Chapter 3 are inseparable from their behaviour as 'coupled circuits' so that, given accurate values for mutual impedance, it should be possible to calculate the gain with equal precision. Studying the subject from this angle sheds light also on important practical aspects, bringing out for example the need to increase coupling by bringing the end of elements closer together as already mentioned.

To illustrate this it will be useful to pursue further the example of the W8JK which, as illustrated in Fig 5.11, uses a pair of elements 'driven' by voltages of opposite phase E

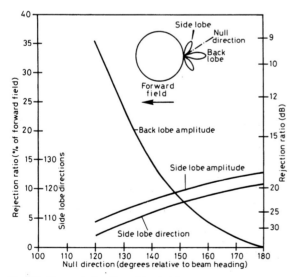

Fig 5.6. Size and direction of back lobes (see key above). For corresponding gain, see Fig 5.5 (Ham Radio)

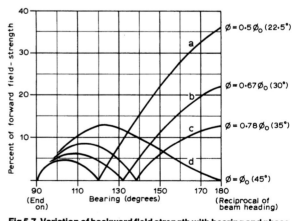

Fig 5.7. Variation of backward field strength with bearing and phase angle (φ). Angles in brackets apply for spacing = λ/8. Curve (a) corresponds to maximum gain and curve (d) to maximum (nominal) front/back ratio. Curve (b) provides near-maximum gain, and better interference rejection than (d) for all bearings less than 147°

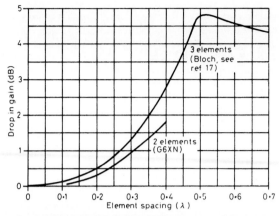

Fig 5.8. Decrease of gain with increase of spacing. Note that gain is a maximum for both two- and three-element beams as spacing diminishes, though practical constraints impose a lower limit of about 0.1λ (Ham Radio)

and $-E$ respectively, the crossover connection being extremely important since otherwise, as already indicated in the discussion of mutual impedance, one ends up with a very close approximation to a dipole and the gain can be specified without further calculation as almost exactly 0dB! The currents in the elements are I and $-I$ respectively, the voltage IZ_m induced from the other element being subtracted from E in

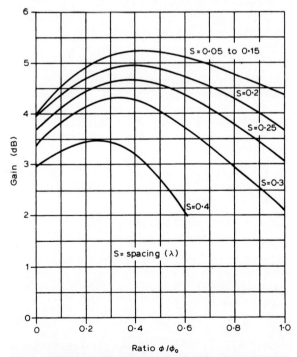

Fig 5.9. Variation of gain with phase shift at large spacings. (Top curve is reproduced from Fig 5.4 for comparison). For 'straight' arrays without current equalisation, maximum gains are only slightly reduced (eg 4.0dB for $S = λ/4$) but F/B ratios are much worse

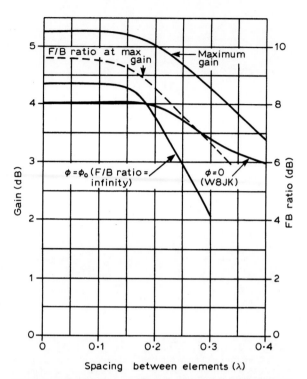

Fig 5.10. Variation of gain with spacing for the conditions of maximum gain, maximum nominal front/back ratio ($\varphi = \varphi_0$) and $\varphi = 0$. Dotted curve shows nominal front/back ratio corresponding to the maximum gain curve

both cases. It then follows from Ohm's law that $E - (-I)Z_m$, or in other words $E + IZ_m$, must be equal to IR. Tuning out the reactive part (if any) of Z_m we have $E/I = R - R_m$ and, substituting known values (p83) for parallel $λ/2$ dipoles spaced $λ/8$, $R - R_m = 73 - 64.5 = 8.5Ω$. This is the 'effective' radiation resistance of each element. Adding the two resistances, $R_{8JK} = 17Ω$ whereas for a dipole we have $R_D = 73Ω$.

The current in each 8JK element is therefore $\sqrt{(73/17)} = 2.06$ times that in a dipole. Adding these with a phase difference of $45°$ (Fig 3.7), it is found that the forward field from the W8JK antenna is 1.58 times that from a dipole, equivalent to a gain of 4.0dB. It is interesting to note that $17Ω$, as well as being the radiation resistance for the two elements in series, would also apply to a single driven element in the event of the other being a parasitic element carrying an identical current in antiphase, since field-strength is proportional to I, power is equal to I^2R and both are unchanged, so R must also be the same. It will later be shown that, in the case of a two-element driven array, the radiation resistances can always be directly added (or, if one of them is negative, subtracted), even though if there is mutual reactance they are always different. (Note that in the case of the W8JK the elements are not connected in series but in parallel, so that the actual feedpoint impedance is $17/4 = 4.25Ω$, though this is not material to the calculation of gain.)

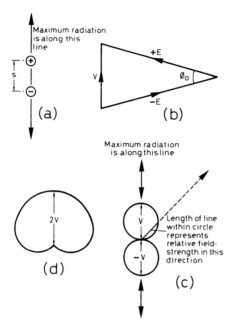

Fig 5.11. (a) Two closely spaced sources separated by distance S. (b) Vector addition results in voltage V that for small angles is proportional to φ_0. (c) Polar plot shows variation of field voltage as a function of the angle to observer. No additional (electrical) phase shift has been introduced, ie $\varphi = 0$. (d) Field pattern if electrical phase shift φ equals physical phase shift (φ_0) *(Ham Radio)*

The next step is to introduce, without altering the current ratio, a phase shift equal to or less than the spacing in order to obtain a null in the back direction or some other direction judged to be desirable from inspection of Figs 5.5 and 5.6; to this end the driving of both elements with the help of a phasing line has attracted numerous experimenters but, despite some outstanding successes in individual cases, the results have been somewhat variable for reasons which will become obvious. The use of controlled coupling on the other hand is

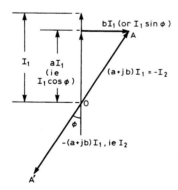

Fig 5.12. Derivation of I_2 from I_1. A fraction a of I_1 has added to it at right-angles another fraction b so that $OA = (a = jb)I_1$. Marking off an equal length OA' in the opposite direction, we obtain $-(a + jb)I_1$. Suitable choice of a and b provides the desired phase angle. Since we are dealing with a right-angled triangle, $OA = I_1 \sqrt{(a^2 + b^2)}$ and it is only necessary to put $a^2 + b^2 = 1$ to make I_1 and I_2 equal in amplitude

simple, completely effective, and in retrospect it seems amazing that it should have escaped attention for so long, particularly in view of the close analogy with coupled circuits.

By retaining both X_m and X as variables and allowing the current ratio also to vary, one enters a complex area which contains an infinite number of permutations and combinations but very few guidelines. If on the other hand the current ratio is assumed to be 1.0 on the basis that this is what is wanted and can normally be achieved by one means or another, the answers can be written down straight away. This avoids going through the normal processes which have involved the author in many pages and wasted hours of algebra, besides causing others to resort to computers or experimental modelling techniques which have in some cases produced the wrong answers. In fact all one needs to know is Ohm's law and the definition of mutual impedance from which, for the driven element

$$E = I_1 R + I_2 Z_m \qquad (1)$$

Little more remains except to express I_2 in terms of I_1 and then write this expression out in full.

To explain the process in more detail, Fig 5.12 shows the current I_2 shifted in phase relative to $-I_1$ by a typical angle as required by Fig 5.4, and it will be seen that in this position it can also be described as the sum of two currents at right-angles, ie $aI_1 + jbI_1$. Pythagoras tells us that for equal amplitudes $a^2 + b^2 = 1^2 = 1$ and, as in previous examples, the phase shift is given by $\tan \varphi = b/a$. Putting $I_2 = -I_1(a + jb)$, $Z_m = (R_m + jX_m)$ and, assuming any j terms to be removed by the normal tuning process, we have for the radiation resistance of the beam

$$E/I_1 = R - aR_m + bX_m \qquad (2)$$

Initially one is not concerned about how to meet the stated condition, but is merely looking at the situation from the point of view of an element having another one alongside it carrying some particular value of current, regardless of how this may have come about. To obtain the conditions for equal amplitudes one need only put

$$I_1 = \frac{-I_2}{a + jb} = -I_2 (a - jb) \qquad (3)$$

substituting this in equation (1) we obtain

$$R + jX = (a - jb)(R_m + jX_m)$$
$$= aR_m + bX_m - j(bR_m - aX_m) \qquad (4)$$

and since the 'real' and the 'j' terms have to be equal to each other separately (because there is no other way of constructing the triangle)

$$R = aR_m + bX_m \qquad (5)$$
$$X = aX_m - bR_m \qquad (6)$$

Notice that (2), (5) and (6) are essential conditions but it does not matter how they are satisfied. In principle one can use parasitic operation with either element driven, or drive both elements, but in practice there are restrictions. In particular, since aR_m is always less than R, condition (5) can only be met

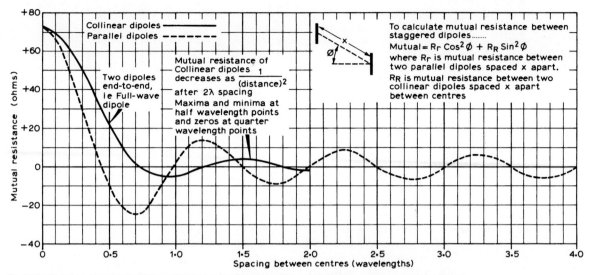

Fig 5.13. Variation of mutual resistance between parallel and collinear λ/2 dipoles as the spacing is altered

if bX_m is positive; thus if X_m is negative b/a must also be negative, which means that in this case parasitic elements must be tuned as reflectors. It is of interest to note from (6) that if $aX_m = bR_m$ we have $X = 0$, so there is no detuning of the reflector and the beam can be reversed merely by switching from one element to the other. From (5) we find this implies a further condition $a = R_m/R$ so that $X_m = bR$. Figs 5.13 and 5.14 illustrate the variation of R_m and X_m with spacing for straight λ/2 dipole elements.

It will be clear from the W8JK example that R_m/R must always be less than one, otherwise as it approached unity the gain would increase to infinity, and from (14) it is evident that I_2/I_1 cannot in fact exceed R_m/R. Also, as may seem obvious intuitively, I is even further reduced by detuning which is essential if $X_m = 0$. It follows that with $X_m = 0$ current equalisation is impossible unless both elements are driven. For further insight, let the reflector be tuned to resonance and the required phase difference obtained by adding reactive

Fig 5.14. Variation in mutual reactance between parallel λ/2 dipoles as the spacing is altered

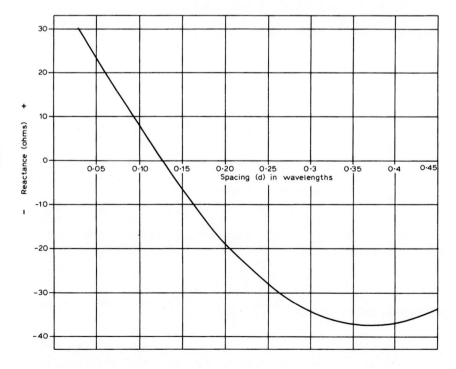

coupling so that $R_m = X_m$ instead of equating R and X. Proceeding along similar lines and referring again to Fig 5.1(c), it is found that $I_1 = 1.0$, $I_2 = 1.24$, and the equivalent dipole current is 1.59. This makes the gain 4.0dB and increases the F/B ratio to 16.4dB, but now instead of undercoupling there is overcoupling, with the reflector current exceeding that in the driven element.

Fig 5.15 shows the variation of φ/φ_0 with a for spacings between 0.1λ and 0.19λ, the point corresponding to $b/a = R_m/R$ being marked on each curve, from which it will be seen that the $X = 0$ requirement is met for $\varphi/\varphi_0 \approx 0.63$ over the whole range of spacings. This is sufficiently low to provide a close approach to maximum gain and, though slightly on the low side for best interference rejection, this is of little consequence, particularly if separate tuners are used for transmission and reception.

There is one more useful result of this design procedure to be noted – the condition $bR_m = aX_m$ also gets rid of the j terms so that there is no detuning of either element by the other. In other words, it follows from Figs 5.7 and 5.15 that the process of making both elements individually self-resonant and bending the ends together so that the currents are equal should automatically ensure infinite rejection of signals on bearings of about $-130°$ relative to the beam heading. The radiation resistance is exactly double the values read from Fig 5.4, apart from any corrections which may be necessary in accordance with the rules stated earlier. The use of two feeders allows remote beam reversal and separate tuning for reception and transmission, though the nulls will not be quite complete for bearings other than $-130°$ unless both phase and amplitude are adjusted. However, Fig 5.3 shows this point to be largely academic, particularly if the difficulty of making practical use of null depths in excess of 20 or 30dB is taken into account.

Referring back to (2) and (5), it will be seen that if X_m is negative (ie capacitive) and b is positive (phase advanced) the radiation resistance of the driven element is equal to $2bX_m$. If, on the other hand, we want to know the radiation resistance of the retarded element (reflector), b must be replaced by $-b$ in which case (5) and (6) are no longer satisfied and the effect on (2) is to make $E/I_1 = 0$, ie the radiation resistance is zero. In a way this is a glimpse of the obvious since if the adjustment is already correct the last thing one wants to do is either to supply power to or take it from the reflector. On the other hand, if equations (5) and (6) are not satisfied the driving of both elements is one way of putting matters right. In this case (with X_m negative) we have from (2) for the radiation resistances of the two elements:

$$R_{dir} = R - aR_m + bX_m \qquad (7)$$
$$R_{ref} = R - aR_m - bX_m \qquad (8)$$

When these are added X_m disappears, ie

$$R_{total} = R_{dir} + R_{ref} = 2(R - aR_m) = 2(R - R_m \cos\varphi) \qquad (9)$$

Note that X_m can cause *one* resistance to be zero or negative but *has no effect on the total*.

Arrays with unequal currents

It is instructive at this point to work out the radiation resistance, power gain, polar diagram and reflector tuning for a two-element parasitic array with straight elements, treating it like an ordinary pair of mutually coupled tuned circuits (Fig 5.1) with which many readers are already familiar.

Referring to Fig 5.1, the voltage induced in the secondary is I_1Z_m and the resulting current I_2 develops a voltage $I_2(R+jX)$ across the impedance of the secondary. This is assumed to be a parasitic element detuned in the direction causing it to act as a reflector; however, since this impedance is short-circuited the sum of the two voltages is zero and we have

$$I_1Z_m + I_2(R + jX) = 0 \qquad (10)$$

Hence $I_2 = -I_1Z_m/(R + jX) = -I_1Z_m \dfrac{R - jX}{R^2 + X^2} \qquad (11)$

But I_2 induces a voltage I_2Z_m back into the primary, so that if this is resonant $E = I_1R + I_2Z_m$ and, substituting for I_2, we have

$$E/I_1 = R - Z_m^2/(R + jX) \qquad (12)$$

To keep the algebra as simple as possible, we need $X_m = 0$ which happens very conveniently for $S = \lambda/8$. This leaves $Z_m = R_m$ which can be obtained from Fig 5.13. Now E/I_1 is the impedance 'seen' by the feeder and the j terms are eliminated by the normal tuning and matching process, leaving the radiation resistance which is given by

$$R_B = E/I_1 = R\left(1 - \frac{R_m^2}{R^2 + X^2}\right) \qquad (13)$$

The phase angle φ is determined by R and X as shown in Fig 5.1(b) but can be found more quickly by obtaining the angle $\tan^{-1}(X/R)$ with the help of a pocket calculator. This is the phase difference between the two currents I_1 and $-I_2$.

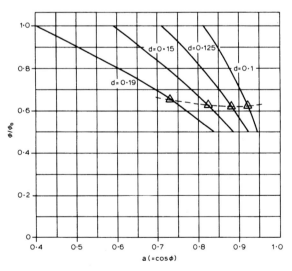

Fig 5.15. Variation of φ/φ_0 with a or $\cos\varphi$ for various spacings. The dotted line links the points for which $a = R_m/R$, showing that no detuning is required for the parasitic element provided φ/φ_0 is made equal to about 0.63

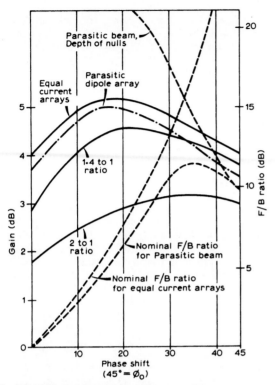

Fig 5.16. Gain and front/back ratio for two-element arrays with unequal currents. Top curve from Fig 5.4 is reproduced for comparison. Spacing = λ/8

Recalling Chapter 3, p25, we may decide to make φ 'equal to the spacing' φ₀, ie 45° for a spacing of λ/8, so that for this example we need $X = R$ and from equation (2) the magnitude of I_2 is given by

$$|I_2| = I_1 R_m / \sqrt{(R^2 + X^2)} = 0.707 \, I_1 R_m / R \qquad (14)$$

From Fig 5.13, $R_m = 64.5\Omega$: putting $R = 73\Omega$ and assuming a power of 73W so that the current in a dipole would be 1A, we have $R_B = 44\Omega$, $I_1 = 1.29$A and $I_2 = 0.805$A. Since $(\varphi + \varphi_0) = 90°$ the triangle may be completed as in Fig 5.1(c) to obtain the forward field which is represented by AB. This gives an equivalent dipole current of 1.54A so that the gain in decibels is 20 log 1.54 = 3.75dB. This is accurate to better than 0.1dB, and represents a loss of only 0.45dB compared with the equal-current condition assumed in Chapter 3. On the other hand, the field in the back direction, which in this case may be obtained by subtracting I_2 directly from I_1, is 0.485/1.54 times the forward field, a front/back ratio of only 10dB, as illustrated by the dotted curves in Fig 5.16.

This performance is rather poor compared with what can be achieved with two-element arrays since about a third of the possible gain has been sacrificed. In practice more than half the missing decibels can be recovered merely by retuning the reflector, but to realise the full potential of two-element beams it is necessary, as we have seen, to equalise the currents

and *shift the null away from the back direction.* This makes it possible to obtain gains of the order of 5dB combined with better than 20dB rejection over all or most of the 180° of back direction.

It used to be taken for granted that for equalisation of currents both elements would have to be driven. Figs 5.4 and 5.9, which were calculated on this basis, tell most of the story [1, 23], and show how gain, directivity and radiation resistance vary with the ratio of phase shift to spacing (φ/φ₀); it should be noted that (except for minor corrections explained below) these curves are applicable to *all* two-element close-spaced beams with equal currents (including quads). There are, however, differences in the case of parasitic beams due to current inequalities which vary between wide limits, depending on the type of beam and whether the parasitic element is tuned as a director or reflector. Though these curves were calculated prior to evolving the simpler method described above, the task was eased by assuming a spacing of λ/8 for which, in the case of straight elements, $X_m = 0$.

Although there is no direct connection between size and gain or directivity, the current required to maintain a given signal level varies inversely as the length and width of the array. This means that the radiation resistances given in Fig 5.4 have to be multiplied by factors nearly proportional to the inverse square of each of the dimensions and if, for example, the spacing is halved, radiation resistance is divided by four.

It may also be necessary to make a further correction to allow for any change in shape of the current distribution. This can be combined with the length correction by use of Fig 3.12 which gives radiation resistances for elements which have been shortened by bending over the ends and discourages the use of other methods. When two such elements are used as a beam, the radiation resistance is reduced in substantially the same ratio as that of λ/2 dipole elements, Fig 5.4.

The total radiation resistance for the two elements is twice the value given in Fig 5.4; it is this *total* value which must be used for calculating the current and it is given correctly by use of the scaling factors. These operations conceal a hidden factor of considerable practical importance, namely that if Z_m includes reactance as well as resistance, the radiation resistances of the individual elements become unequal and, although the total is fixed, one of them can be zero or negative.

This means that, in the case of a driven array, one element is actually returning power to the transmitter for re-issue, as it were, to the other element, the radiation resistance of this being more than doubled which can be of considerable help in the matching process. This will cause little surprise to those familiar with the operation of coupled circuits in receivers; moreover, since the second feeder is handling very little power it does not matter in the least that the SWR may well be close to infinity. A further advantage of this situation is that each feeder can be separately matched for its power-handling role, and beam reversal can then be effected from the shack by a simple interchange of feeders without affecting SWR, a different situation as we shall see from that which exists when $X_m = 0$.

An attempt to repeat the calculation for the case of X_m not being equal to zero defeated the author for a long time due to the increase in the complexity of the algebra, but eventually yielded the curves of Fig 5.9 and 5.10 which show the extent to which 'supergain' assumptions (p21) break down as the $\lambda/4$ limit is approached. At this spacing there is a drop of 0.5dB in maximum gain with driven operation and 1.0dB for conventional parasitic operation. For the $\varphi = \varphi_0$ condition the gain drops even further, from 4.2dB with close spacing to only 3dB with $\lambda/4$ spacing, and front/back ratios are substantially worse.

Another effect of reactive coupling is to improve either reflector or director operation while rendering the other more or less useless, with negative reactance favouring reflectors and positive reactance directors. This makes driven operation unnecessary, since all that is required to achieve optimum results is to increase capacitive coupling between the elements by bringing the ends towards each other. It is a characteristic of the quad antenna (as well as some of the more recently introduced compact dipole arrays) that this desirable condition is achieved, more or less, without conscious effort. This is perhaps the most likely explanation for the particular reputation of the quad since, as will later appear (p109), there is no way that the true gain difference can exceed about 0.5dB.

The usefulness of equations (7) and (8) is illustrated by the following example. In one well-known type of driven array, elements are spaced $\lambda/4$ and a phasing-line of electrical length $\lambda/4$ is used between them in the belief that this produces 90° phase shift. Such arrays are commonly assumed to be reversible. For the moment let us assume that equal currents with a phase difference of 90° (ie $b = \pm 1.0$, $a = 0$) have been achieved; in this case aR_m disappears and for a dipole X_m, from Fig 5.14, is equal to -28Ω. Putting $b = -1.0$ so that the element furthest from the transmitter lags in phase and therefore acts as a reflector, we have for dipole elements $R = (73 + 28)\Omega$ for the front element and $(73 - 28)\Omega$ for the rear element, ie 101Ω and 45Ω respectively.

Reference to Fig 4.4(b) shows that *provided* the phasing line is terminated in a resistive impedance, a length of $\lambda/4$ will indeed produce a phase difference of 90°. (Note, however, that this is a special case and does *not* imply for example that a line of length $\lambda/8$ will produce 45° phase shift). What we now have is two pairs of terminals between which the impedances are respectively 101Ω and $(Z_0^2/45)\Omega$, where Z_0 is the characteristic impedance of the phasing line.

It must next be noted that the equal-current condition requires the reflector to receive less power in the ratio 45/101. This will be achieved by connecting the two impedances in parallel, provided $Z_0^2/45 = 101 \times (101/45)$, ie $Z_0 = 101\Omega$ and the reflector impedance then comes to 227Ω. Unfortunately for this example, 101Ω is not a standard value of impedance and, so far as is known to the author, the required conditions have never been correctly implemented. Indeed a Z_0 of 300 or 600Ω is most usual and clearly quite useless since the impedance which would be presented by the reflector line (if it were possible by some extraneous means to satisfy the required amplitude and phase conditions) would be 2000 or 8000Ω

respectively. Nevertheless, the fact that very little power flows along the feeder going to the reflector may leave this free to operate as a parasitic element. In practice, failure to establish the correct conditions has invalidated the assumptions used to simplify the calculations and created a situation which is extremely difficult to analyse.

Let us suppose then that, realising its importance, the necessary effort has been made to acquire a Z_0 of 101Ω. Calculation can now proceed, the total radiation resistance being equal to 146Ω so that the current is that of a dipole divided by $\sqrt{2}$, and the two fields add in phase to give a gain of only 3.0dB over a dipole. Suppose that, nevertheless, this very poor performance is accepted in return for the apparent ease with which the beam direction can be reversed. Now we could be in trouble again since the calculations have assumed resonance, ie any reactive components of impedance have been tuned out. Note that (2) was derived from the 'Ohm's law' relationship $E = I_1R + I_2Z_m$ which for this case is equal to $I_1(R + X_m)$, so that in fact there is no reactance and no problem. However, this again is a stroke of luck, deriving from the condition $a = 0$. In general $(\pm)$ reactance is transferred, the sign being reversed when the direction is reversed, so that if the beam is required to be reversible any attempt to tune out the reactance only makes matters worse as shown below.

For the next example, consider a spacing of $\lambda/8$ and a phase shift of 45°, ie the antenna is tuned as before for infinite rejection in the direction opposite the beam heading. We have $a = b = 0.707$ and, from Figs 5.13 and 5.14 respectively, $X_m = 0$ and $R_m = 64.5$. The radiation resistance is $73 - (0.707 \times 64.5) = 27.4\Omega$ but putting

$$E = I_1R + I_2R_m = I_1R - I_1(a - jb)R_m$$
$$= I_1(R - aR_m + jbR_m)$$

we find there is a reactance term of 45.6Ω to be tuned out. For the reverse direction the reactance is reversed in sign and, unless these reactances are tuned out, there will obviously be a very large SWR which can be found by entering the Smith chart (p68) at a point

$$1 + \frac{45.6}{27.4} j = 1 + 1.66j$$

which corresponds to an SWR of 4.5. If the j term is tuned out for one direction (it cannot be done for both) beam reversal will result in twice the amount of detuning, and the j term is therefore doubled, resulting in an SWR of 12!

Another interesting aspect which may be noticed with an SWR meter connected in the reflector lead is reversal of *the direction of power flow as the reflector is tuned*, ie R_{ref} goes negative. Lack of reference to this in the amateur literature suggests that those who have observed it may have judged it best to keep quiet! Nevertheless, if it causes surprise and concern this can only be due to the failure to identify amateur beams with 'supergain' antennas, for which negative values of R are a typical feature [1]. Note that if X_m is positive (inductive) parasitic elements should be tuned as directors, not reflectors.

Suppose that, despite X_m being negative, we want to tune a parasitic element as a director. From equation (7) we require $X = aX_m + bR_m = -2aX_m$ if nothing else is changed; this implies considerable shortening of the parasitic element but from (11) there is then, as might be expected, a reduction in the value of I_2 relative to I_1. This is exactly what happens in the case of the quad, where the negative reactance is due to the wide spacing between the top of one loop and the bottom of the other, negative reactance being typical of spacings between about 0.15λ and 0.65λ as shown in Fig 5.14. In the case of the quad it is a matter of common observation that, despite the impressive performance of reflectors, attempts to retune these as directors are singularly unsuccessful.

Similarly, with $\lambda/4$ spacing of dipoles it is well known that reflector operation is more efficient; meanwhile, director operation is impossible with the VK2ABQ (which has element ends very close together) and the miniature beams described later. The opposite effect has been observed in the case of a single parasitic element used with a collinear pair, indicating a positive value of X_m, though it has to be confessed that the reason for this is still obscure.

It will be clear by now that there is no difference in principle between a driven array and a parasitic array but the practical differences can be very important. To realise the above example in practice, both elements must be driven, otherwise the condition $X_m = 0$ means that I_2 cannot equal I_1. Returning to the above example, the feedpoint impedance of element 1 is given by

$$\frac{E}{I_1} = R - aR_m + jbR_m$$
$$= 27.4 + 45.6j \text{ ohms}$$

For element 2, b is negative and we have

$$\frac{E}{I_2} = 27.4 - 45.6j \text{ ohms}$$

It follows from this that if each feeder is made equal to an integral number of half-wavelengths and the system fed off-centre to obtain the required phase shift, the impedance Z_T seen by the transmitter in the absence of retuning is (27.4 + 45.6j)Ω in parallel with (27.4 − 45.6j)Ω.

The system as a whole is therefore resonant and with the help of the chart it is found that Z_T comes to 35Ω, so that for 50Ω line the *SWR for the whole system* is 1.35 for both directions of fire. This unfortunately applies *only* to the short length of line between the transmitter and the phasing device, and effectively conceals the undesirable situation in each of the individual feeders. The resonant condition is nevertheless of some interest, and the use of straight or inverted-V elements with open-wire resonant feeders joined in 'parallel antiphase' and fed slightly off-centre has been the basis of a number of systems described by the author [2, 3, 4], and reviewed briefly below. A limitation of this approach arises from the desirability of avoiding extreme values of SWR, even in open-wire lines, and the difficulty of reconciling this with requirements for compact multiband systems.

Some readers may be worried about extra losses when two

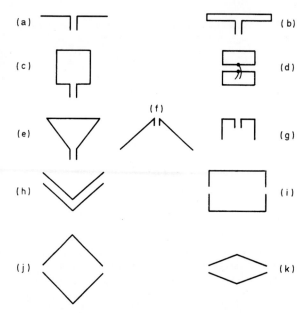

Fig 5.17. Typical shapes of beam element; (a) to (g) are seen in elevation, with the ends hanging downwards in cases (f) and (g): (h) to (k) are plan views of V or U-shaped elements arranged in pairs

feeders are used, and there is some justification for this. Suppose that, having met the $X = 0$ condition, there is a current I flowing in each element, and let the feeder length be a whole number of half-wavelengths, so that for correct operation a short-circuit is required at the lower end of the reflector line, the wave travelling down it being totally reflected. This establishes a sinusoidal current distribution in the feeder, I being the maximum value and $I^2/2$ the mean-square value. Since R is the same for both feeders and the losses in the main feeder are given by I^2/R, this represents a 50% increase in the total feeder loss. Subject to the practical compromise suggested in another chapter (p38), the length of coaxial line will not exceed 40ft (12.2m) so that, assuming a typical loss of 1.0dB/ 100ft (30m) at 30MHz, the *extra loss* comes to 0.2dB in the worst possible case, which is not unduly serious.

It may be interesting to note in passing that with $X_m = 0$ the feeders share the work equally and there is no extra loss, except that due to the high SWR in the event of beam reversal being required; this also comes to 0.2dB.

Arrangement of elements

Typical shapes of elements are shown in Fig 5.17 and there are few restrictions on choice, most types of element except ground-planes being suitable for use in close-spaced beams. However, they must be properly co-ordinated since it would not do to have, say, one element vertical and the other horizontal. Although loop and dipole elements are sometimes mixed in widely spaced arrays, close spacing is difficult to define and almost certainly not advisable when *one* element is split into two portions separated by distances of the order of $\lambda/4$, as is the case with the quad loops, Figs 5.17(c) and (d), the delta loop (e) being roughly equivalent.

V-shaped elements may be mounted directly in line and facing the same way as in Fig 5.17(h), though the arrangements shown at (i) to (k) (or (f) and (g) on which the ends are hanging down) are better since the coupling between elements is readily adjustable for meeting the optimum design conditions specified earlier. However, due to radiation off the ends it is inadvisable for more than half the length to be bent over as in (g) or (i), or for the angle of the V to exceed 90°. Thus in case (i), assuming a square shape and putting $\varphi = \varphi_0$, there is 90° phase difference between the element currents; referring to Fig 2.5 and allowing for phase differences, relative fields for the forward and endwise directions are given by $0.7 + 0.7 = 1.4$ (forward) and $0.15 \sqrt{2} \times \sqrt{2}$ (endwise), ie a ratio of 1.4/0.3 or 13.4dB in favour of the forward field. Since the bent-over ends constitute a W8JK-type pair, about 3dB gain must be assumed, so that the ratio of endwise energy to forward energy is $(0.3/14)^2/1.4$ or 3.3%, a loss of 0.14dB only. This figure escalates rather rapidly if the bending is increased further. A pair of V-shaped elements may be mounted so that they hang down as inverted-V's from a single spreader, coupling being adjusted by bringing the ends together so that the bird's-eye view resembles Fig 5.17(k).

Fig 5.17(i) or (j) may be derived by taking a single quad loop, Fig 5.17(c), tilting it over into a horizontal position and placing insulators in the sides to make it into two elements, Fig 5.17(j). This is the basis of the VK2ABQ antenna which is rapidly gaining in popularity [11, 12]. The spacing as shown is wider than desirable but it has been found possible for a third element to be fitted into the same space, thus yielding an efficient three-element design as described on p201. Alternatively, the square shape may be distorted into a rectangle as in the modified version of the VK2ABQ beam shown on p202.

The earlier discussion in this chapter centred mainly on two-element, equal-current arrays (parasitic or driven), for which the conditions for optimum performance were shown to be clearly defined and more-or-less realisable in practice. As demonstrated later (p103), closely analogous guidelines exist in principle for multi-element arrays, though even with only three or four elements practical implementation is virtually impossible because of difficulties arising from the large number of variables and close tolerances which escalate rapidly with the number of elements. Nevertheless, theoretical limits have been clearly defined by Uzkov [16], and provide useful insight into the nature of the problem as well as solid ground for rebuttal of some of the wilder claims of advertisers. In practical terms this means that with three or more elements it is not possible to specify a 'best' design. However, various sets of guidelines leading to acceptable compromises are available, including the design charts for three-element arrays featured in Figs 5.24 and 5.25 which are well tried and tested. In all cases the available prescriptions avoid the need for values of coupling other than those occurring naturally between straight elements.

In stressing the basic equivalence of loops and dipoles it is important also to retain the customary distinction between open-circuited elements having high RF voltages at their ends (dipoles) and closed-circuit systems (loops) which involve high currents at points furthest from the transmitter, since these aspects as well as the mechanical differences are often crucial in choosing the best type of antenna. Given the usual requirement of low impedance at the transmitter or at any point of connection to a low-impedance feeder, a dipole has odd-harmonic resonances whereas loops tend to resonate on even harmonics, which can be particularly useful for multiband elements, though because of pattern break-up (pp122–125) their useful frequency range tends to be more restricted.

Loops are in general less susceptible to rain static as well as losses in trees and buildings, and provide DC continuity which can be useful for diagnosing faults or for de-icing; another advantage of loops is that mostly they occupy much less width for a given radiation resistance, though this is partly offset by the need for more wire to bring them to resonance. Fig 5.17 shows the main types of element and indicates some of the ways in which dipole elements can be paired to allow for adjustment of coupling which, in the case of loops, tends to be more or less correct with normal spacings.

Factors affecting the choice of element type include the available space, means of support, visual impact, whether multiband operation is needed, and possible trade-offs between operating convenience and some aspects of performance. If the need arises to make a beam as small as possible further considerations arise as discussed later in this chapter and on pp205–206. In general, for monoband operation, dimensions are not very critical subject to appropriate tuning and matching; on the other hand, coverage of five or six bands is subject to elements being large enough for efficient operation at the lowest frequency without causing pattern break-up on the highest band. Given also in the case of two elements the need to maintain suitable spacings, there remains little room for manoeuvre; with dipoles this tends to restrict choice to Fig 5.17(j) or (k) which, by taking advantage of the current distributions, result in a decrease of effective spacing as frequency increases. With three or more elements this is not a significant problem, an increase of spacing to 0.25λ at the highest frequency being beneficial rather than otherwise.

Multiband elements

Most types of element are fairly easy to adapt for two-band operation by means of traps or preferably a centrally located tuning network, but extension to three bands results in a larger number of variables, making optimisation difficult and also exacting a price in terms of additional trap losses or interaction between stacked elements. Unless one is able to erect a large structure such as a log-periodic antenna (which is another compromise since only a few of the elements are in use on any one band) the use of resonant feeders would appear to be a better alternative. In this case it has been found possible (with careful selection of type of element) to construct small

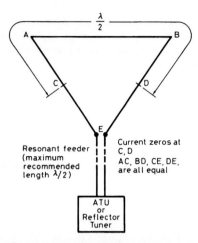

Fig 5.18. Original version of the small delta loop (SDL). The distinctive feature is placement of the nulls in the centre of the sides in the case of the lowest frequency band (the 'main design frequency' or MDF) so that all radiation comes from the top. Reflector and driven elements are identical, tops being spaced about 11ft for 14MHz and the bottom corners brought in towards each other. The position of the zeros is not unduly critical

lightweight antennas, providing efficient coverage of five and in some cases six bands.

Small delta loops elaborated from Fig 5.17(e) have been found particularly suitable, as witnessed by a number of two-element arrays featured in Chapters 7, 12, and 13. The reasons for this are evident from inspection of Fig 7.4, which relates radiation resistance to size for various shapes of loop, and Fig 7.5, which allows the upper frequency limit to be estimated from the rate of increase in strength of the endwise mode of radiation typical of loops operating on frequencies remote from their fundamental resonance. Fig 5.18 shows the small delta loop (SDL) element in its simplest form, the loop size being chosen with the dual purpose of conforming to the guidelines provided by the above figure references and maximising the effective height by placing the current nulls in the middle of the sides so that all the radiation comes from the top of the loops. Despite the small size of these elements, efficiencies in excess of 90% can be achieved with wire diameters down to 1mm (20swg), which means they can be supported by lightweight mast extensions, one method which has proved very successful being the use of four fishing-rod blanks angled upwards and outwards from the top of the mast to provide up to 15ft of additional height. Alternatively, using nylon fishing line for example, fixed arrays can often be supported between trees, buildings, etc, which can be particularly useful if there is a need for the antenna to be invisible.

Resonant feeder systems tend to be disadvantaged, sometimes severely, by impedance discontinuities which usually make 'worst case' situations a lot worse and, although on another frequency band these may be helpful, the first priority is to ensure that 'worst' is good enough. Apart from keeping feeders short, Chapters 7 and 12 feature a number of other ways of 'living with' this problem as well as circumventing

it by getting rid of the discontinuities, a crude but effective recipe for this being the use of two wires in parallel for the element whilst keeping the feeder impedance as high as possible.

Unless the element is larger than it need be, in which case higher-frequency coverage will be restricted, the designer will need to concentrate on the 'lowest' frequency where the radiation resistance and bandwidth will be just adequate for his needs. These will depend for example on how much importance is attached to achieving 95% as opposed to, say, 80% efficiency, or being able to QSY by more than 100kHz without having to fiddle with the ATU. This has been defined as the 'main design frequency' or MDF, and special measures may be invoked such as the use of relays to connect matching stubs adjacent to the elements or an 'impedance transforming loop' (ITL), of which several versions are described in later chapters, pp126, 213. It uses a low-Z_0 dipole, consisting of two or more well-spaced wires in parallel for the top part of the loop, and a short, loaded, high-Z_0 dipole for the bottom part. At the MDF this multiplies R by the square of the Z_0 ratio, the loop being electrically full-wave though physically smaller. In general the higher frequencies can take care of themselves and, subject to a number of constraints, the antenna may be usable on an even lower frequency band with only slightly reduced efficiency.

If short span is not an important requirement, for example if suitably spaced trees are available or the reader is looking for a 'best possible' multiband beam for putting on a tower capable of supporting 40–44ft elements, centre-fed dipoles as in Fig 20.2 offer a number of advantages, including up to 3dB of extra gain with virtual freedom from pattern break-up at the highest frequency plus improved bandwidth at the lowest frequency. Compared with a log-periodic antenna, which is probably the main alternative, Fig 20.2 lacks some of the convenience but uses a much shorter boom and retains the reversal and deep nulling features of equal-current arrays.

The use of resonant feeders for five or six-band operation can easily lead to a very elaborate complex of tuners in the shack, each installation being a special case; to avoid this, a careful study of resonant-line 'basics' (pp60–65) and examples in Chapter 12, p213, is recommended.

The quad antenna

The above explanation of equal-current arrays applies to small elements of almost any shape since it is difficult to bend them in such a way that there is a secondary mode of radiation sufficiently dominant to upset seriously the usual assumption of a cos θ pattern. This rule starts to break down only if the distance between separate concentrations of current exceeds some figure greater than λ/4, or if there are current reversals. In breach of this rule and also in defiance of the basic principles of 'stacking gain' as set out in Chapter 6, claims for additional gain in the case of quad and delta loops continue to be widely publicised and accepted. This unfortunately results in the waste of much time, money, and effort in the construction of 'monsters' which are all too often a recipe for disaster.

Attempts by the author and various others, eg [26], to set the record straight have borne little fruit and, faced as it seems with genuine convictions, it is necessary to look for explanations beyond the relevant facts recorded in standard textbooks, which can be summarised as follows.

(a) The gain attributed to quad loops stems from their resemblance to a pair of $\lambda/2$ dipoles spaced by $\lambda/4$ for which there is a well-established gain figure of 1dB; this can also be easily calculated from readily-available data on mutual impedance. However, since the ends are bent over these are 'short dipoles' and the actual gain is less, not more.

(b) Two or more quad elements arranged as a beam can be closely identified with a stacked pair of Yagi beams; when beams are stacked the total gain is the product of the unit gain and an 'array factor' which is effective only if the stacking distance is sufficient to produce a narrowing of the overall pattern; the higher the unit gain the narrower its pattern and the greater the separation needed. Any stacking gain is therefore reduced by an increase of unit gain, provided both occur in the same plane; since the quad derives its gain from reduction of beam width in both horizontal and vertical planes (as does also a Yagi), the commonly made claim of extra gain independent of the number of elements must be disregarded. A more detailed discussion of array factors, including their application to loops, will be found in Chapter 6.

In addition to its bad features, the quad has a number of useful ones as discussed in later chapters, but the claims of extra gain conflict not only with the facts set out above but a massive weight of experimental evidence, including [26] large numbers of gain comparisons between quads and Yagis with from two to six elements.

This is in full accord with my own experience covering some 30 years of comparative testing with antennas of both types. At no time has there been the slightest hint of gain differences other than those attributable to height, location, or some specific fault condition, except that adding close-spaced directors to quads was found to be completely ineffective, a fact inherent in the capacitive nature of the coupling impedance and possibly not applicable to wider spacings. The above reference presents a long and detailed review of the evidence, including possible explanations of errors, to which must be added the following paradox which is based on the assumption of a rather cluttered environment or ground sloping uphill, both very common situations. This results in a disproportionate increase of low-angle signal strength with height so that the top half of the quad loop becomes correspondingly more effective. On this basis the improvement in the case of the quad could be construed as an injunction to get rid of the lower halves of the loops so that all the radiation comes from the top; in other words the loops need to be changed into dipoles!

In a search for further pitfalls it is of interest to note that the gain of a two-element quad compared with a single element is 0.4dB greater than the corresponding figure for $\lambda/2$ dipoles

which, if added to the 1dB gain of a single loop, begins to look useful; in fact, however, this result is obtained by claiming the 0.4dB twice over! The quad loop is a 'short element' and has to obey the same rules as other short elements, so that the true gain of the loop compared with a $\lambda/2$ dipole is 0.6dB only; moreover the apparent 'extra' gain is not unique to loops but provides yet another instructive illustration of the operation of stacking principles. The $\lambda/2$ dipole owes its 0.4dB gain over a short dipole to the fact that in nearly-endwise directions radiation from near its ends tends to cancel because these are separated by $\lambda/2$; although this shows up as a pinching-in of the sides of the pattern, nearly all of the effect takes place outside the beamwidth of a two-element beam which is therefore not affected.

It follows from this that arrays of small loops or short elements have the same effective gain as arrays of $\lambda/2$ dipoles, although single elements are 0.4dB down, so the gain *relative to a single element* exceeds that for a comparable array of half-wave dipoles.

Two-element driven arrays

The development of controlled coupling as just described casts some doubt on the continued relevance of driven systems but has not ruled them out as alternatives, and a combination of the two methods might be expected to reduce the need for working to close tolerances, a matter of particular importance in the design of very small beams, as will be appreciated in due course. The usual method is to employ a phasing line with its length 'equal to the spacing' so that a null is obtained in the $-180°$ direction, but this usually makes matters a lot worse for reasons outlined above. This is in any case the wrong direction for the null, even for best interference rejection, but more serious consequences arise from the misconception that a line length of $\lambda/8$ produces a 45° phase shift and pro rata. As explained in Chapter 4, this happens *only* if the line is matched, and most of the arrangements thus far described have an inherent mismatch (though the operator may be unaware of this because the SWR meter is connected in the 'common' lead where, as we have just seen, the two mismatches may compensate each other).

Due to the mismatches the 'phasing line' is more likely to result in large current inequalities than it is to produce the desired phase shift, and a better method makes use of the resonance principle based on equal and opposite reactances as illustrated in Fig 5.19. Given that $\omega L = 1/\omega C$, which is the standard condition for resonance, the generator sees equal but opposite reactances ($\pm X$) to the left and right, and the same current flows in each load R. A total phase difference φ is obtained by putting $\tan (\varphi/2) = X/R$. If the loads are unequal, equal currents can still be achieved by using suitable values of L and C, and any reactance seen by the transmitter as a result of this operation can be tuned out in the usual way. Fig 5.19(b) shows this idea applied directly to the W8JK beam for converting it into a phased array [4], but at this point the argument has to be elaborated to take account of mutual impedance.

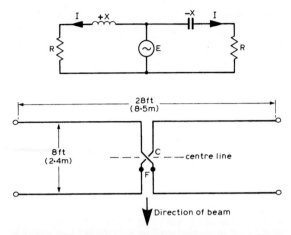

Fig 5.19. The resonance or '±X' method of phasing; if $X_m = 0$ the total phase difference between the currents in the two loads (R) is given by tan $(\varphi/2) = X/R$ or approximately by $\varphi = 2X/R$ radians if X is less than about $R/2$. For parallel $\lambda/2$ dipoles spaced $\lambda/8$ and fed in phase, $R = 137.5\Omega$, the mutual resistance being added to the radiation resistance. Note that with equal values of R the currents are equal only if the reactances are of equal magnitude. Lower figure shows application to the W8JK. The total electrical length from the ends of one element through to the ends of the other is exactly $\lambda/2$. Displacing the feedpoint about 4½in (11.4cm) from the centre line was found to produce the desired directional pattern. CF provides the reactance X which amounts to +21Ω. Due to the short elements, R is halved, giving a value of 0.62 for φ/φ_0, corresponding to a gain of 5dB

If elements are widely separated so that $Z_m = 0$, the phasing-line method has the advantage that any amount of phase shift can be introduced without altering the impedance seen by the transmitter, though the '±X' method is more suitable for providing precise adjustment of phase over a limited range such as ±45°, a 2:1 mismatch being incurred for a 90° shift. In the case of close-spaced beams, however, large phase shifts are not required, and when mutual impedance comes into the picture the '±X' method takes the situation in its stride. Ignoring for the moment mutual coupling between the loads, the generator 'sees' an impedance $(R + jX)$ looking one way and $(R - jX)$ the other, so that the magnitude of the two impedances (ie $\sqrt{(R^2 + X^2)}$) is the same in both cases, the total phase shift φ being given by 2 $\tan^{-1} (X/R)$.

This principle was invoked by the author in the design of his very first close-spaced beam, the consequences being even more startling, though a great deal less useful than the findings described in the last section, creating the impression of some extremely powerful demon in charge of the whole proceedings. To put it in a nutshell the system:

(a) worked perfectly;
(b) ceased to work *at all* when the frequency was shifted a mere 10kHz or thereabouts!

At that time phasing-line systems were much in vogue, the desired total phase shift of 135° being obtained sometimes with an in-phase connection and a $3\lambda/8$ phasing line, sometimes with out-of-phase connection and a $\lambda/8$ phasing line.

The author had applied similar thinking to his reactance method, opting for the in-phase connection. A large amount of algebra aided by a good deal of luck finally produced an explanation, since the phase shift was found to be proportional to $X/(R - R_m)$ for the in-phase connection and $X/(R + R_m)$ for the out-of-phase connection. Hence for the first case adjustment was more critical in the ratio of $(R + R_m)/(R - R_m)$, ie 137.5/8.5 or 16 times! Reversing the connection to one element put matters right, theory being further vindicated by reversal of the beam.

This arrangement was similar in principle to the one illustrated in Fig 5.20 which serves to demonstrate the essentials of phase control in tightly coupled systems, regardless of the method used. An essential precondition is overall resonance for the two elements plus the line joining them, so that off-centre connection of the feeder, eg at AA' or BB', is equivalent to inserting a reactance +X for one direction and −X for the other. Resonance is easy to achieve since if the system is tuned low this brings the shorter side closer to resonance so that more current flows, and vice versa. The current can be checked with a probe (p279) or with a flashlamp bulb bridged across a few inches of conductor. Depending on the result of this test, the loop CABC' can be lengthened or shortened as required.

In view of the low radiation resistance and use of resonant feeders, the bandwidth is rather narrow as explained in Chapter 8, so that for a practical system it was found better to use folded dipoles (p110), which incidentally increased the length AB (which can be regarded as a phasing line) from about 16in (0.4m) to 5ft (1.5m). However, using inverted-V folded-dipole elements spaced $\lambda/8$, it was found that adjusting for current equality in the centre of the 14MHz band resulted in a ratio of 0.7 at the band edges so that the problem was still not fully resolved. The arrangement shown in Fig 5.19(b) is somewhat worse than this, radiation resistance

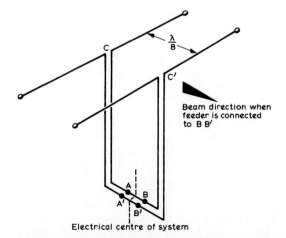

Fig 5.20. Two-element array with resonant (or mismatched) feeders. If the elements are resonant the length CABC' must be an even number of half-wavelengths. AB can be regarded as 'the phasing line' but is much less than $\lambda/8$ if open-wire lines are used. Note that the feeders are crossed over as for the W8JK antenna

being divided by eight whereas the total wire length is only divided by four.

It is of interest to note that in this case the effective phasing line length is 9in (23cm), being equal to CF × 2. This was discovered experimentally in the first instance and later checked by calculation, thus casting more than a little doubt on the usual assumption that a length of λ/8 (or 8ft (2.4m) for 14MHz) is always correct!

The tuning procedure described above has also been found usable with λ/4 spacing despite the reactive coupling, though full analysis of the system under these conditions is rather complicated. In cases which have been described of elements spaced λ/4 (so that the coupling includes negative reactance) and fed with separate coaxial lines, most of the work will be done by the feeder going to the forward element. With the other feeder having, more or less, an 'idling' role only, the adjustment should not be unduly critical; however, as demonstrated by Figs 5.9 and 5.10, λ/4 spacing is too wide.

With λ/8 spacing the elements could each, in principle, be separately tuned and matched but it seems a pity not to take advantage of two feeders for beam reversal. In this case, one needs to start with elements which are individually self-resonant and accept a fairly high value of SWR in each feeder as explained earlier in this chapter.

A number of arrays have been developed in which elements of approximate length λ/2 and spaced λ/8 are connected in parallel antiphase, the physical length of the phasing line being λ/8 and the feeder connected directly to one element which is somewhat shorter than the other. These arrangements, which include the well-known 'ZL Special', are difficult to analyse, though in at least one case the element details appear to be about right for normal parasitic operation and the phasing line would most likely be playing a minor role. Another possibility, consistent with some rather low gain figures quoted for the 'ZL Special' [5], can be inferred from inspection of Fig 5.4. This shows that with increasing φ one enters a region of operation where gain is low but front/back ratio still reasonably good and, since radiation resistance is high, adjustment should be relatively non-critical.

Some of these arrangements closely resemble two adjacent elements of a log-periodic system as described in Chapter 14 and, designated as 'log cells', have been used for the excitation of large arrays with a number of additional parasitic elements such as the one described on p200. In these cases the requirements for a symmetrical current distribution are presumably met and, in considering phase shift, the log cell cannot be isolated from the system as a whole, so further discussion here would not be appropriate. Another type of phased array using the resonance principle is the Swiss quad [7], in which the reactances are obtained by making one loop larger than the other, though the same result plus the possibility of beam reversal can be obtained by off-centre feed on the lines already described. However, quads appear to have acquired their reputation partly as a result of the tighter coupling which makes driven operation unnecessary *provided the spacing is correct*. For parasitic operation the 0.1λ spacing of the Swiss quad would be much too close.

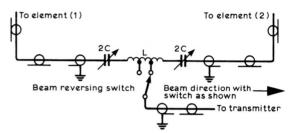

Fig 5.21. Phasing network for two-element beams. Coaxial outers are bonded together. Elements of close-spaced arrays must be antiphase connected, so that if the inner or the coaxial feeder goes to the right-hand side of one element it goes to the left of the other. L and C are chosen to resonate at approximately the frequency in use, but detuning in conjunction with adjustment of tap positions can be used to obtain the required amplitude balance combined with correct phase adjustment, despite modest errors in tuning or matching. Typically for 14MHz, L = 1.6μH and 2C = 200pF (maximum). Method can be adapted for any type of feeder. Too high a value of L results in excessive RF voltages

Summing up, it can be stated as a broad conclusion that to the extent that mismatches exist (as they usually will) it is essential to apply the principle of resonance-plus-symmetry as exemplified by Fig 5.20, though this can probably be regarded as an extreme case.

The above considerations, coupled with the need to make sure of correct operation in the case of very small beams, led the author to devise the lumped-circuit type of phasing line shown in Fig 5.21. Exploiting the resonance (±X) principle, the tuning control is used to obtain amplitude balance with the coil taps providing phase adjustment and beam reversal. This method, though particularly suitable for use with close-spaced beams, is of universal application and can be adapted by means of differential capacitors or ferrite tuning slugs to provide a continuous fine adjustment of phase, though large phase changes result in a mismatch. Despite these merits and the fact that the author still liked to 'have it there just in case', the prototype line quickly found itself demoted to the role of remote tuner for a parasitic reflector, this mode of operation proving simpler and the nulls equally good. Nevertheless, if the feeder length is unsuitable or the coupling badly out, such a phasing device provides a convenient remedy, and if switched into circuit for reception only can be highly beneficial as a nulling device for interfering signals.

Front/back ratios in the region of 25–30dB are readily obtainable with parasitic operation and, although driven arrays can do better by providing the operator with control over amplitude as well as phase, the benefit from this is restricted for two reasons:

(a) high rejection ratios demand a critical balance which holds only for a very small range of frequencies or arrival angles;
(b) interference is often from more than one source or, if from a single source, the arrival angle may be varying or there may be more than one arrival angle.

Adjustment for suppression of a particular interfering signal is unlikely to yield maximum gain for transmission, and a fully engineered system needs to include separate phase and amplitude controls for transmission and reception.

Yagi arrays

These are named after one of their inventors and include conventional two-element parasitic arrays, though they can have any number of elements, of which usually only one is driven.

Parasitic elements take the form of single 'reflectors', placed behind the driven element, or 'directors' (of which there can be many) placed in front. Starting from the antiphase condition, radiation from a director is advanced in phase because (like the front element of a driven array) it is 'nearer the receiver', and also because of detuning in the capacitive direction (by shortening) which gives a phase lead to the current flowing in it. For the forward direction the phase shifts are additive, whereas for the reverse direction the phase lead of the current is cancelled by the lag due to the radiation now having *further* to travel. With two elements, if the currents (and for some direction or other the two phase shifts) are exactly equal, then for that direction there must inevitably be zero signal as already discussed, though with more elements there can be additional nulls.

Reflectors operate on the same principle as directors except for inversion of the phase relationship and reversal of the direction of fire.

Until the comparatively recent emergence of antennas such as the VK2ABQ, the hands of antenna designers (including the author) were tied by the customary assumption that the right shape for antenna elements (loops excepted) was 'straight', despite the rather obvious necessity demonstrated earlier in this chapter for increasing the coupling between them.

It still remains for full advantage to be taken of controlled coupling. This is one of the main concerns of Chapters 12 and 13 since it is felt there need no longer be any excuse for continuation of the relatively poor performance hitherto associated with two-element parasitic dipole arrays.

Nevertheless, there are some further points to be cleared up. Reference has already been made to the non-reactive character of the mutual impedance in the case of $\lambda/2$ dipoles spaced by $\lambda/8$, and this leads also to a symmetrical situation in the case of parasitic excitation, performance being identical irrespective of whether the parasitic element is tuned as a director or reflector. This is a mathematical identity which, in conjunction with the independence of size demonstrated earlier, invalidates claims of better performance in the case of closely spaced directors. The origin of these can be traced back to what is evidently a slight error in the original 1936 paper by Brown [6] who first drew attention to the possibility of obtaining gain with closely spaced elements.

To confirm this, Fig 5.22 was calculated from the data in Figs 5.13 and 5.14 for a two-element parasitic beam having a spacing of 0.05λ, and it will be seen that for a director the gain conforms very closely to the driven element case from Fig 5.4. The depths of null, though reaching infinity only at one point, are very considerable.

The improvement in *directivity* compared with more widely spaced parasitic elements (Fig 5.16) is due to tighter coupling and in part to the positive X_m term, which operates as explained earlier to improve the performance of a director and degrade that of a reflector. For a director the coupling is slightly in excess of critical, reaching a maximum value of 1.035 for $X = 0$, corresponding to $\varphi/\varphi_0 = 1.0$. The radiation resistance curve follows fairly closely that of Fig 5.4, subject to multiplying the latter by two to obtain the total resistance and dividing by $(2.5)^2$ to allow for the reduced spacing, a small increase in R being due to the overcoupling. Such low values of R imply very close tolerances, narrow bandwidth and possible losses as explained in Chapter 3, so that spacings as close as this are not recommended.

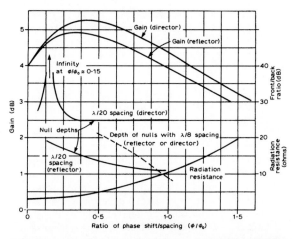

Fig 5.22. The effects of very close spacing; curves are calculated from mutual impedance data, the director gain curve being almost identical with that for equal currents: Fig 5.4. Failure to achieve an infinite depth of nulls is due to slight overcoupling and a small increase of spacing should correct this. The curves demonstrate the superiority in all respects of director operation when mutual reactance is positive, though the gain difference is small. The radiation resistance is almost identical for reflector and director operation, the inferior performance of reflectors being due to too low a current relative to that in the driven element. The dotted curve shows for comparison the depths of null for a spacing of $\lambda/8$

Though admittedly feasible with careful design, there are usually better options available, in particular those based on the use of bent elements as discussed earlier in this chapter and illustrated in Chapter 12. It is nevertheless interesting to note that director operation with closer-than-usual spacing is one method of obtaining tighter coupling and improved directivity, a point clearly brought out in Brown's paper [6], notwithstanding the slight error (+0.3dB) in the actual gain figures. This was quickly put to use in the amateur field by Van Roberts, W3CHO, who developed a two-element beam using a close-spaced (0.1λ) director and having 5dB gain with 17dB front/back ratio [10].

Three-element arrays

In principle, similar reasoning can be applied to close-spaced beams with additional elements but calculation is much more difficult, and it is simpler to rely on design charts such as Fig 5.24 and 5.25. It is, however, easy to see that a three-element beam is capable of producing an infinite front-to-back ratio in a manner analogous to that of a two-element beam if the outer elements are each supplied with half the current of the centre element and subjected to 45° phase shifts in opposite directions. This special case is easy to calculate and, as shown by Fig 5.23, provides a very considerable improvement in rejection of unwanted signals. However, the gain is not impressive, being only 4.6dB – an increase of 0.4dB compared with two elements tuned in the same way.

It may be possible to improve on this, given the wide range of alternative options indicated by the charts, from which it will be evident that any attempt to approach the maximum gain of 7.6dB, which is theoretically possible with equispaced parasitic elements [21], results in a very low value of R, about 2–4Ω only. From inspection of Fig 3.10, it looks as if it should be possible to keep the loss resistance down to something of the order of 0.4Ω, assuming the use of aluminium alloy tubing with an average diameter of about 0.5–0.75in (1.3–1.9cm). This gives an efficiency of 90% and an effective gain of 7.0dB, although 6dB or thereabouts is the most that has normally been achieved in practice [21].

This discrepancy is almost certainly due to the high price which has to be paid for maximum gain (in the form of reduced bandwidth) and the difficulty of keeping manufacturing, erection and maintenance tolerances within sufficiently close limits. It can be overcome to some extent by using additional feeders to effect remote fine-tuning of the parasitic elements but, although it might be thought possible to enlarge on such a facility to obtain instantaneous reversal of beam direction, it has been found rather easy to incur

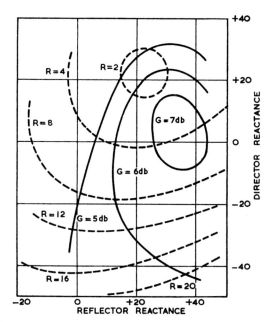

Fig 5.24. Contour chart showing contours of gain (solid lines) and input resistance (broken lines) as a function of the tuning of the parasitic elements. This chart is for a spacing of 0.15λ between elements, but is also typical of arrays using 0.2λ + 0.1λ spacings

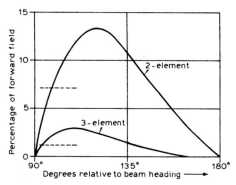

Fig 5.23. Comparison of two- and three-element arrays for rejection of interfering signals from the back direction when the phase shift is equal to the spacing (φ/φ₀ = 1). Currents adjusted to give null at 180° in both cases. Corresponding gains are 4.2dB and 4.6dB. Average levels shown by dotted lines indicate 16dB improvement with three elements. The three-element curve assumes equal currents and symmetrical phase shifts for director and reflector, making it more difficult to achieve in practice unless restricted to the receiving case only (see p155)

substantial losses unless the range of adjustment is kept to a minimum.

Referring to Fig 5.24 with these problems in mind, the lower right-hand corner of the chart is clearly the region to aim for, where the gain is still over 6dB while the feed resistance approaches 20Ω. This region of the chart corresponds to rather long reflectors (+40 to +50Ω reactance) and rather shorter than optimum directors (−30 to −40Ω), and also is found to be the region of best front-to-back ratio.

Although the chart is for antennas with both spacings equal to 0.15λ, the resistance and bandwidth are both somewhat improved, with the gain remaining over 6dB excluding losses, if the reflector spacing is increased to 0.2λ and the director spacing reduced to 0.1λ. Such an array would operate satisfactorily over at least half the 28–29MHz band or the whole of any other band for which it is likely to be constructed.

The overall array length of 0.3λ is practicable on all bands from 14MHz upwards, though the 20ft (6m) boom required for a 14MHz array is rather heavy for a rotary array and there is a temptation to shorten it. Spacings should not be reduced below 0.1λ for either reflector or director as the tuning will again become too critical and the transmitter load unstable as the elements or the feeder move in the wind. It should not be overlooked that, in general, for a given cost and degree of practical difficulty, the lighter the beam, the higher it can be erected; in terms of practical results this may be worth a lot more than additional elements.

The optimum tuning does not vary greatly for the different spacings, and it is therefore possible to use a simple practical design chart (Fig 5.25). An array made with its element

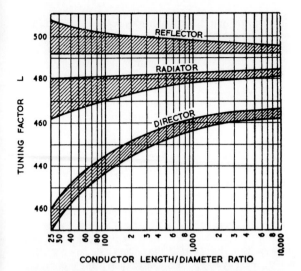

Fig 5.25. Design chart for Yagi arrays, giving element lengths as a function of conductor length-to-diameter ratio. The tuning factor *L* is divided by the frequency in megahertz to give the lengths in feet. These curves are for arrays of overall length 0.3λ, with reflector reactance +40 to +60Ω and director reactance –30 to –40Ω, and give arrays of input impedance between 15Ω and 20Ω. Element lengths which fall within the shaded areas will give an array which can be used without further adjustment, though the front/back ratio may be improved by adjusting the reflector

impressive. If a more ambitious monoband antenna is required, the log-Yagi (p200) can be personally recommended on the basis of signals received from a number of them. On the other hand, the situation is somewhat different in the case of multiband beams, most of which are three-element commercial designs using trapped elements unsuitable for equal current arrays, the extra element being essential in this case for the achievement of reasonable F/B ratio and helping also to offset the trap losses.

X-beams and slopers

One omission from Fig 5.17 is the X-beam which has been reserved for separate consideration in view of its many attractions, combined alas with serious defects. It has appeared in numerous forms, including quad and 'sloper' varieties, but the main essentials are illustrated in Fig 5.26(a) which also shows the radiation pattern for excitation as a W8JK-type antenna. Though not normally used in practical

lengths falling in the shaded regions of the diagram will normally give good performance without further adjustment. The length of the director may be decided in advance and the reflector may then be adjusted experimentally to improve the front-to-back ratio. It will be seen that the radiator is somewhat longer than a normal dipole; this is because the parasitic elements have a detuning effect on it. The addition of a second director also spaced 0.1–0.15λ will not materially affect the above recommendations but major changes of shape such as bending the ends inwards will invalidate use of Fig 5.25.

It will be appreciated that with three elements, as with two, the reactive coupling plays a major part in determining the relative currents and as a result the experimenter aiming for a particular working point on a diagram such as Fig 5.24 must expect to find difficulty unless he sticks to the use of straight elements spaced around 0.125-0.15λ. By way of example, the author was unable to obtain any detectable gain from the addition of a close-spaced (λ/8) director to a two-element quad, this result being fully accounted for by very low current in the added element as a consequence of the negative sign attached to the coupling reactance (p90).

The three-element Yagi shares with two-element beams the possibility of instantaneous reversal, either by means of relays mounted in the antenna or the use of resonant feeders. Comparisons in respect of F/B ratio can be misleading to the extent that performance figures nearly always relate to the 180° direction and, although Fig 5.23 avoids this limitation, it is a special case and not typical of standard practice; moreover, the additional gain of about 1 dB per director is not

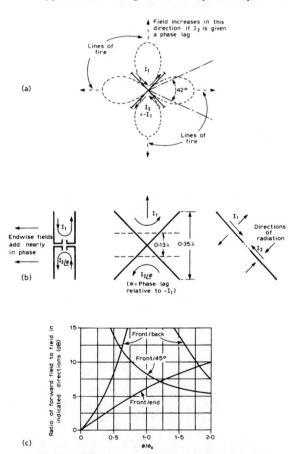

Fig 5.26. (a) X-beam or 'sloper' with elements in antiphase. (b) shows (left to right) resolution of the cross into pairs of dipoles for calculation of front/side, front/back and front/45° ratios. (c) shows variation of each of the rejection ratios with phase angle, front/back ratio being identical with Fig 5.4

designs of X-beam, this provides yet again a useful key to the understanding of an important principle. The first point to observe is the basic symmetry which ensures that the antenna looks identical when seen from any four directions 90° apart. Instead of the figure-of-eight pattern previously experienced with the W8JK connection, there is now a clover leaf, ie two figures-of-eight at right-angles. If now a phase shift is introduced between I_1 and $-I_2$, there will no longer be complete nulls in the 45° directions and the field in *one* direction will be given a boost at the expense of the opposite direction.

Graphical integration with Fig 2.5 as a starting point has produced two results of interest.

(a) For the initial clover-leaf pattern the width of each lobe between '3dB points' is 42° compared with 66° for the normal W8JK mode, but as there are four lobes instead of two one might expect a decrease in gain of the order of 84/66 or 1.05dB.

(b) For evaluating performance in any pair of directions the X may be replaced by equivalent dipoles as shown by the dotted lines in the middle sketch of Fig 5.26(b). The dipoles are assumed to support a sine-wave current distribution and their spacing is equal to 26% of the length of a diagonal, ie 0.13 for a λ/2 cross. When phase shift is introduced, the 'boost' in the direction indicated means that endwise radiation is proportionally reduced and most of the lost 1.05dB can be recovered. The previous curves (Fig 5.4 *et seq*) are useable as a fairly good approximation for obtaining gain, radiation resistance, and front-to-back ratio, provided φ/φ_0 is greater than about 0.5.

Due to length reduction and a small correction factor (0.88) due to the relative ineffectiveness of the centre portions of the elements arising from the close spacing, the radiation resistances in Fig 5.4 must be divided by 2.3 if both elements are driven or 1.15 for a single driven element, assuming that the coupling between elements is adjusted for equal currents. Since the centres are in close proximity it should be possible to devise some form of inductive coupling for this purpose.

For the endwise directions the equivalent dipoles almost constitute a conventional W8JK pair as shown at the left of (b), but can be regarded more accurately as a pair of 'half W8JK's' with a phase difference φ which can (if one needs to be precise) be taken into account by a small field-strength correction factor, 0.92 for $\varphi \leq \varphi_0$ and 0.7 for $\varphi = 2\varphi_0$. The field for the endwise relative to the forward directions, ignoring the correction, is given by

$$\frac{\sin (\varphi_0/2)}{\sin \left(\dfrac{\varphi + \varphi_0}{2} \right)}$$

and is plotted in Fig 5.26(c).

In Fig 5.26 we are looking down on what could be any of several antenna systems. It could for example be a pair of crossed λ/2 dipoles cut in their centres and re-joined to form a pair of V-shaped elements, though by suitable feeding

'plumber's delight' construction may be used and the cutting avoided. It could also be a set of wires sloping down from the top of a mast, in which case the four-way symmetry is an invitation to use them for a beam system with directional switching. It then becomes important to consider the worst directions, ie those at 45° to the lobes shown in Fig 5.26(a). Unfortunately there can be no front/back ratio for these directions, and any success one may have in filling in the dips must inevitably lead to a worse radiation pattern for the back directions. Nevertheless, practical designs of X-beam include the use of sloping wires which form part of the guy-wire system, and UA3IAR [9] has devised a switched-beam quad operating on these lines.

Unfortunately, looking at the right-hand side of Fig 5.26(b), it will be seen that for the 45° directions two of the four half-elements have become invisible. The other two look exactly the same from either direction, this being proof that, despite suggestions to the contrary, there cannot be any back/front ratio on these bearings, the radiated field being proportional (for *both* directions) to sin ($\varphi/2$). It is given relative to the forward field by

$$\frac{0.7 \; \sin (\varphi_0/2)}{\sin \left(\dfrac{\varphi + \varphi_0}{2} \right)}$$

This is also plotted in Fig 5.26(c) which shows for comparison the front/back ratio based on Fig 5.4. To fill in the 45° nulls as much as possible it is clearly desirable to use as large a value of φ as possible, the front/back ratio for the UA3IAR quad being consistent with a (φ/φ_0) of about 1.7. The gain from Fig 5.4 is 2.8dB, the radiation resistance for each of the two driven elements being 50Ω, ie 57Ω read directly from Fig 5.4 divided by 2.3 for the X configuration but multiplied by two as the elements are loops. These figures are the basis for a viable switched-beam system provided that a 'dipole' standard of performance over four narrow arcs is acceptable. It seems difficult to account for the reported drop of only 3dB for these directions, particularly as it is depicted as being combined with reasonable front/back ratio. Possibly the results could be affected by vertically polarised components of radiation which are likely to be appreciable in the case of dipole slopers, though one would expect them to cancel for quad antennas provided a balun is used!

To get X-beams further into perspective it is interesting to compare the crossed-dipole array with Fig 5.17(j), which uses identical dipoles but brings together the ends instead of the centres. This halves the space occupied, increases the radiation resistance by about 32 times and provides a much better radiation pattern. Alternatively the dotted lines in Fig 5.26(b) can be replaced by dipoles of identical size and spacing, resonated by means of bent-over ends; performance will be almost identical but with elimination of the pattern defects and requiring only just over a third of the space, the radiation resistance being nearly doubled because the current distribution is rectangular rather than sine wave. For 'all-round switchable' directivity, vertically polarised arrays are more suitable and might be expected as discussed in Chapter 10 to provide comparable performance even when restricted in height.

To sum up, the very considerable attractions of X-arrays derive from the single point of support and the possibilities of directional switching; the price paid is much larger size for the equivalent performance and a basically worse directional pattern. The reader may well feel, particularly after perusal of Chapters 10, 12 and 13, that there are always better options available.

'Sloper' arrays based on λ/2 dipoles sloping down from a common point are becoming increasingly popular, particularly on the lower-frequency bands. Despite some similarity with X-beams, including some features of the directional patterns, points of maximum current are widely separated and they are thus exempt from criticisms relating to low values of radiation resistance. Inevitably, however, they result in two modes of radiation, acting both as low-height horizontal antennas suitable for short-range, high-angle contacts and vertical radiators having a reasonable DX capability; it is clearly better for DX working to bring the lower ends back towards the mast as described in Chapter 13, p227, so that as much power as possible goes into the vertical mode. A separate low-height inverted-V dipole can be used to take care of any short-range requirements.

Small beams

The beam obtained by adding a third element to Fig 5.17(j), which was mentioned earlier and is described in detail in Chapter 12, occupies only half the area of a conventional 'full-size' beam based on λ/2 elements but differs only very slightly in performance. In effect, the end halves of λ/2 dipole elements add relatively little to the performance and therefore tend to waste space. If an even smaller beam is required it becomes impracticable to use three elements, except by compromises which lead to fairly rapid deterioration of performance with decreasing size. However, since the gain advantage from the third element is normally only 1dB, restriction to two elements is not a serious loss, particularly as the necessity for two feeders, imposed by bandwidth problems, brings with it possibilities for the 'nulling out' of interfering signals as described in Chapter 9.

It is reasonable to suppose the existence at all times of a standing requirement for beams to be as small as possible *subject to meeting a given performance specification*. This may well be set so high in terms, for example, of operational convenience that it can only be met by the use of full-sized monoband elements. On the other hand, the need to retune the transmitter when changing frequency within a band may be accepted as part of the price for multiband operation or fitting an antenna into a small space. Often a rather modest reduction in size is accepted when a different method would have resulted in a much smaller structure, providing identical performance or better performance for a glven size.

It is not intended by this to suggest that a satisfactory

antenna should be scrapped merely because it *could* have been better designed, and there are times when an 'inferior' solution of a problem may result in so much saving of time or expense that it becomes the only alternative to no solution at all! This is likely to apply particularly in cases where it is desired to adapt an existing antenna to operate on 10, 18 or 24MHz. A reader conversant with the basic principles should have no difficulty in working out such compromises if the need arises, and for present purposes the emphasis will be on making beams as small as possible.

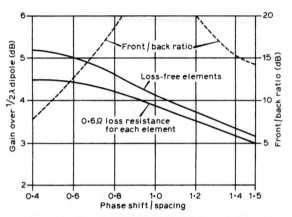

Fig 5.27. Gain and front/back ratio for two elements with and without losses, as a function of phase angle. Note that losses tend to increase the optimum value of phase shift. The lower curve assumes a spacing of λ/8 and a loss resistance for each element equal to 4% of its radiation resistance as measured with the other element removed *(Ham Radio)*

Yet again the W8JK beam is a good point from which to start, being still widely favoured despite a typical feedpoint impedance of only just over 4Ω for the two elements in parallel. Nevertheless, it has already been shown that putting in a phase shift equal to the spacing (apart from other advantages) multiplies the radiation resistance by four, and the top curve of Fig 3.12 shows that the length of elements can be shortened to a mere 30% of λ/2 if division of the radiation resistance by four is acceptable. This merely restores it to the W8JK value, so that if satisfactory performance is assumed in the case of the W8JK it must follow that a phased beam having elements only 0.15λ in length (10ft (3m) for 14MHz) will perform equally well, *provided the reduction of length is carried out in the right way*.

To illustrate the possibilities of size reduction without appreciable loss of gain, the lower curve in Fig 5.27 has been calculated [14] for 14swg (2mm) wire elements 12ft (3.66m) long, spaced 8ft (2.44m), but is equally applicable to a 10ft (3.1m) square design. The upper solid-line curve is part of the gain plot from Fig 5.4 reproduced for comparison, from which it can be seen that the loss of gain is very slight, and in the light of discussion in Chapter 10 would be more than offset if advantage can be taken of the smaller size to gain a few extra feet of height.

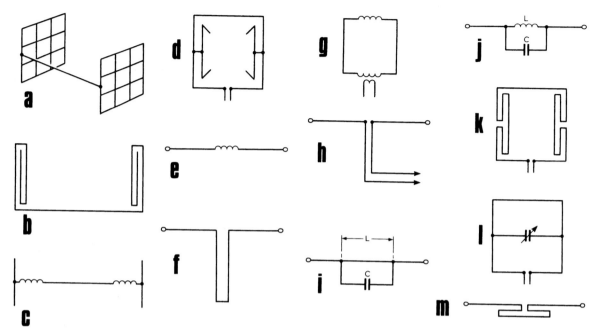

Fig 5.28. This shows 13 different methods for loading short elements. The merits of each type are discussed in the text. (a) Capacitance plates consisting or wire grids. (b) λ/2 elements with folded ends. The length must be increased slightly to maintain resonance. (c) Small capacitance hats – the effective capacitance is enhanced by near-resonance with the inductors. (d) A loop with capacitance hats. This is equivalent to a stacked pair of (b)-type elements with their ends in contact. (e) Centre loading with an inductor. (f) A λ/2 element with a folded centre. This is similar to (e) with a stub instead of the coil. However, the R values from Fig 3.12 are transformed by the stub to give an even lower value at the closed end of the stub. (g) Loop equivalent to (e). (h) Resonant feeders. (i) Version of a two-band element as used by DL1FK. The capacitor tunes the inductance of the centre of the radiator to increase its effective value at the lower frequency. Series resonance of the capacitor with its connections shortens the electrical length for the higher frequency. (j) Lumped-circuit equivalent of (i) as used in one form of the G4ZU minibeam. (k) Alternative version of (d) using linear loading at voltage maxima. (l) Capacitance connected between points of maximum voltage. (m) Linear loading at a point of maximum current *(Ham Radio)*

Fig 5.28, taken from reference [14], shows various ways which have been used for folding or shortening antenna elements in order to fit them into smaller spaces. Of these only (b) and (d) have much practical relevance to the task of trying to make beams as small as possible without loss in performance, though in some cases combination of (c) and (b) to effect a modest degree of additional size reduction may be acceptable, particularly if stubs are used in place of coils. There are two imperatives which follow from the discussion of losses in Chapter 3 (p26) and which may be stated as follows:

(a)   the current distribution in the radiating portion of the antenna *must* be uniform;

(b)   the antenna must be brought to resonance without the use of power-consuming devices, and this rules out the use of loading coils except possibly in an auxiliary role after most of the loading has been provided by other means.

It is impossible to meet these requirements at the size limit set by gain considerations alone without incurring severe overcoupling between the elements. This is because the large 'blobs' of capacitance needed at the ends of the elements for tuning them to resonance also couple them tightly together.

The answer to this problem is neutralisation of the excess capacitance as shown in Fig 5.29. The method is identical to that used for push-pull amplifiers, the current in the neutralising circuits being too small to upset the radiated field, and for monoband operation there are few problems [13].

The arguments just presented might seem to suggest that all beams should be as small as possible, but this is not the intention since gain is only one aspect of performance. If it is not necessary to make a beam as small as possible there are advantages in larger size, particularly in regard to bandwidth and multiband operation which are topics for later chapters. At the smallest possible size it becomes essential to use separate feeders to each element to allow remote adjustment and avoid bandwidth restrictions but, as already stressed, important advantages follow in any case from the use of two feeders.

Loop elements as in Fig 5.28(d) are not envisaged for 'minimum size' arrays since the construction becomes very complicated if taken to the limit. The great virtue of this type of element is that it leads to the smallest possible diameter of turning circle though, owing to their relatively large vertical extent, such beams may still be considered 'large' compared with ones using type (b) elements. With this restriction on the

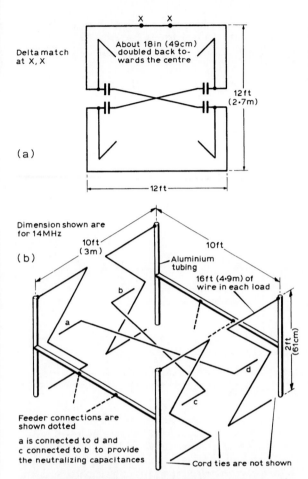

Delta match at X, X

X   X

About 18in (49cm) doubled back to-wards the centre

12ft (2·7m)

(a)

12ft

Dimension shown are for 14MHz

10ft (3m)

(b)

10ft

Aluminium tubing

16ft (4·9m) of wire in each load

b

a

2ft (61cm)

d

c

Feeder connections are shown dotted

a is connected to d and c connected to b to provide the neutralizing capacitances

Cord ties are not shown

Fig 5.29. Miniature beam with neutralisation; (a) based on flat construction, illustrates the principles; (b) shows loading wires folded in vertical plane to achieve further size reduction and improved construction. For further details see Fig 12.13

losses. Furthermore, the loading is essentially inductive so that the current distribution is triangular and the radiation resistance very low. Method (k) was the first small loop to be tried by the author and was quickly abandoned, though it has since been described elsewhere. Because very little current flows in the loading section, the inductive effect is small and it was found to be almost identical with (d) which is a lot simpler.

Another proposed method, (l), breaks the cardinal rule that *paths carrying large currents must not double back;* if they do the current 'flowing the wrong way' is subtracted from the effective total and this brings the radiation resistance down with a big bump! In this case, assuming a 12ft (3.7m) square loop, the current through the capacitor is roughly equal to the loop current so that the signal is equal to that from one wire considered in isolation. This divides the radiation resistance by four so that the current is doubled and the total loss (ignoring the vertical wires) is multiplied by six compared with the 'top-hatted' loop, (d). Method (m), known as 'linear loading', is basically the same as (f) but gets round the problem of how to dispose of the stub and can likewise be used to effect a modest size reduction, particularly if end-loading is used in addition.

In general it is advisable to aim for a more or less square overall shape since otherwise the diameter of turning circle for a given value of R is increased. Thus in going from 10ft (3m) square to a 14ft (4.3m) by 7ft (2.1m) rectangle at 14MHz, R is unchanged but the diameter of turning circle is increased from 14ft (4.3m) to 15.8ft (4.8m), and if 14ft is the element length it becomes more difficult to accommodate the necessary loading. Going in the other direction, 14ft spacing is getting too close to the $\lambda/4$ limit, and gain is decreased partly from this cause but also because radiation from the folded-over ends can no longer be ignored. Additional considerations applicable to multiband operation are discussed in Chapter 7.

High-loss beams

An interesting problem arises [3] if, for any reason, it is necessary to use inefficient elements, a situation likely to arise, for example, when there are restrictions on the erection of visible antennas. A thin wire trailing over a wet tiled roof (or even a thicker wire just inside the roof space) clearly breaks the rules of good antenna design, and resistance losses may be greatly augmented by losses in brickwork or other poor-quality insulating materials. However, the situation is by no means hopeless, remembering that even a few watts of effective radiated power is capable of providing regular DX contacts. For reception, owing to the high external (galactic) noise level a large number of decibels can be sacrificed without adverse effect on signal-to-noise ratios and, however great the losses, unidirectional patterns identical with those of typical high-quality beams may be achieved by the use of two or more suitably-phased elements, although a completely different set of design requirements arises.

These may be derived from calculations similar to those on

use of small loops it can be assumed that neutralisation will not be required.

Of the other arrangements shown in Fig 5.28, (a) provides maximum efficiency but is inconvenient, and it is not practical to accommodate enough loading if the size is reduced to a minimum. Types (c), (e), (g) suffer from losses in the loading coils, greatly aggravated in cases (e), (g) due to the triangular current distribution. (f) is similar to (e), though use of the stub instead of a coil roughly halves the losses, and it is often a convenient method for achieving a modest degree of length reduction not exceeding about 20%.

In the case of resonant feeders (h), the losses in the dipole are multiplied in proportion to the total length of wire in the system, or alternatively the feeder can be reckoned as operating at an SWR well in excess of 100 with consequent large losses. Methods (i) and (j) have been used for multiband systems, including miniature beams, but involve quite large circulating currents in the resonators and therefore increased

earlier pages by adding a relatively large loss resistance R_L to the radiation resistance R, the phase shift due to a series reactance X being given approximately by X/R_L which bears little relation to the previous formula X/R. Because of the assumed high value of R_L, very little current flows in a parasitic element so *both elements must be driven*. Much higher values of reactance X are required to produce a given radiation pattern, but alternatively phasing lines may be used without any of the complications described earlier, since the mutual impedances which give rise to them are negligible in comparison with the loss resistance.

The mathematics are further simplified and it is easy to divide the power equally between two elements, so that if a current I would flow in one element alone, equal currents $0.707I$ flow in each of the two

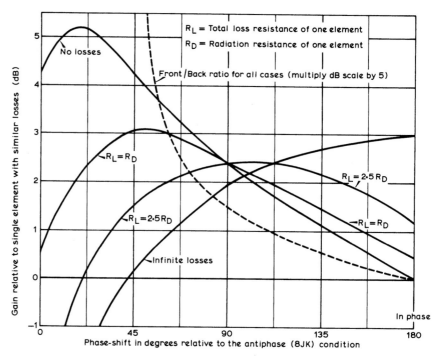

Fig 5.30. Gain and front/back ratio for a pair of lossy elements spaced λ/8. The elements are assumed to be driven with equal currents. Gain or loss relative to a loss-free dipole is obtained by subtracting the loss figure 10 log (1 + R_L/R_D) from the gains indicated

elements. With λ/8 spacing and 135° phase difference (ie $\varphi/\varphi_0 = 1$) the field strength 'in the beam' is identical with that from a single element and is only a fraction $R/(R_L + R)$ of that which would be produced by an efficient dipole, although the radiation pattern is the same as that of an efficient beam having the same spacing and phasing. However, 3dB improvement in the radiated signal may be obtained by driving both elements in phase, which destroys the front-to-back ratio. There is thus a conflict between transmitting and receiving requirements.

Fig 5.30 compares the variation of gain with phase angle for low-loss elements, the extreme lossy situation discussed above and two intermediate cases, the low-loss curve being an extended version of that shown in Fig 5.4. Front-to-back ratio is also plotted over the range of main interest for the case of lossy elements. It will be noticed that losses cause the maximum of the gain curve to shift to the right, the loss of gain due to 'incorrect' phasing being more than offset by the increase of efficiency due to higher radiation resistance as one moves further away from the antiphase condition. For the same reason it would be advantageous, in the intermediate cases only, to use wider spacings. It is notable that with wide spacings, compared with a single lossy element, 3dB gain always exists in some directions, and these can be varied at will, depending on the phase shift.

Reference has been made already to the extreme unsuitability of the W8JK beam for use in lossy situations, eg as an indoor antenna. For proof of this consider first, by way of

example, a two-element driven array tuned for maximum nominal front/back ratio ($\varphi = \varphi_0$) but having a loss of 3dB due to its surroundings, leaving a net gain of 1.2dB over a dipole at the same height but in the open. From Fig 5.4 the radiation resistance of each element is 28Ω and by implication this has been assumed equal to the loss resistance. In the W8JK configuration, however, the radiation resistance drops to 8.5Ω and the efficiency to 8.5/36.5 or 23%. This is a total loss of 6.4dB, being 3.4dB worse than for the phased array and 2.2dB worse than a dipole. Transferred to the lossy location, the dipole is degraded in the ratio 101/73 or 1.4dB only, so that in going from an indoor dipole to the W8JK there is a *loss* of 0.8dB whereas the phased array provides 1.2dB gain.

For a large initial loss the *extra* loss for the W8JK reaches a limiting value which is equal to the ratio of the two radiation resistances, ie 28/8.5 or 5.2dB. Since the W8JK has no front/back ratio, less gain than a dipole, and needs only trivial modifications (p82) to turn it into the phased array which was the starting point for this example, it is difficult to account for its continuing popularity as an indoor antenna, except on the basis that little is expected from indoor antennas, accurate measurements are difficult, it needs no more than a watt or so of effective radiation to produce some DX contacts, and there is usually no accurate way of measuring losses.

If the loss resistance exceeds 40Ω or so it would be better in any event to use a dipole for transmission plus a separate short antenna for phasing out interfering signals as discussed on p156.

Designing an indoor beam

There is no 'best' type of indoor beam since each case is different, but the reader has now been provided with a number of building-blocks which can be deployed to suit the circumstances.

To illustrate some of the possibilities, it will be assumed as a starting point that a 20m beam is required to be fitted into a roof space 10ft square with a lot of plumbing, electric wiring etc in the vicinity. Reasons for rejecting the W8JK beam have been already discussed and Fig 5.29(a) might look like an ideal solution, but is it?

Even in this case the RF voltages remain very high, so after a brief reference to p251 we might decide to try a pair of resonant helices, each wound with about 20m of 14swg copper wire and having, from Fig 3.11, an RF resistance of 1.6Ω. As the current distribution is sinusoidal and the elements are short dipoles, the radiation resistance is equal to 80Ω divided by the square of the shortening ratio; this comes to 7.3Ω but, for two elements putting φ/φ_0 equal to 1.0 and the spacing equal to $\lambda/8$, this comes down to 2.9Ω. The efficiency remains reasonable but several kilovolts of RF can still be expected at the ends of the elements!

By increasing φ/φ_0 to 2.0 and referring to Figs 5.30 and 5.4, the gain drops to 2.4dB compared with a single element which is 0.9dB worse than a $\lambda/2$ dipole. Meanwhile the total for the two radiation-plus-loss resistances has risen to 17.8Ω which is still rather low; however, by end-loading the elements along the lines of Fig 5.29 it would be possible to reduce the electrical length of the helices to about $\lambda/8$, resulting in a nearly uniform current distribution which doubles the radiation resistance (R) and reduces the losses. R can be further multiplied by $(5/4)^2$ if the spacing is increased to 10ft, making a grand total of 56Ω. Gain and F/B ratio are not impressive but it should be a simple matter to optimise antenna characteristics separately for reception (p154) and incorporate this in the T/R switching. It should be noted that if more space is available the size of the antenna should in general be adjusted to fill it, since R is proportional to the square of the area occupied. It may be useful to note also that the shape of the 'inverted' SDL (Fig 7.4) conforms closely to that of many roof spaces.

These are but a few of the many options available for tackling the difficult problems posed by the indoor environment, which is properly a task for Chapters 10 and 11 to which the reader is referred for further guidance.

Vertical arrays

It is necessary at this point to make another brief descent from free space. The majority of amateur beams for the higher-frequency bands use horizontal elements, probably due in large part to the mechanical problems of mounting vertical arrays. In the latter case, for a given *mean* height the *total* height is greater, the lower ends of the elements get entangled with guy wires, and there is coupling between the elements and supporting structures which may result in losses, distortion of the radiation pattern and TVI. The feeding of vertical antennas can also cause problems.

The relative merits of horizontal and vertical polarisation are discussed in Chapter 6 (p118) and Chapter 10 (p162), from which it seems clear that the main virtue of vertical antennas lies in the possibility of obtaining fairly good performance even when height is severely restricted. A typical 'breakeven' height for equivalent DX performance is around 25–30ft (8–9m) at 14MHz and probably proportional to wavelength. Whether this is accurate or not, it is well known that vertical polarisation is relatively better at the lower frequencies.

It is nevertheless the author's view that vertical beams have been greatly underrated as DX antennas for the higher frequencies. It is true that for *equal* performance in the two cases a vertical array needs to be relatively elaborate, but this is less of a problem in 'low height' situations which allow the mechanical problems to be resolved in various simple ways as described in Chapter 13.

It may be that some of the prejudice against vertical antennas has been engendered by that commonest of all excuses for a poor signal, 'I am only using a ground plane'. The ground-plane antenna appears prone to serious shortcomings (p44) and the 'Zepp' feed or J-match in its usual form, though it may seem the obvious method for feeding a vertical dipole, is open to even stronger objections (p47). In practice *at low height* a vertical dipole can usually be centre-fed with a balanced line, the balance (though inherently imperfect) being usually good enough.

The use of coaxial cable plus a balun is also acceptable; alternatively a 'balanced' Zepp feed (p48) or a tuning unit working against a small counterpoise may be employed (p45). A further alternative is to use monopole elements in conjunction with short counterpoise earths as described on p212; these can be regarded as a kind of dipole, being subject to exactly the same rules, and they can be expected to provide almost the same performance for the same height reckoned to the 'centre of gravity' of the current distribution.

One particularly interesting aspect of vertical beams is the ease with which they can be rotated electrically to provide all-round coverage. Whereas horizontal beams are wide angle in the vertical and narrow angle in the horizontal planes, the reverse holds for vertical beams and reasonably good azimuth coverage in the case of two or three elements can be obtained with a minimum of four switched directions. A driven element may be surrounded by a ring of, say, four parasitic elements and the beam rotated by using relays to make small changes in the length of the parasitic elements (p226). Alternatively a ring of four close-spaced elements may be connected in various ways, and the author favours an arrangement of four 'half-loops' or the vertical equivalent of inverted-V elements. These can be supported by a single pole with the top half of the elements forming the top part of the guy-wire system as described on p227. Optimum methods of connection and phasing for three or four close-spaced vertical elements have been the subject of a computer study [15] which has been used as a basis for recommendations in Chapter 13.

Practical beams and the Uzkov limit

Reference has already been made (p21) to the Uzkov limit [16], according to which the maximum gain theoretically obtainable from n elements is equal to n^2. This is a mathematical result based on isotropic sources and the gain figure is slightly reduced when these, together with the standard of reference, are replaced by real radiators such as $\lambda/2$ dipoles for which corrections have been calculated by Bloch, Medhurst and Pool [17], as reproduced in Fig 5.31.

For an equally spaced arrangement of dipoles or other 'point sources' the gains indicated by these curves cannot be exceeded under any circumstances and, from investigations reported in the reference, unequal spacings appear to make matters worse rather than better.

Fig 5.31 also shows for comparison the gain limit (n) for additive systems. It should be noted that the n^2 curve assumes infinitesimal spacings, though it remains reasonably accurate for spacings up to at least 0.2λ, whereas the n curve requires spacings of *not less* than 0.5λ and therefore relates to a much larger type of array. The n^2 curve is in fact correct within 0.15dB for four elements at spacings up to 0.2λ but there is a drop of about 1.2dB in gain for spacings of 0.25λ. The crosses represent the closest practical approaches to the theoretical gain for which there is reliable evidence. The figure for $n = 2$ is taken from Fig 5.4, those for $n = 3$, $n = 6$, and upwards of $n = 6$ being taken from a comprehensive experimental study of long Yagi arrays [19]; this contains one mistake insofar as a gain of only 2.6dB is recorded for a driven element plus reflector, but apart from this the figures are consistent with data from other sources.

Particular interest attaches to the circled point which was the end product of an attempt to reach the Uzkov performance limit in the case of four elements as described in the above reference. Mention has already been made of the very rapid escalation of losses, and practical difficulties in general, as spacing is reduced. Bloch and his co-workers appear to have used the widest spacing consistent with their purpose, ie 0.2λ, and to demonstrate operation of the supergain principle with more than two elements the vector diagrams shown in Fig 5.32 have been constructed from data given in their paper. The apex angles are accounted for by the spacing plus or minus an 8° phase shift. Diagrams on the right have been drawn for a typical two-element array (maximum gain) and demonstrate the underlying similarity. Other data for the four-element array are summarised in Table 5.1 and Fig 5.33.

The measured gain (75MHz) was 8.7dB so that, adding 0.8dB for the known losses, a further 0.6dB remained to be accounted for by losses in the coils and capacitors of matching networks. The measured bandwidth was about 1.7MHz which is sufficient to suggest the possibility of a workable design covering most of any one of the HF bands, though the need for improvements in the feeder system is indicated in the reference.

An interesting problem arises from the negative resistances listed in Table 5.1; these indicate that elements 3 and 4 are returning power to the transmitter for re-issue to elements 1

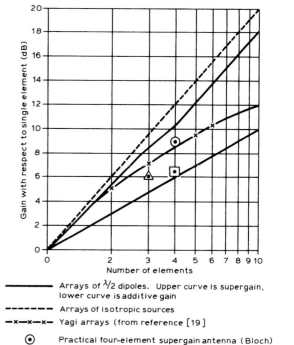

Arrays of $\lambda/2$ dipoles. Upper curve is supergain, lower curve is additive gain

— — — — Arrays of isotropic sources

—x—x—x— Yagi arrays (from reference [19])

⊙   Practical four-element supergain antenna (Bloch)

⊡   Equal-amplitude elements with optimum spacing [18]

▲   Typical three-element beam, $\lambda/8$ spacing

Fig 5.31. Maximum end-fire gain of array of equispaced elements. This figure is taken from the paper by Bloch *et al*, with the two lower curves and points added *(Proc IEE)*

and 2, and it is clear that relative phases and amplitudes have to be carefully controlled, a matter likely to present some difficulty. It appears to the author that this might be achievable by separate feeding of elements 2 and 3 with a phasing unit of the type shown on p92, elements 1 and 4 being excited parasitically from elements 2 and 3 with careful control of coupling, eg by bending the elements inwards or outwards as required. The importance of ensuring the correct current ratios follows from the fact that a maximum possible gain of 6.5dB only has been calculated for a set of four elements carrying equal currents with optimum phase differences [18].

The geometrical principles of Chapter 3 (p21) apply irrespective of the number of elements so that if, for example, the spacings are divided by four, the angles between the vectors in Fig 5.32 must also be divided by four. This means that the currents are multiplied by four and the radiation resistances divided by 16, becoming 0.32, 0.425, −0.1 and −1.25Ω respectively. The reader has already been introduced to the difficulties which arise when radiation resistances fall below 5Ω or so, and these become further emphasised when bandwidth is discussed in Chapter 8. In view of the inherent difficulty of reaching the gain limit for more than two elements, it is evident that any such attempt must be based on using the widest allowable spacings, eg 0.2λ as in the design based on Table 5.1 and Fig 5.32. This assessment is difficult

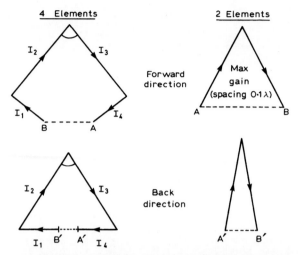

4 Elements

2 Elements

Forward direction

Max gain (spacing 0·1λ)

Back direction

Fig 5.32. Phase and amplitude diagrams for optimised four-element supergain antenna. Based on details given in the paper by Bloch et al, these diagrams demonstrate the mode of operation. Front/back ratio = AB/A'B' = 10.5dB. The marked angle is 'equal to the spacing' plus or minus a small phase shift (8°), this being mainly responsible for the difference in length of AB and A'B'. It will be seen that a very small phase error could make a considerable difference to the final answer, thus demonstrating a characteristic feature of supergain arrays. Corresponding diagrams for a two-element beam (shown on right) exhibit the same characteristic 'pincer effect'

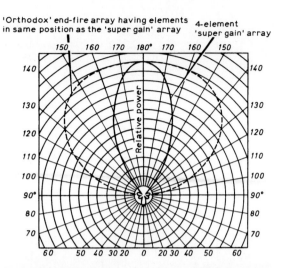

'Orthodox' end-fire array having elements in same position as the 'super gain' array

4-element 'super gain' array

Relative power

Fig 5.33. Radiation pattern of the experimental four-element supergain array compared with 'orthodox' end-fire array (Proc IEE)

to reconcile with gain figures which have been quoted for log-Yagi arrays having element spacings of only 0.05λ, though these can provide impressive performance and designs such as the one featured on p200 deserve consideration by anyone looking for a 'best possible' monoband beam.

The experimental points in Fig 5.31 need some discussion since the measured gain in the 'supergain' case is only slightly above the curve for Yagi arrays of more or less conventional design, and it might therefore appear as a negligible return for a lot of hard work. It is, however, instructive to consider Fig 5.31 in conjunction with Fig 5.34 which shows the gain of Yagi arrays as a function of length on the basis of two separate studies using different assumptions and methods, the spacing between elements being 0.2λ for the crosses and 0.26–0.3λ for the circles. In the design of Yagi arrays with large numbers of elements there are so many variables that it is not possible to specify a 'correct' method of design, but the points in Fig 5.34 are in fairly close agreement with each other and with other comparable studies. General conclusions to be drawn include the following.

(a) There is no difficulty in reaching the limit for two elements but with increasing numbers the difficulties escalate rapidly.

(b) With three or four elements it is still possible to get fairly close to the limit but only if the spacing is increased to the maximum allowable. The 'typical' figure for $n = 3$ is based on amateur beams with spacings of $λ/8$, whereas the Yagi curve assumes spacings of $λ/5$ and demonstrates the likely *improvement* from the wider spacing at

28MHz when close-spaced '14MHz' elements are used on both bands. This counters the widely held belief (justified, alas, for the two-element case) that if 14MHz beam elements are used at 28MHz the spacing is necessarily too wide for optimum performance.

At large n the difficulties escalate to the point where the additive gain curve applies; thus for $n = 10$ there is a shortfall of 6dB relative to the supergain curve, and for a given number of elements only 2dB improvement compared with additive gain, though the latter would demand an increase of array length from 2.2λ to 4.5λ. In general it might be concluded that spacing can be increased with advantage as the number of elements is increased. We return to this topic in Chapter 6.

It may be noted that sources of loss in the case of the supergain antenna described above are known and an improvement of 1dB looks possible. This would leave the

Table 5.1. Theoretical design data for four-element supergain array

	Element number			
	1	2	3	4
Relative magnitude of currents	8.155	18.386	18.386	8.155
Driving point resistances (Ω)	+5.1	+6.8	−1.6	−20.1
Input powers (relative)	+340	+2288	−539	−1336

Power gain relative to λ/2 dipole = 10.1dB
Current in λ/2 dipole to give same field as array, in same units as the above currents = 10.3
Total radiated power (relative) = 753
Ditto for reference dipole (for same field) = $(10.3)^2 \times 73 = 7745$
Hence power gain relative to λ/2 dipole = 7745/753 = 10.1dB
Theoretical maximum power gain for very close spacing (from Fig 5.24) = 10.3dB
Half-power beamwidth = 52°
Front-to-back ratio = 10.9dB
Calculated losses in antenna + feeder = 0.8dB

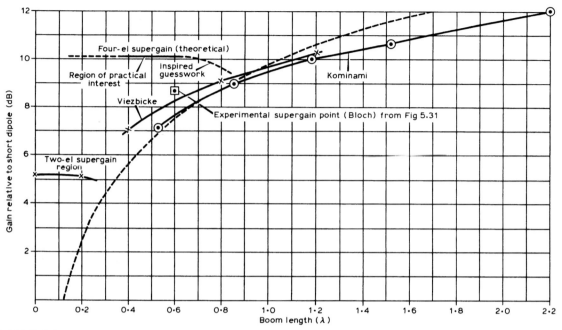

Fig 5.34. Variation of gain with boom length for Yagi arrays, indicating comparison with supergain arrays. The dotted curve is an attempted 'best fit' based on the assumption of gain proportional to length; this has no practical significance for small antennas but the relatively steep slope for large boom lengths suggests that parasitic excitation may not make best use of the available length

shortfall several times greater in the case of the Yagi but the amount of this (2dB) is hardly enough to justify the added complexity of an optimised design.

In choosing an antenna system the gain for a given number of elements is only one of a number of criteria, and reduction of boom length may be more important than cutting down the number of elements.

Were it possible to overlook a few mundane practical details, the prospect of supergain antennas with many elements operating at the Uzkov limit would be quite fascinating, and it is indeed not impossible that one day someone will build a 1000-element beam the size of a matchbox and having a gain of a million! By invoking the principle of superconductivity, whereby the resistance of certain conductors falls to zero at temperatures slightly above absolute zero, the problem of efficiency might be overcome but one would then, alas, be left with a bandwidth so narrow that it could take years to signal the equivalent of a single morse dot!

The nature of the difficulties can be anticipated from a simple numerical example based on the square-law relationship (p85) between radiation resistance and the dimensions of an array; thus at 14MHz a W8JK beam with dimensions of 2in × 1½ in would have a radiation resistance per element of

$$8.5 \times \left(\frac{2}{33 \times 12} \right)^2 \times \left(\frac{1.5}{8 \times 12} \right)^2 = 0.5 \times 10^{-7}\Omega$$

It is not clear how such elements would be constructed and resonated but even a normal full-sized element develops a

reactance of this order if the frequency is shifted away from resonance by about 5 parts in 10^9. On this basis bandwidth (calculated as explained in Chapter 8) comes to 6×10^{-4}Hz and the morse dot can now be signalled in about 1000 seconds or less than half an hour. Unfortunately, after all this (including provision of a supply of liquid helium) the gain is still a mere 4dB! The reader who has studied the earlier part of this chapter may hasten to point out that the W8JK is the worst possible antenna for such an application and the above time could be divided by four, but the prospects are still not encouraging.

Summary, conclusions and recommendations

Two-element amateur beams should consist of closely spaced sources of radiation, equal in amplitude and correctly phased. The majority of designs fail to meet these conditions, and suffer from more-or-less serious defects. This includes loop arrays such as the quad which, though satisfactory in terms of performance, are not advised for rotary beams since they are heavy, unsightly, expensive, and due to high wind loading frequently blow down! In addition to providing optimum performance, the recommended designs result in a minimum of weight, size and cost, besides being relatively easy to tune. *The specified conditions are easily realised in practice since they require only the use of reflector elements having their ends correctly spaced from those of the driven element.*

Unfortunately, up to the time of writing, attempts to

equalise currents have usually relied on phasing lines which work correctly only if mutual coupling can be neglected. As, however, close-spaced beams work solely and entirely by virtue of such coupling, the decline in popularity of phasing-line systems is hardly surprising. However, although good performance is compatible with only a narrow range of options (the same for all equal-current, two-element beams) and requires adherence to strict rules, it is quite difficult to achieve an antenna that does *not* work at least after some fashion. With a little assistance from the long arm of coincidence, even driven arrays based on phasing lines have been known to produce top-line performance; this road, however, is more likely to lead to disappointment.

Three-element beams are less amenable to calculation owing to the large number of variables and there is no clearly recognisable 'optimum' set of conditions, but *designs based on the right-hand lower corner of Fig 5.24 are suggested as a likely means of achieving a considerable reduction in average interference levels.* Higher gains and longer boom lengths tend to result in worse front/back ratios, although this can be largely offset by increasing the number of elements [21, 24]. The available data is not, however, directly applicable to small beams with bent elements, and further design studies are needed for these cases.

The maximum gain that can be expected in practice from small beams varies only from 5dB relative to a single dipole, in the case of two elements spaced by 0.1–0.18λ, up to 6 or 7dB for three elements with boom lengths of 0.25–0.5λ [19, 20, 21, 23, 24]. Similar figures apply to vertical arrays, including monopole elements working against short loaded counterpoises at heights upwards of 2 or 3ft (0.6–0.9m) from the ground, but the pros and cons of vertical versus horizontal polarisation can be quite complicated, as discussed in Chapter 10 (p162).

Even if, for example, due to environmental constraints elements have high losses, there is usually some advantage in using more than one but it is essential (and in this case possible) for all to be driven. Apart from this or as a means of correcting small errors of design or adjustment after erection, driven operation is not recommended.

Two-element beams may be reduced in size to only 10ft (3m) square at 14MHz, and pro rata, without losing more than 1dB of gain but for this purpose it is *essential* to use capacitive end-loading. This results in excess coupling between elements, an effect which can be counteracted by means of neutralisation. Two feeders should be used to effect beam reversal and some degree of remote tuning.

X-beams and a number of other element shapes are not recommended.

References

[1] 'Supergain aerials', L A Moxon, *Radio Communication* September 1972, p586.

[2] 'Two-element driven arrays', L A Moxon, *QST* July 1952, p28.

[3] 'Gains and losses in HF aerials', L A Moxon, *Radio Communication* December 1973 and January 1974.

[4] 'The Moxon beam', L A Moxon, *RSGB Bulletin* August 1953.

[5] *The ARRL Antenna Book,* 12th edn, ARRL, 1970. (The matter is not referred to in the 13th edition).

[6] 'Directional antennas', G H Brown, *Proceedings of the IRE,* Vol 25, January 1937, p78.

[7] 'The Swiss quad beam aerial', R A Baumgartner, HB9CV, *RSGB Bulletin* June 1964.

[8] *The ARRL Antenna Book,* 13th edn, ARRL, 1974, p200.

[9] 'Quad with switchable polar diagram', L Vsevolzhskii, UA3IAR, *Radio* (USSR) No 6, 1978, pp18–19. See also 'Technical Topics', *Radio Communication* October 1978 *et seq.*

[10] 'The compact unidirectional array', W Van B Roberts, W3CHO, *Radio* (USA) January 1938.

[11] F Caton, VK2ABQ/G3ONC, *Electronics Australia* October 1973.

[12] 'Technical Topics', *Radio Communication* March 1980. See also numerous earlier references in 'Technical Topics' from January 1974 onwards.

[13] 'Technical Topics', *Radio Communication* February 1977 and June 1978.

[14] 'High-performance small beams', L A Moxon, *Ham Radio* March 1979.

[15] *The ARRL Antenna Anthology,* 1978, p114. (Material originally presented in *QST* by J L Lawson, W2PV).

[16] 'An approach to the problem of optimum directive antennae design', A I Uzkov, *Comptes Rendus de l'Academie des Sciences de l'URSS,* Vol 53, p35.

[17] 'A new approach to the design of superdirective aerial arrays', Bloch, Medhurst and Pool, *Proceedings of the IEE,* Part III, September 1953.

[18] 'The gain of an idealised Yagi array', D G Reid, *Journal of the IEE* Vol 93, Part IIIA, 1946, p546.

[19] 'Yagi antenna design', P P Viezbicke, *NBS Technical Note 688,* US Dept of Commerce, December 1976.

[20] 'A design of Yagi-Uda antennas by non-linear optimisation techniques', M Kominani and K Rokushima, English text in *Electronics and Communications in Japan,* Vol 61-B, No 1, 1978, pp47–54. (See also 'Technical Topics', *Radio Communication* March 1980).

[21] *Antenna Theory and Design,* H P Williams, 2nd edn, Pitman, p145.

[22] 'Theoretical treatment of short Yagi aerials', W Walkinshaw, *Journal of the IEE,* Vol 93, Part III-A, 1946, p564.

[23] 'Evaluating aerial performance', L A Moxon, *Wireless World* February and March 1959.

[24] 'Yagi antenna design', J L Lawson, W2PV, *Ham Radio* May 1980.

[25] Les Moxon, 'Two element HF beams', *Ham Radio* May 1987.

[26] Wayne Overbeck, N6NB, 'Quads v Yagis revisited', *Ham Radio* May 1979.

Chapter 6

Arrays, long wires, and ground reflections

Thus far, attention has been focussed mainly on antennas which can be regarded as 'point sources' of radiation, or closely spaced groups of sources which when properly co-ordinated can be regarded perhaps·as 'super point sources' since the overall dimensions remain small compared with a wavelength.

To complete the picture it is necessary now to consider 'arrays' of point sources such as the following.

(a) Long wires which, in effect, constitute 'strings' of point sources.

(b) 'Additive-gain' arrays consisting of a number of separate sources, adequately spaced, and co-ordinated by the use of such feeders and phasing lines as may be necessary to cause the radiation to add up in phase in a desired direction.

(c) The two-element array formed by an antenna of whatever size *and its image in the ground*. This is the point of re-entry after the long sojourn in free space, and it is also the 'moment of truth' since it is the effect of the ground in conjunction with height restrictions which determines whether DX performance will be good, bad or indifferent. In this wider context the term 'ground' is to be understood as including structures erected on the ground such as buildings and power lines, as a result of which it may be necessary to depart from the simple 'antenna plus image' concept.

Array factor

Most of the above cases can be handled in the same way, using an 'array factor' which is merely the pattern produced by isotropic sources similarly spaced and phased as in Fig 6.1. This can be obtained very easily by graphical addition as in Fig 3.3 or, for two like-phased sources, more quickly from the expression

$$F_a \propto \cos \left(\frac{\pi d \sin \theta}{\lambda} \right) \qquad (1)$$

where F_a is the array factor and the quantity in brackets is half the phase difference, at the receiver, expressed in radians. A plot of this for $\lambda/2$ spacing has been included in Fig 3.9. Similarly for antiphased sources we have

$$F_a \propto \sin \left(\frac{\pi d \sin \theta}{\lambda} \right) \qquad (2)$$

If F_u is the pattern of the individual units (eg $\cos \theta$ in the H-plane for a horizontal dipole) the overall pattern is given by $F_a \times F_u$, ie for each direction the patterns F_u and F_a are obtained separately and then multiplied together. Thus for a pair of in-phase dipoles spaced $\lambda/2$ the values of F_a given by (1) above are multiplied by $\cos \theta$ to obtain the lower curve in Fig 3.9. A potentially difficult problem, or rather group of problems, can therefore be resolved by breaking them down into two very simple problems, though there is one important limitation to this approach. If the units are in any way dissimilar, the array factor concept is not readily applicable and, despite some extra labour, it is easiest to obtain each point on the overall pattern by the method of Fig 3.3, making due allowance for the relevant amplitude and phase differences in each case.

Fortunately the need to obtain complete directional patterns for arrays rarely arises in amateur work, though an amateur with two beams (which may be different) may decide to operate them as a two-unit array in which case he might like to know, for example, how much the direction can be allowed to vary without having to readjust the phasing. Another problem of this type arises as will be seen later in the case of a *vertical* antenna and its image in the ground.

A rather more complicated problem arises if spacing between units is insufficient so that the presence of one unit modifies the currents and therefore the radiation pattern of another unit. In this case it is the modified unit pattern F_u

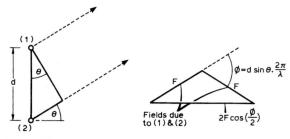

Fig 6.1. Derivation of array factor for point sources in-phase and out-of-phase

106

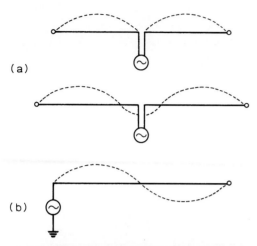

(a)

(b)

Fig 6.2. Full-wave (1λ) dipoles corrrsponding to Fig 6.1. (a) shows two half-waves in phase with the ends close together (collinear pair) and spaced apart (an 'extended double Zepp'). (b) shows a 1λ end-fed wire with out-of-phase current loops

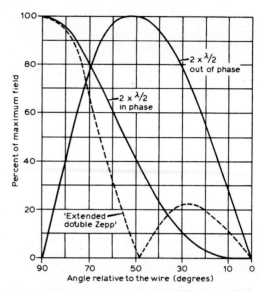

Fig 6.3. Directional patterns corresponding to Fig 6.2 shown in Cartesian form, one quadrant only being shown since the overall pattern is symmetrical

which must be multiplied by F_d. Though this may be difficult in principle, such effects can be corrected in the case of a vertical antenna and its image in the ground. Fortunately, for the most part, amateur HF antenna systems can be divided up into single units, widely spaced groupings of units, and a number of reasonably simple cases in which coupling between units, if not small enough to be ignored, can be allowed for on the basis of mutual resistance data as explained below.

Exceptions to this include long Yagi and log-periodic arrays which are difficult to evaluate without a computer or model range. However, the results of a number of studies have been published and provide adequate guidelines. These include gain figures for long Yagi arrays, as already summarised in Fig 5.34 which is based on several sources. An example of a log-periodic array and a general explanation of its mode of operation will be found in Chapter 14.

Radiation patterns of full-wave antennas

So far the discussion of radiation pattern has been mainly confined to general principles and short conductors. It has been shown that going downwards from, say, λ/2 there is little change in pattern, and such antennas can therefore be considered as 'point sources'. In other words, as far as the pattern (and gain) is concerned it is as if the radiation was coming from a source of infinitely small dimensions, but with due regard of course for angles of inclination and polarisation.

If the length of wire is increased, say, to 1λ the position is changed radically and there are two main cases to be considered: Fig 6.2. In case (a) the wire is centre-fed and there are two in-phase concentrations of current separated by λ/2. This is sufficient to provide some additive gain and, although radiation is still concentrated at right-angles to the wire, the pattern width is reduced from 90° to 50° for 3dB drop in signal. As plotted in Fig 3.9, this provides a gain of just under

2dB, and the length can be further increased with advantage up to about 5λ/4. At this spacing, ie 3λ/4 between the centres of the current loops, the mutual resistance is zero and the power gain is therefore 3dB, being exactly equal to the number of elements as explained on p23.

Strictly speaking, this calculation relates only to a spaced pair of separate elements, but the centre-fed 5λ/4 wire (which is usually known as an 'extended double-Zepp') is more convenient, the current in the short $2 \times \lambda/8$ central portion being too small to affect the directional pattern appreciably.*

In contrast to this example, Fig 6.2(b) shows an end-fed 1λ antenna, which can be considered as a transmission line using the ground as the return path. Since there is now no discontinuity in the centre, the current and voltage can only vary smoothly along the wire according to ordinary transmission-line principles as explained in Chapter 4. Hence the two half-waves are of opposite phase, and radiation must therefore be zero at right-angles to the wire, as well as in the endwise direction. The radiation pattern for Fig 6.2(a) and (b) may be obtained from the above array factors, multiplying in each case by cos θ.

The resulting patterns are shown in Fig 6.3 from which maximum radiation in the case of Fig 6.2(b) is seen to occur at an angle of 50° to the wire. The radiation resistance relative to a λ/2 dipole can be deduced with the help of mutual impedance data, as explained below, and used to derive the gain which comes to 0.5dB. Fig 6.3 applies to one quadrant only but, making use of symmetry, the solid line curve can be used to construct the well-known, clover-leaf pattern (λ case)

---

* This current does subtract about 10% from the total wanted field for a given loop current but, since the directivity and therefore the gain is virtually unchanged, the only practical consequence is a 20% decrease in R.

of Fig 6.4. Though Fig 6.4 is perhaps more pictorial, Fig 6.3 tends to be more informative and this form of presentation has already been used in Chapters 3 and 5.

It is sometimes of interest to know the radiation pattern and resistance of closely spaced, antiphase sources, eg in order to estimate the power lost by radiation of unwanted modes in cases of capacitive end-loading (such as Fig 13.14) or ground-plane radials. For very close spacing the pattern is given by sin $\theta \times \cos \theta$ and differs little from the out-of-phase curve in Fig 6.3, merely pushing it slightly to the right and reducing its width by some 5%. Proceeding by analogy with Fig 2.5 as a starting point, the following formula has been derived (p235) for the unwanted/wanted mode power ratio:

$$P_u/P_w = t^4/4h^2$$

The derivation has been simplified by assuming uniform current distributions, t being the half length of a symmetrical loading wire, and h the length of the radiator. Correction for actual current distributions can reduce this ratio by factors of 8 or more, but not increase it.

For the case of a $\lambda/4$ ground-plane antenna with a pair of $\lambda/4$ radials, the amount of loss is 0.5dB. Also to be considered is the effect of current inequalities. For example, a small difference $p\%$ between the radial currents can be represented by a dipole carrying $(p/2)\%$ of the current, the power ratio for the above example being given by p^2 or only 0.17dB loss for a 20% inequality.

These examples are useful patterns for many other calculations, but there is one important condition to be observed: in these cases the calculations have involved two modes of

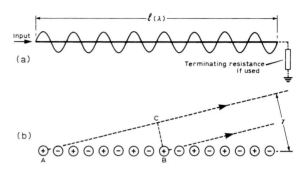

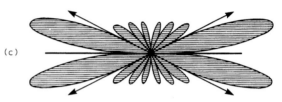

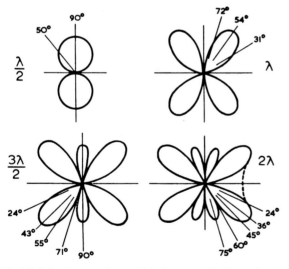

Fig 6.5. Current distribution in a long-wire antenna is shown at (a). Standing wave pattern disappears if antenna is terminated in a suitable load and average current is then the same at all points, barring losses. At (b) the long wire of (a) is represented by point sources of alternate sign. Radiation in direction AC is zero when AB − AC = $\lambda/2$ which occurs when the angle $\gamma = \sqrt{(2/l)}$ where l is in wavelengths and γ in radians. (c) is a typical radiation pattern for an unterminated long-wire antenna, the null directions indicated by arrows being those given by the above formula *(Wireless World)*

radiation and these have been treated independently, which is allowable only because they are orthogonal. In other cases, for example if the radials are sloped downwards or replaced by a counterpoise in line with the radiator, the two modes may tend to reinforce or cancel each other. Misleading answers can be expected, though it is often possible to avoid such difficulties by rearranging the problem as described later.

End-fed long wires

As we have seen in Chapter 4, end-fed wires can be any length, and it will be noticed from Fig 6.4 that as length increases the four main lobes decrease in width and move closer to the endwise direction. With longer wires, smaller lobes known as 'sidelobes' appear in the radiation pattern but, although these are often important in commercial applications, it will be sufficient here to note that they increase in number and decrease in width with increasing length of antenna, being mostly between 5 and 10dB down on the main lobes. Further data for long single wires are given in Table 14.1, p238.

Consider next a much longer wire; assuming this to be unterminated a standing-wave pattern exists as shown in Fig 6.5(a) and the wire can be regarded as a string of dipoles of alternate sign as shown at (b). For most directions each dipole can be paired off with one of opposite sign, allowing where necessary for phase differences resulting from different

Fig 6.4. Polar diagrams for end-fed wires up to 2λ. The angles of main lobes and crevasses are shown, also the angles relative to the wire direction (ie 90° − θ) at which the loss is 3dB in the main lobe. The lobes should be visualised as cones surrounding the wire. As length increases the lobes move closer to the wire direction, so that in the 2λ case there is some radiation at useful wave angles in the endwise direction as shown by the dotted line

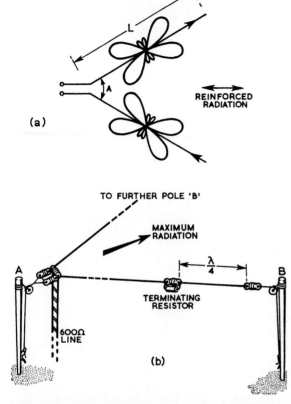

(a)

REINFORCED RADIATION

TO FURTHER POLE 'B'

MAXIMUM RADIATION

$\frac{\lambda}{4}$

A   B

TERMINATING RESISTOR

600Ω LINE

(b)

Fig 6.6. V-beam derived from two long wires arranged at the appropriate angle for alignment of one pair of main lobes. Addition of resistors as shown at (b) results in unidirectional pattern

reasonable performance over about two octaves. Optimum design requires that the lobes of the individual wires should be aligned in the wanted direction and this dictates the shape of the array. Although beamwidths are narrow and rotation is not possible, there are usually sufficient sidelobes, Fig 6.6(a), to provide some useful coverage in most directions. The resistor absorbs the power which would otherwise be radiated in the back direction.

Very impressive performances have been achieved by a few amateurs able to erect arrays of this type but, in view of their limited interest for the average reader, further considera-tion, which is one of the topics for Chapter 14, has been restricted to general guidelines and some possibilities of obtaining increased gain for a given area occupied.

Loop antennas

Single wires are often bent into the form of a loop, the most important examples being the quad, Fig 6.8(a), and the bi-square, Fig 6.8(b). The quad can be distorted into a variety of shapes such as triangular, being then known as a 'delta loop', Fig 6.8(c), or even squashed flat in which case it becomes a 'folded dipole', Fig 6.8(d). The folded dipole is usually λ/2 and has the same radiation pattern as an ordinary dipole, and if used with a resonant open-wire feedline it can give a good account of itself over a frequency range of at least half an octave.

The quad loop is perhaps second in importance only to the dipole. It usually consists of 1λ of wire bent into a square so that its largest dimension is λ/4, and offers a number of practical advantages other than the high gain frequently claimed. This it does *not* provide, as explained below, though this is also self-evident from the small size which rules out any appreciable amount of additive gain, and links its radia-tion pattern closely with that of an ordinary dipole. The

distances of travel. However, nearly in line with the wire, alternate dipoles are separated by nearly λ/2 and thus produce fields which add in phase. The large number of dipoles makes up for the relatively small field which each produces at this angle, even to the extent of providing considerable gain if the wire is long enough, as shown by Table 14.1.

When the wire is terminated in its characteristic impedance there is no standing wave pattern but, taking a 'snapshot' at any given instant of time, the appearance would be very similar to Fig 6.5(a) and to a large extent the same reasoning applies. This, however, is now a 'travelling wave' moving towards the termination, and for the backward direction radiation from any point on the antenna is cancelled by radiation of opposite sign from a point λ/2 further on. This has λ/2 less distance to travel and left the transmitter half a cycle earlier, so there are three phase reversals in all, resulting in cancellation. Hence the radiation pattern is now unidirectional.

Long wires such as these are usually grouped to form V- or rhombic arrays, Figs 6.6 and 6.7, which can provide high gain and are much used for commercial point-to-point services. Such antennas may be terminated or unterminated, and are wideband to the extent that they can be designed to give

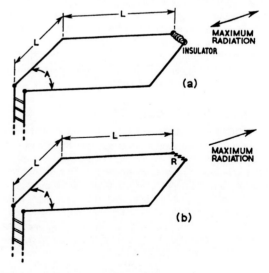

MAXIMUM RADIATION

INSULATOR

(a)

MAXIMUM RADIATION

R

(b)

Fig 6.7. Terminated and unterminated rhombic antennas

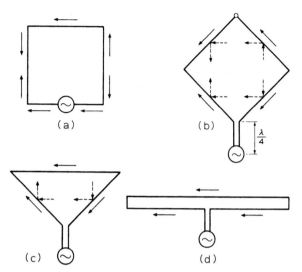

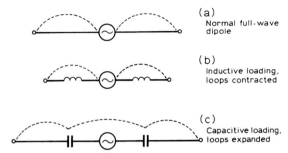

Fig 6.9. Centre-fed antenna (a) can be contracted by inductance as at (b) or stretched by capacitance as at (c)

Fig 6.8. Attempts to form arrays by bending wires into loops. The quad loop at (a) has superficial resemblance to two separate point sources but stacking distance (λ/4) is insufficient to produce significant difference in pattern compared with single source. The same applies to the delta loop at (c), whereas the folded dipole included at (d) for comparison has no pretensions to be other than the equivalent of a dipole. In contrast, the bi-square loop at (b) is equivalent to four elements; each current loop can be represented by a pair of 'equivalent dipoles' at right-angles (Chapter 2, p10) but the vertical components cancel each other, leaving the equivalent of four horizontal (as drawn) dipoles

b-square, on the other hand, has λ/2 sides and thus achieves additive gain, though usually at the expense of height.

Stretched wires

It is possible to 'stretch' a λ/2 current loop to fill the whole of a wire of any length by the use of series capacitors as in Fig 6.9(c). Uses of this principle range from the use of a single pair of capacitors to enable, say, a 14MHz dipole to be used at 21MHz, to the production of a nearly uniform current distribution in a long wire which then bears a close resemblance to the collinear array of Fig 6.11. Inductance as in Fig 6.9(b) has the opposite effect and is used for example as a loading device for mobile antennas.

Wires bent into odd shapes

Wires often have to be bent into 'odd shapes' to fit them into an available space, and in dealing with these cases it is convenient to think of the wire as consisting of a number of point sources, one to each straight section or more than one if a section is much longer than λ/2. If the arrangement is two-dimensional (ie capable of being drawn to scale on a flat piece of paper) the radiation from a given source can then be resolved into two components at right-angles, one in any desired direction and the other at right-angles to it, as explained in Chapter 2 and illustrated in Fig 6.8(b).

For the moment it will be sufficient to note that the 'value' to be assigned to each component is simply the average

current times the apparent length of the wire as seen from the appropriate direction.

The components which are aligned in any given direction can be directly added if the dimensions are small, or added taking due account of phase differences if the dimensions are large. If the problem is three-dimensional, each source has to be resolved into three components mutually at right-angles, but fortunately many important practical cases such as the bi-square antenna referred to above involve only two dimensions.

Centre-fed long wires

One other case of practical interest is the centre-fed long wire such as a 3.5MHz dipole which has been pressed into service at 14, 21 or 28MHz. At 14MHz this becomes a pair of 1λ radiators as in Fig 6.10, which compares the pattern with that of an end-fed wire of the same length, illustrating the tendency for radiation to be concentrated at a much larger angle to the wire when this is centre-fed. These patterns were

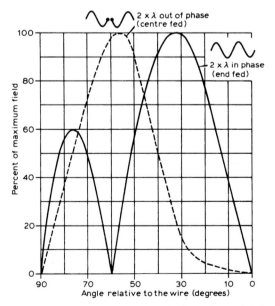

Fig 6.10. Comparison between centre-fed long wire (eg λ/2 dipole for 3.5MHz band used on 14MHz) with the same long wire end-fed

obtained by taking the out-of-phase curve from Fig 6.3 and multiplying it by the array factors appropriate to a spacing of 1λ.

Gain, radiation resistance and mutual coupling

It will by now be evident to the reader that these three properties of antennas are closely interrelated, and the important role of both mutual resistance and mutual reactance in the case of close-spaced beams has been demonstrated.

In contrast to this, additive-gain arrays have been assumed to consist of independent elements which is a valid approximation for demonstrating the principles. This approximation is not strictly true in practice as spacings are dictated by compromises, and mutual resistances can be as high as $R/10$ out to spacings of several wavelengths. Although the amateur is usually not concerned with practical HF arrays involving this kind of spacing, it is instructive to consider the general case of n elements all coupled into each other by complex impedances. This might appear to pose a rather formidable problem, but in practice most of the complication disappears if the currents are assumed to be all in-phase or out-of-phase, this being the condition for full additive gain when elements are spaced by $\lambda/2$ which is typical of practical arrays. We then have at the terminals of the first of n elements

$$E/I_1 = R \pm R_{m1} \pm R_{m2} \pm R_{m3} \pm \ldots \pm R_{mn}$$

where the subscripts denote the mutual resistance couplings to each of the other elements and a negative sign implies antiphase excitation. The reactance terms add in the same way but are automatically eliminated by normal tuning processes.

This result applies equally to large commercial arrays and simple arrays of considerable importance to the amateur, such as the two half-waves in phase shown in Fig 6.2(a). The gain of this has already been worked out for the special case of $R_m = 0$ which requires a centre-to-centre spacing of $3\lambda/4$. More commonly the ends are adjacent so that the spacing is only $\lambda/2$, and the mutual resistance of 21Ω from Fig 5.13 is added to the natural 73Ω resistance of each current loop. Assuming some arrangement of feeders which applies the available power to the two resistances in series, the loop currents are found to be less than those in a dipole in the ratio $73/(2 \times 94)$, ie 0.62, but as there are two loops the field produced exceeds that from a dipole by 1.24, which is a gain of 1.98dB.

The bi-square antenna

The simplicity of this method of calculation can be appreciated by applying it to a more complicated example, the 2λ loop commonly known as a 'bi-square antenna' and illustrated in Fig 6.8(b). Each side can be resolved as just described into equal horizontal and vertical components, but it will be obvious that the vertical components cancel, leaving

only the four horizontal point sources which are in phase for the directions normal to the plane of the loop. Because the wires are inclined at 45° each produces *for a given current* only 70% of the field from a $\lambda/2$ dipole and this halves its radiation resistance.

Mutual impedance data is not available for this arrangement as it stands, but it can be seen from inspection of the figure that, as viewed from any one of the dipoles constituting the loop, the fields produced by those on either side of it cancel each other so that there is no mutual coupling except between opposite pairs, for which the mutual resistance, -10Ω, can be read directly from Fig 5.13. A driving point impedance of 62.5Ω can therefore be assigned to *each* dipole and for a given radiated power the current I relative to the current I_D in a $\lambda/2$ dipole is given by

$$I/I_D = \sqrt{(73/(4 \times 62.5))} = 0.56$$

To obtain the field strength relative to that from a single dipole we have to multiply by the number of dipoles but divide by $\sqrt{2}$ because of the 45° inclination of the wire, so that the gain as a current ratio is $(4 \times 0.56)\sqrt{2} = 1.53$ or 3.7dB, in fair agreement with the 4dB figure usually quoted. The radiation resistance referred to a current point such as the end of the $\lambda/4$ stub in Fig 6.8(b) would be 250Ω if $Z_0 = Z_a$, but typical values in practice are likely to be 600Ω and 1000Ω respectively. Transformer action as described on p34 reduces the impedance to $250 \times (0.6)^2 = 90\Omega$ which provides a reasonable match to 75Ω feeder.

The quad loop

One further example brings us back yet again to the controversial topic of the gain of quads! It has already been pointed out that *as a first approximation* one can regard the quad (like the dipole) as a point source of radiation similar to all other point sources. If, however, one needs to be more precise, there is no objection to regarding the quad loop, Fig 6.8(a), as a pair of stacked $\lambda/2$ dipoles. However, it should be noted that bending over the ends to form a loop will reduce the field strength by a factor of 0.7 and therefore (for the same gain) halve whatever the radiation resistance may happen to be for the unbent dipoles.

From Fig 5.13 it is found that for the appropriate spacing ($\lambda/4$) the mutual resistance is 40Ω, so that the total radiation resistance will be $72 + 40 = 112\Omega$. The two dipoles are, in effect, connected in series so that the current compared with that in a single dipole is given by $72/224 = 0.567$. The total field from the two dipoles is therefore $2 \times 0.567 = 1.134$ times that from a single $\lambda/2$ dipole, which is a gain of 1.09dB only, in agreement with data for stacked dipoles to be found in most standard textbooks. When the ends are bent over to form a quad loop the gain is reduced due to radiation from the bent-over ends in a high-angle endwise mode, and the amount, though small, is certainly enough to bring the gain down to under 1dB. Bending the ends also results in loss of much of the 0.4dB by which the gain of $\lambda/2$ dipoles exceeds that of very short dipoles.

Figures in excess of this have been frequently quoted in professional as well as amateur literature, but whatever their source can be disregarded, particularly as the discrepancy has been allowed to pass without comment. Moreover, in at least one case the excess gain is stated to be irrespective of the number of elements. This assertion is incompatible with the basic principles of stacking which dictate, as explained below, that in multi-element arrays even the 1dB gain disappears. It is not intended by this necessarily to disparage the quad since account must be taken of other advantages, such as the ease with which optimum performance can be obtained in practice, and the good back-to-front ratio resulting (subject to correct spacing) from near-equality of the currents in a driven element and in a parasitic *reflector* as discussed on p78.

Stacking

Gain may be obtained not only by stacking elements to form beam arrays but by stacking beams to form 'arrays of arrays', this being largely an extension of the same principles, though close spacing is no longer applicable. Additive principles apply, and gain results only if the addition becomes significantly less effective *within the beamwidth of the individual units*. Otherwise there will be no narrowing of the directivity pattern and therefore no gain. It is of interest to note that insufficient stacking distance must inevitably be reflected in an increase of radiation resistance, since otherwise the individual antenna currents would be only 3dB down on those for a single element and, with in-phase addition, 3dB gain would result as already explained. Measurement of radiation resistance can indeed be used to determine the *effective* gain of an antenna, though this relates to the antenna at a particular height and in a particular environment.

The required spacing for satisfactory stacking depends on the patterns of the individual units and the method of stacking. Fig 6.11 shows the three usual methods of stacking single elements, these being known respectively as 'collinear', 'broadside' and 'end-fire'. It will be evident that different methods of stacking produce different radiation patterns; for example, the collinear stacking of horizontal antennas tends to produce a very narrow azimuthal beamwidth as illustrated by the lower curve in Fig 3.9. In contrast to this, a broadside array consisting of horizontal antennas stacked one above the other, or an end-fire array of vertical elements, produces a much wider beam in azimuth. This is important if it is desired to cover a large geographical area such as North America or obtain all-round coverage by beam switching rather than beam rotation.

So far as DX signal strength is concerned it makes no difference whether gain is achieved by narrowing of the horizontal or of the vertical beamwidth. It is often thought that because broadside (ie vertical) stacking of horizontal antennas reduces high-angle radiation more low-angle radiation is produced, but the reverse is true for a total height less than 0.8λ. This is due to the reduction in mean height as compared with using the top antenna by itself. However, the reduction

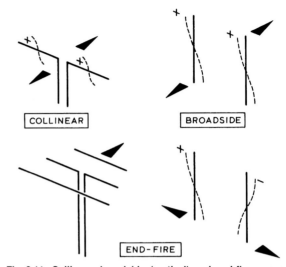

Fig 6.11. Collinear, broadside (vertical) and end-fire arrays, illustrating the terms. The arrows indicate directions of maximum radiation and the voltage standing waves on three of the antennas show polarity and phase. End-fire arrays may be parasitic (ie Yagi type) as shown, or all elements can be driven with close or wide spacing between elements. Broadside and collinear arrays use the additive gain principle and must be widely spaced

in high-angle radiation may have advantages for reception as discussed in Chapter 9.

End-fire arrays such as the Yagi operate by restriction of beamwidth in *both* planes, and with increasing gain need to be spaced further apart both horizontally and vertically. Horizontally polarised quad arrays can be regarded as a pair of Yagi arrays stacked vertically with a separation of λ/4, the azimuthal pattern being that of a single Yagi and the vertical plane pattern obtainable by multiplying that of the Yagi by F_a for a pair of sources spaced λ/4.

To illustrate this, the reverse process was applied to one published directivity pattern for a four-element quad. This was divided by the array factor for λ/4 spacing to obtain the pattern for a single four-element Yagi and, by comparing the 3dB beamwidths, the gain difference was estimated to be 0.35dB only.

In the same vein one recent study (reference [19] of Chapter 5) predicts a vertical spacing requirement in excess of λ for a stacking gain of 2dB in the case of seven-element horizontal Yagi arrays. At 0.4λ spacing the gain is 0.8dB only, and it is evident that it will be very close to zero at a spacing of 0.25λ, though the curve stops short of this point. Even greater spacing is required with collinear stacking.

It is quite inconceivable that the quad should have been granted some special dispensation in regard to stacking gain, and it is suspected that the 'quad myth' has now gained such wide currency that measurements incompatible with it are automatically disregarded while the remainder serve to reinforce the myth. Reliable measurements are virtually impossible at HF (p278) and even measurements at UHF with scale models are liable to serious errors.

In contrast to this, calculation of gain in the case of the simpler types of antenna usually presents little difficulty as already illustrated by a number of examples. The following calculation is however particularly interesting, being a close-enough approximation to the quad for further demolition of the 'quad myth', as well as serving the immediate purpose of demonstrating the reduction in stacking gain when the gain of individual units is increased.

Consider a driven element consisting of two $\lambda/2$ dipoles stacked vertically and connected in series (as in the last example), a similar pair being placed 0.15λ behind them to act as a reflector. We need to work out first the spacing between the upper element of one pair and the bottom one of the other, ie $\sqrt{(0.25^2 + 0.15^2)} = 0.29\lambda$. The value of R_m for use in equation (9), p84, is obtainable from Fig 5.13, allowing for two contributions of 31Ω corresponding to the 0.29λ spacing and another two of 60.5Ω from the 0.15λ spacings. This gives a total of 183Ω for R_m.

Referring to Fig 5.4, we may decide to aim for maximum gain, equating the phase shift (φ) to 'half the spacing'. A spacing of 0.15λ corresponds to $0.15 \times 260° = 54°$ so that $\varphi = 27°$ and $a = \cos\varphi = 0.89$. From the previous example (single pair), $R = 224\Omega$ so that from equation (9) in Chapter 5 we have for the driven element

$$R_{de} = 224 - (0.89 \times 183) = 61.5\Omega$$

If the element currents I are all equal they can be obtained relative to the equivalent 'dipole' current I_D from the ratio of the resistances, ie

$$I/I_D = \sqrt{(73/(2 \times 61.5))} = 0.77$$

The total phase difference between the fields produced by the driven element and by the reflector is $54°$ plus $27°$, ie $81°$. Adding with due allowance for this phase difference as explained on p11, the gain in field strength relative to a dipole is

$$4 \times 0.77 \sin\left(\frac{81}{2}\right)$$

$$= 2.00 \text{ or } 6dB$$

The gain of a single dipole plus reflector with equal currents and $\varphi/\varphi_0 = 0.5$ (from Fig 5.4) is 5.2dB, so that the stacking gain in this case is only 0.8dB compared with 1.1dB for the single pair of the previous example. Though the drop in this case is quite small, the stacking gain disappears rapidly as the number of elements increases.

Although this example approximates very closely to the case of the quad, some gain is lost as discussed earlier (p111) when the ends are bent over to form loops. This is difficult to estimate accurately but a reasonable allowance would be in the region of 0.1–0.3dB. This loss occurs also in other arrangements using bent elements, such as the various versions of the VK2ABQ array.

Stacking gains for collinear and broadside pairs are plotted in Fig 6.12, end-fire arrays being fully covered in Chapter 5. Fig 6.13 shows the performance to be expected from the

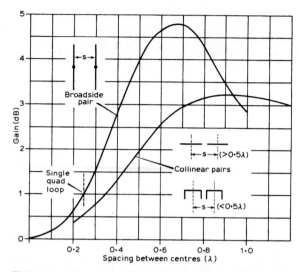

Fig 6.12. Variation of gain with spacing for collinear and broadside pairs

phasing together of two separate antennas, assuming them to be far enough apart for mutual interaction to be neglected, in which case a switched phasing line provides the most convenient method. The three-position switch in Fig 6.14 provides phase shifts of $0°$, $60°$ and $120°$, and with the addition of a phase-reversing switch, shifts of $180°$, $240°$ and $300°$ become

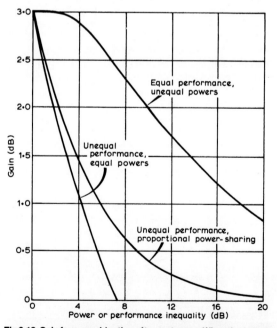

Fig 6.13. Gain from combination of two antennas. When the antennas differ in performance the gain as read from the figure is relative to the best antenna alone, and is maximum when power is shared in proportion to the gain difference, with the better antenna receiving the larger share. Both antennas must have the same polarisation

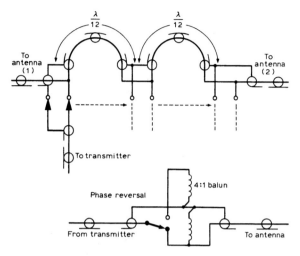

Fig 6.14. Phasing switch. Two λ/12 lengths of cable allow the relative phase to be switched in 60° steps assuming both antennas to be matched. With use of a phase-reversing switch (necessary in any case for setting-up) this provides a total of six steps of 60°, the maximum phase error then being 30°. Receiving-type wafer switches (not miniature) are usually satisfactory. Both poles must be switched. A 4:1 balun can be used in one of the feeders to provide phase reversal (lower sketch), but with balanced lines it is necessary only to reverse one pair of feeder connections. More switch positions may be provided for obtaining sharper nulls on unwanted signals

available. This allows the phase to be adjusted within 30° of the optimum value, the loss in gain for this amount of phase error being only 0.1dB. Unless corrected by a suitable transformer there will be a 2:1 mismatch, assuming an SWR of 1.0 for each of the separate antennas.

Fig 6.13 shows the dependence of stacking gain on relative performance of the individual antennas and the way in which power is shared between them, and it is interesting to note that if the antennas have identical gain a power inequality of 10dB reduces the stacking gain only from 3dB to 2dB. On the other hand, a performance inequality of 6dB reduces the extra gain from addition of the worst antenna to 1.0dB only, even this being subject to arranging an unequal division of power based on the gain ratio.

It is useful to note that directivity in *one* plane does not affect stacking requirements in another, eg adding reflectors to a collinear array does not need an increase of end-to-end spacing.

Effect of ground

After our sojourn in free space it is now time to come down to earth, and by way of softening the impact it is helpful to ensure that initially our antennas are all horizontal, the ground flat, and all interfering structures removed. Provided the height is not too low, and assuming for the moment that we are interested mainly in DX (which usually requires a low angle of radiation relative to the earth's surface), it becomes possible to regard the earth as a perfect reflector. Putting this another way, where before there was one antenna there are now in effect two, the second one being the mirror image of the first.

These two 'antennas' are in antiphase, as pictured in Fig 6.15(a), from which it will be clear that radiation at the angle θ exists *only* by virtue of the difference BC in path lengths. This produces a phase shift which can be determined by measuring AB, converting it into fractions of a wavelength and, if the answer is required in degrees, multiplying by 360. If BC is equal to λ/2 the direct and reflected waves reinforce each other to provide 6dB gain relative to free-space propagation, but halving the height or the radiation angle reduces this gain by only 3dB. For even lower heights the decrease in signal strength becomes more or less directly proportional to height as shown by Fig 6.16. To help in relating this to practical situations, the point marked with a cross applies to a typical DX signal at 14MHz, assuming an antenna height of 50ft (15m). This applies equally to all types of horizontal antenna, thus invalidating claims that one antenna is better because "it lowers the angle of radiation".

On the face of it, Fig 6.16 might appear to be of doubtful value since one does not know the actual angles of radiation required in any given instance, and AB is therefore also unknown. However, the author has found that predictions of relative average DX performance based on radiation angles of 6° are by and large consistent with experience, although

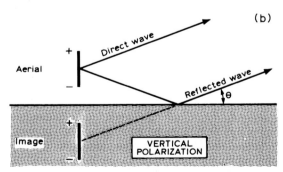

Fig 6.15. Images of antennas in perfectly conducting ground. The horizontally polarised image is in antiphase and cancels the radiation along the earth's surface. At appreciable wave angles the path length from the image is greater by the distance 2h sin θ, resulting in a phase difference of 4h sin θ/λ radians. At (b) the image of the vertical antenna is in phase and supports radiation along the surface

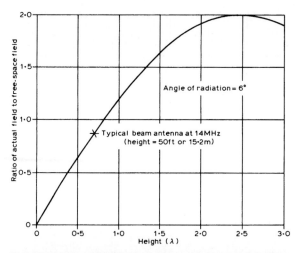

Fig 6.16. Variation of DX field strength with height of transmitting or receiving antennas. Though drawn for a radiation angle of 5.7° the curve is valid for other small angles if height is adjusted in inverse proportion to the radiation angle

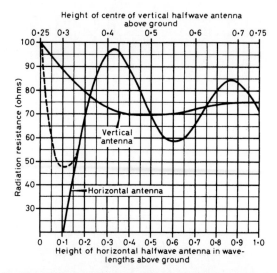

Fig 6.17. Radiation resistance _R_ of λ/2 horizontal and vertical dipoles with height above a perfect earth. Dotted curve shows typical values of feedpoint impedance of horizontal antennas over actual earth. Note that at low heights _R_ in the horizontal case is proportional to _h²_, but due to ground losses the feedpoint impedance rises steeply as indicated by the dotted curve

this is an oversimplification (Chapter 5). There is no doubt (p14) that much lower angles would often be useful so that it is usually best in any case to erect antennas as high as possible. Unfortunately, even in the absence of planning restrictions or other constraints, an increase of height beyond, say, 50–70ft (15–20m) usually leads to rather rapid escalation of costs and practical difficulties for a relatively small advantage.

There are other effects of the ground which (though relatively trivial) have given rise to some confusion. For example, as height is varied there is interaction between a dipole and its image in accordance with the mutual impedance data for parallel dipoles, Fig 5.13, and this causes the radiation resistance to vary with height as shown in Fig 6.17. It is often supposed from this that a height of 0.6λ is specially advantageous since the lower radiation resistance implies a larger current and therefore a bigger signal, as indicated by Fig 6.18. This effect is, however, too small to override the general desirability for DX working of putting the antenna as high as possible, as discussed in Chapter 10 and also demonstrated by Fig 6.16. The variation of resistance with height is likely in any case to be negligible with close-spaced beam antennas owing to the nearly antiphase fields existing directly underneath them.

The 'perfect earth' assumption, despite its validity for low-angle reflected signals, does not apply to vertical incidence. At low heights, say less than λ/4, a horizontal antenna experiences very considerable ground losses which cause the radiation resistance, or perhaps one should say 'apparent' radiation resistance, to depart from the 'perfect earth' value as indicated by the dotted curve.

These losses are often ignored in the literature or even dismissed as insignificant, in which case the consequences would be extremely interesting and indeed somewhat dramatic.

This is because at low height above a perfect earth the radiation resistance varies as the square of the height.

Halving the height therefore doubles the current, so that the DX signal should stay constant from a height of about λ/4 downwards until the antenna is almost lying on the ground, by which time the currents and voltages would be very large.

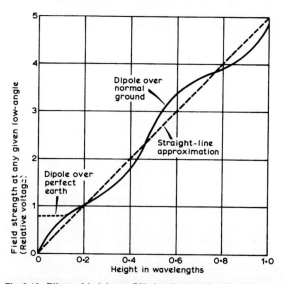

Fig 6.18. Effect of height on DX signal strength with horizontal dipoles. The ripples are attributable to variations in radiation resistance caused by mutual impedance between the antenna and its image, and are greatly reduced in the case of close-spaced beams

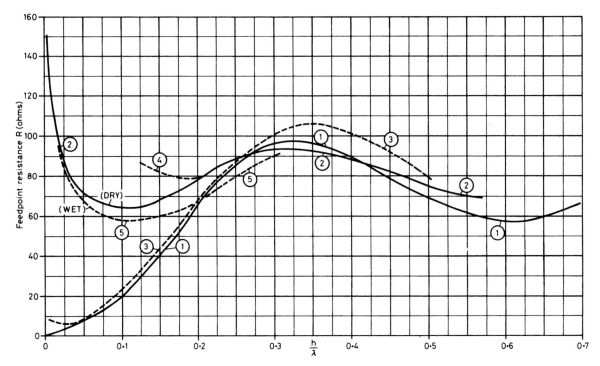

Fig 6.19. Comparison based on reference [1] between perfect ground [5] and measured results for typical ground [1], showing steep rise in resistance at very low heights and the effect of a ground screen (mesh = 0.0003λ): curves 1, 2 and 3 respectively. Calculations [1] for dielectric ground (K = 5) show good agreement with curve 2 except as indicated (curve 4) below h = 0.2λ. Curve 3 checks closely with theory, putting K = ∞. Curve 5 illustrates the effect of wet weather. Note that the difference between curves 1 and 2 below h = 0.25λ consists of ground losses *(ARRL Antenna Compendium Vol 3)*

Incidentally, this is another version of the finding (pp25 and 47) that the directional pattern of small arrays is independent of size, and it is a great pity, after drawing attention to such interesting prospects for what is believed to be the first time, that attention has to be directed also to the earth losses which, despite some references, have received very little attention in earlier literature.

The author was himself caught by this to the extent of much effort wasted, before discovering that the feedpoint resistance of a λ/2 dipole levels out with reducing height, a typical value being 50Ω, and then starts to rise again as illustrated.

Despite wide variation in ground constants and other variables such as operating frequency, there appears now to be general agreement [1, 2], in line with the author's own experience, that the resistance curve for real ground diverges significantly from the 'perfect-ground' case below a height of 0.15 to 0.2λ. As illustrated in Fig 6.17, the rise is quite small down to a height of 0.05λ, but becomes increasingly steep with the approach to ground in line with theoretical predictions [1], the feedpoint impedance reaching in practice a typical maximum value of 130Ω at heights of a few inches.

It is important, however, to realise that this is not radiation resistance, which tends to zero at zero height; in other words the difference must be attributed entirely to ground losses. For matching one is concerned only with the feedpoint impedance and the distinction has no relevance, but in relation

to signals the situation is quite different since the attenuation applies to noise as well as signals. It follows (as the author has found on many occasions) that when there is a very low antenna at one end contacts are 'nonreciprocal', stations with low antennas being able to give much better signal reports than one is able to give them.

The loss in terms of power effectively radiated can be estimated by comparing the solid and dotted line curves in Fig 6.17.

It is claimed that the rise in resistance can be prevented by placing a wire-mesh ground screen underneath the antenna [1, 2] extending for a distance of λ/2 in all directions [2], but in the HF band the provision of such large screens would be no mean undertaking and the practical value in some doubt. As will be appreciated from the basic geometry (Fig 6.15) and the discussion of Fresnel zones in Chapter 10, such screens have no effect on angle of radiation, relying for their effect solely on the reduction of near-field losses in the ground directly under the antenna. However, as these fields are of small extent and we know already that a height of 0.15λ is an adequate substitute for a screen, since also there appears to be no factual data relating size to efficacy, a much smaller one might be worth trying.

For an antenna height of λ/8 the expected gain would be in the region of 6dB, a mesh size of 0.01λ being more than adequate and 0.025λ only about 1dB worse [1]. Fig 6.19, which is derived from reference [1], illustrates the effect of ground screens, expands the low-height region of the horizontal curve in Fig 6.17, and compares some of the measured results with theory.

Other interesting things happen to antennas on the way down to ground level, associated with the change in Z_0 described in Chapter 4, p49. These appear hitherto to have evaded attention, but have major repercussions on low-level tune-up procedures, provide a new method [6] for the estimation of ground losses, and pave the way for resolving in the next section some of the problems of vertical antennas.

It may be recalled that the Z_0 of antennas is determined by the length/diameter ratio of conductors and thus is independent of height, except at very low heights where, for example, a half-wave wire can be considered as a pair of single $\lambda/4$ wires with a ground return, for which the Z_0 is obtained from the height/diameter ratio and is independent of length. As an example, we find from Fig 4.13 that for a typical HF antenna $(2l/a = 10^4)$, $Z_0 = 984\Omega$. At a height equal to 1/10 of the length it is found from equation (2), p49, that $Z_0 = 828\Omega$. Since there is no change of inductance and air is still the dielectric, the resonant length is unaffected and even the likely increase of SWR to 1.18 (the impedance ratio) may well pass unnoticed.

Next suppose the length of the dipole to be only $\lambda/4$, which means that an inductive reactance of 984Ω is needed for resonance; at the lower height this is the wrong value, and consulting the Smith chart it turns out that to achieve a 'fit' requires a decrease of 12% in frequency. Observe now that as height increases a point is reached above which, as illustrated by Fig 6.20, there is no further change in resonant frequency; in other words, the first formula is fully applicable so that the ground is having no influence and therefore not causing any losses.

This of course is also the point at which the two curves diverge in Fig 6.17, and requires for its determination only a loaded wire (L or C, depending on whether the wire is short or long) and a GDO.

Though giving only a rough indication, this method is simple, highly instructive, and consistent with more direct methods of measurement. One important conclusion to be drawn from it is the fact that low level tune-up of any element having an appreciable extent in the vertical plane is likely to be a waste of time, which is how the effect first came to be noticed. The element in question was an inverted-V, and the problem of tuning was resolved by laying it out horizontally. Later the same technique was used very successfully for investigating the change with frequency of current distributions round quad and delta loops of various sizes and relating them to bandwidth. This was the method used for evaluation of multiband loops as described in Chapters 7 and 12.

It may have been noticed in the above discussion that three completely different kinds of ground effect have been involved.

(a) Ground reflections which determine the vertical radiation pattern and hence the DX performance of the antenna. These involve ground areas which may extend a

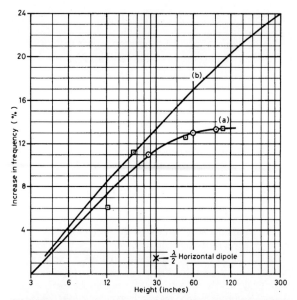

Fig 6.20. Increase of resonant frequency with height of inductively loaded $\lambda/4$ dipole. (a) Measured results at 28MHz starting from a height of 3in for symmetrical (circles) and unsymmetrical (squares) loading. (b) Predicted change assuming return path via the ground, which is seen to be virtually non-existent for heights above about 60in. The point X shows that the frequency change is due almost entirely to the loading and hence to the change in Z_0 (ARRL)

long way from the antenna, and provide one of the main topics for Chapter 10.

(b) Variations of radiation resistance with height, Fig 6.18, which can be explained by mutual impedance between the antenna and its ground image. This has often been wrongly interpreted as indicating an optimum height, and because (seen from below) the elements are nearly in antiphase, the effect is considerably reduced in the case of close-spaced beams.

(c) Losses associated with currents flowing in the ground underneath the antenna. These occur because if the height is low enough the capacitance to ground from each pole of the antenna provides an easier current path than the direct coupling between them, as illustrated by Fig 6.21.

These distinctions, as will be seen, assume added importance in the case of vertical polarisation because of the prevalence of lower heights and even greater scope for confusion. An example of this is provided by advice in [7] to use large numbers of ground-plane radials. From their resemblance to a ground screen these might be expected to remove the ground loss (Fig 6.19), subject to the spacing between their tips conforming to the mesh-size recommendations in [1]. With $\lambda/4$ radials this would require at least 10–20, with a useful maximum of about 100, which agrees well enough with the advice in reference [7] except for the rapid decrease of losses with height which can be inferred from Figs 6.19 and 6.20; a probable explanation for this would be radiation from

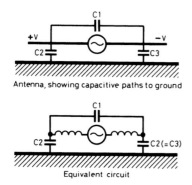

Antenna, showing capacitive paths to ground

Equivalent circuit

Fig 6.21. Equivalent circuit for horizontal dipole at low heights above ground *(ARRL)*

the feeder particularly in view of the problems with active monopoles recorded in Chapter 9.

In the case of vertical polarisation over a hypothetical perfect earth, Fig 6.15(b), the antenna and its image are in the same phase, and maximum radiation occurs at zero elevation (though some allowance may have to be made for the variation of radiation resistance with height as shown in Fig 6.17). In practice, however, one is more interested in the real earth, in which case the magnitude and phase of the ground reflection vary between wide limits as discussed in Chapter 10. Below a certain angle, analogous to the Brewster angle in optics and for the majority of residential areas about 8 to 15° depending on soil constants, the phase of the reflection coefficient reverses and for very low angles its magnitude rises to unity (Fig 10.2). Hence, in the absence of obstructions having a vertical component, there should in principle be no difference between vertical and horizontal polarisation. Over a range of useful angles, however, the reflection coefficient is usually in the region of 0.4–0.7 only, so that even at low heights cancellation of the direct wave is incomplete and some low-angle radiation takes place.

The amount is too small to justify oft-repeated claims that vertical antennas are good low-angle radiators but it is enough to permit reliable DX communication even when height is severely restricted, particularly if a number of such radiators can be assembled to form a beam. This is extremely valuable at the lower frequencies where it is usually difficult with horizontal antennas to achieve sufficient height for efficient low-angle radiation.

However, vertical polarisation is particularly useful over sea water, which is a special case since its conductivity is some two orders of magnitude better than that of other natural ground or even fresh water, and this reduces the Brewster angle to about 2–3°.

The general effect of the Brewster angle and imperfect reflections is illustrated in Fig 6.22 for a ground-based monopole, which with its image looks like a dipole, the radiation resistance being halved because the radiated energy is confined to a half-space. Replacement of the monopole by a λ/2 dipole alters the picture only to the extent that the dipole and its image form a collinear pair, providing a maximum

gain of 3dB at low angles. Radiation at higher angles is restricted in accordance with Fig 6.3.

The commonest form of vertical antenna is the so-called 'ground plane' which has been discussed in some detail in Chapter 4. In this case one pole of the dipole has been replaced by a set of radial wires which provide a return path for the antenna current but generate opposing fields, so that they are non-radiating. The radiation pattern is essentially that of a short dipole which, as will be recalled, differs only slightly from that of a λ/2 dipole so that as the length is halved the radiation resistance (R) is divided by 4.

It cannot be emphasised too strongly that the radials are in no sense a reflecting plane but merely a practical convenience which, by allowing the base of the radiator to be brought down to any height without having to bore a hole in the ground, provides a much wider range of constructional options. At ground level it becomes identical with the short vertical monopole of Fig 6.22, R being doubled due to mutual coupling between the antenna and its image. This leads once again to the generally accepted figure of 36Ω, at the same time providing further rebuttal of the oft-repeated assertion that R is independent of height.

The rate of decrease in R with increasing height is in fact extremely rapid, as demonstrated by Fig 4.22 taken from reference [3] and for convenience reproduced here as Fig 6.23. This shows the variation of radiation resistance with height for any λ/4 vertical radiator, and is based on rigorous mathematical analysis subject to the assumption of perfectly conducting ground. However, any readers sharing the author's allergy to mathematics may like to know that a close approximation to it can be obtained by graphical integration, making use of Fig 2.5, and treating the radiator and its image as a collinear pair. This, as we have seen, is how they have to be regarded, the figure of 'about 20Ω' being in line also with

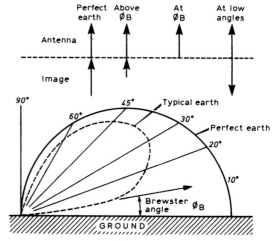

Fig 6.22. Vertical-plane radiation pattern for a short vertical monopole. The dotted curve shows the effect of imperfect ground. Simplified vector diagrams at top show trends of behaviour above and below the Brewster angle

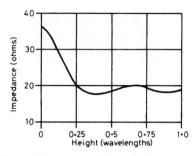

Fig 6.23. Base feed impedance of λ/4 vertical monopole antenna as a function of height *D* above the ground

early published measurements pre-dating the confusion by which the 'ground-plane' scene has since become afflicted.

Having thus established the 'array' status of practical vertical antennas and their image, two further questions remain, the effect of ground reflections and of ground losses. The most striking difference between H and V polarisation from the practical viewpoint lies in the fact that in the H case the DX performance tends to be predictable, more or less, with the help of a curve such as Fig 6.16, whereas in the V case it depends on both the magnitude and the phase of the reflection coefficient. At best, these quantities can only be roughly guessed; also the effect of trees and buildings is much greater. Detailed discussion of the relative effects of various kinds of 'real' ground and the differences between this and 'perfect' ground will be found in Chapter 10. Fortunately, assuming the option to be available, the relative merits of H and V polarisation in a given environment can usually be assessed from tests with simple antennas.

Ground losses with vertical antennas

In the case of vertical antennas, ground losses occur in exactly the same way as with horizontal antennas but are usually much less [6], since the radiator is at right-angles to the ground surface and, referring to Fig 6.24, the 'obviously much easier' path for capacitive currents via the ground, as depicted in Fig 6.21, exists only in respect of radials at very low height.

Even in the case of a grounded monopole, the loss (though some is inevitable) can be held down to a mere 1.6dB by the following tested procedure, based on a measured value of 130Ω (as in Fig 6.17) for the feedpoint resistance of a λ/2 dipole at a height of an inch or so. Since as the height approaches zero there ceases to be any coupling between the two arms, the RF resistance to ground from its centre must be 130/4 = 33Ω, resulting in a loss of 2.7dB, but this can be halved by using two dipoles at right-angles, reducing the loss to the lower figure. The 33Ω figure was checked and found to be little changed by burial of the 'dipole', although its resonance ceased to be measurable. The ground was light, sandy soil of high resistivity, and the RF resistance clearly bore no relation to the DC resistance.

Further to this, the idea of using insulated wires lying on the ground surface or buried just below it, either as radials or as 'secret antennas' [4, 5] has been around for some time and, in the light of the above experiment, looks as if it might be well worth pursuing. The wires can be encased in lengths of hosepipe with sealed ends, with provision if necessary for tuning by partial withdrawal. Due to losses fairly broad tuning can be expected, with a velocity factor of about 2/3, the author being indebted to W0YBF for this information.

In the case of above-ground radials, losses decrease even more rapidly with height than in the case of Fig 6.19, and the main height-determining factor is likely to be head clearance! These results are independent of the length or number of radials which are in no way critical, efficiency being well maintained down to a length of λ/20 for a pair of radials [6]. There is no advantage in exceeding λ/8, and the use of less than λ/12 without some good reason is not recommended; below this, there is marked deterioration in respect of bandwidth, increased end voltages, and risks of feeder radiation as described on pp148, 149. For multiband requirements, the lengths, assuming four radials, can be allowed to vary between about λ/16 and 5λ/16, subject to avoiding λ/4 as explained on p42. This assumes band-switching of the loading-coil inductance, though other options may occur to the reader.

Advocacy by the author of short radials has been countered on a number of occasions by reference to the poor performance of certain commercial products, in which it is alleged

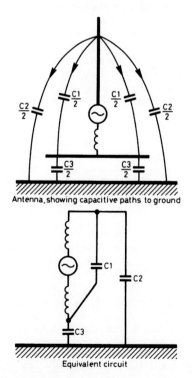

Antenna, showing capacitive paths to ground

Equivalent circuit

Fig 6.24. Equivalent circuit for ground-plane antenna with inductively loaded radials close to ground level

that the radials were bonded to the mast. In this case it must be surmised that the ground connection was provided by the mast or coaxial outer, the role of the radials being purely ornamental and the result in many cases disastrous. Properly used, short radials are simple and as argued above 'the best way of doing the job', but the correct rules must be strictly observed. This cannot be too strongly emphasised, and to this end they can be summarised as follows.

The radials must be well-insulated, clear of any surrounding obstructions, and tuned to resonance by a single loading coil common to all of them.

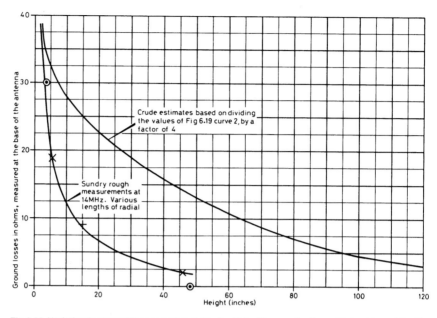

Fig 6.25. Variation in ground losses with height of radials. Measured values obtained by subtracting radiation resistance (in this case 36Ω) from the total resistance at the feedpoint. Note the convergence of the two curves towards a similar high value at zero height, and that ground losses are independent of radial length *(ARRL)*

All normal precautions for preventing feeder radiation must be taken (pp53), and in the event of any detectable current on the outer of the coaxial feeder (p55) this should be minimised by fine tuning of the loading inductance.

With radials of any length large RF voltages may be present, making it necessary to guard against any possibility of accidental contact; this is likely to be easier with shorter radials although, with very short ones, higher voltages are to be expected.

The Marconi antenna has an important place in radio history but, though sometimes used on the lower frequency bands, is of doubtful merit for the majority of amateur applications. This is due to (a) losses due to earth currents, (b) the desirability if possible of raising the antenna somewhat higher above ground level so as to obtain some or all of the potential gain of 3dB. Practical methods of increasing the electrical height without undue increase of physical height include the use of short end-loaded dipole elements supported by catenaries which also provide the end-loading as in Fig 6.27. This also tends to eliminate earth losses.

A favoured height for vertical antennas having their base at ground level is 5λ/8, corresponding to one half of the extended double-Zepp described on p107. It should be appreciated that, although a vertical antenna at sufficient height with its image approximates to a collinear pair, the pattern over a real ground has a 'nick out of the middle' at low angles, ie just where one can least afford it, due to phase reversal of the image for low-angle radiation. Nevertheless, the decrease in radiation resistance with increasing height, as shown in Fig 6.17, means that current increases and whatever low-angle signal there is must therefore also increase.

Thus far the ground has been assumed to be smooth, flat and uncomplicated. The effect of ground slopes is largely predictable but that of power lines, buildings, trees, hills and other objects is mainly a matter of guesswork plus a few empirical guidelines, which are the subject of Chapter 10.

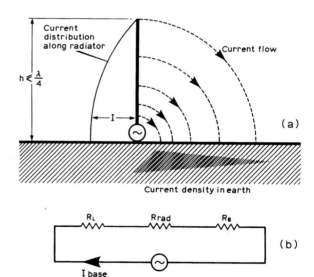

Fig 6.26. (a) The Marconi antenna. Current distribution on a short vertical radiator over a plane earth. The return path for the antenna current to the generator is via the ground which has relatively poor conductivity. The earth resistance is typically around 100Ω. (b) Equivalent circuit for (a): R_L, ohmic losses (usually small); R_E, effective earth resistance (usually large); R_{rad}, radiation resistance

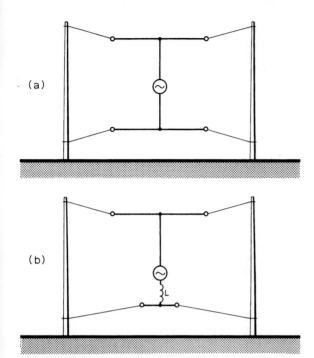

Fig 6.27. Alternatives to Fig 6.26: (a) dipole; (b) dipole or monopole? (see Chapter 4)

One curious effect of the ground is to produce vertically polarised radiation 'off the end' of a horizontal dipole. Thus, if a dipole is disposed horizontally above an earth plane acting as a reflector, there will then be some radiation along the line of the antenna wire. This may be appreciated by holding a pencil parallel to the surface of a mirror and observing the image from the end-on direction at various heights above the mirror. Closing one eye, the pencil shrinks to a dot but the image, though perhaps greatly reduced in length, remains visible. Neglecting ground losses, the amount of radiation is determined by the usual cos θ formula, and is therefore proportional to the apparent length of the image as viewed in this way. Since this image appears to be in the vertical plane if the mirror is horizontal, the radiation is vertically polarised.

Of greater importance, apart from local working, is the considerable high-angle sky-wave radiation 'off the end' of a horizontal dipole. For example, applying the cos θ formula it is evident that there will be only 6dB discrimination against signals arriving at an elevation angle of 30° from an endwise direction as compared with signals in the main lobe, neglecting the effect of the ground, which due to the higher angle is more likely to favour short-skip interference than a wanted DX signal.

In between these two directions the plane of polarisation changes gradually from horizontal to one inclined at 30° to the vertical, remaining of course always normal to the wave direction and in the plane of the wire.

Due to the varying effect of the ground as the ratio of

vertical to horizontal polarisation changes, it is difficult to compute accurately the vertical plane radiation pattern for directions well away from the main lobe. These directions in general are of minor importance but it should be noted that for short-skip (ie high-angle) signals there will be considerable reduction of directivity. On the other hand, it may often be possible to increase the strength of a wanted signal, or reduce interference, by switching to another antenna at a different height. It is useful to note that the dipole tends only to exhibit reasonable horizontal directivity at the lower wave angles, and will tend to become omnidirectional for the higher angles associated with short-skip propagation.

Summary and conclusions

The performance of any antenna system in free space can be analysed by considering it as a number of 'point sources' of radiation or any convenient grouping of point sources. This was done in Chapter 5 for close-spaced sources and has now been extended to include wide spacings, ground reflections and large arrays of various types.

It is important to appreciate the distinction between close-spaced arrays, which rely on tight electrical coupling for their operation, and wide-spaced arrays including antennas *and their images in the ground.* Such arrays, though basically independent of mutual couplings, usually experience some degree of interaction between their component parts, and this may modify the performance to an appreciable extent. There are some borderline cases, and wide-spaced groupings of close-spaced sources are also possible. It is important to appreciate that in general the greater the gain of individual groups the further apart these must be spaced. However, if gain is obtained entirely by restriction of the radiation pattern in the *vertical* plane, the required *horizontal* stacking distance is not increased, and conversely.

Because of the greater influence of soil conductivity and dielectric constant, both quantities varying between wide limits, performance is much less predictable in the case of vertical antennas.

References

[1] 'Input impedance of horizontal aerials at low heights above the ground', R F Proctor, *Proceedings of the IEE*, Part 3, Vol 97, May 1950.

[2] *The ARRL Antenna Book*, 15th edn, 1988, p3-11.

[3] 'The feed impedance of an elevated vertical antenna', Guy Fletcher, VK2BBF, *Amateur Radio* (Australia) August 1984.

[4] 'Sub-surface antennas and the amateur', *The ARRL Antenna Compendium*, Vol 1, 1985, p133.

[5] 'Secret antennas', *Radio Communication* September 1989.

[6] 'Ground planes, radial systems and asymmetric dipoles', *ARRL Antenna Compendium*, Vol 3, ARRL, 1993.

[7] *The Radio Amateur Antenna Handbook*, Radio Publications Inc, Box 149, Wilton, Conn, USA, p93.

Chapter 7

Multiband antennas

It is generally essential to meet operational requirements with the smallest possible number of antennas so that 'multibanding', ie making a single antenna operate on several different frequencies, is a subject of particular importance. It is also perhaps the one which poses the largest number of interesting problems. There are two main essentials: it must be possible to feed the antenna efficiently and the radiation pattern must be acceptable on each band.

The 'odd bit of wire'

As explained in the last chapter, any 'odd bit of wire' can be used as an antenna by attaching one end to a suitable tuning unit operating in conjunction with a suitable earth return path. This latter need only be a short counterpoise if the wire is near $\lambda/2$ resonance but has to be of low impedance if the wire is shorter than about $5\lambda/16$. Subject to provision of these essentials, the 'odd bit of wire' is therefore a multiband antenna, though its efficiency falls off fairly rapidly as the length is reduced below about $\lambda/4$.

Resonant-feeder systems

Reference has already been made to the use of dipoles fed from long resonant lines but it will be evident from the previous chapter that the directional pattern changes considerably with frequency. For example, for a 3.5MHz dipole fed in the centre there is a maximum in the broadside direction at 3.5 and 7MHz, whereas at 14MHz and higher frequencies there is little or no radiation in the broadside direction but four main lobes at angles to the wire which decrease with increasing frequency.

This can provide useful coverage on all the HF bands, especially for short and medium range paths involving high angles at which the nulls in directional patterns are less sharply defined. Dipoles can also be used as beam elements along similar lines, except that their use in this way is restricted to a frequency range of at most 1.5 octaves by rapid decrease of radiation resistance below the half-wave resonance, pattern break-up at higher frequencies, and non-optimum spacing of elements.

Loops can be treated in the same way and come in a wide variety of shapes, some of which offer important mechanical

or electrical advantages such as harmonically related resonances, a shorter span, and a larger number of options, though the range of frequencies which can be covered without some degree of break-up of the radiation pattern is even more limited. In this respect some shapes are worse than others.

The multiband characteristics of a typical quad loop are illustrated in Fig 7.1 which shows how the current distribution in the loop varies over a frequency range of two octaves. It can be inferred from this that efficient operation as a beam element is restricted to the range from 14 to 21MHz, unless some means such as those in Fig 7.2 can be provided for open-circuiting the top corner on 28MHz, which provides a gain of 3.7dB in the case of a single element as explained on p111.

Even without the open-circuit provision, a *single* 14MHz quad loop can provide good performance on all bands from 7 to 28MHz, although at 28MHz the polarisation is changed from horizontal to vertical and the directivity resembles that of a pair of antiphase sources (p110). At 7MHz the radiation resistance is very low, about 7Ω only, but reasonable efficiency can be achieved with care. The current distribution in the loop at 7, 14, 21 and 28MHz is shown in Fig 7.1, and by using a $\lambda/2$ tuning stub (as in Fig 7.3) simultaneous resonance is obtained in or close to each of these bands, the overall length of the system being $\lambda/2$ at 7MHz and approximate multiples of this on the higher frequencies. However, the harmonic relationship is not exact and slight adjustments are desirable when changing bands. It is thus advisable to have access to the lower end of the stub, in which case there is no problem in tuning the loop also to the 10, 18 and 24MHz bands.

For multibanding by the use of resonant feeders, loops have a substantial advantage compared with physically comparable dipole elements since they have much larger radiation resistances. A 14MHz quad loop has nearly twice the radiation resistance and, when used with a long resonant feeder, almost twice the bandwidth of a similarly fed single-wire dipole. If 'squashed flat', so that it turns into a folded dipole, there is a further 2:1 improvement in this respect. If the loop is open-circuited at the top for 28MHz operation, there is a further doubling of the radiation resistance and extra gain (p111).

Diagrams such as Fig 7.1, but with the current distributions

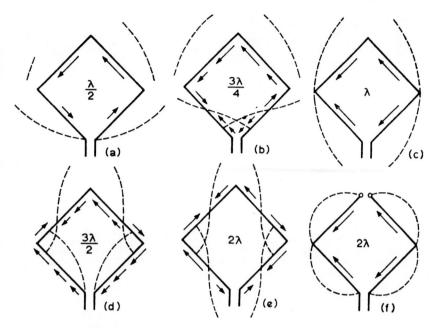

Fig 7.1. Current distribution in loops of various sizes at different frequencies. The arrow lengths indicate very roughly the difference in the relative contribution to the total field strength. Illustrations (a), (c), (d) and (e) represent a 14MHz quad loop excited at 7, 14, 21 and 28MHz respectively, while (b) and (d) correspond to a slightly oversized 21MHz loop used at 14 and 28MHz. Illustration (f) shows the effect at 28MHz of open-circuiting the top corner of a 14MHz loop, thereby turning it into a bi-square element; by using a linear resonator as in Fig 7.2(b) this effect can be achieved without disturbance of operation at 14 or 21MHz

drawn in accurately, can be used for the determination of radiation patterns and resistances (R), recalling that the field at a distance is proportional to current multiplied by the length of conductor through which (as seen from the distant viewpoint) it appears to be flowing, due allowance being made for any phase differences.

Antenna problems such as this appear to be a high-risk area for those with computers but, for anyone gifted with sufficient patience and prepared to settle for rough estimates with Fig 2.5 as a starting point, no special skills are needed.

The results of this process are featured in Figs 7.4 and 7.5 for several different loop shapes, and it may be recalled from Chapter 5 that the small delta loop (SDL), with its horizontal side at the top, is particularly attractive as a multiband element. Small size helps in several ways, effective height being increased at lower frequencies due to placement of current nulls in the centre of the sides so that all the radiation comes from the top, by extension of the upper frequency limit, and by permitting lighter construction.

Problems occur mainly at the low-frequency end of the range where the aim is to find the best ways of living with low values of R, and a lucky accident as related in Chapter 5 led to the development of an 'impedance transforming loop' (ITL) which multiplies R by a factor of 3 or 4. Indirectly, and with various strings attached, it allows the lowest frequency of operation to be extended downwards from the main design frequency (MDF) by a half-octave, features which have to be weighed against greater complexity and reduced storm resistance.

It is instructive to apply this information, added to what we already know about dipoles, to two examples as follows; chosen at random, these demonstrate the versatility as well as the limitations of resonant feeders, and the major improvements

which can often be effected by slightly altering the terms of reference.

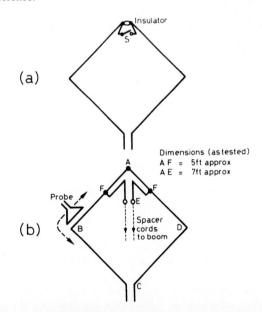

Fig 7.2. Open-circuiting top of 14MHz quad loop by means of a switch S or linear trap AFE (which may be adjusted for zero current at B and D as described on p282) to make it into a bi-square beam, giving high gain on 28MHz. S can be a relay or operated by a long cord. The relay should not be operated with RF power applied. Estimated voltage across contacts with 400W at 28MHz is approximately 1.5kV. Max current (14MHz, contacts closed) is less than 3A. For full UK power use, a solenoid-operated switch is suggested. Switch windings must be bypassed for RF and supply leads not allowed to resonate near any wanted frequency

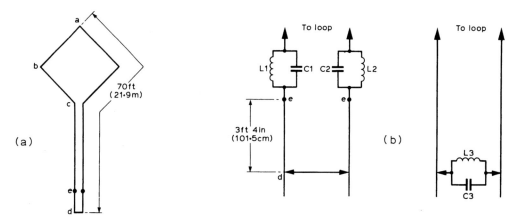

Fig 7.3. A loop and stub arrangement with resonances close to 7, 14, 21 and 28MHz. A low-impedance feeder may be connected at point (d) or a 600Ω line at (e). Resonances are not in exact harmonic ratio so that slight changes in stub length may be needed; for 14/21MHz this may be effected automatically by compensating circuits tuned to about 18MHz as shown at (b) where C1 and C2 are 500pF and C3 is 250pF. By alteration of stub length 18 and 24MHz may also be covered. L3, C3 tune the reflector

Example (a)

On the basis of Figs 7.4 and 7.5 it might be decided to try a right-angled delta loop for a simple antenna based on Fig 7.3(a) covering all HF bands from 14MHz upwards, since this uses the least amount of wire for a given value of *R*. For a circumference of 0.6λ and a Z_0 of 600Ω the SWR is 30, and the loss resistance (from Fig 3.12), assuming 14swg wire throughout, is 3.3Ω. The loss of signal in decibels is therefore given roughly by $10 \log (23.3/20) = 0.66$, which is about equal to that for the same loop fed with coaxial cable and appropriate matching. At 21 and 28MHz, *R* is equal to 144 and 350Ω respectively so losses are negligible.

Fig 7.5 confirms that there is no pattern break-up, though as this is not a beam it might not anyway be a matter for concern, and there appear to be three coincident resonances so that it only remains to complete the matching process by providing suitable transformers. In fact, the example has been oversimplified in two respects but this can be put right as follows. The impedance discontinuity at the bottom corner of the loop has been ignored, and this nearly doubles the losses as well as seriously disturbing the simple harmonic relationship.

For a way to avoid this we can refer to Table 7.1 from which it follows that by using two well-spaced wires in parallel for the loop its impedance can be equated, more or less, to that of the feeder.

The other matter to be put right is the omission of the 18 and 24MHz bands, and since these are nearly in a 3:4 harmonic relationship relative to a fundamental frequency of 6MHz, all that is needed is to patch in about 12ft of additional feeder. More precisely, as calculated, this is very close in each case to λ/4, and the addition inside the shack of short lengths of 300Ω line (9ft for 24MHz and an extra 3ft for 18MHz) as described on p64 is the easiest way to achieve it. Feedpoint resistances are 17 and 70Ω for 18 and 25MHz respectively, but can be multiplied by 4 if 600Ω extension lines are

substituted; lengths must if necessary be multiplied by the velocity factor.

Note the achievement of an extremely compact antenna (13ft span) providing efficient coverage of the most useful DX bands. Use as a beam element would be possible at 18MHz and above. The use of two-wire loops reduces losses and improves bandwidth, besides making it easy to calculate as will be evident from p128. The SWR bandwidth is only 1% on 14MHz but in-shack retuning should not be difficult. This example demonstrates that, even with five bands to be covered, there is still value to be extracted from exploiting the harmonic resonances of loops featured in earlier work by the author but, if the length requirements cannot be met, the methods described in Chapter 4 (pp62–64) provide a suitable alternative.

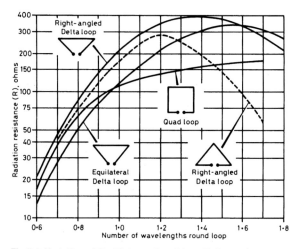

Fig 7.4. Variation of *R* with loop size. *R* is radiation resistance as perceived at top centre, and size is measured in wavelengths of circumference. Values are approximate based on method described on p9

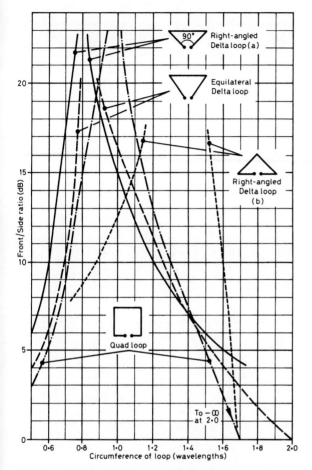

Fig 7.5. Variation in front/side ratio with loop size

Example (b)

In the next example, attention is directed to a 'simplest possible' situation in which a horizontal dipole is centre-fed with open-wire line as in the case of the G5RV antenna, p185, except that, within broad limits, both the antenna and the feeder can be any length, their characteristic impedances being designated by Z_a and Z_0 respectively.

Referring to Fig 3.12, a dipole length of about $\lambda/4$ is the shortest likely to be of interest, and from Fig 4.59 the value of R as seen at its centre is 13Ω. The feeder 'sees' an impedance of $13 + jZ_a$ ohms so that, dividing by Z_0 and consulting the Smith chart, it is found that maximum current occurs at a distance down the line which, because Z_a is normally greater than Z_0, is somewhat greater than $\lambda/8$. For an impedance ratio of 2 the distance is 0.176λ but the value of R, which we also need to know, is too small to read off the chart. However, since the current exceeds that at the antenna by $1/\sin(27)$, we find from Ohm's law that R at this point is only 2.68Ω. This might be a 14MHz dipole fed with 21m of feeder which we are trying to use on 7MHz, and for a typical open-wire feeder

(16swg) the loss resistance from Fig 3.11 is 3Ω, losses in the antenna itself being negligible. The loss in terms of signal strength is not much more than just noticeable and, though the bandwidth (from Chapter 8) is very narrow (0.5%), this is easily taken care of by retuning in the shack.

A more serious problem is likely to be the very large RF voltages existing at the point of entry into the shack and advice on this point will be found on p63. It will also be difficult to match into the very high value of RF impedance without incurring additional losses, feeder lengths of less than 0.4λ or more than 0.65λ being in this respect more suitable.

Going up to 10MHz the situation is already much more favourable, the minimum value of R being 14Ω and the efficiency increased to 80%. At 28MHz the antenna functions as a collinear pair, providing a gain of 2dB and this can be increased to 3dB by a 25% increase in length, making it into an 'extended double-Zepp'. The effect of this at 7MHz is quite dramatic, with R increasing from 2.68 to 13Ω. In this way we have arrived at another very desirable type of multiband antenna, providing useful gain on 25 and 28MHz, together with efficient coverage of all bands except 3.5 and 1.8MHz, though it may be possible to use it as a top-loaded vertical or sloping-wire antenna for transmission on these bands as described later.

Loops are preferable for small rotary beams and, if separate feeders are used to each element, it becomes possible to switch the beam direction so that less than 180° rotation is needed; there is then no serious problem with twisting or short-circuiting even of open-wire feeders. On the other hand, the folded dipole or delta loop is convenient if, for example, an antenna is to be slung between two trees. The ability to reverse beam direction by means of a switch is in itself of great value.

Application of the Smith chart to the design of loops and feeder systems

One approach to the design of, for example, an SDL antenna is to erect any loop or pair of loops consistent with the guidelines provided by Figs 7.4 and 7.5, wiring them to the shack with whatever high-impedance twin feeder happens to be available. Essential in-shack requirements are a GDO, an SWR meter, some form of tuner, an assortment of extension leads and baluns, and, in the case of beams, a pair of double-pole reversing switches or relays.

Undoubtedly DX will be worked on all bands, but there may well be complications or inconveniences which could have been avoided by seeking assistance from the Smith chart. In principle it should be possible in this way to predict in advance exact values for feeder extensions or other matching components, what form of loading, if any, to incorporate in the loops and the benefits likely to accrue from using the impedance transforming loop (ITL) shown in Fig 7.6(g), but one snag is the lack of data for the impedances of loops and parts of loops. The figures in Table 7.1 have little claim to accuracy, but luckily it needs quite large errors in data to produce incorrect guidelines, and results obtained along the

Table 7.1. Characteristic impedance of multiwire and helically loaded dipole elements

Number of conductors or, for helices, the approx no of turns per inch	Diameter		Spacing (in/cm) or, for helices, the resonant length (ft/m)		Z_0
	(in)	(cm)			(ohms)
1	0.04	0.1			1000
1	0.08	0.2			900
1	0.8	0.2			650
2	0.04	0.1	3	7.5	715
2	0.04	0.1	12	30	630
2	0.04	0.1	24	60	590
2	0.08	0.2	12	30	550
3	0.04	0.1	3	7.5	630
3	0.04	0.1	12	30	515
4	0.04	0.1	4	10	490
Helix, 4.8	1	2.5	7	2.1	2350
Helix, 3.5	1	2.5	10	3	1650
Helix, 2.5	1	2.5	15	4.5	1100

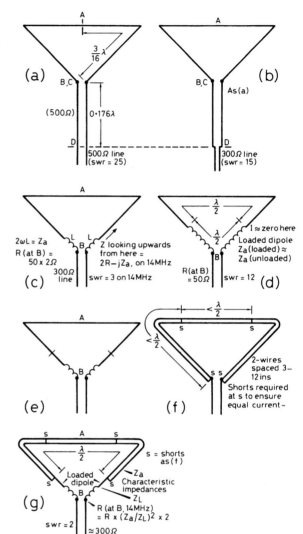

Fig 7.6. Loading of multiband delta loops. (a)-(e) Single-wire loops. (f) Constant-impedance system (CIL). (g) Impedance-transforming loop (ITL)

lines of the following example have proved in most cases to be sufficiently accurate as well as time-saving.

After years of working mainly with equilateral loops, interest has now shifted to the right-angled delta, following the discovery that it yields about twice the value of R at its main design frequency (MDF) for a given front/side ratio at twice the MDF. On the debit side, for the same value of R the span is increased and the height advantage reduced, in each case by about 10%.

Qualitatively, this situation can be inferred from the fact that if a loop is 'squashed' it starts to resemble a folded dipole which would be more difficult to support but has a large value of R and does not radiate endwise; the right-angled delta achieves most of its advantages at very little cost but the shape is not unduly critical and may be influenced by the available hardware.

The following illustrations are based on an R of 50Ω, with a loop circumference of 0.75λ, and are equally applicable to a single loop or a beam element since either can be arranged, eg by a slight alteration of loop shape, to conform closely enough with the assumptions.

For present purposes the loop is a transmission line which has been opened out, thereby increasing its average impedance to about 1000Ω, and the feeder is initially assumed to be 500Ω throughout as in Fig 7.6(a). Starting from point A on the Smith chart, Fig 7.7, the 0.05λ circle is followed round clockwise for 0.375λ, arriving at B where the normalised impedance is found to be (0.1 – j) ; this is seen by the feeder as (0.2 – 2j), point C, which is 0.176λ from resonance on a 0.04 (ie SWR = 25) circle. This means that a resistive impedance of 20Ω will be found at D, Fig 7.6(a). Subject to calculation of losses, we may continue the 500Ω line all the way to an ATU in the shack or, after checking for possible adverse consequences on other bands, decide to change at C to 300Ω line as in Fig 7.6(b).

Another alternative is to eliminate CD by making the loop

self-resonant, one method being to use loading inductances at B, as in Fig 7.6(c), the required reactance in this case being equal to Z_a. This allows 300Ω line to be connected directly at B and, with an SWR of only 3, the problem of 14MHz (ie the difficult one) has been solved very neatly. However, before getting too excited about this, a thought should be spared for 18MHz where the loop was already self-resonant; it does not need the inductance, and in fact has strong objections to it. R from Fig 7.4 is 200Ω, which should be a good match to the line, but instead this sees a normalised impedance (200 + j1270)/300, ie 0.67 + j4.23. The SWR has increased to about 30, but with a feeder length of, say, 20ft (suitably matched) the operator may not notice the difference; losses could be as low as 1dB and the bandwidth four times the width of the

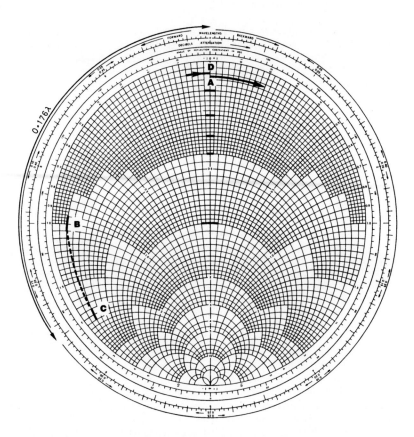

Fig 7.7. Use of the Smith chart to determine stub length and SWR. From A we move round the 0.05λ circle to B at the bottom corner of the loop. Normalising from 1000 to 500Ω takes us back to C, then 0.176λ on 0.04 circle brings us to resonance at D with an impedance of 20Ω

band. Such a system is workable but there is little in hand, and on balance one is probably better off without the loading. The situation is much better, however, with 600Ω line since SWR on 14MHz has been reduced from 25 to 6, and on 18MHz has only risen to 14.

A better alternative is to replace the inductances by helical loading as in Fig 7.6(d). In the case of the 'Claw' construction, p213, the lower half of the sides of the loops can consist of a resonant pair of helices wound on the fibreglass supporting arms. These function as a loaded λ/2 dipole, so that the loop, though still physically of small size, becomes 1λ at the MDF. From reference to Table 7.1 it is found that the impedance of the helices roughly equals that of the wires they replace, both C and L having been doubled so that the velocity factor is halved. Ignoring for the moment some 'small print', R appears at the lower corner unchanged from its original 50Ω value and the SWR, 6 in 300Ω or 10 in 500Ω line, is satisfactory. Proceeding as before, we find at 18MHz an SWR of 10 in 300Ω or 7 in 500Ω line, but a 'worst' situation now exists at 21MHz where the loop, now at its 3/4λ resonance, acts as a 'wrong way' transformer for the 370Ω radiation resistance so that 2700Ω appears at B. With SWR values of 9 and 5.4, either type of line remains useable. This estimation has not allowed for replacement of the original 'tip of a sine-wave' current distribution in the lower part of the loop by a sine-wave, so on 14MHz the effective height is dragged down

slightly by radiation from the lower part of the loop, and on 28MHz there will be some deterioration of the front/side ratio.

Fig 7.6(e) shows an interesting variant of the helical loading which was inspired by the following incident; due to storm damage an ITL, loaded (as it was thought) according to Fig 7.6(g), was replaced under difficult conditions by single-wire loops leaving the loading inductances in place. In view of a long feeder run (140ft of 600Ω line) it was expected that, as an emergency measure, matching stubs would have to be manually connected as close as possible to the antenna, at least on 18MHz for which an SWR of 20 was predicted. In fact no ill effects were observed, SWR close to the antenna being in the region of 5 or 6 on all three of the lower bands. This was eventually traced to the inductances being helically wound over some 2ft of 1in diameter fibreglass at the lower end of the supporting arms. From Table 7.1 the Z_0 of the helices must have been about 1500Ω but the process of transition to 'helical line' from 'merely an inductance', though obviously involving distributed capacitance, is by no means clear. It could be of importance not only as a means of escape from the limitations of uniform helical loading described above but possibly also for optimisation of helically loaded dipoles (p263).

The constant impedance loop, Fig 7.6(f), appears to have been conjured into existence for the first time in the course of contriving example (a) above, but could also be conceived as a missing step in the evolution of the ITL, Fig 7.6(g) and pp88, 213. In the context of multiband antennas using resonant-feeder systems it has the appearance of an important break-through in that it eliminates 'worst case' situations caused by points of high impedance on the antenna coinciding at some frequencies with points of transition to the relatively low impedance of the feeder; it can also provide welcome relief from poring over Smith charts since SWR is simply the ratio of resistances read from Fig 7.4 or (for dipoles) from Fig 4.59, and electrical lengths coincide with physical length. 'Best cases' also fail to materialise, but there is then usually some performance in hand. Bandwidth and efficiency are im-proved, but on the debit side there is more wire to be supported and construction is more difficult.

Similar principles apply also to dipoles, and in both cases it is essential to respect the axiom stated on p42. It might be thought that 'loss' by radiation would satisfy the exemption clause, but it fails to prevent the two wires in parallel from behaving as a high-Q resonator in which large currents can flow as a result of small differences in the lengths of the two wires. The remedy is very simple, consisting of short-circuits between the wires such that distances between them are non-resonant, checks as described on p282 with a current probe prior to erection being recommended. The ITL provides much lower SWR at the MDF and improves bandwidth as well as facilitating operation below the MDF which, in the absence of special measures, would also be the lowest useable frequency. Measures to obtain satisfactory operation at 14 and 10MHz from 21 and 14MHz designs respectively include short feeders, slightly larger-than-optimum loops, and heavier-gauge conductors.

Guidelines for the design of ITL and CIL systems are provided by Table 7.1 which lists very approximate Z_0 data for several parallel-wire and helically loaded elements, lengths of about 20ft (6m) being envisaged for the wires and $\lambda/2$ resonance for the helices. All figures are based on 14MHz, though the dimensions are not critical, typical errors being of the order of 15% if length or frequency are changed by a factor of 2. In the case of loops, constancy of Z_0 will be improved by reduced wire spacings for the sides, but high accuracy is unlikely to be needed and in some cases it may be more important to achieve the lowest possible average value of Z_0, particularly if the object is to achieve band-switching at the antenna; this is a task for which the CIL is particularly well suited.

The main ITL success story was the 'Miniclaw', p217, a two-element beam with a loop circumference of 37ft (ie an MDF of 21MHz). As this only had to cover one octave in all, it was possible, by the use of additional loading, 300Ω feeder and a matching stub biased in favour of 14MHz, to achieve an R value at the transmitter of 24Ω. For comparison, a 0.85λ right-angled delta, constant-impedance loop (CIL) yields an R of 20Ω without the constraints but, at the MDF, the SWR is 6 instead of 2, making it less suitable for use with very long lines unless additional matching is provided, such as stubs switched by relays.

Table 7.2. Estimated values of SWR for various options

Type of element	Band (MHz)	SWR in main feeder 600Ω line	300Ω line stub	300Ω line no stub
Equilateral version of Fig 7.6(a), single wire, no loading, 56ft circumfer-ence ie 0.8λ at 14MHz. Stub (ie matching section) length 11ft	14	16	8	20
	18	4	8	2
	21	4.2	8	6
	25	6	3.7	12
	28.5	4.4	3.3	8
As above but ITL with loading at bottom corner	14	1.8		
	18	8		
	21	8		
	25	6		
	28.5	4		
As above but distributed loading	14	2.5	1.25	
	18	4.5	8	
	21	4	8	
	25	2.5	3	
	28.5	1.8	1.1	
Miniclaw, ITL. Circumference 0.8λ at 21MHz (0.55λ at 14MHz). Stub length 7ft approx except for figures in brackets (11ft)	14	25	16(11)	50
	18	7	2(7)	8
	21	2.5	4	1.25
	25	4	3	2.5
	28.5	3	3.5	6

Notes: Figures based on values of R from Fig 7.4, supplemented by rough estimates, 500 and 1000Ω respectively, for Z_{01} and Z_{02}. In view of the complex shape, bends and assorted stubs, accurate estimates are not possible but Z_0 (measured) was found (coincidentally) to be reasonably close to the 'single thin wire' value of 1000Ω for a helically loaded lower dipole; leading coils yield a higher equivalent value of Z_{02}.

A rough approximation to a CIL can be obtained by end-feeding typical tubing elements with short-circuited 300Ω lines, the loops formed thereby being fed with 700Ω open-wire line. This points the way for possible conversion of existing beams as suggested in Chapter 12.

Based on the above discussion, Table 7.2 presents a number of figures which may assist the reader in making a choice from the large number of options now at his disposal.

Beams based on these options are believed to offer the best, and often the only, chance of achieving a 'good average' level of DX performance on several bands in face of the environ-mental and other constraints by which most of us are afflicted. For those able to erect big beams, recognised multiband options include stacked Yagis, quads and log-periodic anten-nas, but resonant feeder systems remain competitive in the form of either the DJ4VM quad (pp139, 187, 196) or based on elements such as the 44ft dipole featured in Table 7.3 which demonstrates the advantages to be expected from exploiting the constant-Z_0 principle in this case also. This could probably claim to be the ideal multiband beam element in view of its two-octave coverage, although despite its large size the R values are generally lower than those of loops. With three elements the spacing problem can be taken care of by using the outer elements only on 7 and 10MHz. Gains of 10dB can be expected on 24 and 28MHz.

Table 7.3. Radiation resistance and SWR versus frequency for 44ft dipole, with comparison between 'normal' and 'constant-Z_0' systems

Frequency (MHz)	R (at current loop) (Ω)	SWR, normal system, Z_0 = 600/1000Ω	SWR, constant-Z_0 system. Z_0 = 600Ω
10	55	10	11
14	150	5	4
18	240	5.5	2.5
21	190	10	3.1
25	144	17	4.2
28	85	14	7.1

Dipole may consist of tubing 0.5–1.0in diameter or 2–3 wires in parallel with total spacing of about 12in.

Optimisation of spacing

With two elements, whether dipoles or loops, if the spacing is optimised for one band it tends to be non-optimum for another; thus if the spacing is λ/8 at 14MHz, it becomes λ/4 at 28MHz. This is too wide (p81) so that some gain is lost and there is considerable deterioration in front/back ratio. The problem is largely resolved in the case of three elements since the boom length then becomes λ/2 at 28MHz, and a substantial amount of additive gain results as may be inferred from Fig 5.34. There is still some deterioration of front/back ratio but this may be found less important at the higher frequencies, and should in any case be amenable to the use of 'nulling' techniques as discussed in Chapter 9. Due to the increased element length and spacing (these being measured in wavelengths), there is a considerable increase in radiation resistance at the higher frequencies, and this allows operation

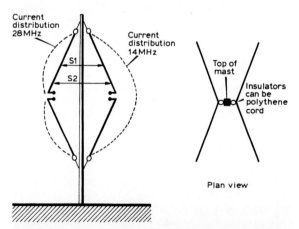

Fig 7.8. End view of a pair of vertically polarised quad loops 'doubling' in the role of guy wires, the loops being pinched in towards the mast at top and bottom. Current distributions for 28 and 14MHz are shown dotted on left and right respectively but each applies to both loops. Effective spacings, ie between 'centres of gravity' of the current distributions, are S₁ and S₂ at 28 and 14MHz respectively. For this version (unbroken loops) the loops must be fed symmetrically at each of the side corners using the DJ4VM method (Fig 7.9)

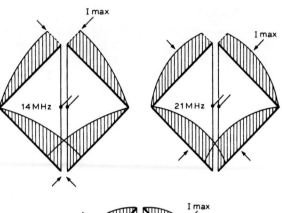

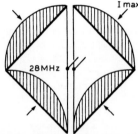

Fig 7.9. Current distribution in centre-driven quad elements. The current loops are always symmetrical. The feedpoint impedance is variable and tends to be highly reactive so that resonant feeders are needed for multiband operation (Ham Radio)

closer to the optimum condition, an advantage which can if desired be traded for greater bandwidth. If a shorter boom is required the problem can be resolved by use of a third element which operates on the higher frequencies only.

Another alternative is tapered spacing, the elements of a two-element array being bent inwards so that the ends (or points of maximum voltage) are brought towards each other. This improves performance at 14MHz as explained in Chapter 5, and at 28MHz it brings the 'centres of gravity' of the current distributions in the elements closer together as shown in Fig 7.8. Tapered spacing is applicable to most types of two-element multiband beam, and is achieved in the case of the SDL by bringing the lower corners in towards each other since at the higher frequencies the lower portions of the loops contribute significantly to the radiation.

In this way it should be possible to achieve reasonable coverage of all bands (including 10, 18 and 24MHz) from 10–28MHz. Bandwidth is expected to be rather narrow at 10MHz but the band itself is so narrow that this is not a problem! Another method for the multibanding of loops is to feed them symmetrically as in Fig 7.9 which shows an arrangement developed by DJ4VM [1]. By providing a symmetrical current distribution, this eliminates unwanted modes which might be expected to result in (a) extra interference at 18 and 21MHz and (b) a relatively poor pattern with reduced gain at 24MHz.

Applications of these principles are described on pp215 and 233.

Use of traps

The most usual method of multibanding, and in the author's view the one with the least merit, is by the use of 'traps' as shown in Fig 7.10. These are tuned circuits which act as insulators to cut a dipole, monopole or beam element down to size at the higher frequencies, thereby throwing away additive gain which is worth almost 2dB when a $\lambda/2$ dipole is used at twice its fundamental frequency. In addition losses are significant, at least in the case of beams; bandwidth is reduced due to the high Q of the traps which is essential for keeping losses as low as possible; elements have to be heavier or wires thicker in order to support the traps; and the traps are a frequent source of unreliability due to ingress of moisture.

It is only fair perhaps to add that most proprietary beams are of this type and many of them produce outstanding DX signals; the loss in performance compared with a monoband beam should according to the author's calculations be no more than just noticeable, though enough to justify the preference of many leading DX operators for monoband beams.

Leaving aside the question of weight, however, there are sound arguments for the use of traps in the case of inverted-V dipoles since these are somewhat unsatisfactory at harmonic frequencies unless cut down to size, or unless the apex angle exceeds about 120°. This is due to (a) a big increase in relative strength of the vertically polarised end-wise mode of radiation and (b) reduction in the effective mean height if the whole element is used, as may be seen from inspection of the current distribution. Due to increased losses in conjunction with the lower value of radiation resistance, traps are not recommended for close-spaced beams using inverted-V elements.

Trap losses can be readily estimated if the radiation resistance is known; thus in the simple case of a two-band beam for 14/21MHz based on Fig 7.10(a), and aiming for 6dB gain in accordance with Fig 5.16, we have $R = 20\Omega$. Z_a from Fig 4.13

is typically about 800Ω so that the impedance as seen between the ends of the driven element at 21MHz is $800/20 \times 800 = 32,000\Omega$. The impedances of the two traps in series appear as a loss resistance across this and are equal to the Q of the coil times its reactance or that of the tuning capacitance.

On such occasions the author finds it saves time to remember a rather approximate but nicely rounded figure of 8000Ω per picofarad at 21MHz, $12,000\Omega$ at 14MHz, and *pro rata*. Thus, having read somewhere or other that 40pF is a typical value of trap capacitance, and confident (however misguidedly) of one's ability to achieve a coil Q of 200, the impedance of each trap comes to $8000/40 \times 200 = 40,000\Omega$, ie a total of $80,000\Omega$. The ratio of power lost to power radiated at 21MHz is the inverse of the impedance ratio, ie 32/80, so that only 80/112 of the power is radiated, a loss of 1.5dB or a quarter of the total gain.

Critics, particularly those who feel that all calculations should go through a computer and be accurate to at least 10 places of decimals, will no doubt contest this figure, but to restore confidence in trapped beams requires drastic measures and could generate even worse situations. For example, one might reduce C to 10pF which consists largely of the coil self-capacitance and probably limits the Q to about 140 though, even so, the loss is reduced to about 0.6dB which is a substantial improvement. At 14MHz, however, there is now a large and lossy inductive reactance which may be obtained by dividing 21/14 = 15 into the 21MHz reactance figure of $8000/10 = 800\Omega$, ie 570Ω. This is shunted by capacitive reactance of 1200Ω and, using the normal rules for impedance in parallel, we have a net inductive *reactance* of

$$\frac{-1200(570)}{570 - 1200} = 1086\Omega$$

or 2172Ω for the two in series. This is added to a reactance $1.7Z_0 = 1360\Omega$ seen looking inwards from the traps, and tunes with about 3pF which is provided by the extension of the dipole beyond the traps.

The length of this extension can be found from the Smith chart, p70; the reactance, being equal to $5.4Z_a$, is equivalent to a 'line length' of 0.028λ or 1.9ft (0.58m). These extensions carry a triangular current distribution and thus add relatively little to the radiation resistance at 14MHz which, with some help from Fig 3.12, is found to be about 17Ω, ie a reduction of 15% only.

So far not too bad, but what about the coil losses? The current at this point in the element is about 0.5 times that in the centre but, because of the circulating current in the capacitor, this has to be multiplied by roughly two. For a coil Q of 200 we thus have to reckon a loss resistance of $570/200 \times 2$, ie 5.7Ω in series with the radiation resistance. This is a loss of $100 \log_{10} 22.7/17 = 1.26$dB. Provided that for some odd reason one would rather lose power at 14MHz than at 21MHz (where the QRM is not so bad!) this result can be construed as a slight improvement. Note, however, that the use of RF speech processing could raise the mean power (for 400W PEP) to 100W, in which case each trap will be dissipating 12.5W. This is enough to melt the solder (unless the traps are

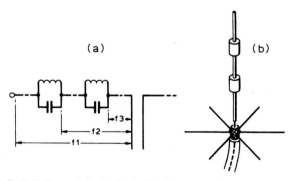

(a)   (b)

Fig 7.10. Trapped dipole. One half is shown at (a). The traps act as insulators, the resonant lengths for f_1 and f_2 being reduced somewhat by the inductive reactance of the included traps. When applied to a ground plane antenna, this may consist of a self-supporting tube as shown at (b), the tube being cut and then rejoined using rod insulators over which the coils are wound. Separate sets of radials are needed for each band. Trap circuits must be well protected against the weather

heavily constructed, in which case the mediaeval hazard of a shower of molten lead will no doubt be replaced by one of falling debris!).

The losses calculated above are only part of the total, since losses in the parasitic elements must be reckoned separately. Assuming a typical current ratio of 0.6, a fraction 2×0.62 or 72% must be added to the above losses, bringing them over the 2dB mark, and some further loss will occur due to the extra traps in the more usual case of three-band operation. These examples are further pursued in the next chapter, demonstrating the adverse effect of traps on bandwidth.

In concluding this part of the discussion, it is perhaps fair to mention that one design of commercial beam uses traps in the driven element only (with separate parasitic elements for each band) and has an enviable reputation for performance.

Doubly resonant antennas

Against the above background it has been pointed out [10] that classic design methods are based on a special case and do not in general yield the best options of those available. Put simply, using traps as 'insulators' to define the ends of a dipole places the highest possible voltage across L and C, and hence for a given inductance might be expected to result in maximum losses, though matters are not in fact as simple as this. An alternative for a two-band design is to choose an antenna length corresponding to the geometric mean of the frequencies and use traps as 'stretcher-shorteners', in which case the term 'traps' seems hardly appropriate and it is less misleading to talk of doubly resonant antennas. Fig 7.11 shows as (a) the classic design, (b) a 'symmetrical' design, as described in the reference, (c) a 'symmetrical' design, single-resonator version, and (d) a series trap suitable for loop antennas.

To appreciate the advantages of symmetrical design, consider an 18/24MHz antenna based on (c); with no trap the resonance is given by $\sqrt{(18 \times 25)} = 21.2$MHz. The frequency ratios f_h/f or f/f_l are 1.18 and the ratio of circulating current to through current is given approximately by $\omega/2\delta\omega = 1/0.36 = 2.8$. The reactance of the coil alone is $Z_a/(2\pi\Delta l/\lambda) = 1000 \times 6.28 \times 0.0225 = 141\Omega$ but, because of the circulating current, an actual reactance of 141/2.8 appears to have this value. Assuming a Q of 200, it has a resistance of 0.25Ω and to arrive at the effective loss this must be multiplied by the square of the current, giving a figure of 2Ω which is negligible compared with estimated values of R, 40Ω at 18 and 116Ω at 25MHz. It is a disadvantage of this method compared with the two-trap version (b) that because of the shorter length the radiation resistance is reduced.

W0JF has drawn the author's attention to the fact that even the symmetrical design is a special case from a wide range of options which allow a great deal of flexibility, and readers may already be familiar with the linear resonator [7] which is much easier to design and adjust when restricted to two bands only, the whole of the element being used on both frequencies and operation at the lower frequency being virtually unaffected by the upper resonance. Another example of non-interacting resonances is provided by Fig 12.5 which, if

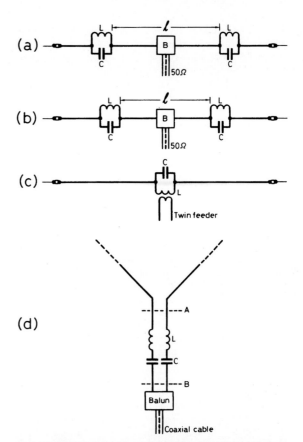

Fig 7.11. (a) Classic design. L, C and the length *l* are all resonant at f_H. Overall length is less than $\lambda/2$ at f_L. (b) Symmetrical design. L, C, *l* non-resonant. Optimised by computer. (c) Symmetrical design, single resonator. L, C provides inductive loading at f_L and capacitative shortening at f_H. (d) A loop as Figs 7.1 or 7.2 is resonant at f_L with stub short-circuited at A, and at f_H with short-circuit at B. L, C is resonant at f_H so that the stub length AB is not affected, but capacitative at f_L where it tunes out the inductance of AB. Note that because of difficulty in getting an exact match on both frequencies an ATU must always be used with dual-resonant antennas. For 14/21MHz, AB is *roughly* 11ft with most loop shapes and sizes

erected as an extended double Zepp, provides 3dB of extra gain at the highest frequency, though this may be lost by folding it to fit into a smaller space. Operation on 28MHz is completely unaffected by the capacitors since these are located at points of zero current, their values being chosen to provide resonance on 14MHz or any of the intermediate bands. As there are no circulating currents at the lower frequencies, losses are minimal, though the capacitors must be of high quality and, in some cases of folding, of high voltage ratings.

Series traps, as illustrated in Fig 7.11(d), exploit a 'special relationship' of certain loop resonances and are more efficient because there are no circulating currents. Typically, loops having a circumference between about 0.8 and 1.1λ at the lowest frequency should be suitable.

Using a suitable stub and GDO, the fundamental resonance

should first be established and, in the case of a 14MHz loop, the 21MHz second harmonic resonance will then be found by moving the shorting bar about 9ft down the stub. The trap is placed about half-way between these two positions.

On 21MHz the trap is series resonant so that tuning is not affected, but on 14MHz the inductance of the portions of stub above and below the trap, between the two resonance points (each about 250Ω), has to be tuned out by the capacitive reactance of the trap. At 14MHz we have $X_l/1.5 = 1.5X_c$ where X_c, X_l, are the reactances at 21MHz. Equating the difference at 14MHz to 500Ω we have $X_c = 600Ω$, ie C = 12.9pF and L = 4.25µH. With coil resistances of 3 or 4Ω and no circulating current, the trap loss should be negligible even with SDL elements, but large voltages are developed across the components which must be of high quality and well protected from the weather.

A two-element reversible beam was constructed on these lines using 0.9λ loops, each with its own 50Ω feeder and 1:1 balun, an SWR of less than 2 and deep tunable nulls being obtainable on both bands. In comparison with Fig 7.3, only marginally better efficiency and bandwidth can be expected but there may be considerable advantage in not having to dispose of a pair of long open-wire stubs. Trials, though fully supporting the theory, were never completed owing to a shift of interest following release of the WARC bands.

Stacking

Another common method of multibanding is 'stacking' in its various forms. Fig 7.12(a) shows λ/2 dipoles for different frequencies connected in parallel, in which case only the one for the frequency in use presents a low impedance to the feeder. The others are highly reactive with impedances of several hundred ohms, except that a 7MHz dipole, if included, does duty also on 21MHz. The same principle may also be applied to radial or counterpoise systems for the grounding of vertical antennas. Some systems have been described in which dipoles for adjacent frequencies are formed from 300Ω feeder so that they are stacked within a few millimetres of each other. This is, to put it mildly, difficult to reconcile with the usual stipulation that when beam antennas for different frequencies are mounted on the same mast the separation must be *at least 6ft (1.8m)*.

The usual method of resolving the conflict is apparently to make sure that both statements do not appear in the same chapter, but there could be a simple explanation since both statements are evidently based on experience, and it is likely that when one beam is being tested the feeder of the other one is pushed aside with careless abandon. There will then be a significant chance that the other beam *plus its unspecified length of feeder* will resonate near enough to the wanted frequency to result in considerable mutual coupling.

Adding 6ft (1.8m) to the mast is one possible remedy though it would be (a) simpler, (b) better, and (c) cheaper to short-circuit the unused feeder or, if already short-circuited, to try an open-circuit instead. This is little more than conjecture, but some evidence that the trouble arises from the driven

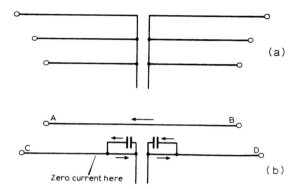

Fig 7.12. (a) Multiband λ/2 dipoles. The dipoles are cut to the appropriate length for each band and the centres joined by short lengths of low-impedance feeder. (b) Traps for suppression of currents induced from neighbouring dipoles. The object is to prevent any disturbance to an element AB as a result of currents which it may induce in CD. The trap lengths are not critical, the required capacitance being inversely proportional to length. See Table 7.4 for dimensions

element only *and is therefore controllable from the shack* can be inferred from the commercial practice of mounting parasitic elements for different bands in fairly close proximity on the same boom, and the author has even stacked a 21MHz quad a few inches inside a miniature 14MHz quad with negligible interaction. This result appears to be in conflict not only with the experience of DJ4VM [1] but other findings of the author, whose enthusiasm for stacking declined markedly after the following incident.

After finding that the addition of a close-spaced driven element for 21MHz to a 14MHz beam left the received signal unchanged, checks with a current probe revealed a large increase in driven-element current, the effect of this being offset by a large 14MHz current flowing the opposite way in the 21MHz element!

Another disconcerting example involved the modified VK2ABQ-type beam (p202), serious disturbance of 28MHz operation being found to occur due to 28MHz current flowing in adjacent 21MHz elements; this resulted in critical adjustments and narrow bandwidth but was curable by the use of simple linear traps inserted each side of the centre of the 21MHz element, Fig 7.6(b). Each trap consists of a single capacitor plus a long lead, whereby it is connected across part of the existing element to form a resonator. It has only a modest task to perform and there is negligible disturbance of normal operation on either band. Use of traps in this way

Table 7.4. Typical trap dimension for 2in (5cm) spacing and 14swg (2mm) wire as shown in Fig 7.12(b)

Frequency (MHz)	Length (in)	Length (cm)	Capacitance (pF)
28.5	16	40.6	50
25	16.3	41.4	68
21	20	50.8	68
18	24	61.0	80
14	30	76.2	128

whenever the need arises should in principle allow the use of parallel dipoles to be extended to include coverage of 10, 18 and 24MHz.

Unfortunately, as demonstrated by the previous incident, interaction can take subtle forms and may not be obvious, as for example when it alters the coupling factor between driven and parasitic elements. A likely explanation for conflicting experiences with stacking emerges from inspection of Fig 5.2, since one can clearly expect to find, in general, a complicated 'mix' of opposing electric and magnetic couplings involving near-field regions. Unless and until such effects have been more fully investigated, or unless the operator has plenty of time, patience, and experience, this method cannot be recommended when the frequency separation is much less than a half-octave, and even in this case careful checks are advisable prior to erection. On the other hand, it appears that, provided spacing is not of the 'almost touching' variety, interaction can often be cured by sufficient detuning of an offending wire, though bandwidth may be degraded. This adds further to the range of options opened up by the use of resonant feeders.

The so-called 'multiband quad' consists of separate arrays for 14, 21 and 28MHz stacked inside each other. This is another instance of 'cutting down to size', but even worse than before since using a quad loop at twice its fundamental frequency provides 3–4dB of additive gain (p111), ie nearly twice as much as in the case of a dipole element. It seems a great pity to throw this away, besides being quite unnecessary since there are several alternatives, two of which are described below. In the case of stacked arrays, instances of interaction have been reported and this could be due either to unused feeders of unsuitable lengths or to higher-frequency currents flowing in lower-frequency elements as discussed above.

Multiband operation by retuning

An antenna intended for one frequency may, in principle, be used on any other simply by retuning and making any necessary changes to the matching arrangements. For example, starting with a $\lambda/2$ dipole for 14MHz, the length becomes $3\lambda/4$ at 21MHz, ie the half-length increases from $\lambda/4$ to $3\lambda/8$ and, remembering that the reactance of a $\lambda/8$ length of line is always equal to Z_0, this is the amount that has to be removed to restore resonance. Since the reactance of the antenna is inductive (Fig 4.7), capacitance must be inserted and for a typical wire dipole ($Z_0 = 1000\Omega$) the required value comes to 8pF. At 28MHz an insulator is required, and this can take the form of a tuned circuit which is usable also as a matching device. Fig 7.13 shows how band-switching might be effected using, say, a Ledex switch mounted in a waterproof box, though an equivalent arrangement can be worked out using relays.

At least one such arrangement has been described in the literature but objections on grounds of reliability may have some validity, unless there is easy access to the antenna by climbing or lowering the mast. This is because components

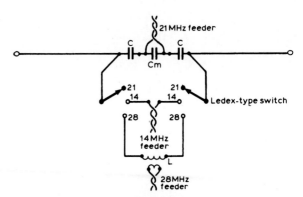

Fig 7.13. Centre tuning of 14MHz $\lambda/2$ dipole; C, C_m, C resonate with L at 28MHz, a low-impedance feeder being coupled into L as shown, though a high-impedance feeder tapped across L may also be used. At 21MHz the capacitors are series resonant with the excess inductance of the antenna and C_m is chosen to match any desired feeder impedance. At 14MHz the element is series fed in the normal way with low-impedance line, the shunting effect of C_m being negligible. A common low-impedance feeder may be used via two extra poles on the switch. This is only one of many possible arrangements

specifically 'designed for the job' are not available at the time of writing except at high prices. Nevertheless, some relays such as RS type 349-658 have been found suitable; these are small, light and relatively inexpensive, contacts being rated at 5A, 250V AC. A number of measures as follows may be taken to ensure reliability.

1. Use relays, preferably in conjunction with other methods such as double resonances or the linear resonators described below. This simplifies the switching as compared with more basic methods involving switched networks as in Fig 7.13.
2. Take precautions to ensure that switching operations are never carried out while RF power is applied.
3. Test thoroughly on full power before erection.

Referring again to Fig 7.13, another alternative is to use 'passive' switching by suitable electrical networks which provide appropriate reactances at each frequency. Fig 7.14(a) shows one of several arrangements developed by VK2AOU and DJ2UT [2], and Fig 7.14(b) a somewhat similar scheme developed by the author. In Fig 7.14(a) one circuit could be tuned to act as an insulator at 28MHz, and the other detuned to provide the required capacitance at 21MHz. At 14MHz there will be some added inductance which can be compensated by adjustment of element length.

Three-band matching is achieved with the aid of auxiliary driven elements for 21 and 28MHz, and it is possible to think of many variations on this theme which has also been applied to quad antennas. In Fig 7.14(b) the circuit L1, C1 is resonant at 28MHz and C2 provides the additional capacitance required for 21MHz. C2 can be switched by means of a relay or as in Fig 7.14(c) by the circuit L3, C3, which is also resonant at 28MHz and acts as a passive switch. Matching was achieved on all three bands by tapping the feeder across a suitable

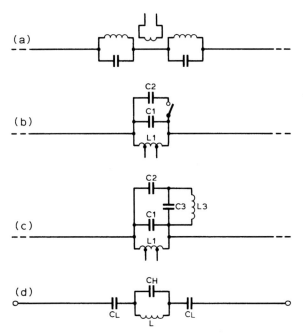

Fig 7.14. Multibanding networks with passive switching: (a) as developed by VK2AOU; (b) semi-active network (G6XN); and (c) passive version of (b); (d) L, C_H act as an insulator for the highest frequency, C_L tunes out the inductive reactance at a lower frequency

fraction of L1. Another method, Fig 7.14(d), uses capacitors C_L at the higher-frequency current nodes where they have no effect; at a lower frequency they tune out the inductive reactance of the system, thereby providing two-band operation.

The linear resonator

A disadvantage in each of the above cases is the need to split the element in the centre which is no great hardship in the case of, say, a λ/2 dipole since the insulator need not be of particularly high electrical quality. Unfortunately at 28MHz the dipole is full-wave so that high RF voltages exist across it and the situation is entirely different. It was frustration due to delay in the delivery of a 'better' insulator that caused the author to look for a different solution. This took the form of using *part of the element itself* for the inductance L as shown in Fig 7.15. This allows the element to be supported in the centre and is compatible with 'plumber's delight' mechanical construction.

An unexpected bonus was provided by the accidental discovery that, due to a highly asymmetrical type of resonance, the addition of C had very little influence at 14MHz. In effect L virtually disappeared at 14MHz by reverting to its normal role as the 'middle bit of the antenna', so that normal monoband dimensions could be used and performance was virtually unaffected by multibanding. With C adjusted for 21MHz operation there was a downward shift of only 1½% in the design centre frequency at 14MHz but this increased to

about 5% in a later design as a result of increased diameters and spacings of conductors.

For three-band operation without relays the necessary reduction in capacitance at 28MHz is effected by additional linear resonators formed by C2, C3, as shown in Fig 7.9(b), and both arrangements have also been applied to quad antennas (see p189). A detailed explanation and analysis of linear resonators will be found in an appendix to this chapter and antennas using this principle are described on pp123, 137, 190 and 201.

Although two-band operation is easy to achieve with this method and three-band operation not unduly difficult, the inclusion of further bands would require either a servo-controlled variable capacitor at the centre of each element or banks of preset capacitors selected by relays or a Ledex-type switch. The method currently favoured by the author would use two-band elements according to Fig 7.14(d) or 7.15(a) selected by relays, which also ensure that any element likely to cause problems on a given band is open-circuited or detuned. To avoid the need for protecting coils against the weather (Fig 7.14(d)), turns must be of large diameter, self-supporting with at least 4in spacing between turns; alternatively open-wire stubs may be used and can if necessary be folded into the form of a four-wire cage (p199).

The linear resonator was first employed by DL1FK as a means for obtaining multiple resonances of small beam elements [4]; in this case, at the lowest frequency, the resonator is acting as a loading device and there is inevitably a large circulating current which increases losses and restricts the amount of size reduction which can be achieved without serious inefficiency. In contrast to this, at the higher frequencies the radiation resistance is much higher and losses should be negligible. Other applications of linear resonators are described in later chapters, an important feature being the ability to isolate or detune any metal structure without cutting into the structure as would be necessary with ordinary resonators.

In linear resonator systems, three-band matching may be achieved by connection of the feeder across an appropriate fraction of L as in the case of the inductive stub, Fig 7.14(b).

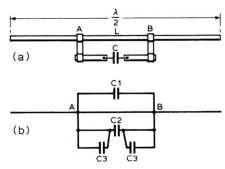

Fig 7.15. Linear resonator. An electrical conductor AB having an inductance L is bridged by a second conductor which includes a capacitor C. At (b), capacitors C3 form additional resonators which act as passive switches to remove C2 at 28MHz

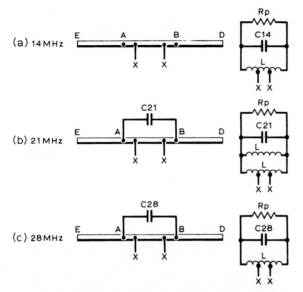

Fig 7.16. Principle of multiband matching (not to scale). (a) Inductance (L) of AB is tuned by the capacitance of AE, BD. R_p is the radiation resistance referred to the terminals of L which acts as a step-down autotransformer. Value of feedpoint impedance depends only on the distance XX so that A, B are arbitrary points which can be chosen to coincide with the terminals of the linear resonator of (b) or (c). (b) Inductance L is roughly equal to the inductive reactance of AE, BD which appears in parallel with it. C_{21} tunes both reactances and the radiation resistance can again be represented by a parallel resistance R_p. (c) L and C_{28} form a parallel-resonant circuit to act as an insulator between the two half-waves and allow them to be energised in phase. It also acts as a transformer to match the radiation resistance R_p into the feedline. To compensate for borrowing part of the antenna to form the inductance, the value of C_{28} is slightly increased

The principle is illustrated in Fig 7.16 where (a) represents any λ/2 element with a parallel feed, such as a T or delta match. Selecting points A and B at random, the wire joining them can be regarded as an inductance L tuned by the capacitance C_{14} of the outer portions, as shown on the right. As an approximation, provided L is not too large or too small, the current-loop radiation resistance R can be regarded as being in series with it, giving rise to an equivalent parallel resistance $\omega^2 L^2/R$ between A and B.

To use the same antenna at 28MHz we need only connect a small capacitance C_{28} across L, thereby tuning it to resonance so that it acts as a centre insulator and the dipole becomes two half-waves in phase (Fig 7.16(c)). By 'borrowing' some of the dipole to act as an inductance, the half-waves have been shortened, ie capacitance has been subtracted, but it is easily replaced by a slight increase in the value of C_{28}. The loop radiation resistance is stepped up by the antenna itself acting as a λ/4 transformer, so that it appears as a resistance Z_a^2/R across L, where Z_a is the characteristic impedance of the antenna.

On 21MHz the antenna, looking outwards from AB, is an inductance L_a in parallel with L as shown in Fig 7.16(b). It is convenient to choose the length AB so that L and L_a are

Table 7.5

Band (MHz)	R (dipole)	R (beam)	ωL or Z_a	R_p (dipole)	R_p (beam)
14	70	20	200	570	2000
21	200	100	300	450	900
28	200	150	600	1800	2400

roughly equal, and a radiation resistance R measured at a current antinode becomes roughly 2R when the reference point is altered to the centre of the element. If I is the current in the element at this point, the total circulating current in C_{21} (Fig 7.16(b)) is 2I, and the parallel impedance R_p is again given by $\omega^2 L^2/R$. Typical values for these quantities are given in ohms for dipoles and beams by Table 7.5.

For an SWR better than two, which is adequate for most purposes, an impedance variation of 4:1 is allowed, so the above impedance figures provide a reasonable starting point for the design of a matched feeder system. In principle, all that is needed to use the linear resonator itself as the matching device is to tap the feeder across the appropriate fraction of L, given by $\sqrt{(Z_0/R_p)}$ where Z_0 is the feeder impedance. For example, if a 300Ω feeder is tapped across 45% of L, a 5:1 impedance ratio is obtained and the worst SWR in the case of the beam will be 1.7.

This example is based on arbitrary assumptions and in fact does no more than establish a 'tendency to match', but with this as a starting point it is usually possible to obtain much lower values of SWR than those implied by Table 7.5.

Linear resonators have also been successfully used with quad loops, two being required for each loop in the case of 14/21MHz operation with coaxial feed. This somewhat cumbersome arrangement proved difficult to reconcile with the much more important role illustrated in Fig 7.2(b), where the resonator open-circuits the top of the loop on 28MHz to provide 3.7dB of extra gain as featured on p111. The price paid for this is restricted bandwidth, of the order of 300kHz only, as determined by erecting the loop horizontally within reach of the ground and observing the position of the current zeros which precess rapidly around the loop with changing frequency. This procedure is highly educational and recommended for the initial testing of all new loop designs! In this case, since the resonator is the cause of the narrow bandwidth, the addition of long stubs (which are *relatively* broadband) as in Fig 7.3 not only does little to make matters worse but, by ensuring that adjustments can be made at ground level, helps towards the achievement of a viable system.

Miniature beams

Both the lumped circuit, Fig 7.14(b), and linear resonator methods were first applied to the parasitic elements of centre-loaded small beams, the loading being provided by the resonators [3, 4]. Centre-loading has already been criticised (p27) because of very low values of R, and the situation is made a lot worse by multibanding since the circulating currents in the resonators are much greater than the element currents. On the other hand, with short elements there is no question of 'additive' gain and therefore no objection in principle to stacking.

In one case, a small 14MHz beam similar in principle to Fig 5.22 was used in conjunction with a separate, centrally placed, driven element, having a linear resonator to give 21/28MHz operation. Separate (stacked) parasitic elements were used for 21MHz, and for 28MHz it was found possible to incorporate linear traps in the 14MHz elements without detriment to their performance. Despite some good signal reports, all adjustments proved to be rather critical, bandwidth was narrow and the feeling developed that this was not an ideal system, one problem being excessive coupling on 21MHz via the 14MHz elements. This required separate neutralisation and the complications were felt to be excessive.

Reference has already been made to the 'Miniclaw', an SDL array using the ITL principle and described in detail on p217. This is the smallest multiband beam that can be recommended unless at the lowest frequency it is switched so that, on transmit, it operates as a two-turn loop. The small size has been achieved in part by heavier construction, and certain trade-offs may be possible; as an alternative the CIL, Fig 7.6(f), might be found more convenient but remains as yet undeveloped.

Advantages of multiband operation

In the case of Yagi beams currently available on the commercial market, the universal use of traps for multibanding means that best DX performance is being achieved by those with monoband antennas to the disadvantage of those unable to erect separate antennas for each band. However, multibanding (if properly executed) results in *better* than the usual monoband performance at the highest frequency, since in effect one ends up with two beams stacked side by side. In the case of three-element beams the advantage should be greater than the figures quoted, due to a threefold increase in radiation resistance at 21 and 28MHz which enables the design parameters to approximate more closely to the theoretical maximum gain condition.

Use of high-frequency antennas at lower frequencies

Another aspect of multiband operation arises if after, say, giving priority to DX working at the higher frequencies, there is a desire to operate also on lower frequency bands and possibly 'have a go' at some DX on these bands, as well as using them for shorter ranges. Vertical antennas, provided they are used at *both* ends of a contact, are best for ground-wave communication and a vertical antenna is usually best also for DX (although in the case of 7MHz, if a fixed wire beam can be erected at a good height, say 50ft (15m) or so, this may provide the best choice for a particular direction). A vertical antenna is poor for the shorter ranges beyond ground-wave range, due to the lack of high-angle radiation, and in this case it may be best to use a horizontal antenna and bounce the

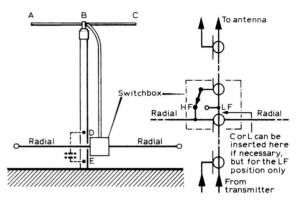

Fig 7.17. Use of 14MHz beam as top-loaded ground-plane antenna for 3.5MHz. Feeder should be brought down well clear of the mast if possible, but in the case of a metal mast it should be possible to achieve isolation by using a linear resonator DE. For LF operation the feeder could probably then be tapped onto DE! but illustration assumes either a wooden mast (preferably dry!) or adequate clearance between feeder and a non-resonant metal mast, the beam element being insulated from the boom. C or L can be inserted as shown in order to resonate the vertical structure. Text assumes that the 14MHz feeder continues to the mast base (E) and runs along ground to a remote point F

signals off the ionosphere at about vertical incidence. In this case very little height is needed, ranges of up to several hundred miles being consistently achieved with powers of a few watts and antennas only a few feet off the ground.

Fig 7.17 provides an instructive example, typical of situations which frequently arise in practice and which can be exploited very effectively. AC is a 14MHz dipole or beam element with a feeder BDEF supported by a wooden mast. A break at D with, say, a plug-and-socket connector allows BD to be used as a vertical $\lambda/4$ antenna top-loaded by AC on 3.5MHz. This is operating against a 'two-radial ground plane', or more precisely the centre of a horizontal dipole which serves as an artificial earth, connection to the feeder being made as shown. If the length of the radiator is not exactly resonant, it may be tuned by a series inductance or capacitance as indicated, and the 'radials' may be bent or loaded as necessary to fit them into the available space. In view of the advantages of being able to switch polarisation, provision may be made to use the radial wires as a horizontal dipole for short-range working.

Using baluns as necessary, there is little difficulty in adapting this idea for any type of feeder, a 4:1 balun being recommended for 300 to 600Ω line feeder, although an ATU will then almost certainly be required in the shack unless the feeder length does not differ greatly from $\lambda/2$. For use as horizontal radiators the 'radials' can be made from 300Ω ribbon and connected as a folded dipole. These and similar vertical ground-plane arrangements are capable of excellent DX performance on 3.5MHz, but may be adversely affected by wet weather unless the top is insulated and the feeder brought down clear of the mast. These precautions may also allow a metal mast to be used provided it is non-resonant.

To recommend such an arrangement in view of the remarks

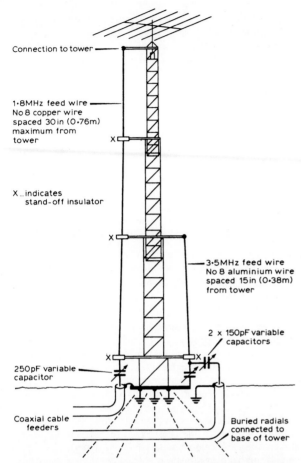

Fig 7.18. Details of shunt-fed tower as used at W5RTQ. The 1.8MHz band feed on the left side connects to the top of the tower through a horizontal arm of 1in (2.5cm) diameter aluminium tubing. The other arms have stand-off insulators at their outer ends made of 1ft (30cm) lengths of plastic water pipe. The connection for the 3.5MHz band, right, is made similarly at 28ft (8.5m), but two variable capacitors are used to permit adjustment of matching with large changes of frequency (ARRL Antenna Anthology)

about ground planes on p172 may seem inconsistent but it is difficult to convert such structures into dipoles and, provided the reader is fully conversant with the earthing requirements (p172) and measures for prevention of feeder radiation (p53), there should be no difficulty in achieving a satisfactory compromise.

Metal masts and towers can themselves be used in many cases as vertical radiators on low-frequency bands as shown in Fig 7.18 [5]. For this it is usually assumed that the tower height should not be much greater than $5\lambda/8$, since otherwise the current distribution contains two loops of opposite phase and low-angle radiation tends to be cancelled. However, it should be possible to overcome this limitation by use of a linear resonator near the mast centre as shown in Fig 7.19. Given the availability of, say, a tall mast supporting a TV

antenna for reception in a fringe area, this could be pressed into service as an all-band vertical and Fig 7.19 is a suggested method of achieving this. Such an arrangement breaks new ground and has not been tried up to the time of writing, though its feasibility has been indicated by the author's experiments with linear resonators.

On the other hand, towers and masts supporting HF beams have often been used as low-angle radiators for the longer wavebands and are capable of giving excellent DX performance. Cables attached to HF beams should preferably be run down inside the metal structure and earthed for RF at the base of the support. This is to ensure that RF currents do not stray along unpredictable paths such as via the mains wiring to ground. If the cables have to be run down externally they should be screened, the screens being bonded to the structure at several points if this is possible, though usually this is not essential. The structure should be checked for DC continuity, any junctions liable to develop high resistance due to rust or corrosion being bridged if possible, though this is not feasible with telescopic towers or masts.

The broadband approach

The methods described thus far have achieved operation on several bands by providing multiple resonances, some or all of which may be quite sharp. There are, however, a number of 'broadband' antenna systems capable of providing continuous coverage over a band of one octave or more, thereby meeting all or most of the user's multiband requirements for DX communication. The snag about this approach lies in the impossibility of combining high gain with large bandwidth and small size.

Due to the difference in their requirements and in particular the nature of their frequency allocations, commercial operators have hitherto been more interested in extensive frequency coverage (wide bandwidth) than in gain or small size, but the allocation of 10, 18 and 24MHz to amateurs tends to bring their needs more closely into line with commercial ones. From the initial reactions of many amateurs to these

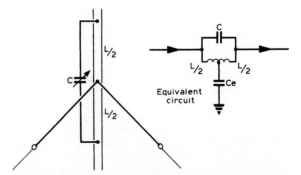

Fig 7.19. Use of linear resonator to convert a tall mast into a collinear vertical array for a higher-frequency band. The tuned circuit acts as an insulator and phase inverter but for this purpose the centre must be earthed. The impedance to earth need only be small compared with the end impedance of the collinear elements and can easily be provided by portions of the guy-wire system

frequency allocations the log-periodic antenna may well have a start over its competitors and is likely in many cases to provide the best compromise between performance and operating convenience. However, it needs to be appreciated that at any given frequency only part of the array is operative, so that performance will be inferior to a well-designed monobander of the same size.

The design of log-periodic arrays is one of the topics for Chapter 14 and reference may be made to Fig 14.8 which shows a typical log-periodic antenna designed to cover a frequency range of 10–30MHz. This uses 11 elements increasing progressively in length by about 4 to 1, the overall length of the array being in the region of 40ft (12m). The elements are connected in alternate phase so that, looking at two elements only, they bear some resemblance to the driven arrays of Chapter 5. The rear element of the pair is 'delayed' by an amount 'comparable with the spacing between the elements' so that radiation takes place in the direction of the shorter elements. At any one frequency only the three or four elements nearest to resonance are doing useful work, so that from the point of view of performance a rough equivalence with a monoband close-spaced Yagi might be expected. Conversely a monoband beam with a 40ft (12m) boom length would provide several decibels of additional gain at 14MHz.

The calculated gain for the example in Fig 14.8 is 6.5dB and another typical design [6], using 12 elements on a 26.5ft (8.1m) boom to cover 14–28MHz and having a longest-element length of 38ft (11.6m), also provides about the same gain. Reasons which currently cause many amateurs to opt for monoband beams rather than multiband beams using traps would therefore apply in this case *a fortiori*. Moreover, quite apart from size, the extra weight and windage of the large number of elements must be included in the reckoning. It is most unlikely that a log-periodic antenna with a frequency range of 10–30MHz (or even 14–30MHz) could be built which would be comparable in size as well as gain with, say a two-element quad having resonant feeders as in the DJ4VM design.

The root of the matter is that with the log periodic antenna one is paying for *continuous coverage with no gaps*. This is a major facility which, even with 10, 18 and 24MHz taken into account, is more relevant to commercial than amateur needs; one rarely gets something for nothing and in this case the price in terms of size and weight, performance, or both, is considerable. On the other hand, the log-periodic antenna dispenses with tuning units and band-switching, thus making for maximum operational convenience, and for amateurs free from planning constraints but deterred by the engineering aspects there are now commercial models available.

Also, for those not too cramped for space, an arrangement of three or four vertical log-periodic arrays suspended from a single main support as suggested on p234 has considerable attractions.

The broadband log-periodic antennas discussed above are not to be confused with those intended for *monoband* operation and discussed in the next chapter.

Arrays using various combinations of long wires (pp239–242), though in general optimised for a particular frequency, are essentially broadband. They usually provide high gain over at least an octave, though in the case of single wires provision of suitable earths presents something of a problem. The author believes however that it should be possible without affecting gain to erect a very long wire as an inverted-L with one end brought into a tuning unit in the shack.

Six-band beams

In conclusion it may be useful to review the above discussion in the context of the WARC frequency allocations, with the object of achieving a close approach to full 'monoband performance' on as many as possible of the six bands from 10 to 28MHz. Log-periodic arrays, however attractive in other respects, are not admissible for the present purpose because of poor performance in relation to size, and this leaves at our disposal:

(a) loops or dipoles with resonant feeders;
(b) stacked loops or dipoles, matched feeders;
(c) multiband elements;
(d) various combinations of (a), (b) and (c).

Ignoring for the moment resonant-feeder systems, the possible combinations are endless, but each of the options, though 'easy' for two bands, turns out to be 'difficult' (or unsuitable) for three, and impossible for more. Stacked monoband elements may be slightly more amenable, but in view of the difficulties which can arise the odds would appear to favour *stacks of two-band elements*.

It is important, in view of the earlier emphasis on making full use of the available aperture, to realise that 'stacking' does not mean that elements have to be cut down to size, even though this happens to be the usual practice. Elements such as Fig 7.14(d) can be arranged to fill the whole of the available space and the 'capacitive stretching' makes them particularly suitable for stacking [9].

The linear resonator holds little promise in its present passive form for operation on more than three bands but, subject to the development of servo-controlled capacitors, it is believed that it could enable three-element beams to be tuned continuously over the range 14–28MHz with possible extension (at slightly reduced efficiency) to 10MHz. Some difficulty would arise in matching the driven element at 18MHz, where L is short-circuited by the capacitive channel, and at 10MHz where the circulating current in L, C will be large, resulting in a high impedance at the normal feedpoint. However, at worst, the driven element could support a separate thin-wire stretched dipole for 18MHz and the feeder could either be switched or allowed to operate as a resonant line for 10MHz. The beam would be reversible at all frequencies but a programming device would be needed to enable settings, once determined, to be memorised and reproduced. There seems little doubt that (given the demand) such a system could be developed for an economic price, but this would require considerable development effort of a kind currently in short supply.

Following the precedent set by G5RV for multiband dipoles, the same treatment can (as we have seen) be applied to beam elements except that the frequency range is more limited and with $\lambda/2$ or VK2ABQ-type dipole elements one is restricted to the use of very short feeders. Alternatively, matching stubs for the lowest frequency band, located close to the antenna, can be switched by relays. Compared with stacks of two-band elements, this results in a much simpler and smaller antenna, though these advantages added to beam-reversal and deep-nulling may have to be weighed against bandwidth penalties and the relative inconvenience of open-wire lines.

The case for resonant feeders has gradually strengthened since it became clear, to the author at least, that there was no other way to meet the new requirement for five- or six-band beams without relatively large structures or sacrifice of performance. This in turn led to a search for better methods of implementation, and the SDL array, originally conceived as an 'improved version of the VK2ABQ', progressed through further stages of development [11] which yielded a number of useful options as featured in this and other chapters. The particular merit of this type of element derives from (a) highly efficient end-loading at the MDF, this being one of the primary functions of the sides of the loops; (b) relatively large values of R, attributable to its 'folded-dipole' resemblance; and (c) easy, lightweight construction.

Notwithstanding the above, the much older system featured in Figs 7.1 and 7.3 should not be overlooked. Full-wave (14MHz) loops tuned in this way can be used as beam elements on all bands from 21 to 10MHz where the narrow bandwidth is immaterial and, because of lower RF voltages, are particularly suitable for mounting in trees. With the added possibility of high gain on 28MHz by open-circuiting the top corner, five-band coverage is achieved, but regrettably 25MHz is the 'odd one out' and zero gain is to be expected. The DJ4VM quad should also not be overlooked, though it suffers from the same defect unless both top and bottom corners of the loops can be open-circuited, which should result in high gain on both 28 and 25MHz.

Additional possibilities based on Fig 7.8 exist in the case of vertical loop arrays.

Conclusions and recommendations

Multiband operation is usually regarded as a compromise and it is true that in some cases practical advantages can be realised in return for accepting a reduction in bandwidth. However, most existing multiband systems waste energy quite unnecessarily in the form of heat, besides failing to realise the improvement in gain which should result from the increased aperture at the higher frequencies. There is felt to be no excuse for this, and it is unfortunate that so many amateurs have no choice but to purchase commercial antennas which have hitherto, for the most part, followed the dictates of fashion rather than the principles of sound engineering.

The best choice of method usually involves a delicate balance of conflicting factors. For the amateur constructor

suitable methods include the use of resonant feeders, stacked elements or some form of central tuning unit with band switching. Switching may be active (eg using relays) or passive, such as Fig 7.15(b). In general, two-band operation involves fewer problems of design and adjustment, and passive switching is likely to be difficult for more than three bands. Due to mutual interaction, a similar restriction tends to apply in the case of closely stacked dipoles. On the other hand, switching by relays alone becomes rapidly less attractive as the number of 'switch positions' increases due to escalation in the number of relays required.

After some nine years of intensive use on the air of small delta loop arrays in their various forms, the author's preference for resonant feeders is now firmly established, but the ability to recommend them unreservedly derives in no small measure from the new in-shack tuning arrangements described on p64, a development enforced by the proliferation of additional wavebands! It is frequently asserted that the use of open-wire line is no longer an acceptable option in view of the greater convenience of coaxial feeder and EMC problems due to radiation from this type of line (which in fact is very small if the line is well balanced, whereas radiation from coaxial line can be large); this is an issue which can all too easily be 'resolved' either way by a recital of special cases. The advice here is to keep line spacings within the shack down to an inch or less, use plenty of care and commonsense, and pay due heed to the guidelines in Chapter 4. It seems to the author that ample precedent for the use of balanced high-impedance line is provided by the popularity of the G5RV antenna, the most significant difference in the case of beams being the lack of alternatives other than to forgo activity on some bands or tolerate (and add to) the congestion.

It is not difficult to cover five or six bands with gain and directivity equal to that of monoband beams, the price for this being the acceptance of resonant lines to each element which allows all tuning to be carried out at the operating position and confers a number of additional benefits, including the possibility of instantaneous beam reversal and deep-nulling of interfering dignals under the control of the operator. The use of remote tuning devices in each element, though more demanding in terms of engineering skills, is a possible alternative; the linear resonator, though attractive in this context, demands full-sized elements and rigid construction but possibilities for smaller beams include rotary switches driven by impulse motors or dual resonances (p131) switched by relays, all of these methods being greatly assisted by measures which reduce the characteristic impedance of the antenna as described earlier in this chapter.

Extended dipoles, the DJ4VM type of quad loop, or the standard quad with provision for open-circuiting a top corner are suitable elements for large beams as they provide extra gain at the highest frequencies and can also be used singly. For more modest installations, small delta loop elements have been found the most versatile, providing efficient operation (avoiding trap losses) over a frequency range from about 0.8 to 1.6 times the fundamental resonance.

The use of multiple wires for improving bandwidth is well

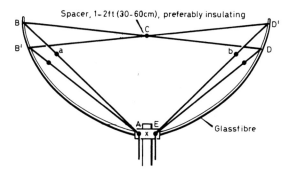

Fig 7.20. Low-Z_0 loop. ABCDE, AB'CD' spaced by BB', DD', and C are effectively in parallel, with wire bridges at a,b for getting rid of unwanted resonances. For use as beam elements providing coverage of 14–28MHz, the shape should preferably be right-angled with a circumference of about 16m. A four-wire top with three-wire sides is possible by the use of insulating spacers at B' and D' secured to the arms. Wire bridges at a, b destroy harmful resonances (see Fig 7.6(f) and italics, p42). Some additional spacers may be needed. Glassfibre arms are preferred but well-treated bamboo with insulating extensions can be used. A central 'prop' can be added if necessary: see photo, p143. (Based on a suggestion by G4CTO.)

established but is only just emerging as the key to resolving problems of multibanding, its value being emphasised by the experience of G3GJX who found, contrary to prevailing expectations, that his portable 14MHz ground-plane antenna derived from Fig 11.10(a) and using 3ft (1m) radials could be made to work efficiently on any of the higher HF bands by retuning the radiator alone. The explanation emerged from recognition of the radial system as a typical case of wires in parallel yielding a very low Z_0 of about 70Ω. With λ/8 radials suitably tuned at 14MHz this would leave a residual reactance at 21MHz of 57Ω in series with 220Ω of feedpoint resistance which could be translated into an SWR of 1.2 and, although with the shorter radials an SWR of about 2.5 would be more likely, this is clearly a problem solved. It seems clear that the way ahead will be linked to the achievement of lowest possible values of Z_0 and Fig 7.20, based on a new method of loop construction proposed by G4CTO, has proved highly effective as well as mechanically attractive since it eliminates most of the spreaders, this being an additional function of the supporting arms. In effect it replaces the parallel wires by parallel loops and, although the loops are highly asymmetrical, this is irrelevant, overall symmetry being preserved because each loop is a mirror image of the other. Achieving lowest-possible values of average Z_0 is likely to be more important than maintaining uniformity of Z_0 within the loops, though this will be assisted by tapering the sides as shown. Though originally conceived for use with resonant feeders, impressive results have been claimed for band-switched beam elements using this form of construction.

Horizontal antennas for the higher frequencies, plus feeders, can frequently be used as top-loaded verticals for the lower frequencies, though for optimum coverage of shorter ranges a horizontal antenna is required; this can be at a low height. The use of centre-fed, horizontal, low-frequency antennas at the higher frequencies is common practice and

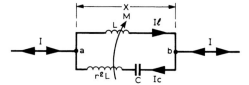

Fig 7.21. Lumped circuit equivalent of linear resonator

can be a useful compromise, despite the narrow angular coverage which, in association with Murphy's law, ensures that wanted signals are always in an unfavourable direction. This tends to outweigh any slight gain there may be in the favoured directions. Long wires may be end-fed on all bands, apart from the increased risk of EMC problems which may result from bringing a 'hot' wire too close to the mains wiring.

Appendix – the linear resonator

For all its apparent simplicity the linear resonator is a complex device. Its main features are summarised in Fig 7.21, which shows the equivalent 'lumped circuit', and Fig 7.22, which illustrates the frequency response of typical resonators, assuming conductors of equal diameter and varying degrees of coupling between them. To assist interpretation Fig 7.23 gives a rough idea of the way the coupling factor varies with spacing of the conductors. For the more advanced amateur who may wish to develop his own designs a number of basic formulae will now be given. If r is the turns ratio, k the coupling factor and $y = \omega LC$ (where $\omega = 2\pi \times$ frequency) we obtain

$$X = \omega L \left(\frac{yr^2(1 - k^2) - 1}{yr(r - 2k) + y - 1} \right)$$

Parallel resonance ($X = \infty$) is given by

$$y_p \doteq \frac{1}{2r^2(1 - k)}$$

The series resonance ($X = 0$) is given by

$$y_s = \frac{1}{r^2(1 - k^2)}$$

The frequency at which $I_1 = 0$ is given by

$$y_0 = \frac{1}{r^2 - kr}$$

For resonators with equal-diameter conductors ($r = 1$) the frequency ratios are

$$f_0/f_p = \sqrt{2} \text{ (ie half an octave)}$$

$$f_s/f_p = \sqrt{\left(\frac{2}{1 + k} \right)}$$

$$f_s/f_0 = \sqrt{\left(\frac{1}{1 + k} \right)}$$

Current ratios are given by

$$I = I_1 + I_c$$

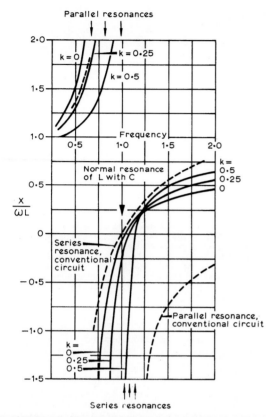

Fig 7.22. Reactance curves for linear resonators showing effect of mutual coupling. Frequency scale is relative. *X/ωL* is the ratio of reactance between the terminals of the resonator to the natural reactance of the conductor. Mutual coupling shifts the curves to the right and brings the series and parallel resonances closer together. Dotted curves show for comparison the characteristics of conventional resonators

$$\frac{I_1}{I_c} = \frac{y(r^2 - kr) - 1}{y(1 - kr)}$$

which reduces to $-kr$ at series resonance. Practical values for linear resonators are $k = 0.2$–0.5, $r = 1.0$–1.3.

In Fig 7.22 it will be seen that one effect of coupling is to bring the series and parallel resonances closer together, so that if, for example, this type of resonator is used to generate the series capacitance needed for bringing a 14MHz dipole to resonance on 21MHz, the effect at lower frequencies is reduced. There are several ways of using such a device to achieve multiband resonances, and perhaps the most obvious would be to use the series resonance for 'shorting out' about one third of a 14MHz dipole and thus bring it to resonance on 21MHz. However, this tends to create difficulties at 14MHz since the parallel resonance in the absence of coupling is exactly half an octave below the series resonance, so that the short-circuit at 21MHz would be expected to result in an open-circuit at the lower frequency. By increasing the coupling factor so as to bring the resonances closer together, the

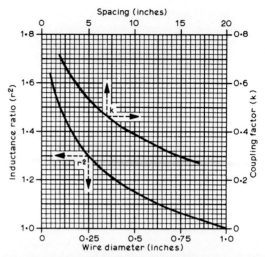

Fig 7.23. Variation of coupling factor with spacing, and inductance ratio with diameter of smaller conductor. Figures based on length of 7ft (2.1m) and large conductor diameter of 1in (2.5cm) but these are not critical. Values for *k* assume 1in diameter for both conductors but decrease by only 11% if one conductor is reduced to 0.1in (2.5mm). Use scales indicated by arrows

idea appeared feasible, and was even tried with some success – although interaction between the tuning of the series circuit on 21MHz and the length of element required for 14MHz was sufficient to make the adjustment extremely difficult.

Unfortunately Fig 7.22 does not tell the whole story, and it could be argued that bringing the resonances together does not get rid of the problem but merely brushes it under the carpet. This is because series resonance might be defined in two ways: the frequency at which the reactance between terminals is zero, and the frequency at which the series circuit can be regarded as an effective short-circuit so that no current flows through the inductive path.

Normally with lumped circuits these frequencies would be identical, but this does not apply when mutual coupling is present. In this case the parallel resonance and the short-circuit frequency retain their half-octave separation, whereas at the zero-reactance frequency there is no short-circuit and at 21MHz there could well be a large and undesirable circulating current, causing appreciable losses and perhaps a reduction in bandwidth. This depends on the dimensions of the 'trombone', Fig 7.15, with close spacing resulting in high current but considerable enhancement of the 'disappearing inductance' effect. Typically, this shift in the 14MHz resonance as a result of adding the 21MHz capacitance varies from about 1% to 7% as the spacing increases from 1in (2.5cm) to 10in (25cm). However, due to the increased circulating current, bandwidth reduction and the onset of appreciable losses, spacings less than 5in (12.5cm) are not recommended for 'mainstream' applications, though suitable for some purposes such as those covered by Fig 7.12(b).

It is useful to be aware of what happens as the length of the 'trombone' is varied. At 28MHz this is acting as an insulator and the voltage across it tends to stay constant so that both RF current and losses are inversely proportional to length. The current is about four times the loop current of the dipole, so that for comparison with the radiation resistance any losses must be multiplied by 16. For a 5ft (1.5m) trombone a typical calculated value of loss resistance is 0.15Ω which translates into a negligible power loss of only 1.6%. At 21MHz the situation is more complicated, but with the recommended dimensions the current I_c through the capacitor divides into roughly equal proportions between L and the inductance L_a of the outer portions of the dipole, each of these being somewhat less than the current IR associated with the radiation resistance.

As a rough guide, I_c should be roughly equal to $2IR$, and anything more than $3IR$ is definitely excessive. The ratio increases rapidly as the length is decreased, but as the length is increased it gradually falls to unity so that all the current is flowing in the capacitor and none through L, which can no longer be used as a matching device. This of course is the 'short-circuit' series resonance and is somewhat lower than the true series resonance as defined by 'zero reactance'. The gradual transition means that the usual distinction between series and parallel resonance has become somewhat blurred and there are matching complications but it is still the basis for a workable system. The 21MHz radiation resistance is so large that the capacitive arm of the trombone can be routed directly via the balun terminals and the element becomes series-fed. However, the low-frequency resonance has now been moved considerably lower, due partly to the larger trombone and partly to the 'capacitive end-loading' effect produced at 14MHz by moving the ends of the trombone outwards. This was found to reduce the required element length by about 14%.

Referring to Fig 7.15, any increase of C beyond the value required for 21MHz will have an appreciable and eventually catastrophic effect at 14MHz, though under proper control it can be used to convert a director into a reflector. On a reflector it has the opposite effect, turning it into a director. This may at first sight be surprising but the explanation will be obvious from careful inspection of Fig 7.22.

As well as by use of mutual coupling, the resonant frequencies may be brought closer by increasing the inductance of the series circuit. This is not subject to the same restrictions, though it is important to ensure that losses remain negligible in comparison with the radiation resistance. Some increase of inductance is possible by decreasing the conductor diameter, but it is difficult to achieve a ratio greater than about 1.5 without loading coils, and in general any diameter from about 0.1in (2.5mm) to at least 0.5in (13mm) is electrically acceptable, with mechanical and bandwidth considerations tending to favour the higher value.

Spurious resonances

Under certain 'fault' conditions, or when adjustments are badly out, it is possible to excite spurious modes of radiation in elements using linear resonators. The most obvious one is the full-wave resonance involving two half-waves in antiphase. DL1FK [4] warns against this to the extent of ruling out the

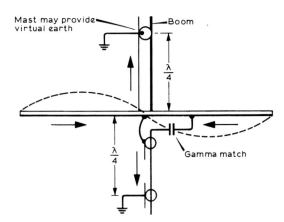

Fig 7.24. Excitation of 1λ mode by unbalanced feed. Centre of element is virtually isolated from earth so an incoming wave could set up the current distribution shown dotted. Voltage can therefore be developed across the feeder. By reciprocity this mode can also be radiated, but not with a balanced feed. Arrows indicate current flow and the feeder length may be any odd number of quarter-waves. The linear resonator capacitor is not shown as it has no effect on this mode

use of full-wave elements, but this mode cannot in fact be excited with a symmetrical feed system and is easily detected. It is predictable that it could be excited quite efficiently with an unbalanced feed under certain extreme conditions (Fig 7.24). Due to normal tolerances its presence has been detected when using a balun, but only in a very weak form, and for this purpose the resonator had to be badly detuned, since otherwise the unwanted mode was completely swamped by the wanted one. The unwanted mode is associated with current flow in the boom, and if both modes are present there will be unequal currents in the two halves of the radiator. If the full-wave mode is present alone, a pick-up loop moved along the radiator indicates a null in the centre. It is likely that under some conditions this mode could cause confusion when looking for resonances with a GDO.

It is possible, when using a GDO or with sufficient mistuning, to excite a mode in which current is wholly or mainly confined to the trombone section and there is little or no radiation from the antenna. This is most likely to be experienced at 21MHz and a low value of SWR is no guarantee that it is not occurring. Conclusive evidence of its presence is provided by the following symptoms:

(a) equal currents in the inductive and capacitive branches, little or none in the remainder of the elements;
(b) inability to tune the parasitic elements or obtain useful field strength readings;
(c) smoke rising from the balun!

If capacitance is being increased from a low value this is the *first* mode encountered. The remedy is to increase the capacitance until a reasonable ratio of inward- to outward-flowing inductive current is achieved. This is typically about 0.3 to 0.6.

Measurements of this kind need only be very rough. Fig

Two-element beam based on Fig 7.20. The basic construction differs from the Claw (p220) by virtue of the added central support, the supporting arms being attached to this at a median position. The side wires are brought down well clear of the arms to a short lower boom. These measures allow the use of even lighter construction or lower-grade materials which happened to be all that was available at the time

18.13 shows a simple 'relative current' meter which may be calibrated against any other RF indicator of known characteristics, such as an oscilloscope. Small size is important for avoiding capacitance pick-up, and the meter should be held at a constant distance such as 0.5in or 1cm (which can be judged roughly by eye) from the conductors carrying the current to be estimated. The distance should be slightly increased for conductors of smaller diameter. It will be found useful to remember that at 21MHz the current flowing into the capacitor must of necessity be equal to the sum of the two inductive currents, provided the point of observation is close to the junction of the conductors.

If a GDO is coupled in off-centre, many spurious modes will be observed. This happens with any 'plumber's delight' beam, the modes corresponding with the many different ways in which a wave can wrap itself round the structure as discussed in Chapter 18.

References

[1] 'A new multiband quad antenna', W Boldt, DJ4VM, *Ham Radio* August 1969.

[2] 'A different multiband aerial system', H F Ruckert, VK2AOU, *Amateur Radio* April 1978.

[3] 'More about the Minibeam', G A Bird, G4ZU, *RSGB Bulletin* October 1957.

[4] R Auerbach, DL1FK, *DL-QTC* July 1960.

[5] *The ARRL Antenna Anthology,* p34.

[6] *The ARRL Antenna Book,* 15th edn, 1988, pp208, 161.

[7] 'The 'disappearing inductance' – a new trick and some better beams', L A Moxon, *Radio Communication* April/May 1977.

[8] 'High-frequency antennas and propagation modes in relation to the amateur service', L A Moxon, *IEE International Conference on Antennas and Propagation,* 28–30 November 1978. See also resume in *Radio Communication* May 1979.

[9] 'Loaded wire aerials', F C Charman, G6CJ, *RSGB Bulletin* July 1961.

[10] 'Designing trap antennas: a new approach', Yardley Beers, W0JF, *Ham Radio* August 1987.

[11] 'All-band beam antennas', Les Moxon, G6XN, *Radio Communication* August 1991.

Chapter 8

Bandwidth

The term 'bandwidth', when applied to antenna systems, can have a number of different meanings. For example, in commercial systems an antenna may be required to operate without readjustment over a band of several octaves, perhaps even simultaneously on a number of frequencies disposed at random. In such cases the antenna can be accurately described as broadband, though it is certain to be inefficient unless based on some massive structure or the use of very long wires. In contrast, the amateur requires coverage only of a small number of narrow bands well separated in frequency and, although in principle this object can be achieved by broadband operation, in the above sense this is usually neither feasible nor desirable.

It is comparatively easy to design an antenna to operate on several of these bands, this being the process known as 'multibanding' which formed the subject of the last chapter. It needs to be distinguished from the 'broadbanding' typical of commercial systems, even though in some cases these may be alternative ways of achieving the same objectives. To be fully 'broadband' in the amateur context, an antenna only needs to operate satisfactorily over the whole of each of the frequency bands for which it is intended without requiring re-adjustment of the transmitter. This needs to be achieved if possible without significant change in gain or directivity, and these conditions are fairly easy to meet in the case of monoband dipoles or loops, long wires, and some of the methods of multibanding discussed in Chapter 7.

In the case of close-spaced beams, short dipoles and a number of multiband systems, compromise in one form or another is unavoidable, and it is important to observe the distinction between SWR bandwidth and directivity bandwidth. In each of these cases it may also be necessary to distinguish between the bandwidth for satisfactory operation without retuning, and the bandwidth over which acceptable performance can be achieved subject to adjustments capable of being carried out by the operator.

The SWR bandwidth

This is a property of the antenna plus feeder system and, although a high SWR can always be corrected so far as loading of the transmitter is concerned, it may be accompanied by appreciable extra losses and (with high power) a risk of voltage or current breakdown in the feeder system. Poor SWR bandwidth is often accompanied by poor directivity bandwidth which takes the form of a drop in front-to-back ratio or gain, or both, as the band edges are approached. These effects are not directly connected and may manifest themselves quite independently.

Directivity bandwidth

A large front-to-back ratio is the result of a very accurate balancing out of signals from the rear direction and is critically dependent on tuning, being upset by even a small change in the relative phase or amplitude of the quantities being balanced. Thus in the case of two elements it is readily shown that a phase error of $1/10$ radian (5.7°) limits the front-to-back ratio to a maximum of 20dB, regardless of whether the initial adjustment achieved 30dB, 40dB, or even infinite rejection.

This drop does not, however, necessarily mean that the directivity is *worse*: it may merely be *different*, as in the case of Fig 3.8(b) where the null instead of disappearing has split into two in different directions. In the case of most current antenna designs, nothing can be done in the shack to correct a drop in performance at the band edges. This is because the directivity is obtained by means of elements which are parasitically excited or connected in some way which likewise predetermines the phase and amplitude relationships. On the other hand, by using separate feeders to each element or the use of some mechanical form of remote tuning, this limitation can be overcome and arrangements will be described in a later chapter which enable an antenna to be adjusted from the shack for peak performance on any given frequency.

For reception, it is possible on the HF bands to trade sensitivity for bandwidth by taking advantage of the relatively high noise levels, as featured in the next chapter.

Operating bandwidth

By the use of resonant feeders as described in Chapter 7, antennas can be made capable of operation over a very wide band such as two or three octaves, subject to retuning by the operator, the price paid being *narrower* bandwidth in the absence of such re-adjustment. A wide operating bandwidth

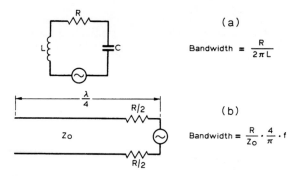

Fig 8.1. Comparison of lines and tuned circuits. The two expressions for bandwidth are comparable except that at (b) $\pi Z_0/4$ has replaced ωL

may also be achieved by remote tuning, eg the use of servo-controlled capacitors as suggested in the last chapter.

Log-periodic antennas, together with rhombics and (to a lesser extent) some monopoles or dipoles using multiple wires, can claim to be 'broadband' in all three of the respects listed above. HF receiving antennas tend to be broadband in the operating sense since, as explained in Chapter 9, 'efficiency' is not important.

Estimation of SWR bandwidth

In the case of antennas other than beams it is usually not difficult to estimate SWR bandwidth using a simple tuned circuit, Fig 8.1(a), as a model. The bandwidth of a tuned circuit between '3dB down' points is found by equating the reactance

$$\omega L - \frac{1}{\omega C}$$

to the resistance R in which case

$$R \approx 2\omega L \times (\delta f/f)$$

where $(\delta f/f)$ is the fractional frequency change. This can also be expressed in the form:

$$\text{Bandwidth} = 2\delta f = R/(\pi L)$$

Carrying out a similar operation for a resonant line or antenna, Fig 8.1(b), the reactance (from p37) is equal to $Z_0 2\pi \Delta l/\lambda$, and for a $\lambda/4$ line or $\lambda/2$ dipole $\Delta l = (\lambda/4) \times (\delta f/f)$. The resistance is therefore equal to the reactance when

$$R = Z_0 \cdot \frac{\pi}{2} \cdot (\delta f/f) = \frac{\pi}{4} \cdot 2Z_0(\delta f/f)$$

and the bandwidth $2\delta f$ is given by

$$\frac{R}{Z_0} \cdot \frac{4}{\pi} \cdot f$$

Compared with the result for the tuned circuit, $2\pi L$ (ie $\omega L/f$) has been replaced by Z_0/f and, although there is a small additional factor $4/\pi$ or 1.27, it is evident that the ωL of the

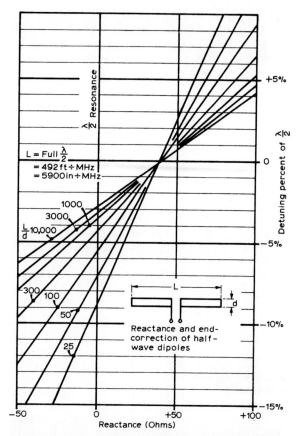

Fig 8.2. Tuning and reactance chart for $\lambda/2$ dipoles. Resonant lengths are slightly shorter than the physical length and decrease with increasing diameter of conductor. For practical HF dipoles L/d varies between about 50,000 and 300 so that the length correction can vary between about 2.4 and 4.5% with R (at resonance) varying as the square of the resonant length. These corrections vary with height and other environmental factors and are not applicable to beams or folded elements. Bandwidth is given by the percentage detuning for a total reactance change equal to $2R$

tuned circuit has been more or less replaced by the Z_0 of the line. This result is to be expected in view of the equivalence between lines and tuned circuits when used as transformers, as explained on p34. Applying this result to a $\lambda/2$ dipole having a radiation resistance of 73Ω and Z_0 equal to 1000Ω, we have

$$\frac{2\delta f}{f} \cdot \frac{73}{1000} \cdot \frac{4}{\pi} = 0.093$$

This is a bandwidth of 9.3% and it is clear that in the case of a simple dipole the bandwidth is proportional directly to R and inversely to Z_0. The '3dB down' points correspond to an SWR of 2.6 which may be found excessive, but the figures thus obtained need only be multiplied by 0.75 to obtain the bandwidth for an SWR of 2.0. Alternatively, the reactance at the centre of a $\lambda/2$ dipole near resonance may be obtained from Fig 8.2 which shows also the variation in resonant length with diameter. Shorter lengths imply some reduction in R which is roughly proportional to L^2.

If a wire is bent in some complicated manner it is difficult to predict bandwidth exactly, but a rough idea is sufficient for most purposes. The lack of a formula for Z_0 which takes shape fully into account is not important, as will be appreciated by looking at Fig 4.13 and visualising the major changes which have to be made in order to alter Z_0 significantly.

There is no difficulty in making a rough estimate if each section of wire is resolved into orthogonal components as explained on p10 and illustrated in Fig 6.8(c), which shows a right-angled delta loop fed at the right-angle.

A practical application of this is shown in Fig 11.13(f), p187, where dimensions are given for a 21MHz loop attached to a resonant feeder, and it is interesting as an example of the method to consider whether this might be used on the 10MHz band. To simplify the examples it will be assumed that the dimensions are adjusted slightly so that a half-wavelength fits exactly round the loop at 10.1MHz.

The long side of the triangle is 0.36 of the total length. Referring to Fig 2.5, it can be seen that the middle 36% of the current distribution yields a square count of 408 compared with the total of 760, so that if the sides of the triangle could be ignored, the radiation resistance would be $(408/760)^2 \times 73\Omega$. However, each side contributes 176 'squares' and each of the orthogonal components in Fig 6.8(c) is equivalent to $176 \div \sqrt{2}$ or 126 squares. Two of these represent current flow in the wrong direction so that (126×2) must be subtracted from the 408, which is more than a little unfortunate since there are only 156 left and the radiation resistance has come down with a big bump, ie to $(156/760)^2 \times 73$ or an insignificant 3.1Ω.

The vertical components have been ignored, but to make sure this is a reasonable assumption they can be considered as a 'W8JK pair' with an average separation of around $\lambda/4$, corresponding to a 90° phase difference. The field they produce corresponds to $126 \times \sqrt{2}$ squares but, allowing 3dB gain for the W8JK, the current needed to produce it is reduced by $\sqrt{2}$, leaving 126 squares as the reckonable contribution for working out the radiation resistance. This yields another 2Ω, so that the assumption was somewhat inaccurate.

Clutching at this further straw, we have a total of 5.1Ω and there are still some losses to be reckoned. The total wire length, including the resonant feeder, is 1.5λ at 10MHz so that, referring to Fig 3.11 and dividing by two for the more-or-less sinusoidal current distribution, the loss resistance (assuming 14swg (2mm) copper wire) is found to be 1Ω.

Though nothing to do with bandwidth, it is perhaps interesting to note in passing that 3.1/6.1 of the total power goes into a horizontally polarised wave at right-angles to the wire. For this mode, therefore, we have a 3dB loss with respect to a dipole, whereas the vertically polarised endwise 'W8JK' mode is only 2dB down on a dipole.

These figures are by no means useless but, to get to the point, what has happened to the bandwidth? The resonant feeder is an unsuitable length, and to cover all bands it is necessary for matching to use an ATU (which complicates

any arithmetic) or 'play around' with feeder lengths and matching transformers whenever the band is changed. However, if the system length can be reduced from 70ft (21.3m) to 50ft (15.2m), this will improve performance at 10MHz and simplifies the example. Because the 'line length' is $\lambda/2$ instead of $\lambda/4$, the bandwidth for a given Z_0 is half that given by the previous formula. However, because half the system consists of 600Ω line the average Z_0 should be only about 800Ω, ie

$$\text{Bandwidth} = 2\delta f = \frac{R}{Z_0} \cdot \frac{2}{\pi} \cdot f$$

$$= \frac{6.1f}{400\pi}$$

or about 0.5% of the frequency. This is 50kHz, which is equal to the width of the band, so that the system is viable, if somewhat marginal. Restoration of the length to 70ft can be expected to increase the SWR on the transmitter side of whatever matching device is used to about 3 or 4 at the band edges, assuming correct matching at band centre. This calculation is typical also of a 14MHz loop used at 7MHz.

Accurate calculation is difficult in the important case of short end-loaded elements, but R can be obtained with the help of Fig 3.12 and, as a very rough approximation, a Z_0 of 1000Ω can be assumed. Thus, for a 10ft (3m) element at 14MHz, $R \approx 14\Omega$ and, assuming the same cross-section and total length of wire, a bandwidth reduction of 14/73 compared with a $\lambda/2$ dipole can be expected; this comes to 250kHz which is adequate for coverage of the phone band.

Where the antenna or antenna-plus-feeder system consists of sections of known length and Z_0, it is a simple matter to work out SWR at the band centre and band edges by making use of the Smith chart as explained on p285. Assuming a match to have been established at band centre, the changes in electrical lengths corresponding to given percentage changes in frequency can be translated into reactances by means of the short-line formula $Z_0 2\pi l/\lambda$, and appropriate values entered in the chart to arrive at the approximate band-edge SWR. The lengths could be entered directly, except that one is then working with very small differences which it is not possible to read accurately.

A simple 'rule of thumb' in line with the above examples is illustrated in Fig 8.3 and provides 'answers at a glance' with sufficient accuracy for most occasions. This shows two lines, one of which can be the antenna. R_a is the radiation resistance and R its value as seen at the transmitter. The lines have

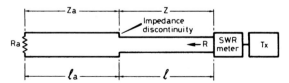

Fig 8.3. Lines in tandem. If l_a, l are multiples of $\lambda/4$ and there is no impedance discontinuity, $R = R_a$. In the worst case l_a, l are odd multiples of $\lambda/4$ and we have $R = (Z/Z_a)^2 R_a$ or $(Z_a/Z)^2 R_a$

impedances Z_a, Z, and lengths l_a, l. In accordance with the above formulae a change δl in the electrical length of a line, measured to a point of maximum current, results in a reactance $Z.2\pi\delta l/\lambda$ appearing in series with R. For 1% change in frequency and a line length of n quarter-wavelengths this becomes $\pi n Z/200$ or approximately $3nZ/200$. Z/R can be identified with the SWR (r_1, r_2 etc) and for the immediate purpose it will suffice to identify 'best' and 'worst' cases, the best (and simplest) occurring when $4l_a/\lambda$, $4l/\lambda$, the numbers of quarter-wavelengths in each line (n and m respectively) are even integers, in which case $R = R_a$. For each 1% of frequency change, R will have in series with it a reactance $\pi n Z_a/200$ due to the first line plus a further $\pi m Z/200$ from the second, and from inspection of the Smith chart it is found for a matched load R and an SWR limit of 2 that the reactance (X) must not exceed $0.7R$.

For a bandwidth of $p\%$ we have therefore:

$$nZ_a/R + mZ/R = nr_1 + mr_2 \approx 90/p$$

Though the derivation was simplified by assuming resonant lines, this is not an essential condition and the formula can be applied to lines of any length, in accordance with the following rule which can be readily established by moving round any circle on the Smith chart in fixed increments of λ.

If a conjugate match is established along a loss-free feeder system, at whatever distance from the load, any given small change of line length will always result in the same mismatch.

This is in line with the fact, already established, that if the feeder length is doubled its bandwidth is halved since only half as much change in frequency is needed to produce a given length change expressed in wavelengths. The line is assumed to be operating at a fixed value of SWR and caution is needed in applying the rule to a composite system such as Fig 8.3.

A 'worst case' arises when n and m are odd integers and $Z_a/Z > 1$. R_a is presented to the second line as a larger value Z_a^2/R_a.

We now have $r_2 = r_1 Z_a/R_a$. Things may indeed be a lot worse but the above formula remains valid. To see why this should be so, refer again to Fig 8.4 and assume an impedance ratio of 2. If the first line is short by the amount Δl this will be made good by the capacitance of the initial portion of the second line, the length subtracted from it for this purpose being only $\Delta l/2$. Thus, although the reactance change per unit length is double in the case of the first line, the effect as 'seen' by the second line is the same as if there was no change in Z. Though calculations are now more difficult, the bandwidth formula remains unchanged, although the bandwidth, alas, does not; putting $m = n = 1$ the two lines become instantly recognisable as $\lambda/4$ transformers, and in this case both R and the bandwidth are divided by 4.

The 'impedance-transforming loop' featured on p126 exploits this effect to advantage by using it in reverse. In this case the loop itself functions as a pair of $\lambda/4$ transformers, a typical radiation resistance of 50Ω being stepped up to a value of 200Ω for presentation to an open-wire feeder. Extending

the above analysis to include 2λ of feeder operating at an SWR of 3 we have

$$r_1 + r_2 + 8r_3 = 10 + 5 + 8 \times 3 = 39$$

giving a bandwidth of $2 \times 50/39 = 2.5\%$, in good agreement with a measured figure of 2.1%. Note that with $\lambda/2$ of feeder the overall bandwidth would be doubled, being little less than that of the antenna alone (6.6%); for a comparable single wire loop the antenna bandwidth is 2.5%, and roughly halved by adding $\lambda/2$ of feeder.

One further example concerns the use of traps and is complementary to the investigation of trap losses in the last chapter, p130. In view of the difficulty in allowing for 'coupled circuit' effects, the example relates to a single-wire dipole, but a 14/21MHz element and a typical trap capacitance of 40pF are again assumed. Taking a value of 1000Ω for Z_0, the impedance between the dipole ends at 21MHz comes to $(1000/73) \times 1000 = 13,700\Omega$. This appears across the two traps in series, these being equivalent to a single tuned circuit of 20pF, ie $X \approx 400\Omega$, giving a Q of $13,700/400 = 34$ which corresponds to a bandwidth of 624kHz. This is adequate for band coverage at 21MHz but drops to only 171kHz for a radiation resistance of 20Ω, corresponding to that of the beam but taking no account of the coupling which improves matters. However, even if this is doubled it remains inadequate, and the answer probably is to reduce the trap capacitance.

The SWR bandwidth of a coupled pair of elements may be greater than that of a single element, this being closely analogous to broadening the bandwidth of amplifiers by the use of coupled pairs of circuits. The reduction in impedance of a primary circuit as a result of detuning is offset due to a decrease in the impedance transferred from the secondary, and this effect was most noticeable in experiments with small, slightly overcoupled beams, the SWR bandwidth being much greater than the pattern bandwidth.

Estimation of SWR bandwidth in the case of two-element beams is more difficult because of the additional variables but, in most cases, assuming equal-current arrays with parasitic reflectors and keeping within recommended limits, it tends to be not very different from that of single elements in spite of the lower values of R. By analogy with coupled circuits, an improvement of the order of 2.5 times might be expected, though the analogy is flawed to the extent that instead of being reactive the coupling impedance is a mixture of resistance and reactance.

Estimation of directivity bandwidth

The same methods may be applied to parasitic elements in order to obtain the directivity bandwidth, except that in this case there is no recognised definition of bandwidth. For a three-element beam this could be based on keeping within the shaded areas of Fig 5.25, although the antenna will work with only slightly reduced performance well outside these limits.

For two-element beams it will be noted from Figs 5.4, 5.7 and 9.4 that adjustment of phasing is less critical if the main interest is less QRM rather than maximising gain. Above a phase-angle ratio of 0.7 up to some value well in excess of 1.0 there should not be any noticeable difference in average interference levels, though gain is dropping off fairly steeply. On the other hand, a decrease to 0.5 results in a 10dB increase in QRM for some 0.5dB of extra gain, the maximum gain condition being also much more critical from the point of view of matching, and resulting in greatly increased interference from some directions as well as a possible increase in average interference levels.

A reasonable compromise, referring to Fig 5.4, might be to let φ vary from φ_0 at the highest to $\varphi_0/2$ at the lowest frequency, eg for $\lambda/8$ spacing the reactance can be allowed to change from 36.5Ω to 73Ω. For a typical wire beam (Z_0 = 1000Ω) we have (see p35)

$$\Delta l/\lambda = 36.5/(1000 \times 2\pi) = 0.0058$$

To convert this into a *percentage* change in the *length of a $\lambda/4$ line* there are multiplying factors of 4 and 100, ie the bandwidth as a percentage is given by $0.0058 \times 400 = 2.32$. This amounts to 329kHz at 14.2MHz so that reasonable band coverage is possible, though no account has been taken of possible amplitude changes which could affect the depth of nulls, and full band coverage has been achieved at the price of accepting a marked increase of interference levels over the lower third of the band.

On the other hand, if the reflector is remotely tunable, for example by the use of resonant feeders as in the case of several of the beams described in these pages, there is little or no variation of null depth over a given band. However, one pitfall has been identified: recommendations for fine adjustment of coupling between elements have included the use of capacitors between feedlines in the shack, but if this is attempted too close to points of maximum current the voltages and therefore the coupling will be varying rapidly with frequency. To guard against such hazards, one must not merely be aware of the axiom stated on p42 which has tripped up designers of ground-plane antennas in such spectacular fashion, but prepared for the same effect to appear in even more subtle disguises which, after many wasted hours, have left the author's ego badly deflated.

With tubing elements the bandwidth can be increased by at least 50% which could be important if one has strong views as to the choice of working point on Fig 5.4, particularly if this choice veers in the direction of maximum gain. However, an even more important consideration may well be the need for lightweight structures leading to wire beams with directional switching (p202) or compact rotary beams such as those described on p207.

The directivity bandwidth for a 14MHz beam folded into a 10ft (3m) square (p206) is reduced relative to that for full-sized elements by the same factor 14/73 as the SWR bandwidth of the individual elements but, compared with the previous example, there is a 25% increase due to the wider spacing. This results in a bandwidth of 77kHz which can be roughly doubled if the gain is allowed to drop by an additional 1dB ($\varphi/\varphi_0 = 1.5$), at which point the front-to-back ratio is still quite high. Alternatively one might, for example, be interested in

the bandwidth for better than 20dB front-to-back ratio for which, from Figs 5.4 and 5.7, the allowable reactance change is 36% of the value which would produce a phase change equal to φ_0, ie $14 \times 1.25 \times 0.36 = 6.3\Omega$. This translates into a bandwidth of about 60kHz, in good agreement with measured values.

This example follows usual practice in relating front/back ratio to a single bearing off the back instead of taking an average based on all back directions, which would be more meaningful but also a lot more difficult. In some cases what appears to be a worsening of the front/back ratio is merely a *shift in direction of the nulls*. The difficulty is accentuated if one tries to compare beams with different numbers of elements. For example reference [23] of Chapter 5 presents large numbers of curves showing the variation of front/back ratio with frequency for various three- and four-element beams, and these show quite dramatically the advantage in terms of directivity bandwidth of operating in the lower right-hand corner of Fig 5.24. It appears from the reference that (with three elements) better than 26dB of F/B ratio can be obtained over a bandwidth of 2% using boom lengths of 0.2 to 0.3λ, though the gain is then no better than that of a two-element, equal-current array. By accepting ratios of 10 to 15dB and boom lengths of 0.3–0.5λ, at least 2dB of extra gain becomes available. With four elements on a 0.7λ boom it should be possible to obtain 3dB gain advantage over the two-element beam, with 20dB F/B ratio over a bandwidth of at least 1%.

These figures are difficult to compare with this author's results for critically coupled pairs of elements. Being for one direction only, they fail to show improvements in *average* front/back ratio as illustrated for example by Fig 5.28, and to obtain the full story one needs to plot the *complete* directivity patterns which has been done (though only for a single frequency) in reference [21] of Chapter 5. Between them these two very valuable references provide a fairly complete but rather complicated picture, from which an attempt has been made to distill the aspects likely to be of most concern to the reader.

Effects of loading

As we have seen, antennas and beam elements often have to be reduced in length by folding or loading to fit them into the available space. Loading in its simpler forms means replacing part of the antenna by an equivalent inductance or capacitance, and the incremental reactance resulting from a given small percentage of detuning is not greatly altered for loading of up to about 50%. This leaves the bandwidth determined mainly by, and proportional to, the radiation resistance, which for single radiators can be obtained from Fig 4.60 or calculated with the help of Fig 2.5. It will be seen to come down very steeply with length in the case of inductive loading, though (as explained in Chapters 11 and 16) matters can be improved by careful placement of the loading. It is important to appreciate that this only applies to loading of a *radiator*, and this means that in the case of an asymmetrical dipole such as the ground-plane the radials can be loaded

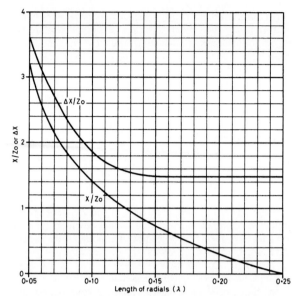

Fig 8.4. Variation of X/Z_0 and $\Delta X/Z_0$ with length (λ) for single wires. Z_0 = characteristic impedance of the wire and ΔX is the change in reactance corresponding to 1% change in frequency (ARRL)

equal-diameter conductors have been assumed throughout, and the reference SWR bandwidth is 3.5% for typical wires at heights above 0.2λ or 7% for the same wires at ground level. As examples, note that these bandwidths are reduced by only 30% for a set of four $\lambda/16$ or a pair of $\lambda/8$ radials, and a pair of $\lambda/20$ radials covers the European 7MHz band. Except with very short radials, the radiator is the main source of reactance and bandwidth is therefore improved by the use of tubing in accordance with normal practice.

End-fed antennas

Hitherto the most usual method of end-feeding antennas has been one or other version of the Zepp feed, as described in Chapter 4, p49, where attention was drawn to the large bandwidth penalties incurred by such methods in the absence of losses. (It may be recalled that use of the G6CJ matching stub allows the feedpoint to be moved inwards which should improve bandwidth, although the antenna is then no longer strictly end-fed.) Alternatives include the use of tuners, which also restrict bandwidth, and the new method of end-feeding with coaxial cable described on p47 (based on the 'end-fed Windom' idea but with the single-wire feeder reduced to zero length).

A surprise feature of this system as applied to the vertical beam described on p227 was the extremely wide bandwidth, an inherent property of this type of antenna previously masked by the narrow bandwidth of the Zepp feed.

A further unexpected development has been the discovery that, applied to the end-feeding of a $\lambda/2$ dipole, it results in virtually the same bandwidth as if the dipole were centre-fed in the usual way with an identical feeder. It was in fact this exercise which first drew attention to the rule featured in italics above. Previous to this, matching of two-wire systems

without affecting R. With further increase of loading the reactances rise as shown in Fig 8.4 with X exceeding the Z_0 of the wires which it replaces so that $Z_0.2\pi\delta l/\lambda$ also increases and bandwidth decreases [1]. (It is worth noting however that efficiency is not affected unless the loading coil is so large that its resistance is comparable with R.)

On this basis Fig 8.5 shows the variation of bandwidth with number and length of radials, taking a $\lambda/4$ radiator with four radials as a standard of reference. To simplify the computation,

Fig 8.5. Variation in bandwidth with number and length of radials. (All conductors are the same diameter. A set of four $\lambda/4$ radials are taken as standard) (ARRL)

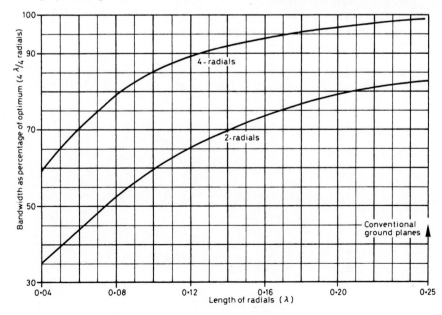

by series capacitance close to voltage antinodes had been much used by the author as a best solution to a number of problems, despite a suspected bandwidth penalty which, in fact, turns out to be non-existent. Referring to Fig 8.4, it does not require a very large frequency change to wipe out the incremental length Δl and thus, one might think, render the system inoperative. In fact, as Δl decreases, the impedance to which matching is effected increases steadily until, at resonance, the matching process becomes identical with that provided by an odd number of quarter-wavelengths of line, and the rule continues to hold.

Other factors affecting bandwidth

The line-reactance formulae indicate that if a resonant system such as an antenna or antenna-plus-feeder contains several half-wavelengths, the reactance arising from any given departure from the resonant frequency will be increased in proportion to the total length, assuming a constant value of Z_0. This results not only in a proportionate decrease in bandwidth in accordance with the formulae, but also increased losses due to the greater length of wire. Such effects may or may not be important depending on the value of radiation resistance, the possibility or otherwise of retuning from the shack, and the importance or otherwise attached to rapid changes of operating frequency.

As we have seen, bandwidth is a property of the *antenna-plus-feeder system* and could well involve several changes of Z_0. Where large transformation ratios are involved it is usually best for impedance matching to perform the operation in two or more stages, and if it is necessary to use two different feeder impedances the respective lengths should be chosen to minimise any mismatches in accordance with advice on pp146, 147.

It has been found that changes in the matching arrangements can have a considerable effect on SWR bandwidth. In one case a big improvement resulted in going from a gamma match to a balanced system; conversely it was found that a large 'delta', in which matching was controlled by choice of wire diameter, resulted in less than half the bandwidth obtained with a smaller series-tuned delta match, which in effect connected the feeder directly to points of the correct impedance. Unfortunately there seem to be no guidelines available in regard to this aspect of matching, and the author can do no more than invite the reader to share his own misgivings about gamma matches!

In the case of a beam the radiation resistance cannot be related directly to bandwidth, owing to the 'coupled circuit effect' which tends to improve matters as indicated earlier.

Discussion

Having read this chapter, the reader will appreciate that *the term 'bandwidth' can mean a lot of different things*. It tends to be used rather loosely but the meaning can usually be inferred from the context and it would be awkward to have to define or qualify it on all occasions. In general, better directivity bandwidth can be traded for gain, particularly if there are a lot of elements. SWR bandwidth, though often used as the main criterion of 'bandwidth', is of little *intrinsic* importance which is a pity in view of the impressive figures which can be achieved with overcoupled elements. It is true, however, that a poor SWR bandwidth may have undesirable practical consequences, especially in terms of convenience for the operator who likes to move around the band a lot. In some cases it may be necessary to reckon that an antenna is 'unusable' when SWR exceeds some specified value; this defines the edges of the usable band of frequencies and therefore the 'useful bandwidth'.

Since directivity and gain are closely linked it has not been thought necessary to define a separate 'gain' bandwidth, but it may be noted that maximum gain does not in general coincide with best directivity; at one edge of the useful band, gain may be falling off rapidly although the directivity remains fair, whereas at the other edge, front/back ratio tends to become poor before the gain has dropped significantly. In this case there can be only a subjective definition of bandwidth depending on what the individual user regards as acceptable.

Reference

[1]   'Ground planes, radial systems and asymmetric dipoles', *ARRL Antenna Compendium*, Vol 3, ARRL, 1993.

Chapter 9

Antennas for reception

Capture area

As might be expected, a good transmitting antenna can be expected to do well as a receiving antenna and, *in terms of signal power delivered to a matched receiver,* there is full reciprocity between the transmitting and receiving properties of an antenna. This may be a good point at which to explain the term 'antenna aperture' since this will be encountered quite frequently in the literature. It is easy to fall into the trap of thinking 'there is no substitute for it', a frequent claim which distracts attention from the possibilities of 'supergain' (subtractive gain) arrays, to which class most amateur HF beam antennas belong as explained in Chapter 5.

A *large* antenna system can be loosely regarded as intercepting most of the signal energy passing through the space occupied; this space is defined as the 'aperture' or 'capture area', and doubling it can be expected to double the amount of signal energy collected. This ties in with the fact that in the case of large beams, as already explained, doubling the size doubles the transmitting gain, thereby endorsing the principle of reciprocity.

As array size is reduced, eventually a point is reached where the additive gain principle on which large arrays depend is no longer operative, because if fields are additive for one direction they must be additive for all directions, the dimension being too small to generate significant phase differences. The antenna system is now small enough to allow use of the subtractive principle as explained in Chapter 3, so that as size is further reduced 'directivity gain' stays constant but the bandwidth shrinks instead. The antenna now has a high Q and, just as tuned circuits couple together more tightly if the Q is increased, so the smaller the antenna, the more tightly it couples into the surrounding space.

If it is desired to retain the concept of aperture this is still possible provided a short dipole, for example, is regarded as *effectively* occupying the same space as a $\lambda/2$ dipole. This is important to remember in the context of stacking since, if the dipoles of individual beam-units of a large array are replaced by smaller units, the separation required between them remains unchanged. The apertures of the individual units should be not quite touching so that the respective collecting areas are completely separate and not partially shared. It will be recalled also that in an earlier chapter stacking distance was

linked with the *directivity* of the separate beam units and not their size. These are merely different ways of looking at the same problem. Capture area is formally defined by the expression

$$A = G_0 \frac{\lambda^2}{4\pi}$$

where G_0 is the power gain (as an arithmetical ratio) relative to an isotropic antenna. For a dipole this becomes

$$A = \frac{1.64}{4\pi} \lambda^2 = 0.13\lambda^2$$

The shape of the capture area can be deduced from inspection of Fig 5.13, bearing in mind that apertures can be regarded as 'just touching' only when the mutual resistance is small. For the collinear pairs in Chapter 6 it was found that the mutual resistance falls to zero at a spacing between centres of 0.71λ, the corresponding separation for the broadside pair being 0.44λ, so that pairs of elements having these spacings will provide exactly 3dB gain. The approximate ratio of two-thirds for equivalent couplings is applicable to closer spacings as well. Assuming an elliptical shape, it follows that the capture area as defined by the formula above has a major axis of 0.51λ along the line of the wire and 0.34λ at right-angles to it, as shown in Fig 9.1. The corresponding spacings provide gains of 2.2dB only, so that the capture areas as defined above are somewhat imprecise and to some extent overlapping. Nevertheless, the 'just touching' rule tends to provide a reasonably good compromise between gain and overall size.

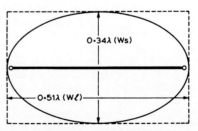

Fig 9.1. Capture area of dipole; this is most easily conceived as a rectangle but is in fact elliptical, being given more accurately by the area W_lW_s of the rectangle multiplied by $\pi/4$. Equating it also to $0.13\lambda^2$ and making use of the two-thirds shape factor as explained in the text enables W_lW_s to be determined

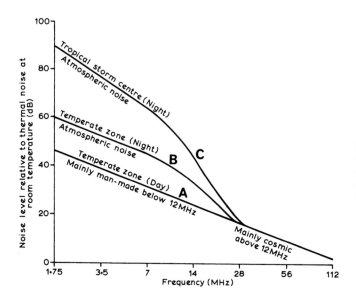

Fig 9.2. Variation of external noise level with frequency, indicating the cosmic noise level which provides a realistic basis for the design of receivers and antenna systems from about 10 or 14MHz upwards. The man-made level, though typical of some suburban locations, varies between wide limits and the atmospheric noise levels, though typical of night-time extremes, are also very variable

In most treatments of antenna gain, this book being no exception, there is an implicit assumption that the transmitted (or received) energy is concentrated within a 'beamwidth', within which there is no discrimination, but which embraces the whole of the transmitted energy* apart perhaps from that contained in a few small 'sidelobes'. This simplifies explanations but falls short of being an accurate description of real-life situations. Fortunately, for the most part, no great precision is needed and the definition of beamwidth as the 'width between half-power points' usually leads to acceptable answers.

The above figures for gain versus separation distance may also be obtained from the array factors plotted in Fig 3.9, thus demonstrating the identity between receiving and transmitting gain expressed as a power ratio.

In putting this into figures it is easiest to assume a rectangular capture area A_r in which case (Fig 9.1)

$$A_r = \frac{G}{4\pi} \lambda^2 = W_1 W_s = \frac{\alpha_1}{\alpha_2} W_1^2$$

where G is the gain over an isotropic antenna (or 1.64 times the gain over a dipole) and α_1/α_2 is the ratio of the beam angles. It will be seen that if the capture area is held constant the gain increases (beamwidth decreases) as $1/\lambda^2$, ie as the square of the frequency.

In view of conflicting figures elsewhere in the literature some readers may be a bit confused at this point, but any difficulty can be resolved by realising that the ratio of the axes of the ellipse is also the ratio of the radiation-pattern widths in the E and H planes. A long thin ellipse means the beam

angle is much narrower in one plane than the other, and it is impossible to have a narrow angle without gain, which must in fact be at least equal to the ratio of the axes. It is no coincidence that the ratio in Fig 9.1 is almost the same as the gain of a dipole over an isotropic radiator. A ratio of three, for example, would involve a gain of three and could not be achieved with a single dipole. Because of this the apertures of the dipoles comprising the top and bottom parts of a quad loop are mainly overlapped, and the gain is only 1dB compared with a dipole. Additional elements increase the apertures so that there is more overlap and the stacking gain is even less.

Signal-to-noise ratio

The principle of reciprocity is useful up to a point, since in most cases it is a mistake to use different antennas for transmitting and receiving. It can, however, be misleading if an antenna is being designed for receiving only; it can happen that, given two equally good antennas for transmission, one may be better for reception. This is because in reception one is not concerned with signal strength alone but with the ratio of signals to noise or interference. HF receivers usually have, and can always (unless the antenna is very small) be designed to have, much lower noise levels than the external noise normally arriving from outer space (cosmic noise), even if atmospheric noise (which is commonly regarded as the major source) is ignored. Any losses in the antenna system therefore decrease the signal and the noise equally, leaving reception unaffected, and thus allowing full benefit to be obtained from whatever directivity is available.

Fig 9.2 shows the ratio of external noise levels to the internal noise level of a low-noise (3dB noise figure) receiver, the allowable reduction in antenna efficiency for less than 1dB drop in signal-to-noise ratio being only 6dB less than the noise levels given by the curves. This demonstrates the

---

* There is a close analogy between beamwidth of antennas and bandwidth of receivers. In the case of receivers 'energy bandwidth' tends to be nearly equal to '3dB down bandwidth', a single tuned circuit being the main exception. Similarly, with antennas the approximation is least accurate in the case of a single element.

possibility in the case of 'receiver only' applications of exploiting superdirectivity to a much greater extent, any bandwidth problems being overcome by remote tuning using variable-capacitance diodes or the use of short 'active' antennas as described later in this chapter.

Antennas with strong high-angle lobes can be expected to pick up more cosmic noise since the ionosphere is transparent at high angles – this is consistent with the author's own experience in a 'quiet' location of lower noise levels when using vertical antennas. Unfortunately vertical antennas are usually worse in regard to pick-up of man-made noise, and there must be many cases where the ability to switch polarisation would be useful for reception. Using horizontal antennas, maximum discrimination against noise arriving at vertical incidence occurs for heights which are a multiple of $\lambda/2$, and in theory there might for reception be some advantage in using these heights. However, at the higher frequencies the ionosphere will usually be transparent to cosmic noise over a range of angles extending downwards well into the vertical patterns of most antennas.

With long-wire antennas and some large arrays, the situation is rather different since high-angle lobes are greatly reduced. Terminated long-wire antennas such as rhombics can be expected to have lower noise levels since the resistance (ideally) absorbs half the noise power. It also of course absorbs half the transmitter power, but this is energy which would otherwise be radiated in the back direction and leaves the forward signal unaffected.

A reduction in noise level, particularly if it is achieved by the use of low-efficiency superdirective antennas, will demand greater receiver sensitivity. This could involve a clash of interests since some receiver designers have wisely taken advantage of the high external noise levels to combat the overloading effects of strong signals. The measures adopted, such as the omission in some cases of RF stages, degrade the sensitivity so that there may be no reserve for exploiting the virtues of some types of low-noise antennas. In the case of lossy antennas strong signals are of course less of a problem and there could be some value in providing a wider range of front-end options in receivers. This would also allow advantage to be taken of abnormally low noise levels such as can occur in the early stages of recovery from an SID (sudden ionospheric disturbance).

A first step towards improving the ratio of signal to noise of man-made origin is usually to place the antenna as far away as possible, not only from known interference sources, but also mains wiring or other conductors by which their range may be extended. This may be difficult, especially in the case of an indoor environment, but with the help of a portable receiver it may be possible to find quieter areas. The smaller the antenna, the better the chance of finding a good location, except that then there is a greater chance of the wanted signal being masked by noise picked up on the feeder. Some of the measures described in Chapter 4 for the prevention of feeder radiation are useful in this context also, such as an RF choke near the feedpoint; this could consist of several turns of feeder wound through a ferrite ring.

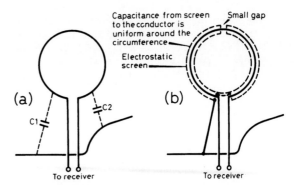

Fig 9.3. At (a) the loop is unbalanced by capacitance to its surroundings. At (b) the use of an electrostatic shield overcomes this effect *(ARRL Antenna Book)*

Reference [2] describes extensive tests with a five-turn loop, 4ft square, designed for reception on 1.8 and 3.5MHz. Compared with a vertical transmitting antenna it was found to be better "by a substantial margin when it comes to digging weak signals out of the (man-made and atmospheric) noise", even when used indoors, though on some occasions the vertical was better and the loop responded to some kinds of noise such as switching transients which were not picked up on the external antenna. Even better performance can be obtained by the use of screened loops, as confirmed by later tests with a four-turn electrically-shielded loop only 13.5in in diameter, which in the course of a DX contest was found to be "in all instances as good or better than the 75ft (22.86m) vertical".

The easiest way to construct a shielded loop is to use one or more turns of coaxial cable, the outer braid being broken in the centre of the coil so that it does not act as a short-circuited turn. This is illustrated in Fig 9.3 which shows also the reason why shielding is necessary [3]. This is often referred to as the 'antenna effect', and its elimination gets rid of most of the noise picked up from house wiring and results in sharper nulls in directions at right-angles to the plane of the loop. These nulls can be extremely useful for the reduction of noise and interference from other sources, particularly if the loop is rotatable from the operating position. The lower sensitivity of loops may make it necessary to use a low-noise preamplifier, and for the higher-frequency bands no more than one turn should be used, size limits being imposed by self-capacitance in the case of screened loops. It is also to be noted that for best directivity the current distribution round the loop needs to be uniform and to this end [3] a conductor length of 0.1λ should not be exceeded.

Interfering signals

In most of the examples in this book the emphasis is on transmitting gain, and usually if, say, 1dB improvement is obtained there is no need to worry about where this comes from, ie whether it is due to less back, side or high-angle radiation. Indeed, if noise and interference were to arrive uniformly from all directions, then the performance in reception, in terms of mean ratio of wanted-to-unwanted signal or noise power, would by definition be identical with the transmitting gain. This point is usually overlooked, greater importance being attached to front/back ratio defined for an arbitrary angle (the reciprocal of the beam heading). As will be seen, however, it usually makes more sense, even from the point of view of interference reduction, to aim for somewhat greater gain.

All antennas radiate some energy in nearly all directions and likewise receive from these directions. The radiation pattern may contain, in addition to the wanted 'main lobe', a number of smaller ones known as 'sidelobes' (p108) which may account for most of the unwanted signals received. With conventional low-gain antennas, the ability to reduce sidelobes is limited by the fact that the number of possible nulls (which is loosely related to the number of elements) is quite small. Increasing the *depth* of a null does not affect its *width*, and for benefit to be obtained from what is in effect better balancing out of an unwanted signal, this has to fit into a relatively narrow slot in the pattern. Given this situation, it may be possible to rotate the beam so that the interference drops into the slot. This may, however, reduce the wanted signal and it is no help if there is more than one signal or, as is often the case (particularly with short skip distances), more than one angle of arrival.

Using a computer to control phases and amplitudes, there are possibilities in the case of n elements of nulling out $n-1$ signals, though such a system would normally be beyond amateur resources. However, multiband antennas based on resonant feeders, as described in other chapters, have the important feature that the antenna directivity and gain is under the control of the operator in the shack, and in this case it is not difficult to arrange relays so that different phasing networks are brought into use for reception. A single source of interference can then be nulled out without too much difficulty, provided it is not in the same direction as the wanted signal.

The sidelobe problem is an important one for designers of large arrays, particularly for reception, since often sidelobes can be greatly reduced by sacrificing a certain amount of gain, but does not greatly concern the average amateur operating on the HF bands.

Amateurs will of course be anxious not only to reduce interference in reception but also to cause as little interference as possible, so that if a separate receiving network is used as suggested above, it must be switched out when checking whether or not a channel is already occupied. Similarly, if different antennas are used for transmission and reception, it is important to switch over to the transmitting antenna for channel checking since a null in one pattern may well coincide with a sidelobe of the other.

Another point to be noted is the possibility of interference by one antenna, or even overhead wires, with the pattern of another antenna. An antenna can of course act as a reflector of interfering signals, rather in the manner of a radar reflector, and it is important to realise that from this point of view its

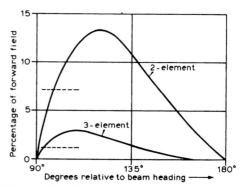

Fig 9.4. Comparison of two- and three-element arrays for rejection of signals from the back direction, currents being adjusted to give a null at 180° in both cases and the gains being 4.2dB and 4.6dB respectively. The dotted lines indicate 'average' levels

radiation pattern is not directly related to the normal pattern which is derived in terms of voltages delivered to the feeder system. The reflector of a beam, for example, will in general respond fully to signals coming from *either* direction and re-radiate them in *both* directions. A degree of coupling between two antennas sufficiently low not to affect the transmitting gain of the one in use may nevertheless result in an unacceptable level of interference due to re-radiation of signals from the back direction.

Advantages of three or more elements

It has been shown in earlier chapters (notably on p101) that, in practice, increasing the number of elements from two to three or four with close spacing has comparatively little effect on transmitting gain. In contrast to this, it might be conjectured that quite a small current flowing in a third element would suffice for cancelling out the residual response of two elements in the back direction, which is likely to be at least 10dB down on the main lobe.

Calculations are difficult and laborious for more than two elements, except in a few simple cases such as the three-element array described on p94, which it is useful to recall at this point, noting in particular Fig 5.23 which has been reproduced as Fig 9.4. This compares backward radiation for two-and three-element arrangements, the big reduction in *average* signal strength for the back directions in the case of three elements being clearly demonstrated. The forward gains are 4.6dB and 4.2dB respectively, so that in terms of transmitting gain the larger beam is slightly down, even compared with the best that can be achieved with two elements, and it is unlikely that much improvement in this respect can be affected without loss of front/back ratio.

It will be recalled that the 'best possible' (for gain) four-element design (p103) is quite poor in this respect, so that there seems to be here a particularly strong case for the use of separate tuning units for transmission and reception. With two elements a deep null can be created in any given direction, but this is in no way equivalent to the kind of rejection demonstrated in Fig 9.4 since it has to be carried out afresh for each case of interference.

Nevertheless, nulling is seen as a very useful *additional* facility, equally applicable to two or three elements and capable of improving discrimination by a further order of magnitude. In the process it takes care of reflections from other antennas and structures, which can otherwise seriously compromise the interference-rejecting properties of both two- and three-element beams. Whether the three-element performance indicated by Fig 9.4 is achieved in practice will depend on whether the mutual couplings happen to be such as to give the required current ratios and phasing; and this will certainly *not* happen in the case of a quad because, as already explained (p90), the current in a director is very small.

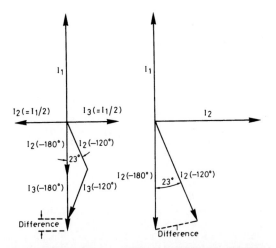

Fig 9.5. Derivation of Figs 9.4 and 5.23. (a) Three-element array. (b) Two-element array. Solid lines with no angle markings show current amplitudes and phases relative to I_1 as they might appear from the forward direction, and the lines with downward arrows show them for the −180° and −120° directions respectively. At (a) the forward field is accounted for solely by I_1, the field in any back direction being proportional to what is left after vector subtraction of I_2, I_3 as shown. This is zero for −180° and equal to $I_1(1 − \cos 23°)$, ie $0.08I_1$ only, for the −120° compared with $I_1(2 × \sin 11½°)$ or $0.4I_1$ for the two-element case. After allowing 3dB for the increase in forward field (for a given I) in the case of two elements, there remains an 11dB advantage in favour of three elements

The possibility that (for three elements) Fig 9.4 is not far removed from being an optimum design for reception can be inferred from inspection of Fig 9.5 which compares the derivation of the two curves. It can be seen that so long as I_2, I_3 remain equal the phase of their sum is unchanged and its amplitude varies comparatively slowly as the signal direction alters, whereas any variation of these conditions tends towards closing the gap between the two curves which become identical when one of the currents falls to zero. Further insight is obtainable from [4] which provides a set of 360° radiation patterns covering the full range of options and both axes; these demonstrate a fairly-well defined optimum for reception corresponding to the bottom right-hand corner of Fig

5.24. This yields also the closest approach to the lower curve of Fig 9.4 but the current ratio, of the order of 2.5, falls a long way short of meeting the equal-current requirement. In other words, in this case, as with two elements, optimum design targets for reception cannot be fully met with parasitic operation based on straight elements. Other difficulties in the three-element case may ensue from the need to preserve symmetry (eg by ganged tuning of parasitic elements) when frequency is changed, and a lower value of radiation resistance resulting in tighter tolerances.

In Fig 9.4 the placement of nulls at 180° from the beam heading provides a useful basis for comparison, though it is essentially a non-optimum condition, not only in respect of gain but also for the reduction of QRM levels. As pointed out earlier, in the case of *omnidirectional* interference, eg noise or large numbers of signals arriving from all angles with equal probability, maximum gain coincides by *definition* with minimum interference but this is based on energy considerations and is no more realistic than the usual practice of considering only a single arrival angle. In practice, with maximum gain the nulls have moved round towards the end-on directions for which there is already considerable rejection.

A more useful measure of discrimination against interference is the number of degrees in the back direction over which the signal strength exceeds some given percentage of the forward field strength. This can be interpreted in terms of the probability of a given level of interference as has been done for the two-element case in Fig 9.6 based on Fig 5.7. It will be evident that minimum interference requires the beam to be tuned for nulls at 140° and 220°, *not* the usual 180° which results in slightly more interference and 0.5dB less gain.

On the other hand, tuning for *maximum gain* results in much greater likelihood of interference, a substantial drop in radiation resistance (which could have consequences such as restriction of bandwidth), some operational inconvenience and perhaps (after taking due account of side effects) a net reduction in gain, all for a theoretical increase in gain of only another 0.5dB. If therefore the same adjustment has to serve for both reception and transmission, the 140° null condition is easily the best compromise, and this applies equally to a quad, bi-square, or two-element dipole array, regardless of whether elements are driven or parasitic. Possible exceptions include extreme cases of miniaturisation and other 'lossy' situations (eg some indoor antennas) for which a rather larger value of phase shift may be beneficial as discussed on p97. Similar considerations apply in principle to three- and four-element arrays, though actual figures are not available.

Out-of-band signals

A point that needs to be watched is the risk of interference from strong out-of-band signals, due to the narrow pattern bandwidth of most beams combined with the poor strong-signal performance of most receivers. A monoband beam is likely to be better in this respect and remote tuning can also help.

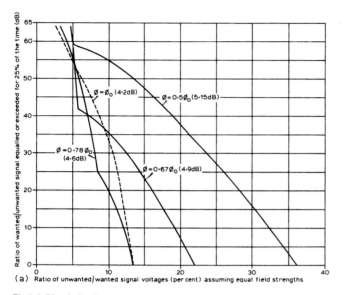

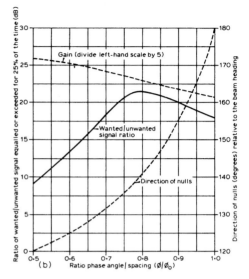

(a) Ratio of unwanted/wanted signal voltages (per cent) assuming equal field strengths

(b) Ratio phase angle/spacing (ϕ/ϕ_0)

Fig 9.6. Discrimination of two-element beams against interfering signals, in terms of the probability of given ratios of unwanted to wanted signal voltages. Interference is assumed to be coming in on the back of the beams from a single continuous source which moves around, so that all directions over a 180° arc are equally likely, the unwanted signal being equal in field strength to the wanted signal. Note that minimum interference requires $\phi/\phi_0 = 0.78$, corresponding to a gain of 4.6dB (as marked on the curve) and, from (b), the placing of nulls in directions of 140° relative to the beam heading. The solid curve in (b) is the effective front/back ratio based on the stated interference probability. It shows an improvement of 3.5dB, coupled with 0.5dB increase of gain, compared with the condition $\phi = \phi_0$ implicit in the usual procedure of tuning for 'maximum front/back ratio'

Nulling of interference

The nulling out of an interfering signal is a critical balancing operation involving both phase and amplitude as shown schematically in Fig 9.7, being closely analogous to the use of an AC bridge. It requires two knobs and a sensitive indicator, the human ear being more or less adequate provided the AGC is not operating. A good S-meter is preferable, and in this case also the AGC should be disconnected or the RF gain turned well back. With a little practice, by simultaneous two-handed operation of phase and amplitude knobs a null may be quickly obtained on a single source of interference, provided the arrival angle is constant or the two antennas respond in the same way to changes in arrival angle, a condition most likely to be secured if the two antennas are close together and have similar radiation patterns.

In a system devised by G3JKF [1] the normal connection to a beam antenna provides one signal and the other is obtained by means of a separate connection to the reflector. In principle the idea is applicable to any type of antenna subject to availability of the nulling signal, which does not require an efficient pick-up device since 'receive only' conditions apply (p152). However, low efficiency may have to be made up by additional gain in the nulling channel; thus a small active 'probe' associated with a dipole as in Fig 9.8 can

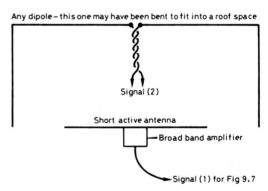

Fig 9.8. Equivalent, for reception only, of a two-element beam. This is suggested for use where space is insufficient for a normal beam. Reference to Fig 9.2 indicates the number of decibels of allowable losses in the second signal path, including any losses in the networks of Fig 9.7. The broadband amplifier will need protection during transmission but, depending on the space available and the operating frequency, may not be needed in all cases

Fig 9.7. Use of 'two knobs' for balancing out a given signal from two sources subject to phase and amplitude differences. The high noise levels prevailing in the HF band allow the use, if necessary, of considerable attenuation without degradation of signal/noise ratio

provide, for reception only, the *exact* equivalent of a two-element beam plus the advantages of (a) instantaneous beam reversal and (b) greater flexibility, so that the direction of a null can be altered in a few moments.

Nulling is of course not possible if the unwanted signal is in the same direction as the wanted signal, and for a British station maximum benefit is likely to accrue when trying to work to the west from the UK at times of short-skip interference from Europe. However, by using two separate antennas, a useful degree of discrimination should be possible, assuming bearing separations in excess of some 30–50°, depending on beamwidths. Ideally, for this application the antennas should be beams separated by about 40–50ft (12–15m). The attractions of such an arrangement as a means of obtaining increased gain and/or directional switching were discussed in Chapter 6, and one antenna rotated so that it has a null in the direction of the wanted signal could be used for the nulling of interference from other directions.

Nulling is difficult and may be useless when more than one interfering signal is involved, but it follows from Fig 9.4 that the likelihood of two or more interfering signals being experienced together or in quick succession could in principle be greatly reduced if the starting point is a three-element rather than a two-element beam. The extent to which this objective is, or could be, realised in practice has yet to be clearly established in view of the difficulties listed earlier, but in both cases major benefits can be expected from the separate optimisation of beam patterns for reception and transmission. For reception there is in principle no need for good front/back ratios to remain the monopoly of those able to erect transmitting beams and, to this end, two separate lines of development will be suggested, following a digression on the subject of active antennas.

Active antennas

Antennas consisting of single active elements have for some time been available on the amateur market. These are ideal for listeners who have only a confined space for the erection of antennas and may be helpful in other cases, for example whenever small size makes it easier to locate an antenna in the best position. Designs are typically geared to the provision of near-optimum reception at all frequencies (inclusive of LF and HF bands) and, as will be seen, this involves difficult design problems which have nevertheless been successfully overcome. Arrays of active elements [5, 6, 7], allowing large structures to be replaced by much smaller ones with similar or even better performance, have already made a considerable impact on the commercial scene and it can be inferred that the development of relatively simple two- or three-element arrays geared to the needs of amateurs unable to erect beams for transmission should be only a matter of time.

Basic principles

The description 'active' normally relates to inclusion in the antenna of an amplifier with the specific object of separating the problems of antenna matching and feeder matching. It

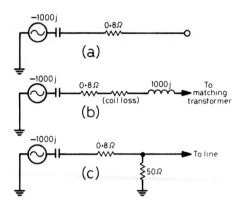

Fig 9.9. Equivalent circuits for typical 4ft whip receiving antenna. (a) Antenna only. (b) Antenna with conjugate match. (c) Antenna with direct coupling to matched line. Values are for 14MHz (all in ohms)

may be recalled from earlier chapters that, in the absence of losses, nearly all small antennas have the same gain since they have identical (ie cos θ) radiation patterns. However, to realise this in practice it would be necessary to maintain a conjugate match at all frequencies which, with typical receiving antennas, is an extremely difficult task, as demonstrated by Fig 9.9. The values indicated are typical of small whips such as those fitted to portable receivers, and it can be seen that even if it were possible to achieve a Q of 2000 for the matching inductance there would still be a loss of 3dB. For a more realistic Q of 100, the losses would rise to 10dB but, accepting some further loss, one could then envisage the connection of a 50Ω feeder. In view of the prevailing noise levels as illustrated in Fig 9.2, this would be an acceptable result except that the matching circuit is high-Q and, for the antenna to be useful, almost certainly out of reach. Seeking a broadband solution, one might next try connecting the antenna directly to the feeder but the loss then rises to 37dB. By adding a transformer and restricting coverage to the HF bands, this could probably be reduced to 30dB.

By incorporating an untuned amplifier, the antenna can be caused to 'see' a high value of load impedance over a wide range of frequencies. This does not eliminate mismatch loss, and unfortunately the amplifier also 'sees' large numbers of very powerful broadcast signals. However, as one writer puts it [5], the amplifier is able to use the very high external noise levels illustrated in Fig 9.2 to "mask its own deficiencies". In other words, the higher the noise level, the larger the amount of attenuation which can be placed in front of a receiver before its own noise becomes significant, and the less the risk of overloading by strong signals. The above reference considers three arrangements based respectively on monopoles, dipoles, and loops, finding that in each case the characteristic gain curve exhibits a decrease with frequency closely following the increase in noise level, which means that if gain is correct at one frequency it should be more-or-less right at others, though noise is a variable quantity and factors such as antenna height and polarisation may affect the 'mix' of different noise sources. Intermodulation products generated in the amplifier must be negligible, interference picked up on the feeder must not be allowed to find its way into the receiver, and other design parameters must be chosen to ensure that (a) the receiver is not overloaded by abnormally high signal levels and (b) the combined noise contributions of the receiver and amplifier remain negligible compared with the external noise.

The required performance

The following recommendations based on reference [5] add up to a somewhat daunting prospect for the amateur designer, and it might be thought that the intermodulation product (IP) figures could be relaxed by using filters to restrict the frequency range to amateur needs. Certainly this should help, but strong signals tend to be concentrated in the range 5–18MHz, with some broadcasting bands very close to the edge of amateur bands, and prospects for the removal of all IPs are not encouraging. The author's only venture into this field was an attempt to copy a published design for a small active loop element; the amplifier, which used small-signal transistors, appeared to be designed along conventional lines and, despite the small size of the antenna, nothing could be heard other than IPs except by inserting a tuned filter ahead of the amplifier.

Recommended amplifier gains for professional applications [5] are –20 to –12dB at 10MHz, decreasing 6dB per octave. Assuming –20dB gain, third-order products at the output terminals should not be allowed to exceed 1µV from a pair of +90dB signals, 82dB being acceptable for second-order IPs. The amplifier noise factor, defined as the ratio of the noise at its output when the antenna is replaced by an equivalent reactance to the thermal noise power, should not exceed 5dB, and the need is also stressed for very good common-mode rejection, since signals picked up on the feeder may be much greater than those induced in the antenna.

Implementation

After overcoming the extremely difficult problems of amplifier design, manufacturers have been understandably reluctant to publish details, though these are understood to include such obvious measures as using power transistors with lots of feedback. The common-mode problem appears to have caused a lot of difficulties and after a study of Chapters 4, 6, and 17 it may come as no surprise to readers that one author [5] refers to a short monopole, when raised above ground level, as "becoming with its feeder some sort of a distorted dipole with a very much higher and uncertain pick-up at some frequencies", suggesting a small earth mat as the remedy, though the recommended conversion whenever possible of monopoles (particularly short ones) into dipoles (p189) applies with even greater force to active antennas. Even so, there remains the very difficult problem of ensuring that any signals picked up on the feeder are unable to find their way through the amplifier, the use of baluns being ruled out by the necessity for very high input impedance. Solutions have emerged based

on push-pull amplification combined with ingenious circuitry, though full details are not available.

A somewhat different situation exists in the case of loops, the required input impedance being very low and the achievement of adequate sensitivity more difficult, as can be appreciated by considering opposite sides as a pair of opposing elements. As explained in Chapter 17, correctly designed small loops owe their outstanding performance as transmitting antennas to a very high value of Q, in marked contrast to the 'total absence of Q' which is the usual requirement for active antennas.

Active antennas, though small by normal standards, are large compared with 'smallest possible' sizes for non-active receiving aerials at frequencies of, say, 14MHz upwards as demonstrated by the example above. For clarification of this, and a number of other issues, the author is indebted to Dr Tong of Datong Electronics Ltd, who has explained that the length is entirely determined by the need for band noise to override circuit noise without undue overloading of the amplifier; contrary to what one might expect, more length is needed for the DX bands due to the fact that noise levels are much lower than at the lower frequencies. He also points out that in this matter there is a lot of scope for special compromises.

Arrays of active elements

As with passive arrays there are two methods of beam formation, additive and subtractive as explained on pp22, 23, and in this case also some engineers appear reluctant to recognise this distinction which is particularly relevant in the case of active antennas. Arrays of active elements connected in phase (ie additive) offer the advantages of simplicity and the ability to replace much larger structures, though the amount of real estate required remains unchanged. In contrast, due to mismatch, the coupling between active elements is very small, allowing elements to be adjusted independently and elements as well as arrays of elements to be stacked in closer proximity, though one might perhaps expect a lower limit (not exceeding about $\lambda/8$ to $\lambda/12$) to be set by the reduction of wanted signals relative to those picked up on feeders. Arrays based on these principles have yet to appear on the amateur market, but would-be experimenters may be encouraged by the following notes giving an outline of two commercial projects featured in the literature.

Reference [4] describes a mobile Adcock (DF) array using a special type of 1m diameter loop element at a height of 1.5m, replacing 10m passive elements, the required distance between pairs of active elements being only one-seventh that between passive elements, a wide range of other applications being envisaged.

Reference [5] describes an active log-periodic array in which the connection to each element is made through a bandpass filter which determines its contribution to the array output at any given frequency. The filter parameters of centre frequency and Q-factor replace the more familiar l and l/D ratio, and omnidirectional coverage over the band 2–24MHz with a directivity of 10 ± 1dB is obtained using six rows of 14 elements.

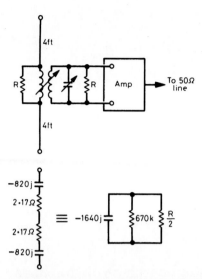

Fig 9.10. Active dipole with half-octave filtering for use with two- or three-element array. For phasing see Fig 9.11. With R = 10kΩ and 2.5× critical coupling, the 3dB bandwidths are about 14–21MHz and the 'circuit' noise factor is 670/5 or 21dB

Against this background, Figs 9.10 and 9.11 are suggested as starting points, one active and the other passive, for further research geared to the specific task of enabling amateurs unable to erect beam antennas for transmission to enjoy the same freedom from QRM as their more-fortunate colleagues. In both cases, the elements are assumed to be sufficiently mismatched to ensure negligible coupling. In the event of common-mode problems, some of the measures described in Chapter 4 for the prevention of feeder radiation are applicable. Fig 9.10(b) shows how a dipole formed from a pair of whips based on Fig 9.9 might be integrated into a tuned circuit forming part of a broadband filter covering, say, 14–21MHz for use in conjunction with an active amplifier.

Conclusion

Interference levels in the HF bands are likely to increase. It will be necessary to develop optimum methods for reducing average levels of interference as well as nulling out individual sources of interference. There is enormous scope for new developments and in this chapter it has been possible only to

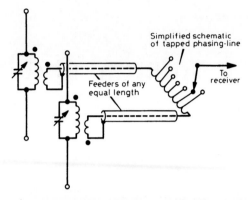

Fig 9.11. Suggestion for monoband superdirective array, non-active. M1, M2 to be in antiphase. Circuit impedance to be about 50kΩ, giving 13dB noise factor at 14MHz. Feeder-interchange switch to be added for beam reversal. Receiver must be protected against strong signals from the transmitter

suggest a few tentative guidelines. Nevertheless, the desirability of separate feeders run back into the shack from each element of a beam for the improvement of transmitting performance has been featured in other chapters, and is a starting point for the development of systems fully and separately optimised for transmission and reception.

References

[1] 'Technical Topics', *Radio Communication* May 1980, p489.
[2] 'Beat the noise with a 'scoop loop', *ARRL Antenna Anthology*, 1978, p76.
[3] *The ARRL Antenna Book*, 1988, pp5.2–5.5.
[4] D G Reid,'The gain of an idealised Yagi array', *JIEE*, Part 3A, 1946, p564.
[5] B M Sosin, 'HF active antenna performance requirements and realisation', *Communications and Broadcasting* Summer 1976, Vol 3 No 1, pp29–34.
[6] B S Collins,'A new high-performance receiving array', IEE Conference on Antennas and Propagation, 28–30 November, 1978.
[7] H K Lindenmeier, 'The short active receiving antenna, an appropriate element for application in antenna arrays', IEE Conference on Antennas and Propagation, 28–30 November 1978.

Chapter 10

The antenna and its environment

It is often remarked that "it's the antenna that counts", though from the point of view of DX performance the author's first priority would be to have a good location, preferably as illustrated in Fig 10.1. Matching the antenna system to this environment, half-a-dozen simple inverted-V dipoles, possibly with reflectors but each requiring nothing more than a clothes-prop for support, could be expected to provide unbeatable performance in any direction at the flick of a switch. Unfortunately, unless one is able to acquire a castle in Spain or is 'operating portable', nothing much can be done about this and usually, far from boosting the signal, ground reflections are the main obstacle to good performance.

At a more practical level we are faced by the fact that some locations are good, others bad and, although in many cases the reasons are obvious, there are others that appear to defy rational explanation. Often conclusions are reached from faulty reasoning which usually by implication invests soil conductivity or some freak of antenna construction with magical properties. Though much is known, there are still large areas of ignorance as well as grey areas which invite speculation. The author proposes to indulge freely in these, hoping that proofs will be forthcoming in due course; in the meantime there are many cases where, even on the basis of existing knowledge, better performance should be obtainable. Let us therefore start with the simplest case, that of a flat unobstructed site.

Flat ground with no obstructions

The average amateur may not recognise this as relevant to his own circumstances. What about, for example, all the telephone wires and television antennas, to say nothing of the house itself, its neighbours and the tree at the end of the garden? It would appear in fact that these items can mostly be disregarded, though there are important exceptions and reservations as discussed later. The first point to note is that in most cases a wave leaving a horizontal antenna and heading upwards towards the ionosphere with a typical take-off angle of a few degrees will clear all or most of any surrounding obstructions, and is 'unaware' of the ground, except indirectly to the extent that the radiation resistance (hence the antenna current and the corresponding field strength) varies slightly with height (p115). The ground for its part is a *virtually perfect reflector at low angles of incidence* and this is true for homogeneous flat ground, whether this be desert sand, agricultural land, lakes or seawater.

In the case of horizontal polarisation and low angles, therefore, the situation is very simple as already discussed in Chapter 6. The direct wave and the reflected wave are of equal amplitude, and combine in phase to give a gain of 6dB relative to the free-space condition when the angle of radiation θ (in radians) is equal to $\lambda/4h$. At 14MHz for a typical radiation angle of 6°, this corresponds to a height of 170ft (52m), the gain being reduced to 3dB for a height of 85ft (26m); below this low-angle field strengths can be reckoned as more or less directly proportional to height. It makes virtually no difference whether the ground is electrically good, bad or indifferent, as may be judged from the reflection coefficients listed in Table 10.1. There is some uncertainty as to the true effective height since this is influenced by the depth of penetration of the reflected wave into the ground, and is likely to be greater in the case of poor soil. However, the author has found in his own case (heavy clay soil) that the linear relationship between height and signal strength is more or less valid on the basis of the actual physical height, and others have reported similar findings.

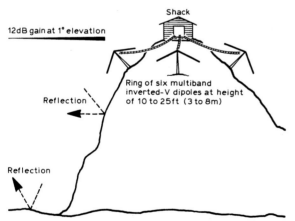

12dB gain at 1° elevation

Shack

Reflection

Ring of six multiband inverted-V dipoles at height of 10 to 25ft (3 to 8m)

Reflection

Fig 10.1. Artist's impression of the ideal location. This provides high effective gain at low angles due to reflections from the foreground and the far distance. Polarisation must be horizontal

160

One other factor to be taken into account in the case of single-element antennas is the variation of radiation resistance with height due to interaction between the antenna and its image; the effect of this on field strength was illustrated in Fig 6.18.

Vertical polarisation

In the case of vertical polarisation and perfectly conducting ground, the antenna and its image are in phase so that maximum radiation takes place at zero angle. Over real ground the position is very different, as illustrated by Fig 10.2. This shows how, with increasing angle above the horizon, the reflection coefficient drops rapidly to reach a low value at the 'pseudo-Brewster angle', thereafter increasing again until at high angles it becomes equal in magnitude to the coefficient for horizontal polarisation. Meanwhile, the phase angle, starting at −180° as for the horizontal case, also decreases, being −90° at the Brewster angle and thereafter dropping rapidly to a low value. In other words, phase reversal takes place around the Brewster angle so that at high angles the antenna and image tend to be in phase; this is in fact the situation for *all* angles over perfectly conducting ground.

This phase reversal means that there would be 6dB gain at very low angles but for (a) the imperfections of the ground

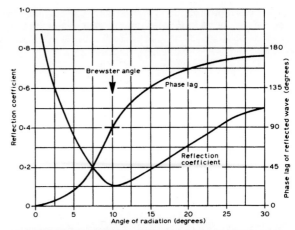

Fig 10.2. Typical variation in magnitude and phase of the reflection coefficient above and below the Brewster angle. At vertical incidence the reflection coefficient approximates to the values given for horizontal polarisation in the 90° column of Table 10.1

and (b) mutual impedance, which in the ideal case would reduce the antenna current by 3dB, an effect which also shows itself as a broadening of the radiation pattern in the vertical plane: Fig 10.3(a). Fig 10.3 compares typical radiation patterns

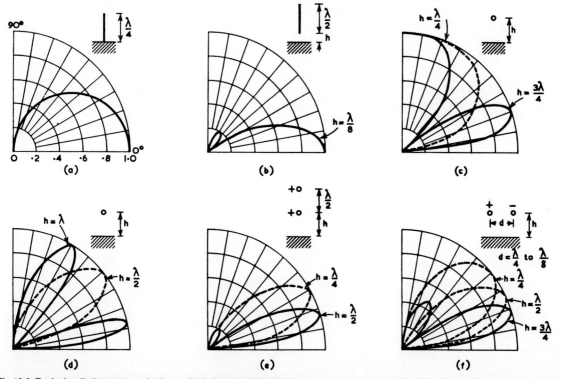

Fig 10.3. Typical radiation patterns in the vertical plane. (a, b) Vertical antennas over perfect earth. (c, d) Horizontal dipoles and collinear arrays. (e) Broadside horizontal arrays. (f) End-fire horizontal systems. Only half of each pattern is shown, the antennas being symmetrical about the vertical axis unless reflectors are used. Diagrams (a) and (b) hold for all azimuth directions, the remainder only for the direction of maximum radiation, ie broadside. Beamwidth in azimuth depends on the length of the arrays

Table 10.1. Typical values of dielectric constant, conductivity, Brewster angles, depth of wave penetration and reflection coefficients for various types of ground at frequencies in the range 3–30MHz. Based on data given in references [1, 2]

Type of ground	Dielectric constant	Conductivity, typical (mho/m) [12]	Brewster angle (approx degrees)	Depth of penetration (approx metres, 3–30MHz) [12]	Reflection coefficient at stated angles for horizontal polarisation					Reflection coefficient and phase angle (degrees) for vertical polarisation at stated angles				
					1°	3°	6°	10°	90°	1°	3°	6°	10°	30°
Seawater	80	4–5	1	0.14–0.04	1.000	0.999	0.998	0.98	0.97	0.4, 80	0.5, 150	0.75, 160	0.85, 170	0.95, 175
Fresh water (best (conductivity)	84	10^{-3} to 10^{-2}	6	9	0.997	0.99	0.98	0.97	0.82	0.75, 1	0.38, 5	0.1, 90	0.2, 180	0.65, 180
Very moist ground	30	5×10^{-3} to 2×10^{-2}	10	3	0.995	0.987	0.968	0.94	0.7	0.88, 2	0.5, 7	0.3, 16	0.1, 90	0.5, 170
Average ground	15	5×10^{-4} to 5×10^{-3}	17	16	0.99	0.97	0.94	0.90	0.55	0.89, 0	0.7, 1.5	0.5, 4	0.25, 10	0.26, 176
Very dry ground (lowest end of conductivity range)	3	5×10^{-5} to 10^{-4}	28	90	0.97	0.93	0.88	0.80	0.25	0.92, 0	0.8, 0	0.6, 0	0.45, 0	0.05, 180

for horizontal and vertical antennas, while Fig 10.4 shows how in the case of vertical polarisation the patterns are modified by the presence of the ground.

Inspection of Table 10.1 shows that for the majority of practical cases the 'pseudo-Brewster angle' varies from about 1° for sea water to 28° for very dry soil and, because the magnitude of the reflection coefficient is less than one in all cases, it can be deduced that there is *some* residual radiation even at very low angles and over the worst ground. This is shown in Figs 10.5–10.7 which compare vertical and horizontal antennas at 14MHz for various types of ground and radiation angles between 1 and 10°, demonstrating that height dependence is much less in the case of vertical antennas, particularly at the relatively low heights typical of most amateur antenna systems. Though calculated for 14MHz,

these curves are valid as a rough approximation for other frequencies in the HF band, and it will be seen that vertical antennas are much superior at low heights. Moreover, low-height vertical beams such as those described in Chapter 13 are very much cheaper and easier to erect than the usual horizontal rotary beam, which at 14MHz needs to be at a considerable height to justify the extra cost, though it has to be remembered that the site under discussion is flat and unobstructed.

The lower curve in Fig 10.8 shows the break-even height

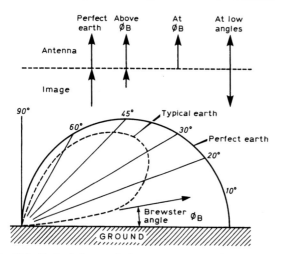

Fig 10.4. Vertical-plane radiation pattern for a short vertical monopole. The dotted curve shows the effect of imperfect ground. Simplified vector diagrams at top show trends of behaviour above and below the Brewster angle

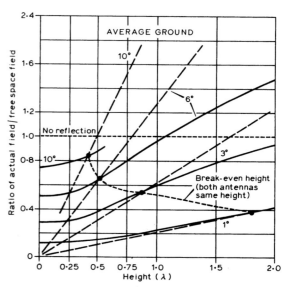

Fig 10.5. Dependence of field strength on antenna height and angle of radiation for average ground. Solid lines are vertical, dashed lines horizontal polarisation. Points above the horizontal dotted line illustrate a gain relative to free-space propagation. Dotted curve links points of equal performance for both polarisations, horizontal being best when the indicated heights are exceeded and vice versa

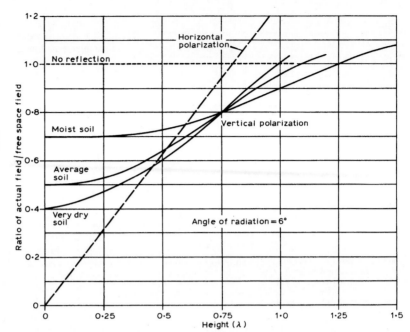

Fig 10.6. As Fig 10.5 for a radiation angle of 6° but showing the effect of extremes of soil conditions

for vertical and horizontal polarisation for average ground and a wide range of elevation angles, the vertical antenna being assumed to 'have its feet on the ground' which makes for maximum convenience and ease of erection. The mean height of λ/4 is a reasonable approximation for most antennas erected to this specification. It will be seen that in this case the

break-even height is not critically dependent on angle of radiation, which is rather fortunate since this is normally

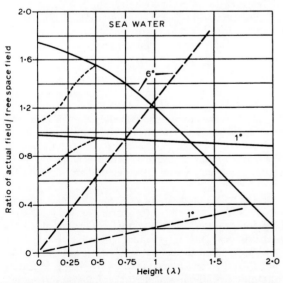

Fig 10.7. As Figs 10.5 and 10.6 but showing the very different situation which exists in the case of sea water. The solid lines are based on the assumption of constant antenna current, and the dotted lines allow for the decrease in this current (rise in radiation resistance) over a perfect earth

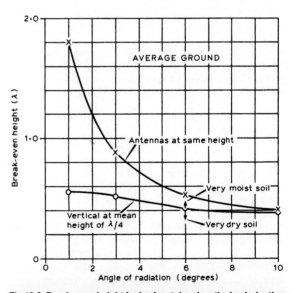

Fig 10.8. Break-even height for horizontal and vertical polarisation. Lower curve shows the height required for a horizontal beam to achieve the same performance as a vertical beam at a fixed height of λ/4. Top curve assumes both antennas at the same height, and implies that in theory for angles below 2° or so it would usually be an advantage if the elements of the average horizontal beam could be rotated into the vertical position. However, reference to Fig 10.5 shows the improvement to be small. The effect of extremes of soil conditions is indicated for a 6° angle, the horizontal being always better if its height exceeds 0.6λ

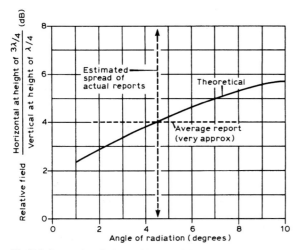

Fig 10.9. Comparison between theory and observed performance of vertical beam at low height (λ/4) relative to horizontal beam at 3λ/4. The theoretical curve assumes equal free-space performance for the two beams. Note the good qualitative agreement, though precise measurements were not feasible

unknown and in any case likely to vary between wide limits. For 6° elevation the break-even heights taken from Fig 10.6 for very dry and very moist ground are also indicated, and again the differences are not very great.

Fig 10.9 shows the calculated improvement in signal strength for a horizontal antenna at a height of 0.75λ together with experimental averages obtained for several antennas used over a nine-month period. It will be seen that a horizontal antenna needs to be erected at a height of about 50ft (15m) to gain an advantage of about one S-unit at 14MHz; it would, however, be nearly as good (and often much easier) to use two low-height vertical beams, suitably spaced and phased.

The theoretical results show that the signal strength from a vertical antenna should increase with height and, although the increase is much less steep than in the horizontal case, the break-even height becomes much greater if both antennas are assumed to be at the same height, as shown by the top curve in Fig 10.8. In the author's case, however, tests on the air failed to establish any height advantage at all when this was increased from 0.25 to 0.6λ. If anything, there was a drop in signal level, the same result being obtained with two different antennas, although theory predicted an increase of about 2dB. Apart from this one anomalous result, good agreement has been found between theory and practice, and there is no reason to believe the results are not typical for the specified site conditions which were met at the author's location for the long path to VK/ZL over which all the tests were conducted.

Even so, it should perhaps be stressed that performance is much less predictable in the case of vertical polarisation, and especially so when receiving performance is taken into account as discussed in the last chapter. Moreover, it will be found later, when considering the effect of obstructions, that the issue becomes even more complicated and this situation can best be resolved by experiments with temporary antennas

before making a final choice of polarisation. It is considered that in most cases the logical choice lies between vertical antennas at low height and horizontal antennas at heights upwards of about λ/2.

The effective mean height of a vertical antenna may be reduced below λ/4 by the use of short end-loaded elements or monopoles. Elsewhere (pp42, 155) it is recommended that monopoles should be operated against a short, inductively loaded counterpoise, not a buried-earth or λ/4 radial system, in which case it can be regarded as an asymmetrical dipole, the equivalent 'height above ground' of a λ/4 monopole being about λ/12 above its base. However, the term 'effective height' when applied to a ground-based monopole usually refers to its actual physical height.

A low-height vertical antenna (λ/4 or less) with its image closely resembles a single dipole, in contrast to a vertical dipole with its image which resembles a collinear pair, so that there is a broadening of the vertical pattern with (in the case of perfect ground) a loss of 3dB. It is therefore to be expected that, although reducing the height of the centre of the current distribution to λ/4 has no adverse effect on gain, there will be some loss, say 2dB, with further reduction in height, including the use of near-ground-based monopoles. Something of this order has been observed by the author, although good DX performance is still achievable.

High vertical antennas tend to be unattractive for several reasons, as follows.

(a) The relatively small return for the extra height.
(b) Elements project both above and below the top of the mast; the extra height tends to be unwelcome and there are usually problems due to the lower ends getting entangled with the guy-wire system!
(c) Interaction between the elements and supporting structures. Methods of getting round this (eg p193) are more easily implemented for low heights.

When antenna height in wavelengths is translated into actual height the balance tends to swing strongly in favour of vertical polarisation for 7 and 3.5MHz, particularly for fixed arrays which can, for example, use short elements supported by catenaries and providing end-loading as on p231. Guidelines for 7MHz are provided by Fig 10.10, from which it may be deduced that a mean height of at least 60ft (18m) and more likely 100ft (30m) is required before a horizontal beam becomes competitive with a good vertical array, though this needs further experimental confirmation.

Going up in frequency to 28MHz, horizontal antennas should be easy winners to the extent that the break-even height drops to 12–15ft (3.7–4.6m); for normal heights about 6dB additional gain over a vertical antenna can be expected. However, a different picture emerges if it is assumed that the 14MHz array is conventional and the same size of element (or the same element) is used at the higher frequency. A vertical λ/2 dipole, for example, can then be used as a collinear pair at 28MHz and, if theoretical height gains are realised, the advantage of the horizontal antenna at 28MHz compared with 14MHz is reduced to 2dB. Even this should be partly

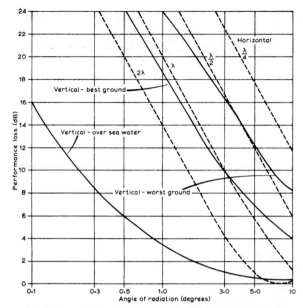

Fig 10.10. Comparison of short horizontal and vertical radiators at 7MHz, assuming flat, open country. 'Zero loss' occurs with in-phase addition of the direct wave and a reflected wave of equal amplitude. Antenna heights are indicated in wavelengths for horizontal polarisation. Low height assumed for vertical radiators, the effect of the ground on radiation resistance being neglected in both cases

neutralised as a consequence of the decrease in radiation resistance; the dotted curves in Fig 10.7 illustrate this for a λ/4 grounded vertical antenna over perfect ground. Sea water provides the best approximation likely to be available, but the effect will be less in the case of a beam and over 'normal' ground.

Fig 10.7 demonstrates the possibility of achieving very low angles of radiation by using vertical polarisation over sea water but, as we shall see, occupants of seaside cottages may well find themselves disappointed in this. An alternative is indicated by the horizontal dotted lines marked 'no reflection' in Figs 10.5 and 10.6. Without reflections, free-space field strengths would be obtained at all times regardless of height, polarisation or angle of radiation and, although most of the recent discussion has hinged on the fact that reflections are inherent features of an earthbound environment, readers may by now be cautious over accepting appearances at their face value. At this point, however, we find ourselves moving away from the initial assumption of a flat, unobstructed, homogeneous site, and before the discussion can continue the reader needs to be conversant with Fresnel zones.

Fresnel zones

Thus far the discussion has been simplified by assuming reflection to take place at that point on the earth's surface which gives the shortest distance of travel for the reflected ray. Looking at this 'point' more closely, it is found to be not

a point at all, but an area – defined by the fact that reflections from all parts of it add up more or less in phase. For low angles and large heights, such as can sometimes be achieved in the course of portable operation, the zone can be a very large area which may well be broken up by hills and valleys or even disappear over the horizon. At the other extreme, important when considering sloping ground in the next section, complications may arise because the zone (though relatively small) is nevertheless too large to be accommodated on the available slope.

To obtain the distances to the near and far edges of the zone for any given angle of radiation [3] the antenna height h may be multiplied by the factors given in Fig 10.11, the shape of the zone being an ellipse having a width of $5.66h$. As a compromise d_N may be increased by 1.6 times, d_F reduced by 40% and the width by 30% for a reduction of 2dB in the amplitude of the reflected wave. The height of obstructions should not exceed $h/4$ from d_N to $0.25d_F$, $h/2$ from 0.2–$0.6d_F$ and h thereafter, though larger obstacles may be tolerated if they block less than 5% of the horizon; these figures are also a compromise. Some values of d_F and d_N are listed in Table 10.2, based on the above compromises and an antenna height of 50ft (15m). It should be noted that these are 'flat earth' figures, d_F being reduced considerably due to earth curvature for low angles and large heights.

The higher angles are included due to their relevance to the case of sloping ground, but it should be noted that if half the beamwidth is less than the angle of radiation the zone will not be fully illuminated and, since the reflection if any would be additive, some loss of gain can be expected. This effect can be reduced by angling the beam halfway between the direct ray and the reflected ray. The negative distances mean that the zone extends *behind* the antenna and explain the experimental fact that it is better to place the antenna on the side of a hill than at the top.

The conditions specified above for the Fresnel zones imply the possibilities in some cases of losing at least part of the reflected wave, thereby achieving good results in what might appear to be unlikely circumstances.

Sloping ground

Fig 10.12 shows two environments which are very different despite the similarity of the foregrounds. In Fig 10.12(a) the antenna with its reflection constitutes a two-element array, with the hill acting as a very tall mast. For a very low angle relative to the earth's surface, a gain of 6dB in the direction of the slope is obtained from the foreground reflection provided

$$h_g = \frac{\lambda}{4 \sin \varphi_s}$$

where φ_s is the angle of slope, and another 6dB (ie 12dB in all) from the distant reflection from the sea or a flat plain, provided $2h_s \sin \theta = \lambda/2$. As an example, this requires a height of 1000ft (300m) for a radiation angle of 1° at 14MHz, though the heights can be divided by 1.5 for a loss of just over 1dB

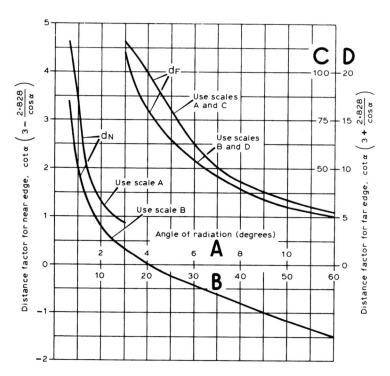

Fig 10.11. Factors for estimating position of near and far edges of Fresnel zones. The distances are equal to the antenna height multiplied by the factors shown

in each case. The further edge of the foreground zone is about one-sixth of the way down the slope for a 20° slope, this fraction tending to be constant with slope angle, since doubling the angle halves the optimum height and hence the distance to the far edge.

In this type of situation the near edge of the distant Fresnel zone could get cut off by the slope, but in the present instance it is nearly three miles (5km) out and requires a slope of only about 3° for clearance. On the other hand, the far edge is at 40 miles (64km) (ie beyond the horizon) so that simple geometry is no longer applicable. However, if very low heights or angles are involved the ideal solution is to get rid of the distant reflection, in which case the disappearance of part of the zone over the horizon should be helpful.

This example has considerable bearing on requirements discussed in Chapter 2 (p16), and is indicative of exciting

Table 10.2. Fresnel zones

Angle of radiation (degrees)	Near edge (ft)	(m)	Far edge (ft)	(m)
1	800	244	10,290	3136
3	272	83	3500	1067
6	120	36	1660	506
10	59	18	1002	305
20	0	0	460	140
30	(−21)	(−6)	320	97
45	(−50)	(−15)	210	64

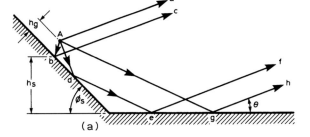

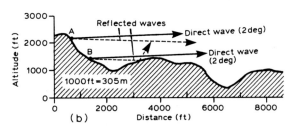

Fig 10.12. (a) Ground sloping down to the sea or flat plain. The direct wave and three reflected waves all add in phase if $h_g = \lambda/(4 \sin (\theta + \varphi_s))$ and $h_s = \lambda/(4 \sin \theta)$, these being the heights of A above ground and sea respectively [13]. Alternatively, the antenna with its image can be regarded as a two-element array at a height h_s. At (b) is shown a typical ground profile for mountainous country; distant low-angle reflections are non-existent for transmitter at B and probably unimportant (due to break up of Fresnel zones) for transmitter at A. In both cases low-angle reflections (not shown) are obtained from the foreground

prospects for anyone prepared to pack portable gear into a rucksack and take to the hills. Moreover, though not directly applicable to the average home environment, it focusses attention on several important principles.

The main unknown in the equation is the optimum angle of radiation; the author has pointed out elsewhere [4] that most experimental results can be explained by assuming an average angle of 6° in the case of the long path between Europe and Australasia. One such contact was achieved with only 1.5W PEP from a location such that lower angles were firmly blocked off by a mountain ridge. On the other hand, the evidence available [5, 6, 7] indicates considerable advantage from the use of angles of 1° or less. These findings can be reconciled on the assumption that the 6° angle, which is representative of what can be achieved with good antenna systems in a typical environment, is low enough to provide good propagation, but that an angle of 1° or less results in extra focussing gain (p16) or reduced attenuation to the extent of at least 10–15dB. To realise this fully it would be necessary to involve exceptional circumstances such as those now under discussion.

The type of location shown in Fig 10.12(b) is in general much easier to find than case (a) and is representative of some home locations; here we look out across mountain ranges or rolling hilly country which occupies the near distance and fails to meet the Fresnel zone requirements specified earlier. As a result, the distant reflecting area is broken up, but there is still a gain of 6dB from the foreground reflection and comparatively little height is needed. In terms of the previous example (assuming 20° slope) we can in effect remove the top one-sixth of the slope, complete with antenna, and put it down wherever we like, provided the ground in front of it is broken up but without disturbing the horizon as seen by the antenna.

The author has found it quite easy to achieve long-path contacts from many such locations with very low powers in the range 0.5–3.0W PEP (SSB), inverted-V dipole antennas with apex heights of 10–24ft (3.0–7.3m), and slopes of 20°–50°, though other locations approximating more closely to Fig 10.12(a) have been markedly better. Even if angles below 6° are cut off, very good results can still be expected, particularly if the reflecting area is bowl-shaped so that it acts like a concave mirror to focus the signal in the desired direction, Fig 10.13(a). Some relatively poor results (including total failures) have been attributed to convex ground which disperses the wave as shown at (b).

As we have seen, there is an optimum antenna height for down-slope working which is in complete contrast to the flat ground case, and also in conflict with requirements for other directions for which the antenna must be as high as possible. Working against the slope is usually difficult, but in some cases one might expect to find an optimum height for the up-slope direction as in Fig 10.14, where the reflected wave is blocked off by the top of the hill. Although one attempt by the author to prove this point ended in failure this is not regarded as conclusive and the idea might well repay further study, bearing in mind that antenna position will be critical. A fixed wire beam for the down-slope direction is easily erected since

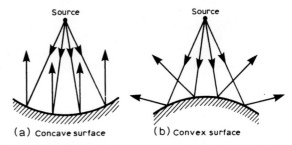

(a) Concave surface   (b) Convex surface

Fig 10.13. This shows how rays are dispersed by reflection from a convex surface but converge after reflection from a concave surface. In accordance with the laws of optics the angle of reflection of each ray is equal to the angle of incidence. The surfaces are assumed to be spherical and suitably placed between the source and the observer

little height is needed, and a conventional rotary beam could be used for coverage of other directions. This would also provide a very valuable beam-switching facility.

Vertical polarisation tends to be unattractive when the ground is sloping. Fig 10.15 illustrates the situation in the case of a steep slope, the image being tilted back so that it makes little or no contribution to the wanted field strength. If, on the other hand, 'vertical' is interpreted as 'normal to the slope', the situation is represented by the dotted lines which are inclined to the wanted direction by the angle φ_s, the signal being directed down the slope instead of towards the horizon. A similar situation applies to high-gain, end-fire, horizontal beams and a maximum of three close-spaced elements is recommended, with collinear stacking if more gain is needed.

With gentle slopes these arguments are less cogent and choice of polarisation may be more difficult, particularly when allowance is made for ignorance of the angles of radiation actually required. The surest way to resolve the matter is probably to try both, but the break-even height for horizontal polarisation will be considerably reduced even for a slope of only 3–5°. At 14MHz and above this will almost certainly make a horizontal antenna the more attractive proposition.

Exceptional locations

Relative performance for flat unscreened sites with properly designed and adjusted antenna systems tends to be predictable (at least for horizontal polarisation), but anomalies are

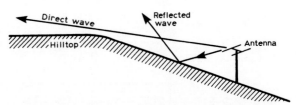

Fig 10.14. Demonstration of possible launch of low-angle wave by antenna on 'wrong side' of a hill. Note that height and placement of antenna is critical, which may account for poor results usually obtained

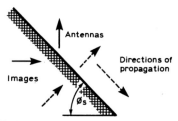

Fig 10.15. Uselessness of vertical polarisation for the exploitation of steep ground slopes. Image is tilted back into the slope so that it is end-on to the direction of propagation and therefore wasted; it is in any case attenuated due to the reflection coefficient being less than unity. Situation could be even worse with antenna normal to slope as shown dotted

not unusual. In cases of abnormally bad performance it is clearly important to eliminate faults in equipment or antenna design before looking for more subtle explanations, and the author is not aware of any case histories relevant to the present discussion.

On the other hand, reference has already been made to the possibility that good performance from an apparently poor location might be explained by absorption of the ground reflection, and one case of exceptional performance from a good location deserves mention as it is well documented and witnessed. The high signal levels in the UK from VK3MO are well known and, even when this station was using only a dipole, the author was consistently reporting the signals as about two S-units stronger than any other Australian stations. Later (in the course of portable activities described on p256), contact was held with VK3MO down to less than 25mW of radiated power, thus establishing the two-way nature of the effect. Further evidence of something unusual was provided by measurements using an aircraft as reported by VK3MO and VK5TT [11]; these revealed a lobe at 4° in the vertical plane as compared with 10° which would have been expected on the usual assumptions of plane homogeneous ground.

The present author's own estimate of the signal enhancement [7] was at least 12dB, making it necessary to account not merely for apparent ray-bending at the ground but excitation thereby of a propagation mode involving considerable ionospheric focussing. Since rays are capable of penetrating fairly

deeply into some types of ground (p162), it seems to the author that the possibility of ray bending analogous to that in the ionosphere and requiring some form of inhomogeneity in the ground might be a possibility. Amateurs, by virtue of numbers and variety of locations, are well placed for adding to knowledge in this area. It is perhaps also worth noting the discrepancy between the standard assumption that horizontally polarised waves are fully reflected at low angles, even in the case of 'worst ground' including city industrial areas, and the basic requirements for Fresnel zones (Table 10.2), which include conditions for full reflection that are certainly not met in all cases.

At the seaside

The behaviour of vertically polarised waves over sea water as illustrated in Fig 10.7 allows efficient low-angle radiation to be achieved very easily in the case of maritime mobile operation, but is somewhat more difficult to exploit from a shore base. There will usually be a stretch of foreground or foreshore separating the antenna from the sea, as shown for example in Fig 10.16. From inspection of Table 10.2 it seems likely that for angles of radiation of a few degrees the reflecting zone will lie partly on land, partly on water, so that two reflected waves, each of somewhat reduced amplitude, can be expected. This is a complicated situation which is difficult to analyse, though it can be assumed that for some very low angle (possibly well under 1°) even the near edge of the zone will be pushed out to sea. This suggests dramatic possibilities but (from the lack of published information) either these have not yet been explored or there is a hidden catch somewhere. It is hoped that readers in suitable locations will be encouraged to experiment on these lines.

The effect of obstructions

Any objects in the vicinity of an antenna are potential absorbers or reflectors of radio waves but, unless they are very close or else comparable in dimensions with the wavelength, the effect is usually negligible. There are two possible ways in which an obstacle can affect the wanted radiation from an antenna.

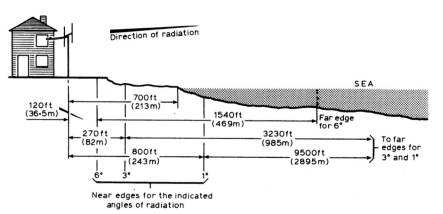

Fig 10.16. Typical seaside location showing position of Fresnel zones relative to the land-sea boundary for radiation angles of 1° to 6°

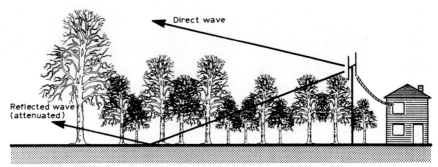

Fig 10.17. Low-angle radiation with vertical polarisation by the use of trees for absorption of the reflected wave

(a) If a non-conducting object is subjected to an electric field it acts like the dielectric in a capacitor and can be regarded as having a current flowing through it. If, therefore, the object is of electrically poor quality, ie if the power-factor of the dielectric is high, losses will ensue; in any event there will be some distortion of the electric field in the vicinity. Such effects are confined to objects in very close proximity to the antenna.

(b) If the object is a conductor, a current is induced in it and this in turn sets up its own field so that energy is re-radiated. Conceivably some of this energy may be radiated in the desired direction and the correct phase but, on average, it represents wasted power from the transmitter. The conductor will also have some losses so that part of the power is in any case wasted as heat. However, normal rules are applicable so that very little current flows in the object unless it is fairly close to resonance.

Common objects likely to have a significant effect are listed below:

Trees
Houses, including their internal wiring and plumbing
Power lines and supporting structures
Telephone lines and supporting structures
Trolley bus wires etc
Lightning conductors
Lamp posts
Guttering (metal)
Other antennas (amateur and TV)
Antenna supporting structures (towers, masts)
Gasometers
Tower blocks

Some of these items can be grouped together and a few general rules can be identified.

Trees

As potential hazards these are usually much overrated. Horizontally polarised antennas can usually be more or less buried in trees with little or no ill effect, though to be sure of this it is best to use full-sized quad or delta loops, due to their relatively high values of radiation resistance. The use of resonant feeders or stubs reaching down to ground level from

such loops, apart from the uses discussed in Chapter 7, allows the performance to be monitored by comparing the element currents which should be about equal for both directions of fire; if this is the same as for quad loops out in the clear it proves they are not being affected by the tree since any losses would show up in the form of undercoupling (p100). The sizes even of inductively loaded loops have been reduced to 12ft (3.7m) square for 14MHz for an average loss of less than 3dB which might have been due to losses in the tree, the radiation resistance being reduced to one-quarter. This can be translated back into a probable loss of less than 0.75dB for full-sized elements. In line with this, experience at a new location suggests a loss resistance of the order of 15–20Ω for loops completely buried in a large beech tree.

A very different situation existed when two 14MHz loops with their feeders, one each side of the tree-trunk, were tuned as λ/2 vertical elements spaced λ/10 for 7MHz; in this case it appeared that the tree trunk was acting as a highly efficient attenuator, though further experiment is needed to establish whether or not a tree can be used to support a vertically polarised array of the type shown in Fig 13.9. A single row of trees spaced some 30–40ft (9–12m) from a vertical antenna was found to be innocuous but 50yd (46m) or so of thick woodland caused several decibels of attenuation at 28MHz. This would be sufficient to absorb most of the reflected wave at angles suitable for DX working.

Under the same conditions no attenuation was observed in the horizontal case, and there would certainly be no appreciable attenuation of the reflected wave over the kind of distances that this might have to travel through flat woodland at a radiation angle of, say, 6°. The range available for these measurements was not sufficient to establish whether or not horizontally polarised rays at very low angles such as 1° would be absorbed or not. However, it seems at the very least highly probable that, at least in the case of vertical polarisation, trees can be used to achieve low-angle radiation as in Fig 10.17 by attenuating the reflected wave so that it no longer interferes with the direct wave from an antenna located at tree-top level.

The observations with vertical antennas in trees were repeated after moving to a new location, to the extent that signals to and from a dipole in a large beech tree were heavily attenuated through the trunk, nearly all signals being attenuated when it was caused to 'fire into the trunk' by adding a reflector. The idea of using the tree, ringed by vertical dipoles, as a direction-switched receiving array remains untested due to demolition of the tree by the 1987 hurricane.

Obstructions other than overhead lines

The effect of houses and their contents is difficult to predict. In some data tables [8] city industrial areas are listed as having a dielectric constant of 3–5 and an effective conductivity of 10^{-3} to 10^{-4} mho/m which puts them in almost the same category as (though slightly better than) the 'very dry soil' of earlier examples in this chapter, ie they are nearly perfect reflectors of horizontally polarised waves at low angles and require no special consideration.

Though doubtless satisfactory as an approximation in dealing with medium-wave propagation from high antennas, it seems obvious that for amateur HF communication tall buildings must inevitably infringe the Fresnel zone specifications quoted earlier. This is particularly so as buildings include wiring, plumbing, lightning conductors and metal guttering, all having resonances in the HF band. Some of these resonances may be sufficiently damped to be ineffective at least in relation to outside antennas, but in other cases a marked screening effect or even a slight 'boost' could be exerted up to distances from the transmitter antenna of 50yd (46m) or so. This figure is based on observations of the effect one antenna can have on another; if, however, objects responsible for screening are accessible, detuning may be possible by the use of linear resonators as described on p193.

In general the influence of vertical or horizontal conductors tends to be confined to radiation from vertical or horizontal antennas respectively except at very close ranges, though a long inclined conductor, even if nearly horizontal, will respond to vertical radiation. A loop of wire such as a quad element does not, however, have a 'way up' but responds equally to both polarisations. As a kind of informed 'guesstimate' it is believed that the screening effect at 50yd (46m) *could* be as much as one S-unit, though in many cases it is a lot less. Screening in excess of two S-units has been observed at about 30yd (27m) range in the case of a second beam in the line of fire of the one in use. It might be thought that this could be avoided by ensuring that the second beam has a good front-to-back ratio, but in practice this is no help at all because the reflector of the second beam reflects *backwards* the signal from the first.

Back-to-front ratio applies only to voltages at the terminals of a beam, which is of course where it is normally wanted, and *does not relate to the properties of the beam as a reflector of other signals*. If the beam which is causing the screening is rotated to an end-on position, the effect on the radiated signal should be negligible, but in reception an unwanted signal from the back direction reflected from the second beam could still be greatly in excess of the signal received directly on the *back* of the first. This means that reflections from metal objects of all kinds (but particularly other antennas tuned to the same wavelength) can very seriously degrade the interference-rejecting properties of the beam in use.

In a built-up area it is reasonable to expect that the reflected wave will be to some extent absorbed by brickwork; 2dB has been quoted as the effect of a brick wall [9] and the author has observed some 3–4dB loss at the 'wrong side of a house'. Part of the wave will be used in setting up currents in loops of electric wiring, conduit, plumbing, lamp posts etc, and the aggregate of such effects must inevitably reduce the reflection coefficient to some extent. This will be beneficial if, at the required angle of radiation, the reflected wave is opposing the direct wave, and conversely if the waves are additive the signal amplitude will be reduced. The direct wave can be expected to escape into space without encountering these obstructions.

As discussed earlier, the 'additive' case is exceptional and it might be expected that (other things being equal) those in built-up areas would be better off than those in the country but, although examples could be cited in support of this, other evidence points in the opposite direction. Considering the two extremes, if the reflected wave is not absorbed, signal strength should be proportional to height (which is a fairly common experience), whereas with complete absorption, which leaves only the direct wave, height should make no difference to the signal strength. However, raising the height may also have the effect of clearing a small number of objects in the immediate vicinity, and this almost certainly accounts for a number of known cases in which the improvement from raising the height was disproportionately large.

Overhead wires

There is very little information on the effect of overhead wires on signal strength, though power lines are a frequent source of interference in reception. Nevertheless, the resemblance of such wires to long-wire antennas suggests that if, say, 10% of the radiated power were to find its way into such a conductor the re-radiated field could be comparable with the direct field which it might assist or oppose. Referring to the dotted curve in Fig 5.13, the mutual resistance between $\lambda/2$ dipoles spaced 3.25λ can be as much as 10% of their self-resistance, and if 72 × 1.1W are fed into one of them the currents will be respectively 1A and 0.32A.

Although the calculation gets more complicated, it takes little imagination with this as a starting point to imagine tight coupling between an antenna and neighbouring power wires, even to the extent of achieving power gains in directions nearly in line with the wires as in Fig 10.18(a). This would be accompanied by reduced signals in other directions. The power line could therefore be expected to distort the radiation pattern in ways which might be helpful along the direction of the line but would be harmful for other directions. Use of vertical polarisation would be the most obvious way of avoiding this problem.

Fig 10.18(b) illustrates other likely aspects of the situation by assuming a sharp bend in the power line. If the line is very long in each direction and the capacitance of insulators can be ignored, each leg can be thought of as a separate terminated long-wire (p238) since the waves propagated along it will gradually diminish and eventually die out before being reflected.

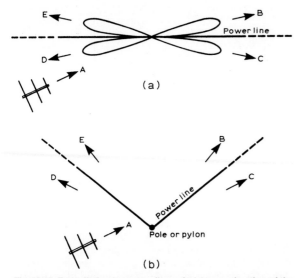

Fig 10.18. Re-radiation by power lines. At (a) some fraction of the power in the wave A is re-radiated in directions B, C, D and E. For the wanted direction A, radiation may be enhanced or opposed by the lobe B. At (b) it is assumed that energy travels outwards along the power line in both directions from the corner, becoming gradually attenuated without reflection. If reflection does take place, eg at insulators, there will be radiation also in the reciprocal directions of B, C, D and E

High-rise buildings

If it is possible to get a horizontal beam onto the roof of a tall building, say a block of flats, the DX prospects are excellent. In the case of full-sized elements there is no need to have much clearance above the roof, provided any detuning effects are corrected, though there seem to be no useful figures available. Clearances would probably need to be at least double in the case of a miniature beam such as Fig 12.3, on account of the larger voltages and currents. There is no certainty that horizontal polarisation will give best results in all cases, though this is the most likely situation. Severe screening can be expected in the case of waves propagated through buildings.

Portable operation

The exploitation of sloping ground (as described on pp235–237) for DX contacts using very low power and simple antennas such as the inverted-V dipole is a fascinating hobby in itself, but suitable locations are not always ready to hand. Finding the best ones demands intensive study of maps, much travelling, probably a long climb on foot in the early hours of the morning to a height of 1000ft (300m) or so, and a lot of luck with the weather. However, good results can usually be expected from a cliff top or steep ground with a drop of 100ft (30m) or so to the sea, and one exceptionally good location found by the author was near the top of a steep-sided railway cutting which appeared to be acting as some kind of horn radiator! In general, steep bowl-shaped contours are usually

effective but (as explained earlier) convex foregrounds should be avoided.

In the case of a cliff top the centre of the dipole should be pushed out horizontally from the edge using, say, a pair of 8ft (2.4m) garden canes tied together, and the ends can be strung back to tufts of grass, points on a guard rail or anything else available. Polarisation must be horizontal and a typical set-up is illustrated in Fig 16.9. There is still much to be learned, however, and the less-enthusiastic experimenter, content merely to try the best locations that happen to be handy in the course of, say, a holiday camping trip, may be in for a few surprises.

On one occasion, a very gentle ground slope provided the author with three UK contacts from Tasmania with 1.5W PEP, although the dipole was hanging from a tree branch at only 20ft (6m). After much puzzling an explanation was conjectured on the lines of Fig 10.19, the lack of any gain from reflections being compensated by the low-angle focussing gain. This is a fairly common situation which might apply to some home locations, and it is interesting to note that if the antenna height is doubled the reflected wave clears the distant hill and cancellation takes place. If this explanation is correct, success may have to be attributed on this occasion to the author's lack of prowess in aiming for a higher tree branch!

To exploit vertical polarisation over sea water the same portable antenna could be used as a top-loaded ground-plane operating against a small counterpoise as illustrated in Chapter 16, p215.

DX working is not normally possible from a flat site with powers of 1–2W SSB and the sort of antenna heights (less than 20–30ft (6–9m)) which are easy to achieve. On the other hand, at 14MHz single-hop working over distances of 800–1600 miles (1300–2600km) has usually been found possible,

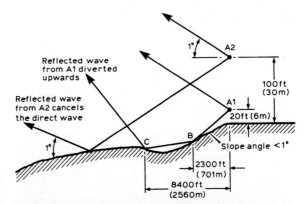

Fig 10.19. Geometrical model of situation giving better low-angle propagation from lower antenna, assuming a ground slope less than the angle of radiation. For radiation angles around 1° there is no reflected wave from A₁ in the same direction as the direct wave. Higher angles are cancelled by the foreground reflection, lower angles by the distant reflection. Horizontal scale is longer than the vertical, the angles being multiplied in proportion. For a typical 6° angle the situation is reproduced if the horizontal scale is divided by six, and good low-angle propagation can then be expected over the range 4° to 6° approximately

in many cases with an antenna height of only 8–10ft (2.5–3.0m).

The indoor environment

Indoor antennas tend to be coupled rather closely into their surroundings and this is liable to generate a lot of problems. Factors to be taken into consideration include:

(a) absorption in brickwork or wet (ie external) woodwork;
(b) losses and distortion of radiation patterns by currents induced in mains wiring, plumbing, telephone wires etc;
(c) TVI and other interference due to the same cause;
(d) difficulty in accommodating full-sized elements, and aggravation of the above effects in the case of loaded elements and particularly small beams;
(e) earthing problems, closely related to (b);
(f) height limitations;
(g) shortage of engineering guidelines;
(h) the prevalence of unsound design practices.

To minimise the difficulties it is important to keep the radiation resistance as high as possible unless large clearances can be arranged, and (except for reception) there may be no advantage in using a beam. Particular attention must be given to earthing, and it is believed the best answer in most cases is likely to be a short counterpoise tuned with a series inductance, arranging the antenna feedpoint and the counterpoise to be as far away as possible from wiring or plumbing. All other conductors near the antenna need to be checked for possible in- or near-band resonances with a grid dip oscillator having a coil of large area (p273), and any that are found should be removed, eg by means of inductively coupled traps (p55).

The earth connection

The ground underneath and around the antenna has a number of functions. Its role as a reflector of signals has just been discussed at length but it is often required to provide all or part of the return path for the antenna current, ie the RF circuit comprising the antenna system is completed via current paths in the ground as in Fig 6.26. This illustrates the Marconi antenna, the lower side of the generator (eg the outer conductor of a coaxial feeder) being connected to a buried earth which in its simplest form is a metal spike driven into the ground. The efficiency of such a system, neglecting losses in the antenna wire, is given by $R/(R + R_e)$ where R is the radiation resistance (36Ω for a λ/4 radiator) and R_e the resistance of the ground connection – typically about 100Ω, giving a loss of 6dB.

Even to get it as low as this may involve a lot of hard work such as driving a 2in (5cm) diameter 6ft (1.8m) rod into heavy clay soil, a procedure which the author strongly deprecates and has no intention of repeating.

To overcome this problem, the method usually recommended is the burial of a large number of radial wires around the base of the antenna as in Fig 10.20, typically 50–100 wires

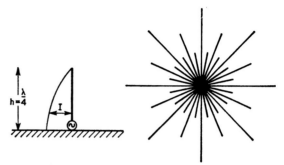

Fig 10:20. Typical radial earth system for short vertical antenna

of lengths up to 3λ/2. In the amateur context this involves a somewhat mindboggling expenditure of time, money and effort which confers no significant benefit. One of the main attractions of vertical antennas is the possibility of achieving good performance *without* using any appreciable amount of horizontal space, let alone the large amount of real estate required for an efficient buried radial system. Neither is it necessary to incur the wrath of the XYL by the digging up of flower beds, or risk the lethal potential gradients that must almost certainly exist at the ground surface in the event of a lightning strike.

It would be a different matter if one could surround the antenna with a high-conductivity ground system extending to the outer limit of the Fresnel zone, thereby realising not merely a low earth resistance but the enormous benefits of efficient radiation at very low angles. This has indeed been achieved with impressive results [10] but such attempts at controlling the environment are incompatible with amateur resources.

Fortunately, the earth resistance can be held to a low value by using the rather simple type of counterpoise earth shown in Fig 6.27(b), which requires very little space and, in effect, converts a monopole into a dipole. In this case the main source of loss is the resistance of the loading coil which, even for a counterpoise of only a few feet in diameter, could be as low as that of one of the 'mind-boggling earth-mats' described earlier. In many cases the counterpoise need consist of no more than a short rod. However, if shortening of counterpoises or radials is carried too far, the consequences include reduced bandwidth, increased RF voltages, and difficulties in preventing radiation from feeders (p55). With all radial (or counterpoise) systems, in the absence of a ground screen (p116) there will be extra losses due to earth currents if the ground clearance is insufficient, and multiband operation requires arrangements such as those illustrated in Fig 11.17. Often the vertical monopole can be re-arranged as a dipole with some advantage (p184).

These things said, there are cases where the attractions of a buried ground remain considerable especially for multiband operation. It is important to realise that there is little or no correlation between DC resistance and RF resistance, and it is implicit from Fig 6.19 that an effective ground resistance of about 36Ω can be obtained by using the centre of a λ/2 dipole

"...the ground plane ... this likewise has an environmental impact"

lying on the ground, or presumably 18Ω from two at right-angles. This implies a loss of less than half an S-unit. Insulated and buried (making due allowance for the dielectric constant of the ground), the wires will have low Z_0 and low Q, any resonances being much reduced in frequency. This reasoning is supported by excellent results known to have been achieved on the main DX bands using only short buried radials, but to be on the safe side it might be advisable to choke as well as bury the feeder. It should be possible to obtain a fairly accurate figure for losses by measuring the feedpoint resistance and, for a λ/4 vertical, subtracting 36Ω. Nevertheless, earlier advice to use wherever possible end-loaded dipoles (or inverted ground-planes) rather than ground-based monopoles should be heeded.

The more usual way of avoiding the need for an earth mat is the ground plane (p42), a variant of the counterpoise but possessing fewer advantages. Though demanding less space than the earth mat, this likewise has an environmental impact and also encourages the feeder to radiate.

Summary

For working DX from a flat unobstructed site at 14MHz and above, the choice lies between a horizontal beam (which should be as high as possible) and a vertical beam, which can be almost 'sitting on the ground', though there is some advantage if its electrical centre can be placed at a height of about λ/4 to 5λ/16. The relative merits of horizontal and vertical polarisation depend on the height available, ground constants and possible obstructions. Rough tests may be advisable using temporary antennas before proceeding with a permanent installation, though for avoidance of ground losses this should not be less than 0.16λ, in line with Fig 6.19.

Advantage can be taken of sloping ground to obtain optimum performance in down-slope directions using horizontal antennas at low heights. On the other hand, obstructions may result in an optimum position, height or polarisation which in general needs to be found by experiment, though some guidelines have been suggested.

On simplistic assumptions, ground conductivity is of no significance for low-angle propagation of horizontally polarised signals but there is evidence in some cases of 'bending' of the reflected wave or some equivalent effect, with important practical consequences.

In portable operation, advantage can be taken of steep ground slopes to achieve DX contacts with very low power and a simple horizontal antenna at low height. This advice has been strongly reinforced by the author's experience at a new location where the DX performance of vertical antennas relative to horizontal ones is at least 6dB worse than previously. The two locations are very different, with light sandy soil and lots of trees (having thick foliage) replacing the heavy clay plus a single row of pine trees (with a few scattered oaks and some hedges) of the previous location.

Short-range working may involve high-angle reflections from the ionosphere, in which case vertical antennas are relatively inefficient and horizontal antennas are preferable. In this case, however, there is no need for height, which can be as little as a few feet even at the lower frequencies.

In seeking to relate environmental factors to DX performance there is still much to be learnt and in this field amateurs, by virtue of the number and diversity of their locations, enjoy a considerable advantage over professionals. Areas of interest include situations such as those illustrated in Figs 10.14, 10.15, 10.17 and 10.19, also the investigation of radiation angles which can be inferred from whether or not signals clear obstructions such as a range of mountains. A suitable methodology can be based on regular comparisons with other amateurs operating preferably from flat, unobstructed sites.

References

[1] *Radio Engineers Handbook*, F E Terman, McGraw-Hill, 1943, pp700–707.

[2] *Radio Communication Handbook*, 5th edn, RSGB, 1977, p11.9.

[3] 'Siting criteria for HF communication centres', W F Utlaut, *NBS Technical Note 139*, US Dept of Commerce, April 1962.

[4] 'Low-angle radiation', L A Moxon, *Wireless World* April 1970.

[5] 'Effect of antenna radiation angles upon HF radio signals propagated over long distances', W F Utlaut, *Journal of Research of the National Bureau of Standards* Vol 65D, No 2, March–April 1961.

[6] 'A comparison of long-distance HF radio signal reception at high and low receiving sites', M R Epstein, *et al, Radio Science* Vol 1, 1966, pp751–762.

[7] 'High-frequency antennae and propagation modes in relation to the amateur service', L A Moxon, IEE International Conference on Antennae and Propagation, 28–30 November 1978.

[8] *Radio Engineers Handbook*, F E Terman, McGraw-Hill, 1943, p709.

[9] 'Attenuation through trees and brickwork', K Bullington, *Bell System Technical Journal* May 1957, p593.

[10] 'A low delta surface-wave interferometer array for HF radio communication', J F Ward, *Nature*, 205, 13 March 1965.

[11] 'The effect of ground on the directional pattern of a 14MHz antenna', A G Bolton and I J Williams, *Amateur Radio* July 1977.

[12] *Radio Communication Handbook*, 5th edn, RSGB, 1977, Chapter 11.

[13] 'The maximum range of a radar set', K A Norton and A C Ormberg, *Proc IRE*, Vol 35, 1947, p17.

Chapter 11

Single-element antennas

A beam (though desirable) is far from essential for reliable long-distance communication, while for shorter ranges a single element has some advantages since all directions tend to be of equal interest. The likelihood of replies to a CQ call tends to be increased more by the absence of directional discrimination than by a slightly bigger signal limited to a single direction. The operator is moreover spared the time wastage and inconvenience of waiting for a rotary beam to rotate! The importance of beam antennas rests primarily on the need for conservation of the HF spectrum which is a scarce and diminishing natural resource. To this end, it is clearly desirable as far as possible to restrict both transmission and reception to wanted directions only, but for many of us, and in the case of the lower bands for most of us, the erection of a transmitting beam is out of the question. In principle the receiving problem should in most cases be soluble as discussed in Chapter 9, but this requires the development of new techniques and hardware.

In general, a single element is much easier to construct and erect than a beam, relatively inexpensive and less likely to lead to problems of planning consent and trouble with neighbours. The decrease in signal strength compared with a beam is no worse than results from switching out the linear amplifier, and is small compared with average differences between one signal and another. The signal is admittedly less competitive, it is more difficult to find a clear channel, and interference is also much more likely, but (except in this last respect) the owner of the single-element antenna is not seriously handicapped. Moreover, current developments should enable interference to be nulled out with the help of a relatively small antenna as described in Chapter 9, and in a few favoured cases both forward gain and screening against signals from the back direction may be provided by the environment itself as described in Chapter 10.

In this and the following six chapters antennas have been grouped according to common features or objectives, though inevitably there is a lot of overlap. This chapter is concerned primarily with loops, dipoles, and asymmetrical dipole (alias ground-plane) elements having dimensions more-or-less closely related to the wavelength, though efforts are made to 'squeeze' them into smaller spaces without losing decibels. This means that whenever possible lengths are reduced by bending over the ends (which contribute relatively little to the

radiation) in such a way that, though occupying less space and no longer radiating, they continue to exercise their function of resonating the antenna without incurring the losses inherent in the use of traps or loading coils.

Half-wave horizontal dipoles

Fig 11.1 illustrates those types of horizontally polarised $\lambda/2$ dipoles likely to be of interest to the reader who has digested the arguments in Part 1. Some of these are important building blocks for beam antennas to be described in the next chapter, and have been included partly or mainly for this reason. In the first instance the discussion is confined to monoband operation.

A straight dipole such as Fig 11.1(a) or (b) is mainly of interest when at least one support (such as a tree or chimney) is already available though it is often best to use this for supporting the centre of a loop or an inverted-V. A tree may be difficult to climb so that it is impossible to use it for anything more complicated than the attachment of one end of a dipole, and in any case a single element of any kind supported at its centre might overhang a neighbouring property. Straight dipoles may be made rigid enough to require supporting only at their centres, for use as rotary beam elements, but they may be useful in other ways; for example, it may be found that they can be erected in a tree without climbing it (eg by throwing a rope over a branch) or at a substantially greater effective mean height than would be possible for a loop or inverted-V. For such applications it is also possible to construct a bamboo 'bow' with a wire dipole as the 'bowstring'.

The folded dipole, Fig 11.1(b), provides almost twice the bandwidth (and for a given weight of copper has only half the losses) of a single-wire dipole, though for most purposes this is adequate and slightly simpler. Taking mechanical considerations into account, one can arrive at a complicated set of trade-offs between single and two-wire dipoles, though the pros and cons are mostly trivial. The author tends to favour folded dipoles using, say, 18swg (1.2mm) hard-drawn copper wire with a central gap between conductors of about $\lambda/30$ for all bands from 7–28MHz, but further discussion of the mechanical aspects will be found later in this chapter (p178).

There is usually no need for insulators as such,

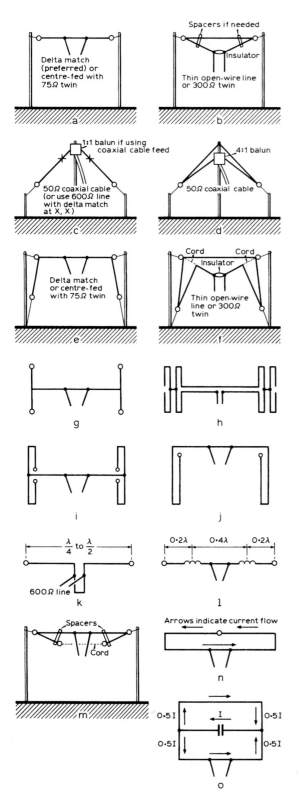

recommended practice being the use of nylon fishing line or polythene cord; these are light, strong, cheap and provide excellent insulation with little or no 'visual impact'. However, so as not to extend this last feature to the diagrams, insulators are included to indicate ends of wires throughout this and other chapters.

Even when no insulators are used, the resonant length of a dipole is slightly less than the free-space half-wavelength, depending on the ratio of length to diameter, but typically 2.4% for wire elements rising to 4.7% for 1in (2.5cm) diameter tubing at 14MHz or half this at 28MHz. Tapering both in its usual form and as illustrated in Fig 11.1(b) will require some slight increase of length but, neglecting this, the correct formula to use for bare wire dipoles without insulators is

$$\text{Length (ft)} = 478/\text{frequency (MHz)}$$
$$\text{Length (m)} = 145.7/\text{frequency (MHz)}$$

It is, however, advisable (if possible) to check resonance or SWR before erection (pp272–274).

The inverted-V, Fig 11.1(c), has important advantages since the single support also carries the feeder which blends in with it so that there is less visual impact. Moreover, since there is no feeder drag on the wire, this can be much thinner and the antenna perhaps even rendered completely invisible. The effective mean height with 90° apex angle is about 5ft (1.5m) less than the height of the support, but this is largely offset by the absence of sag and since there is very much less pull only a flimsy support is needed. It should usually be possible therefore to achieve considerably greater height, and the risk of serious damage in the event of breakage is much reduced.

The ends may be attached to relatively short supports depending on the space available, the base-line required being not less than $2(h_a - h_s)$ where h_a is the apex height and h_s that of the auxiliary poles or other available anchoring points such as a garage roof or tall bush. If necessary the ends of the dipole may be bent over slightly. As an alternative to additional poles two short lightweight spider arms (eg bamboo) may be fixed to the mast, the arm lengths and their distance from the top of the mast being at least 12ft (3.7m) for a 14MHz dipole. The apex angle should be as large as possible and not less than 90°, for which angle the radiation resistance and bandwidth are roughly halved.

In those cases where the antenna is required to be invisible the wire size can be reduced to about 28swg (0.4mm) [1], the main problem being to render it invisible to neighbours

Fig 11.1. Dipole elements. (a) Conventional λ/2 dipole. (b) Folded-dipole or 'squashed delta loop'. (c) Inverted-V dipole; coaxial feeder plus balun may be used as the mast takes the weight directly. (d) Folded inverted-V dipole. (e) Inverted-U dipole. (f) Folded inverted-U dipole. (g) End-loaded dipole; this is suitable as a low-height vertical or, in its horizontal form, fitting into an attic. (h), (i), (j) are as (g) but allow further length reduction, (j) being suitable for suspension horizontally between two poles or use as a beam element. (k) Centre-loading. (l) Coil loading. (m) Loading by bending the ends over. Due to excessive current flow in the reverse direction the folded-back dipole (n) and equivalent loop (o) are not advised. Lengths are λ/2 or less in all cases including (l) for which the marked figures should be halved

without becoming a navigational hazard for birds! It is essential, however, to ensure that in the event of breakage there is no risk of accidental contact with power lines or hazard to pedestrians or traffic. An inverted-V with a 90° apex angle has only half the radiation resistance of a straight dipole, so that if wire size is also reduced there may be a case for using a folded construction as in Fig 11.1(d) in order to maintain efficiency and bandwidth.

The U shape, Figs 11.1(e) and (f), is closely equivalent to the V and has a number of applications. Suppose that operation is required on 7MHz, given two supports only just far enough apart for a 14MHz dipole, Fig 11.1(a) or (b). All that is needed is to bend the ends over to form a U-shaped element. For fitting dipoles into an even smaller space, including indoor locations, any of the arrangements (g) to (j) may be used, depending on the space available; (g) to (i) are preferred on grounds of symmetry but (j) provides a somewhat lower resonant frequency for a given area. Some bending over of ends is allowable if necessary but it is essential that any wires running parallel with the centre of the element should be very short or carrying only very small currents (p99). In case (g) roughly 3ft (0.9m) (total) of extra wire is required at the ends for each 2ft (0.6m) reduction in overall length.

It is usually more convenient to fold the centre of the element as in Fig 11.1(k) but the radiation resistance is then halved for a reduction in length of only 20% which should not be exceeded in the case of a beam element. Reasonable efficiency is possible in the case of, say, a 14MHz heavy-gauge single dipole used in this way at 7MHz, the radiation resistance being 7Ω, loss resistance typically about 1Ω and the bandwidth about 1% which is adequate for operation over the European phone or CW bands. The efficiency in this case is 85%, ie there is a loss of 0.6dB. Similar use of 28 or 7MHz dipoles is more restricted since the 14MHz and 3.5MHz bands are relatively wide. Tuned feeders if used in these cases must be very short; alternatively a matching stub should be used as close as possible to the antenna with some means of switching it out of circuit for multiband operation.

Fig 11.1(l) shows another common method of shortening, with suggested lengths. For the same 20% reduction in length the radiation resistance is reduced to 52Ω. Thus the loss is only 0.4dB, this being increased to 1.2dB if the end sections are halved, reducing the length by 40% in all. The method shown at (m) is equivalent to (l) in terms of radiation resistance, but preferable since it cuts out the coil losses and can be used for fitting an inverted-V into a smaller space.

The folded-back dipole, Fig 11.1(n), and equivalent loop (o) are included as examples to be avoided, although they will be encountered from time to time in the literature. As shown by the arrows, current flows in both directions, thereby greatly decreasing the radiation resistance. For a half-size dipole or a loop as illustrated, the radiation resistance is divided by four approximately compared with end-loaded elements such as Fig 11.1(g) or 11.4(d).

Fig 11.2 shows alternative methods of feeding these antennas; (a) is the most efficient but scores lower on convenience and may be unsuitable if the feeder has to travel any distance

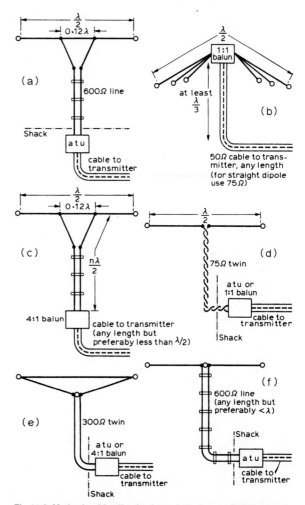

Fig 11.2. Methods of feeding horizontal dipoles. (a) Delta match to 600Ω line. (b) Coaxial feeder with balun. (c) Combination of open-wire and coaxial feed. (d), (e) Balanced twin feeder. (f) Resonant-line system for multiband operation

inside a building or very close to it. Fig 11.2(b) shows the best way of using coaxial feeder, and this is recommended in particular for use with multiband inverted-V dipoles since direct connection of an open-wire line as in Fig 11.1(a), (b) or (e) is not practicable whereas coaxial line can be fixed to the support, there is no drag problem and the visual impact is nil. On the other hand, in the case of straight dipoles, Figs 11.1(a) and (b), its use imposes penalties in the form of extra weight, windage and visual impact. The extra losses (and cost) of coaxial feedline, though not of major importance for lengths up to 100ft (30m) or so, are to be avoided if possible and the arrangement of Fig 11.2(c) seeks to make the best of both worlds. For feeder lengths exceeding λ/2, open-wire line is used in multiples of λ/2 so that the antenna impedance is 'repeated' at the terminals of the balun. The spacing of the delta and the precise length of the open-wire line should be

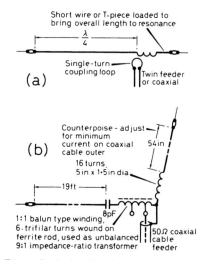

Fig 11.3. Two methods of end-feeding antennas with coaxial cable. (a) Length of radiator, shown as λ/4, can be any length subject to appropriate tuning so it presents a low impedance at the feedpoint. Coupling coil to be carefully positioned for feeder balance. (b) The G6XN version of the Windom as illustrated in Fig 4.28 except that the feeder has been reduced to 'zero length', allowing end-feeding from coaxial cable using a short resonant counterpoise (ARRL)

adjusted for minimum SWR in the shack. In the case of the inverted-V the open-wire feeder needs to be at least 6in (15cm) clear of the support and (b) may well be preferred on grounds of appearance.

The use of matched twin feeder as at (d) and (e) is the simplest and neatest method for centre-feeding of horizontal wires, but suffers from wet-weather problems with the types readily available, and a further drawback in case (e) is the additional windage. On no account should the transparent plastic type of 300Ω line be used since it can deteriorate very rapidly but, provided phase stability is not required and runs are fairly short, other types may be used if given a coating of silicone grease.

Resonant open-wire line as at (f) allows an antenna to be erected quickly without matching adjustments or accurate measurement of length, but requires an ATU and is particularly applicable to multiband systems as described later. Alternatively, for long feeder runs the line can be operated in the resonant condition as far as some convenient point at ground level, where use of a stub (as explained on p39) allows the rest of the feeder to operate as a matched line. Alternatively the arrangement at (c) allows a dipole to be centre-fed with open-wire line operating at a relatively low value of SWR, eg 2 or 3.

Fig 11.3 shows two methods [12] of end-feeding antennas with coaxial cable, requiring in each case the use of some form of short, loaded counterpoise. In effect these methods start by turning the antenna to be fed into an 'asymmetrical dipole' and bear a strong resemblance to the recommended methods for feeding 'ground-plane' antennas (p47) except that the counterpoise has a much lighter task to perform since the antenna impedance is much higher (see also Fig 4.30).

Mechanical aspects of horizontal wires

In the case of centre-fed horizontal wire dipoles, Fig 11.1(a) or (b), there will inevitably be some sag resulting from the weight of the feeder; referring to Fig 11.4(a) this translates into tension in the horizontal portion according to the relation

$$W = 2T \sin \theta$$

The weight of the antenna wire should be added to that of the feeder, but in addition there is wind pressure which can be reckoned as producing a sideways force of up to 20–30lb/sq ft (950–1400N/m²), depending on geographical area [9]. For a 14MHz dipole with a λ/2 open-wire (20swg or 0.9mm) feeder and a wind speed of 100mph (160km/h) we obtain from Table 11.1 a drag of $66 \times 0.7 \approx 5$lb (2.3kg); if the feeder is allowed to billow out away from the wind direction to the extent of 15° and anchored at its lower end this turns into an

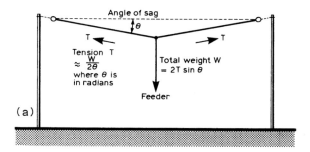

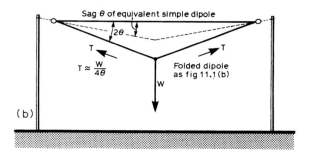

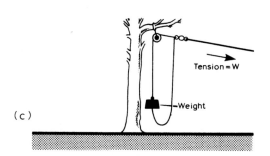

Fig 11.4. (a) Tensions in centre-fed horizontal wires; advantage can be taken of the folded dipole (b) to reduce tension by reduction of W and increase of θ. (c) Method of ensuring constant tension in the antenna wire. The counterweight is equal to the allowable tension T

Table 11.1 (from reference [8]). Calculated wind drag at 100mph (160km/h) on tubes and taut wires with the wind perpendicular to the axis of the tube or wire

Diameter		Drag	
(in)	(mm)	(lb per ft length)	(kg per metre)
2	51	5.8	8.6
1	25	2.9	4.3
0.5	13	1.47	2.2
0.128 (10swg)	3.25	0.29	0.43
0.08 (14swg)	2.0	0.17	0.25
0.036 (20swg)	0.9	0.07	0.10

endwise pull of 10lb (4.5kg) which is the effective value of W for use in the above expression. For a sag of 3ft (0.9m) the tension in the antenna wire comes to 27.5lb (12.5kg), which from Table 11.2 requires the use of 16swg (1.6mm) hard-drawn copper.

A counterweight of 29lb (13.2kg) can be used as in Fig 11.4(c) to ensure that this figure is not exceeded. The windage is roughly doubled for coaxial feeder of 4in (6mm) diameter but this can probably be accommodated by allowing more sag and billowing! Fortunately wind speeds of 100mph (160km/h) are rare, and unlikely in the UK to coincide with conditions of severe icing for which no allowance has been made. The counterweight is essential if trees are used for support because a very small movement of the tree represents a large increase of tension; the length occupied by the dipole is given by $\lambda/(2 \cos \theta)$ and if, one end being fixed, the other moves away by only 4in (10cm), θ is reduced from 10° to 5° and the tension is doubled.

The use of hard-drawn rather than soft copper wire is frequently stated to be mandatory and this is confirmed by the above example for the case of Fig 11.4(a). In case (b), the sag is doubled for a given change in mean height and the dipole can even be allowed to turn into a delta loop (Fig 11.5) without much ill effect, since reduction in mean height is largely offset by the slight gain (1dB) of the single loop compared with a dipole. The feeder wire size cannot be reduced since halving the diameter only halves the drag but reduces the breaking strain to a quarter.

The above examples serve to highlight the problems and provide basic engineering guidelines, though the rules are commonly disregarded without serious repercussions. Antennas like those under discussion are often constructed from

Table 11.2 (adapted from reference [2]). Maximum recommended tensions for hard-drawn copper based on 15% of the breaking strain

Wire size		Tension	
(swg)	(mm)	(lb)	(kg)
10	3.3	126	57
12	2.6	78	35
14	2.0	48	22
16	1.6	30	14
18	1.2	16	7.3
20	0.9	10	4.5

'any odd length' of soft copper wire out of the junk box, maybe off some old mains transformer, the occasional breakage being easily mended. Moreover, in most of the other antennas described in this book, wires are subjected to relatively little tension, and annealed copper (which is more readily available and easier to handle) is usually satisfactory. It is of course vital, in any case where danger or serious embarrassment might be caused by failure, to stick to the rules and make sure of an adequate safety margin.

Further discussion of mechanical aspects of nylon line will be found in Chapter 19, p299.

Full-wave antennas

Use of $\lambda/2$ dipoles at their second harmonic, ie as full-wave (1λ) dipoles, is discussed later in the context of multiband operation but the topic may also arise in respect of monoband systems. Given an available span of 1λ, the options include two half-waves in phase (the 1λ dipole) and two half-waves out of phase, in addition to the basic $\lambda/2$ dipole. The question may arise as to which of these is the best arrangement. None provides all-round coverage and, if all directions are of equal interest, there is little to choose between the $\lambda/2$ dipole and the half-waves out of phase, provided the requirements for efficient end-feeding (p47) can be met. On the other hand, the 1λ antenna is the best choice given a special interest in a particular direction, since it provides useful gain and reduces interference from unwanted directions, assuming it can be aligned properly. Using spreaders it can be backed by reflectors to provide a high-gain beam system.

Loop antennas

Loops have two main advantages over $\lambda/2$ dipoles: they fit into a much narrower space and have a higher value of radiation resistance (p111), the width required for resonant loops being only 0.5–0.7 times the length of a straight $\lambda/2$ dipole, assuming no loading in either case. The loop at its fundamental resonance contains 1λ of wire, in which respect it resembles the folded dipole, Fig 11.1(b), which can also be considered as a loop 'squashed flat'. In some climates they have a further important advantage, being much less susceptible to rain static.

Figs 11.5(a) and (b) show the two most usual forms of the quad loop. These are strictly equivalent, though one or the other may be more convenient, (a) being more usual in the case of rotary beam elements, whereas (b) is more convenient for fixed antennas, allowing them to be suspended from a single support as shown. A spreader can be used in lieu of the cords if space is restricted. By virtue of its size, shape and high value of radiation resistance, this type of loop antenna is particularly suitable for erection in trees, losses usually being negligible so that, if a suitable tree is available, high performance can be attained with a more or less invisible antenna.

For more than 20 years the author relied for most of his DX contacts on pairs of loops wholly or partly buried in trees and operating as fixed but reversible beam antennas. Although

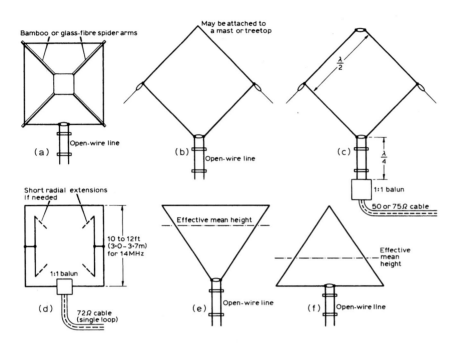

Fig 11.5. Loop antennas. (a), (b) are quad loops, (a) being most suitable for rotary beams and (b) more convenient for fixed arrays. At (c) the top of the loop is open-circuited to provide operation at twice the frequency with 3dB gain. At (d) loading by means of capacitive 'hats' allows considerable reduction in size. Delta loops are shown at (e) and (f) with dotted lines to illustrate the effective mean height; this is much lower in case (f)

much more stringent conditions apply in the case of a beam, no adverse effects were observed except on rare occasions due to extreme deposits of snow or ice. In the preferred arrangement the top corners of the loops were held up by a 9ft (2.7m) spreader attached to a short extension pole secured to the main tree trunk, and the corners were pushed into position by stout bamboos secured to tree branches with occasional help from 2in by 1in (5cm by 2.5cm) wooden struts. *There should be at least 6in (15cm) of polythene or nylon cord between the corners of the loops and the bamboo supports because wet bamboo is a very bad insulator.* An alternative would be the development of a fully proven method of weather protection but this has yet to be established.

On the other hand, there is no need to worry unduly if at times a few leaves (even wet ones) come into contact with the wires. An 11ft (3.4m) long ⅝in (16mm) diameter aluminium alloy tube with a hook at one end was used for threading wires over tree branches etc, and a pruning saw tied to the end of the same rod was used for removing remote branches that could not be avoided. Bamboo rods, though slightly less satisfactory, can also be used. Needless to say, this kind of operation should not be undertaken without climbing experience or adequate advice and ample safety precautions. It is essential for the constructor to be tied securely to the main tree trunk or a very thick branch for all such operations, and trees should not be climbed in wet weather or with inadequate footwear. The erection and maintenance of quads in trees can be difficult and time consuming and, although the author's domestic reputation for being always 'up a tree' is grossly exaggerated, such activities do not have a wide appeal; as an alternative to the quad, therefore, the small delta loop featured in Fig 12.18 is strongly recommended since in many cases it

can be pushed up into a tree from below or from the top of a ladder, and it is simple enough to be easily and quickly installed by someone with no knowledge of antennas, such as a professional tree climber (look up 'tree surgeon' in the 'yellow pages').

The basic quad loop contains 1λ of wire and the methods of feed shown at Fig 11.2(a), (b), (c) and (f) are equally applicable in this case. However, the points of connection for matched open-wire lines are somewhat further apart and require to be found by experiment, the spacings indicated being rough guidelines only. In case (a) or (b) a 4:1 balun and 50Ω feeder may be used; the SWR is about 1.5 but can if desired be improved by using a T-match as shown in Fig 11.6. The required wire length is given very approximately in feet by 990/f, assuming single-strand bare wire.

By open-circuiting the top of the loop as at (c) it becomes a bi-square antenna, having its main resonance at twice the frequency and a gain of 3–4dB as explained on p111. There remains a resonance at the lower frequency where the loop now operates as a kind of vertically polarised W8JK antenna with the beam direction rotated 90°. The dimensions are, however, non-optimum; this is not normally used and has little to recommend it beyond the 'fact that it is there' which may nevertheless be worth noting. Unlike the quad the bi-square is essentially monoband, though it will work as a *single* element on other frequencies if various odd mixtures of polarisation are accepted.

As explained in Chapter 5 (p99) the standard quad loop, Fig 11.5(a), can be considerably reduced in size with very little adverse effect by the use of end-loading as in Fig 11.5(d). A 12ft (3.7m) square loop and a 1:1 balun as shown present a good match to 75Ω coaxial feeder, but further size

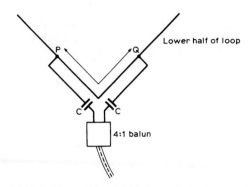

Fig 11.6. Use of T-match for improved matching between a single-loop antenna and a coaxial feeder. A 1:1 balun or a delta connection may be substituted, dimensions being found by experiment. Typical values for 14MHz are PQ 6–10ft (2–3m); C, 70–150pF, though C is not required if the loop size is reduced somewhat. Alternatively adjustment of PQ and C can be used to compensate for small variations in loop size. The method is applicable in most instances where the radiation resistance of an antenna is not suited to available values of feeder impedance

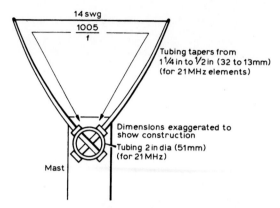

Fig 11.7. Self-supporting delta loop. Typically for 21MHz the sides are made from aluminium alloy tubing, tapering from 1¼in (32mm) to ½in (13mm) diameter while the top may consist of 14 or 16swg (2 or 1.6mm) copper wire. The total length of conductor is given in feet by 1005/f(MHz) [4]. Feed (not shown) as in Fig 11.6

reduction is possible with about 9ft (2.7m) as the likely minimum, the SWR then being of the order of 1.5 using 50Ω cable. This is recommended as a means of fitting a horizontally polarised antenna into a very short span without significant drop in performance. For a 12ft (3.7m) square loop the drop in gain, treating it as a broadside pair and referring to Fig 6.12, is found to be 0.5dB and, after allowing (say) another 0.2dB for the short-dipole effect (p20), there is still a slight gain compared with a $\lambda/2$ dipole.

Loops can be any shape. Figs 11.5(e) and (f) show the popular delta loop which is very similar to the quad, although the gain is about 0.5dB less; the two sloping sides between them contribute one third of the radiated field, the effective heights being given approximately by $(h - \lambda/12)$ in case (e) and $(h - \lambda/4)$ in case (f). The delta loop (e) can be suspended between two supports as in Fig 11.1(b); it is mechanically advantageous since the downward pull is not communicated to the horizontal section and use can be made of a much shorter span. At 14MHz and low angles, assuming 40ft (12m) supports and an effective mean sag of 2ft (0.6m) for the horizontal dipole, the delta loop is only 0.5dB worse than the dipole. Performance is equal at 80ft (24m) but the delta loop is 1.7dB worse for a height of 20ft (6m).

It will be seen that Figs 11.1(b) and 11.5(e) are similar except for the angle between the wires which in the first case is very small. An intermediate shape may be preferred and a triangle with a right-angle at its base is probably about optimum for this application, though likely differences are no more than small fractions of a decibel. This form of delta loop is good also in respect of visual impact. Other versions of the delta loop, Figs 11.7 and 11.8, require only a single support and these are even more attractive, assuming some increase in visibility to be acceptable.

In Fig 11.7 the sides of the delta loop can be regarded as a kind of mast extension and the effective height is roughly $\lambda/4$ greater than the height of the support. The feasibility of this

will depend on the strength of the support and acceptance of an appreciable degree of visual impact. Fig 11.8 is somewhat less ambitious, the mean height being roughly equal to that of the support. The particular interest of this arrangement, which was evolved by ZL1OI, lies in the method of erection which requires only a halyard over a pulley fixed to the top of the support.

Comparing Fig 11.5 (e) and (f) it will be seen that (f) is less 'height-effective' so that it might be better to use the top portion on its own as an inverted-V, subject to increasing the apex angle to 90°; this is desirable also, though less essential, in the case of the loop. In favour of (f) it is often easier to support and this has made it a popular choice for the lower-frequency bands; it is also more suitable for multiband operation.

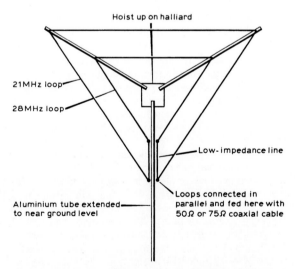

Fig 11.8. Delta loop for 21/28MHz; this light, simple and unobtrusive antenna is hoisted into position by a halyard (CQ Magazine)

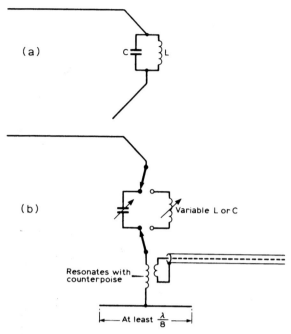

Fig 11.9. End-fed single wire. Arrangement (a) is suitable for lengths of $n\lambda/2 \pm \lambda/8$ but (b) should be used if the length approaches an odd multiple of $\lambda/4$. Suitable values for case (a) are $L = 85/f$ (MHz) and C (max) $= 450/f$ (MHz), the units being microhenrys and picofarads respectively. The loading inductance at (b) tunes out the capacitive reactance if the antenna is short and the capacitance removes the inductive reactance if the antenna is long, reckoning (roughly) 300Ω for a length error of $\lambda/16$, and *pro rata*. The counterpoise must present a reactance small compared with the end-impedance of the antenna and can be very small (3 or 4ft, approx 1m) if the antenna length is near $n\lambda/2$. If the antenna is near an odd multiple of $\lambda/4$ the counterpoise should be at least $\lambda/8$, centre-connected and series-tuned to resonance with a suitable inductance

End-fed wire antennas

Arrangements such as those illustrated in Fig 11.9 (though at one time commonplace) are now largely obsolescent; nevertheless, they still have important virtues, particularly in regard to simplicity of construction and the ease with which they can be improvised or concealed. Virtually any bit of wire bent into any shape can be used though, if possible, the length should be at least $\lambda/2$, it should be as high as possible, and if it has to be fitted into a small space the rules on p98 are applicable.

The feeding of this type of antenna is discussed in Chapter 4 (p42) and is simplified by avoiding lengths which are near to $\lambda/4$, odd multiples of $\lambda/4$, or less than $\lambda/4$, since in these cases much more attention must be given to the design of an efficient counterpoise. This has to be tuned which is an added complexity in the case of multiband operation. If a length of 133ft (40.5m) can be achieved, this is ideal since the desired condition is met (nearly enough) for all bands (including 10, 18 and 24MHz) from 3.5MHz upwards. There is one drawback to this, insofar as the antenna is brought into the shack at a point of high RF voltage, which in a few cases may lead

to increased losses and coupling into TV antennas or mains wiring. However, such couplings will be cancelled, at least in part, by equal voltages of opposite sign existing on a short counterpoise and the size or positioning of this may be important.

Every case under this heading is different, the dimensions and values given in Fig 11.9 being intended only as rough guidelines, though at least in case (a) they are not at all critical. In most cases, except perhaps those involving a lot of bends and close proximity to lossy objects, such antennas in their best directions are equal in general effectiveness to a $\lambda/2$ or λ dipole at the same height. In *some* cases there could be an increased risk of picking up mains-borne interference or causing TVI.

At the higher frequencies performance is poor at right-angles to the wire but there is likely to be some gain in near-endwise directions, eg 2dB for a straight 133ft (40.5m) wire at 28MHz. Due to loss of energy by radiation (or in the case of a thin wire, dissipation) as the wave travels outwards along a single wire, this is partially terminated (p108), resulting in a somewhat stronger signal at the higher frequencies in directions away from the feedpoint.

Earlier remarks about insulation are applicable and it is generally possible to use thin wire supported by equally thin nylon or polythene cord; in addition to this there is no feeder to be concealed and, for meeting 'invisible antenna' requirements without loss of performance, the end-fed wire and the inverted-V are the only serious contenders. The inverted-V may also be end-fed, though care should be exercised in such cases to ensure that as far as possible the current maximum is at the highest point in the system. For monoband operation the alternative method of end-feeding featured in Figs 4.28 and 11.3 can be strongly recommended as it allows high RF voltages to be kept out of the shack. Multiband operation may also be feasible, assuming suitable lengths, access to one end and (for example) an arrangement of plugs and sockets.

Slopers

When, for example, only a single support is available, an antenna problem can often best be resolved by a wire or wires sloping down from it. Radiation patterns can be anticipated with the help of Chapter 6, being dependent on heights, lengths and methods of feeding. Radiation tends to be best in the direction of slope and it is usually desirable, at least for DX, for current concentrations to be located as near as possible to the top end of the wire. To this end, some form of top-loading is desirable, such as a set of radials or, if that is not possible, a short counterpoise with inductive loading (such as Fig 11.9(b) but upside down) may be suitable. Bottom-end feeding by the method of Fig 4.28 is highly recommended since without elaborate precautions the alternative of top-end feeding with coaxial cable will almost certainly result in the feeder becoming part of the radiating system.

Vertical antennas

Experience with $\lambda/2$ vertical antennas (p164) led to the conclusion that, provided they are not in close proximity to trees or buildings, these work nearly as well with their 'feet on the ground' as when raised up to the sort of height that is commonly feasible. In the case of monopoles at ground level there is a basic loss of 3dB plus some ground losses [12] although, as explained in Chapter 6, these effects disappear very rapidly with increasing height. After exhausting the possibilities of vertical antennas at low height, the only way to obtain better performance is a change to horizontal antennas at a height depending on the location, typically about 30ft (9m) but capable of varying between wide limits; the situation may, however, become more complicated if it is not possible to accommodate the span required for a horizontal antenna or if the vertical antenna has to be raised to clear local obstructions or sources of interference. There was also one slightly speculative idea (p169), requiring a vertical antenna to be erected at tree-top level. Despite these exceptions, it seems reasonable to suppose that in most cases the lower end of a vertical antenna will be more or less accessible, and the recommendations below reflect some bias in this direction.

Fig 11.10(a) illustrates a conventional vertical monopole with a somewhat unconventional earth connection inspired by the arguments presented in Chapter 4 (p43). The shorter the antenna, the more important it is to have a low-resistance earth connection; this determines the allowable size of the loading inductance, which must have a loss resistance small compared with the radiation resistance of the antenna. The value of inductance in turn fixes a minimum size for the counterpoise. VK3AM has been using a basically similar idea (often using small helixes as counterpoises to short loaded verticals) in a successful project aimed at developing efficient antennas for use in confined spaces, including small boats. When the length exceeds about $3\lambda/8$ the loading coil shown in Fig 11.10(a) becomes unnecessary and the arrangement shown in Fig 11.9(a) may be used, though this has the disadvantage of requiring a weatherproof box. Alternatively, if the length is very close to $\lambda/2$ the modified Zepp feed, Fig 11.11(d) or (e), may be used.

Top-loading as in Fig 11.10(b) allows much shorter radiators to be used but the loading wire needs to be supported. Typically, for 14MHz a 6ft (1.8m) radiator could be hung from the centre of a 15ft (4.6m) horizontal wire which makes no significant contribution to the radiation (p226); the radiation resistance is about 9Ω so that a loading coil resistance of 2.3Ω would cause a loss of only 1dB. For a Q of 150 at 14MHz this gives an inductance of $4\mu H$ and a required length for the counterpoise of about 16ft (4.9m). This example, in conjunction with the discussion of vertical polarisation on pp161–165, suggests the possibility of efficient DX communication even when height is severely restricted, though an increase in height with suitable attention to loading and tuning can be expected to result in greater efficiency due to the removal of ground losses. Up to 3dB of height gain can be expected as well as a better chance of clearing obstructions. This process, pursued to its limit, results [12] in antennas such as the inverted ground-plane, Fig 11.11(a); the two-wire form shown at (b) improves bandwidth, reduces end-voltages, and assists with matching to coaxial line along the lines of Fig 4.28.

Asymmetrical dipole developed by VK3AM for marine use. Only 2m high, this can be mounted on the cabin roof of a small boat. As set up in the photo and using only 60W PEP, good signal reports were obtained from Europe

It may be noted that this method requires shortening of the radiator by about $\lambda/16$, a matter of little consequence since R is reduced by only 15%. Fig 4.11(b), which scores heavily in terms of convenience, was compared experimentally with the Zepp feed, Fig11.11(c), with and without the G6CJ balancing stub. Apart from establishing the credentials of the new method, the results were highly instructive, differences in field strengths being small provided the current on the outer of the coaxial cable was sufficiently low, a condition achievable in the case of the Zepp by using either the stub or the more-convenient linear trap. As this was a one-off experiment it should not be assumed to apply in other cases without further checking, but it would appear that the absence of any path to ground ensures that the same current has to flow in both feeder wires. In the case of Fig 11.11(b) the trap was needed only in the event of maladjustment of L. Bandwidth was adequate for coverage of the 21MHz band even in the case of the Zepp.

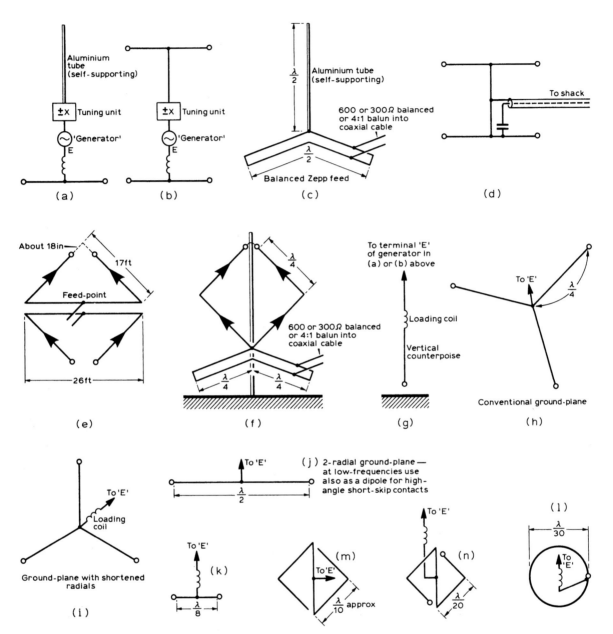

Fig 11.10. Vertical antennas. (a) Monopole with counterpoise; as antenna length is increased the size of counterpoise may be reduced as for other end-fed antennas. (b) Top-loaded monopole; the 'generator' represents some combination of transmitter, feeder and matching system. (c), (d) Dipoles. (e), (f) Two forms of quad, insulators being added at points of zero current, which leaves the operation unaffected but helps to keep high voltages away from the mast and, in the case of beam elements, is needed for directional switching; (e) covers all bands 10–30MHz, (f) is monoband. (g) to (n) illustrate alternative forms of counterpoise for monopole elements with (l), (m), and (n) requiring least space. Note also Fig 11.3(b) which is strongly recommended as an alternative to the Zepp feed, (c) and (f) above

Alternative forms of counterpoise are shown in Fig 11.10(g) to (n), and it will be evident that a short vertical one as in Fig 11.10(g) can be regarded alternatively as one half of a shortened dipole, thereby demonstrating that the distinction between monopole and dipole is somewhat arbitrary. Pursuing

this line of thought a stage further, Fig 11.10(c) and (d) will be instantly recognised as dipoles but differ from (a) plus (g) only to the extent of being more symmetrical. For a given vertical extent without top-loading, symmetry doubles the radiation resistance, and (c) or (d) should therefore be used in

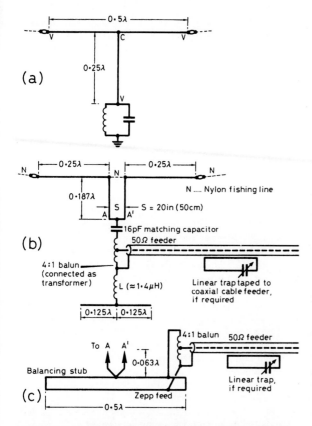

Fig 11.11. (a) The G3VA inverted ground-plane antenna; inversion increases effective height and eliminates ground losses but makes it even more important for the radials to be non-resonant, at least 5% increase or decrease in length of top being suggested. (b) Improved version based on Fig 4.30 ensures equal currents, improves bandwith, and avoids the limitations of the Zepp feed. Values of L and the matching capacitor are for 21MHz. The counterpoise length can be varied between wide limits subject to alteration of L. (c) The Zepp alternative. Note restoration of radiator length to the usual λ/4

preference to (b) wherever possible; the limitation here is the need for longer loading wires when a whole dipole instead of a half-dipole has to be fitted into the same vertical distance.

Apart from possible difficulty in finding room for the longer wires, there could be appreciable radiation from them in a high-angle mode; this can be checked with the help of the formula on p108. Fig 11.10(d) includes a form of gamma match; the outer of the cable should be connected to the electrical centre of the system which is not quite the same as the physical centre, though the difference is not significant provided the feeder is non-resonant.

The main application for (a) and (c) is in the important case of self-supporting antennas when top-loading is not possible, (a) being applicable to λ/4 and (c) to λ/2 radiators. Minimum sizes for counterpoises have not been fully investigated and the dimensions for (l) and (n) are tentative.

Vertical radiators are frequently supported by standoff

insulators mounted on wet wood, which is a recipe for large losses. A much better method of supporting a vertical antenna from a wooden (or even a non-resonant metal) mast is to use two wires which 'billow out' from the mast as in Fig 11.10(e) or (f); this may be Zepp-fed as at (f) or symmetrically as at (e) which is derived from the DJ4VM quad [7], these providing the basis for beam and multiband antennas described later. As it stands, this arrangement has some slight directivity, to the extent of a 2dB loss in the plane of the loop and 1dB gain at right-angles to this relative to a short dipole. In case (e) the feeder should be brought away at right-angles if possible, otherwise it crosses a point of high RF voltage, in which case it must be checked for balance and the measures described in Chapter 4 (p55) put into force if necessary.

Fig 11.12 shows a number of alternative feeder arrangements, (a) being the standard method for a λ/4 vertical antenna, while (b) shows the use of a ferrite transformer to obtain a better match when the antenna and feeder impedances are widely different, as happens for lengths other than λ/4. In the case of a λ/4 vertical antenna at a considerable height, a 4:1 impedance step-up ratio provides a good match to 72Ω feeder. A method of connection to 300 or 600Ω lines is shown at (c), while (d) and (e) are two versions of the modified Zepp feed (p48). Either a balanced line (300 or 600Ω) or a coaxial feeder with 4:1 balun may be connected as indicated in Fig 11.10(c). On the other hand, mutual coupling as in Fig 11.12(e) may be preferred to direct connection as it may reduce the extent to which any imbalance in the open-wire stubs can be communicated to the feeder; the coupling is close to unity so that the required length of stub is increased by at most a few inches. The feeder may also be mutually coupled as at (f) into the counterpoise loading coil, instead of the direct connection shown at (a); an example of this will be found in Fig 13.3 and another at the end of this chapter.

Multiband antennas based on resonant lines

The principles applicable to multiband operation were outlined in Chapter 7 with numerous examples. The task here is to make a selection geared to the solution of particular practical problems.

Although many different designs can be based on the use of resonant feeders, the best known is probably the G5RV antenna, Fig 11.13(a) and (b). This derives from the fact that a length of 102ft (31.1m) has been found by many amateurs to be a good compromise for covering all HF bands, though this depends largely on whether the lobes at the higher frequencies coincide with directions of particular interest.

The G5RV antenna can be fed in either of the ways illustrated in Fig 11.13. In the left-hand diagram, tuned feeders (300 to 600Ω) are used all the way; on the right, Fig 11.13(b), the high-impedance feeder is 34ft (10.4m) long and is connected into a 72Ω twin or coaxial cable. At this junction, the antenna impedance is low on most bands, as can be checked with the aid of Fig 4.49 for a length of 34 + 51 = 85ft (25.9m).

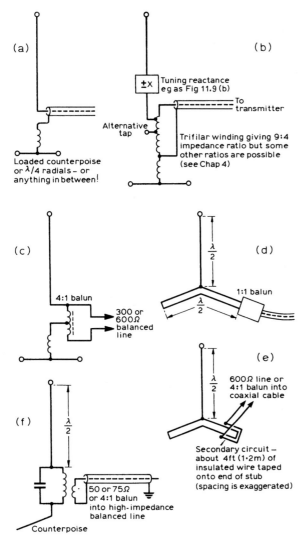

Fig 11.12. End-feeding of vertical antennas. (a) λ/4 monopole. (b) Addition of transformers for impedance matching. (c) Monopole with balanced line. (d), (e) End-feeding of dipole with unbalanced or balanced line. (f) Lumped-circuit equivalent of (d). (e) is equivalent to Fig 11.9(c) but uses an indirect feeder connection, a loop of insulated wire (typically 3–4ft long) taped onto the end of the stub

It has previously been suggested that there is an optimum height for this antenna, ie λ/2 or 1λ above ground, but, although in some cases these heights may provide better matching (and due note should be taken of Fig 6.18), the G5RV is no exception to the general rule that antennas should normally be erected as high as possible.

On 1.8MHz the two feeder wires are connected together at the transmitter end, or the inner and outer of the coaxial cable joined, and the top plus 'feeder' used as a Marconi antenna with a series-tuned coupling circuit and a good earth connection.

On the 3.5MHz band, the electrical centre of the antenna commences about 15ft (4.6m) down the open line (in other words, the middle 30ft (9.1m) of the dipole is folded up). The antenna functions as two half-waves in phase on 7MHz with a portion 'folded' at the centre. On these bands the termination is highly reactive, and the ATU must of course be able to take care of this if the antenna is to load satisfactorily and radiate effectively.

At 14MHz the antenna functions as a 3λ/2 antenna. Since the impedance at the centre is about 100Ω, a satisfactory match to the 72Ω feeder is obtained via the 34ft (10.4m) of λ/2 stub. By making the height λ/2 or 1λ above ground at 14MHz and then raising and lowering the antenna slightly while observing the SWR on the 72Ω twin-lead or coaxial feeder by means of an SWR bridge, an excellent impedance match may be obtained on this band. However, if low-angle radiation is required, height is all important and, as most cables will withstand an SWR of 2 or greater, any temptation to improve the SWR by lowering the antenna should be resisted.

On 21MHz, the antenna works as a slightly extended 2λ system or two full-waves in phase, and is capable of very good results, especially if open-wire feeders are used to reduce loss. On 28MHz it consists of two 1.5λ in-line antennas fed in phase. Here again, results are better with a tuned feeder to minimise losses, although satisfactory results have been claimed for the 34ft (10.4m) stub and 72Ω feeder.

When using tuned feeders, it is recommended that the feeder taps should be adjusted experimentally to obtain optimum loading on each band using separate plug-in or switched coils. Connection from the ATU to the transmitter should be made with 72Ω coaxial cable in which a TVI suppression (low-pass) filter may be inserted.

In the case of tuned feeders there is in principle no particular merit in the length of 102ft (31.1m). It should also be noted that the radiation pattern is of the general long-wire type, and the position of lobes and nulls will vary with length and frequency.

A length of 102ft requiring two supports is not always convenient, particularly if due regard is paid to the mechanical considerations on p178. In principle the G5RV antenna could be erected as an inverted-V but, in view of its length, the ends will then be close to the ground, the effective height reduced and DX performance impaired, except that the slope of the arms will result in vertically polarised radiation for some directions and frequencies. In particular there will be a vertically polarised 'W8JK mode' in the endwise direction on 7MHz which could be quite useful, and on 14MHz probably about half the power will be radiated in a two-element, wide-spaced vertical, end-fire mode. For operation on all bands, inclusive of 10, 18 and 24MHz, open-wire feeder should be used throughout. In this case the top can be reduced to about 60–70ft (18–21m) without serious drop in efficiency at 3.5MHz, provided heavy-gauge wire is used. However, unless plenty of height or sloping ground is available, it will certainly be much better *for DX only* on the lower frequencies to excite the feeder as a top-loaded vertical radiator operating against a suitable artificial ground (Fig 11.10) or, if near λ/2 resonance, voltage-fed on the lines of Fig 11.12(e) or (f) or

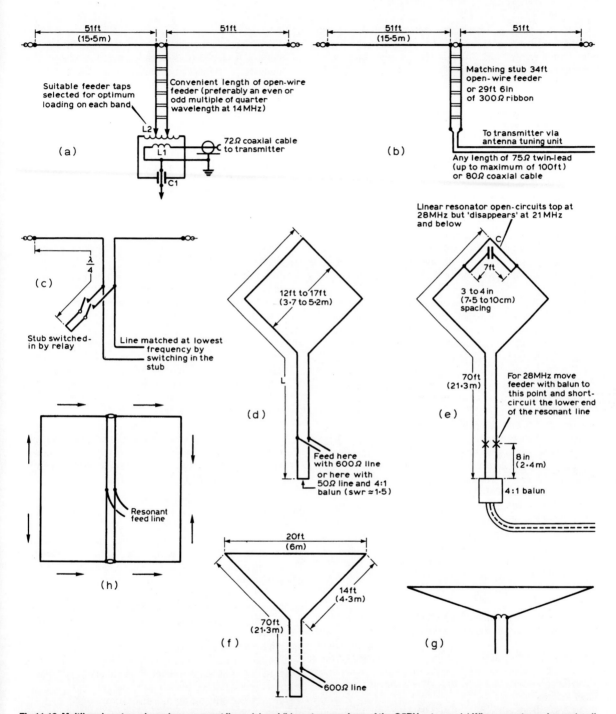

Fig 11.13. Multiband systems based on resonant lines. (a) and (b) are two versions of the G5RV antenna. (c) When an antenna is used well below its normal resonance or if it is a long way from the shack, losses in a resonant feeder tend to be excessive and the bandwidth narrows; to overcome this a matching stub may be switched in as shown. (d) Quad loops with resonant feeder, L = 70ft (21.3m), can be used on all bands from 7–28MHz, though some additional tuning will be required for 10, 18 and 24MHz, and 7MHz is only practicable with the larger loop size. (e) Addition of linear resonator to (d) to provide bi-square operation with extra gain at 28MHz, C ≈ 8pF. (f) Delta loop for 14MHz. (g) 14/21MHz folded-dipole with coil to tune out the capacitive reactance of the two half-dipoles at 21MHz. (h) Horizontally polarised (original) version of DJ4VM quad loop

11.10(f). It may be noted that with a length of 102ft the pattern at 10MHz will consist of narrow lobes at right-angles to the wire, with a gain of 2dB. At higher frequencies the pattern tends to favour the endwise directions with perhaps 2–3dB gain.

For a fuller explanation of the mode of operation (including current distributions) on each band reference [9] may be consulted, noting the feasibility of a half-size version covering all HF bands from 7MHz upwards.

At this point the reader should perhaps be reminded of the basic limitation by which resonant-feeder systems covering a number of closely spaced bands are unavoidably afflicted, as set out in Chapter 4. Looking closely at any normal combination of feeder and antenna, at least one impedance discontinuity can be discerned, usually at the feedpoint but this is immaterial; if it occurs near a point of maximum voltage (as can be expected on at least one band) there will be an additional mismatch equal to the square of the impedance ratio superimposed on what may already be a very large value of SWR.

In this respect the G5RV antenna is better than most and the discontinuity tends to be helpful rather than otherwise, but in the case of Fig 11.13(b) at 10MHz the SWR in the 75Ω line comes to about 40 which is unlikely to be acceptable.

The obvious solution is to get rid of the discontinuity, which in practice means using two or more wires in parallel (spaced a few inches) for the radiator while keeping the feeder impedance as high as possible. This applies equally to loop and dipole elements and, though in some cases it may pay to be more precise, there is no need for a computer. Two to one is a typical impedance ratio and this is somewhat imperfectly compensated by using a wire spacing of 6in (15cm) throughout. In the case of the above example the SWR in the 75Ω feeder is reduced to 10 and a feeder loss (if there is no breakdown) of about 2dB can be expected, so that it would be much better to use open-wire or 300Ω line or, better still, a matching unit as shown at (a).

Note that, in deference to the axiom stated on p42, long wires in parallel should be bridged across at distances less than $\lambda/2$ at the highest frequency, taking particular care also to ensure that any open ends (ie beyond the last of the bridges) are non-resonant. Some Z_0 values calculated [11] for wires in parallel are given in Table 7.1.

The use of wires in parallel is well known as a method for the broadbanding of antennas, but is only just emerging as an aid to tackling multibanding problems following introduction of the WARC bands. It is applied to beam elements in the next chapter, where data will be found for loop elements, and Table 7.3 gives data for 44ft dipoles which can be scaled for other lengths.

As possible alternatives to the G5RV antenna, horizontal loops have been attracting much attention, but an effort to disentangle something useful to the reader from the literature at his disposal has yielded nothing more substantial than a renewed urge to try and set the record straight in several important respects as follows:

(a) *For DX communication the vertical angle of the main lobe in the antenna pattern is completely irrelevant.* It has nothing whatever to do with its quality as a low-angle radiator, nor is there any reason to suppose that this is the angle from which signals are arriving. Low-angle performance is determined solely by the gain which the antenna would have in free space (a three-dimensional property of the antenna) and the ground reflection factor (pp114, 162), which for horizontal polarisation at relevant angles depends only on height. Readers who find this difficult to believe may find it helpful to refer to the comparison of small loops and dipoles on p262. As background, p16 is useful reading, taking particular note of the references.

(b) The gain from *n* wires, unless these are long enough to have appreciable gain (or very closely spaced) cannot exceed *n*, give or take a decibel or so, and it is generally difficult to approach this figure.

(c) In general a small number of decibels in one direction can only be gained by losing a larger number in other directions which may be equally important. Lack of gain is therefore not a disadvantage for a general-purpose antenna such as the G5RV.

(d) If SWR shows little variation with frequency, contrary to expectation, *this is usually synonymous with losses.* These can and do occur due, for example, to energy being pumped into the ground by current flowing on the outer of a coaxial line. The effect is likely to be provoked by any asymmetry in the antenna.

(e) Due to the dependence of vertical radiation on highly variable ground constants, attempts to compare the gain of vertical and horizontal antennas, or estimate the relative H and V content in the response of a given antenna from observed signal strengths, can be highly misleading.

Despite such strictures, any symmetrical design of loop may be worth trying, Fig 11.14 being offered as a suggestion.

If the open-wire feeder is a long one it may be necessary or at least desirable to connect appropriate matching stubs for one or more bands as in Fig 11.13(c). This can if desired be done from the shack by means of relays. In this case only the lengths of line from the stubs to the antenna are resonant, bandwidth may be greatly improved, and losses can be held to an acceptable level for line lengths up to 200yd (180m) or more. Relays as shown have to handle large currents at the lowest frequency, high voltages at higher frequencies, and must have low capacitance.

Contrary to general belief, the quad loop makes a particularly good multiband resonator as explained in Chapter 7, p122, and good results have been obtained on the 7, 14, 21 and 28MHz bands using the arrangement shown in Fig 11.13(d), though SWR (not measured) could have been fairly high on 7MHz and 28MHz. Nevertheless, results included 28MHz SSB contacts with North America using only 300mW on each of three occasions when it was attempted and, with full power on 7MHz, S8 reports from Australia. There are, however, a number of points to be observed:

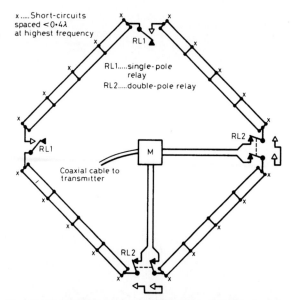

x.....Short-circuits
spaced <0·4λ
at highest frequency

RL1

RL1.....single-pole
relay
RL2.....double-pole relay

RL2

M

RL1

Coaxial cable to
transmitter

RL2

Fig 11.14. Horizontal constant-Z_0 loop antenna. Using four relays and two feeders, many different modes are possible, eg small rhombic covering 21–28MHz, phased pairs of delta loops with beam switching on 7MHz, high- or low-angle loop on 3.5MHz, pair of G5RV substitutes on 14MHz. M = master switch box with tuners (need not be central but simpler if it is). A side length of 100ft (30m) is suggested. Other loop shapes and sizes or single-wire versions are feasible. Wire spacing is not critical, gauge determined mainly by mechanical considerations

(a) Resonances do not quite coincide for all bands and compensating circuits, Fig 7.3(b), may be used to achieve this for 14 and 21MHz.

(b) Because of the very low radiation resistance on 7MHz the wire gauge should be as heavy as possible if operation is required on this band, and particular care must be taken to avoid any high-resistance connections. In the case of a 14/21MHz beam based on Fig 7.2, both loops should be connected in parallel for use as a single loop on 7MHz, efficient operation as a beam being out of the question.

(c) The line of fire for a single 14MHz loop used on 28MHz is in the plane of the loop with a basic end-fire gain of 3dB, from which must be subtracted 3dB due to radiation of half the energy in a vertically upwards mode, leaving the gain roughly equal to that of a dipole.

(d) By using resonant feeders, preferably with matching stubs as in Fig 11.13(c), operation can be extended to include 10, 18 and 24MHz.

(e) Operation of the loop plus the λ/2 resonant feeder as a grounded λ/4 vertical for 3.5MHz is feasible in this case also.

(f) Operation as a bi-square beam with 3dB gain is possible at 28MHz by open-circuiting the top of the loop. This has been done using a linear resonator, Fig 11.13(e), with little disturbance of operation at the other frequencies, but for connection to a matched line the feeder system at the lower end must be altered as shown in the figure. The bandwidth is fairly narrow, about 300–400kHz; if this is

insufficient it may be possible to dispense with the resonator and use a relay. This would, however, require thorough testing at full power prior to erection, with the loop laid out horizontally a few feet from the ground.

(g) The loop can be reduced in size to about 12ft (3.7m) square, keeping the total electrical length (Fig 11.13(d)) constant with little or no loss at 14MHz. Even as a beam element buried in a tree, good results have been obtained with such loops, though a slight loss was suspected compared with the use of a full-size element. In this case, most of the radiation comes from the top half of the loop and in theory, for typical heights and in the clear, this should at least neutralise any slight drop in gain.

The delta loop may be treated in a similar manner but, up to the time of writing, has not been studied in the same depth and there may be appreciable differences. The delta loop, Fig 11.13(f), (despite some fairly strong end-wise radiation at the top end of the frequency range) radiates most of its power in the normal direction over the whole frequency range from 14–28MHz, and could also be used at 10MHz on the same basis as the standard 14MHz quad loop at 7MHz. The bandwidth and efficiency for this mode have been calculated in Chapter 8, p146. The radiation resistance at 14MHz is about 70Ω. In view of its smaller size it could be attractive as an alternative version of the loop in Fig 11.7, though for monoband 14MHz operation into a matched line the loop needs to be loaded by an open-wire stub about 12ft (3.7m) in length. In tackling the problems posed by introduction of the WARC bands, this has emerged as a preferred option for small beam elements covering five or six bands as featured in the next chapter.

In the case of a folded dipole or 'squashed delta', Fig 11.4(b), there is virtually no radiation at the second harmonic unless the top side is open-circuited, eg by the same method as that used in Fig 11.13(e). A 14MHz folded dipole can, however, be used efficiently on 21MHz where it is not far from resonance, its radiation pattern being much the same as at 14MHz. For a total electrical length as defined by Fig 11.13(d) or (e) of 1λ at 14MHz, it is necessary to shorten the system by about 4ft (1.2m) to retain resonance at 21MHz, due to the capacitive reactance of the two halves of the dipole acting in series. This can alternatively be tuned out by an inductance of about 7.5μH, as shown in Fig 11.13(g), but an exact value cannot be given since it is rather large and influenced by its own self-capacitance, which in turn depends on precise constructional details; these are not available, the author's experiments having got no further than establishing the principle. This inductance has no effect at the fundamental resonance.

An alternative method [7] of multibanding the quad loop, due to DJ4VM, is shown in Fig 11.13(h) which is basically similar to Fig 11.10(e). This relies on resonant feeders but has the advantage of ensuring optimum current distribution and a 'clean' radiation pattern at all frequencies, the antenna being completely symmetrical. All bands (including 10, 18 and 24MHz) from 7MHz upwards can be covered as previously described, but in this case the loop size can be increased with advantage to 21ft (6.4m) square; this increases gain slightly at the higher frequencies and, at the lower frequencies, improves the bandwidth and allows the use of somewhat thinner wire without detriment to the efficiency.

A number of other types of multiband loop and dipole elements featured as beam elements in Chapters 5, 7, and 12 can also be used separately but, with beams usually restricted to 1 or 1½ octaves, the requirements tend to differ.

Multiband operation without resonant lines

Earlier discussion (Chapter 7, p139) has emphasised the importance, in the case of, say, a conventional full-sized dipole or quad beam element for 14MHz, of using the whole of it at the higher frequencies. It was, however, also explained that, when the element is folded or otherwise modified to fit it into a smaller space, any attempt to use the whole of it results in a lot of energy being radiated in unwanted directions.

So far in this chapter comparatively little use has been found for the straight dipole, but reference has already been made to the use of linear resonators to increase the versatility of loops and, by using two such resonators as in Fig 11.15, two-band operation can be achieved with a non-resonant line. A more elaborate form of resonator (p134) allows three-band operation but it is difficult to see this being extended to cover additional frequencies, and a more elegant solution would make use of variable capacitors. Given the genius of Heath Robinson plus a well-stocked junk box, this should present no difficulty but, until some manufacturer is enterprising enough to market suitable servo-controlled variable capacitors, most of us will have to be content with something inferior. Nevertheless, the availability of very small and light relays with short leads and 5A contacts makes it possible to switch capacitances and add one band per relay per element as discussed in Chapter 7, p139. There a preference is expressed for hybrid options which combine stacking with the use of linear resonators and relays.

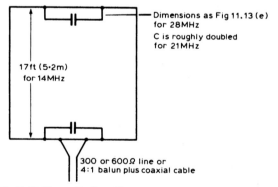

Dimensions as Fig 11.13 (e) for 28MHz

C is roughly doubled for 21MHz

17ft (5·2m) for 14MHz

300 or 600Ω line or 4:1 balun plus coaxial cable

Fig 11.15. The application of linear resonators to provide two-band operation of loops. This can be adapted for any shape of resonant loop

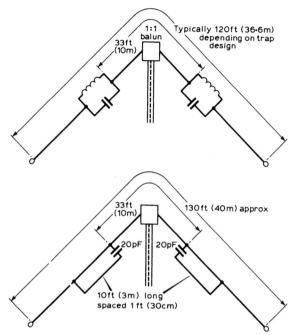

Fig 11.16. Inverted-V dipoles for 14/3.5MHz. (a) Conventional traps. (b) Linear traps. The principle can be extended to provide coverage of some additional wavebands; estimated losses are 0.7dB at 14MHz, virtually nil at 3.5MHz

Objections to the use of traps were recorded in Chapter 7 but, though not favoured in general, they were shown to have some merit for the multibanding of inverted-V dipoles, and improved design procedures are now available (p131). A very common situation is illustrated in Fig 11.16, which shows how a 3.5MHz inverted-V dipole can be adapted as a DX antenna on one or more higher-frequency bands. Isolating the top portion in this way increases the effective height and provides a simple solution to the matching problem. Traps based on high-Q coils are available as proprietary items, and in view of the problems of waterproofing plus the need to maintain the highest possible value of Q at all times, purchase is recommended rather than construction.

An unusual form of trap using linear resonators is also shown in Fig 11.16; this avoids the need for weatherproofing, except that, depending on their construction, it may be necessary to give the capacitors a protective coating of Araldite. It is also light and low loss but the bandwidth is somewhat narrower than with conventional traps. Exact design data is not available but guidelines are indicated and the idea may commend itself to experimenters.

The multiband dipole shown in Fig 7.12 has the advantage of eliminating trap losses as well as being easy to construct; moreover, there is in principle no definite limit to the number of dipoles which may be connected in parallel, so that it could be of particular interest for adding 10, 18 and 24MHz band coverage. Nevertheless, as pointed out in Chapter 7, interactions between dipoles can occur, particularly in the form of

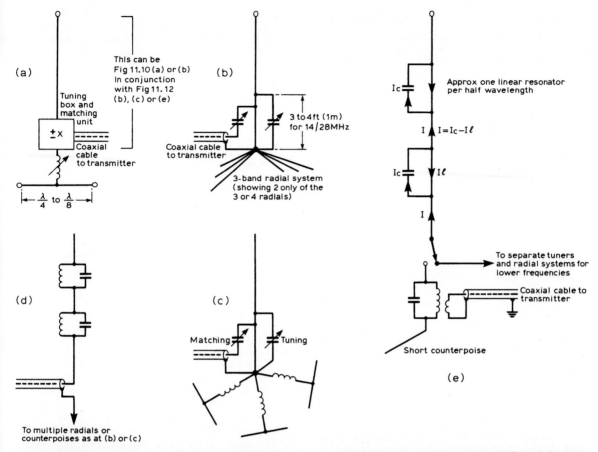

Fig 11.17. Multiband vertical antennas. (a) Use of variable L and C for covering a frequency range of 1–2 octaves. (b) Ground plane uses switched tuning unit based on linear resonator with a separate set of radials for each band. (c) Equivalent arrangement using counterpoises. (d) Use of traps. (e) Use of linear resonators to provide capacitive stretching whereby the whole of the antenna is used at the highest frequency; a 7MHz monopole can be used as two half-waves in phase at 28MHz, operation on 7MHz being unaffected

28MHz current flowing in the 21MHz element. With more dipoles more such effects will manifest themselves but, up to a point, these can be controlled by the use of capacitors as illustrated in Fig 7.12(b).

Multiband vertical antennas

Assuming access to the lower end of a vertical monopole antenna as previously discussed, it is possible to tune it over a frequency range of at least 3 to 1 without incurring significant losses or seriously upsetting the radiation pattern in the vertical plane. All that is required therefore is a suitable tuning box and an appropriate earth connection for each frequency. Since all the recommended 'earths' are frequency selective the choice lies between a single earth, the tuning of which is linked with that of the antenna, Fig 11.17(a), or a set of earths individually resonated to include all the desired bands, one common version of this being the multiple ground plane shown in Fig 11.17(b). A rather similar option is the multiple counterpoise of Fig 11.17(c). These also illustrate

the use of a linear resonator as a tuning unit, though this is not recommended for a tuning range much in excess of one octave.

The most usual method, and probably the easiest, for coverage of a frequency range greater than 2½ or 3 to 1 is the use of traps as in Fig 11.17(d), but there are interesting possibilities for the experimenter based on the use of capacitive stretching (p238) of the antenna at the highest frequencies by means of linear resonators as in Fig 11.17(e). These should preferably be located within $\lambda/8$ of points of maximum current. The required design procedure is to lay the antenna out horizontally within reach of the ground and check the current distribution along it as C is varied. The value of I, which is equal for the resonator sections to $(I_c - I_L)$, should be as constant as possible. However, except at the end of the antenna, *there must not be a zero* since this would imply a phase reversal, and the object of the exercise is the maintenance of constant phase and amplitude. Capacitive stretching results in the equivalent of a collinear array and hence extra gain at the higher frequencies.

Tuning units as in (a) may be switched remotely by relays or Ledex switches, but the linear resonator can be used as in (b) or (c) for two-band or three-band operation within a range of just over one octave, subject to acceptance of some reduction in bandwidth at the highest frequency.

Some readers will no doubt be prepared to accept sacrifices in return for the extra convenience of trapped verticals which are available as proprietary items covering all or most of the HF bands. In comparison the stretched or collinear vertical antenna produces much less radiation at higher angles, so that in addition to some extra gain for DX there will be less short-skip interference and less cosmic noise. Conversely the trapped vertical gives better performance for medium-range working though, as previously pointed out (p173), all vertical antennas (unless the feeder is radiating) result in poor performance over shorter distances.

Indoor antennas

The choice of a single element or beam for an indoor antenna depends on the interplay of a number of influences which are different in each case and can probably be resolved only by experiment, though some guidelines will be indicated in the following pages. An indoor antenna is usually a last resort, but unless one is unfortunate enough to live in a steel-framed building it should be possible to radiate a useful, and even in some cases a fully competitive, signal. For best results the guidelines in Chapter 10 (p172) should be strictly followed, each case being treated on its merits and ready-made solutions regarded with suspicion. In the case of a building with three or more storeys and an accessible roof space (not too severely cluttered by plumbing and electric wiring), a horizontal dipole with end-loading as necessary in accordance with Fig 11.1(e) to (j) is likely to provide the best answer.

In some very favourable cases it may be possible to accommodate a fixed but reversible beam (even, in the case of a few very large houses, a rotary beam for 21, 24 or 28MHz) but good results are not in general to be expected if a small beam is fitted into a space only just large enough to accommodate it. This is because very high RF voltages exist at the ends of the elements and any adjacent 'lossy' material will introduce severe losses. It is possible that in some cases a beam such as Fig 12.3 may give good results, at least in dry weather, but the experimenter with limited time at his disposal would probably do better to use a single element for transmission with perhaps (when such techniques are more fully developed) a separate small 'active' antenna for nulling out interference in reception (p156).

This advice could, however, be at fault since there seems to be no body of reliable experience on which to draw. An ideal single element is probably a small or rectangular 'quad loop' lying down in a horizontal position; this may be 'end-loaded' capacitively as in Fig 11.5(d). The radiation resistance is fairly high, being 72Ω at 14MHz for a loop 12ft (3.7m) square, and RF voltages are correspondingly low. It therefore looks like an ideal antenna for fitting into a small roof space but spacing between the sides should not exceed 12ft, otherwise

too much energy is directed upwards, to the extent that with 17ft (5.2m) spacing the gain is 2dB down on a dipole. With additional folds or inductive loading it could be reduced in size to 8ft (2.4m) square or even less although, if this is the only space available, some loss in performance is almost certain to ensue.

The 'odd bit of wire' type of antenna cannot be ruled out even for indoor applications, and in the case of a large house a long wire wandering through the various roof spaces and ending up if necessary in a number of folds to provide end-loading may be a good choice, at least for the low bands, if RF can be kept out of the mains wiring, eg with the help of the measures discussed below.

In good conditions some DX communication should be possible with nothing more than a dipole in the roof space of a bungalow and, if the house or bungalow is on a steep hillside, outstanding results *in the downhill direction* can be expected with no more than this. Failing such a slope or a tall house, the advice to try vertical polarisation if possible before finalising the antenna system holds for the indoor case also.

Absorption effects may be worse in the vertical case, but on the other hand a vertical antenna in an attic space, even if it has to project down through the ceiling into an upstairs room, is less likely to find itself tightly coupled into the electric wiring system. A vertical at ground level may experience more absorption but otherwise should be nearly as good as one in the attic. Methods of shortening vertical antennas are discussed on p263 and the possibility of a phased pair of fairly widely spaced verticals may be worth considering. One antenna particularly favoured by constructors of indoor antennas is the W8JK beam, but this is in fact the 'worst possible' choice. This is because for its size the W8JK has (p100) the *lowest* radiation resistance which it is physically possible to achieve, and correspondingly high voltages. In contrast the single-element loop discussed above minimises the losses.

This brings us to what is perhaps the real crux of designing a good indoor antenna system: keeping RF currents out of other wiring. We have here yet another example of the problem of coupling between wires which has already shown up in many different forms. Although in principle this could perhaps be favourably exploited in a few cases, to do so would be decidedly tricky and possibly even involve some fire risks. The only sound rule is to ensure that the RF is confined to the antenna system. Unfortunately in the case of a typical small home any resonant wire or pipe, unless very close to the ground (eg under the downstair floorboards) or running at right-angles, can be expected to show some coupling, and in consequence current will flow in what is likely to be a very lossy system. As well as being dissipated, however, power will almost certainly be radiated in unwanted directions and some of it carried to TV sets in adjoining houses or other undesirable destinations. A short list of such conductors includes:

Mains wiring
Metal conduit enclosing mains wires

Central heating pipes
Hot and cold water pipes
Telephone wires
TV antenna feeders
Bell wires
Extension speaker leads
Gas pipes

Resonances can usually be located with a GDO having a coil of sufficiently large area as described in Chapter 18; this should be held against two or three well-separated points on each of the conductors under suspicion, the reason for more than one point of application being failure of resonances to show up on the GDO if the test is made at a current node. Some amateurs have apparently had success in removing resonances by the use of plug-in capacitors at various mains outlets [5], but although this may shift the frequency it seems likely in many cases to have no effect. This is because wires going to an outlet tend to be effectively in parallel, whereas plugging in an appliance having a suitable length of lead, or just an odd bit of lead ending in a terminal block, must inevitably have some effect on resonances.

Another useful trick is to put a trap in the wire which is causing the trouble, but it is *not* necessary to cut into the wire in order to do this. Instead, a linear-resonator type of trap can be made from a short length of open-wire line tuned to the required frequency, Fig 11.18(a). One wire of this line is then taped onto the conductor in question but without breaking into the insulation. In the case of a pipe (not gas pipe), however, direct contact should be made to it (eg with earthing clips) so that it becomes one conductor of the line, the other conductor of which should preferably also be tubing, though the diameters need not be equal (Fig 11.18(b)). This idea has many applications.

It is particularly important in the case of indoor antennas to make sure that any earth current associated with the antenna system is provided with a suitable return path. *It must not go through the mains wiring, and this includes the mains earth.* The problem is basically the same as in the case of an outside end-fed antenna, and arises also to a greater or lesser extent whenever there is any loss of balance in the antenna system. An indoor antenna, even if of a balanced type and fed with a balun, may become unbalanced due to proximity to the other conductors in the house, which may still affect balance even though resonance has been averted. Whatever earthing system is adopted must be regarded as part of the antenna and cannot be considered in isolation.

Conclusions and recommendations

This chapter has provided a wide choice of single-element ideas from which it is hoped that readers will be able to select those best suited to their needs or by which they may perhaps be inspired to think of better ones. It is felt nevertheless that some readers will be confused by the amount of choice available and may be helped by the author's personal selection of 'best buys'.

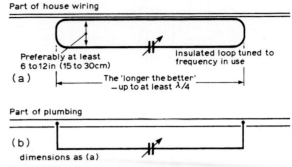

Fig 11.18. Use of linear trap to suppress an unwanted resonance. (a) shows how this result may be achieved without making the electrical connection to the conductor shown at (b)

1. The end-fed single wire has fewest problems of erection and, subject to a few reservations (see earlier text), can give a very good account of itself. Typically, one fixes a TV-type antenna mast to the chimney, runs a wire up to this from the shack window and then out to any convenient support as far away as possible, 133ft (40m) being a desirable length. With a similar arrangement during the mid-'thirties, using all bands from 3.5 to 28MHz, the author almost equalled the previous year's winning score in the W/VE contest. Though not remarkable in view of improved conditions, this result was good enough to inspire considerable respect for this type of antenna, particularly as a W8JK beam at the same mean height (about 35ft or 11m) and a two-element vertical beam failed to produce any improvement in signal reports. A lot depends of course on whether the wire runs in an 'interesting' direction, and a tall tree at the mid-point would probably be an improvement over the TV mast. In the event of EMC problems, several feet of the mains cord should be wound around as much ferrite rod as possible and either a short loaded counterpoise or a single 'λ/4 radial' wire used as an earth connection for the rig.

2. The inverted-V dipole, Fig 11.1(c), or the monoband version of Fig 11.2(b). *This is usually the easiest way to achieve the greatest possible effective height on the most important DX bands.*

3. For mounting in trees which can be climbed easily, use a quad loop with a resonant feedline extending at least to within reach from the ground, along the lines of Fig 11.13(d) or (e), but consider the possibility of replacing the linear resonator by a relay as discussed on p189. Note that this also can be excited as a top-loaded vertical for lower-frequency bands. By suitable tuning provisions at ground level 10, 18 and 24MHz can be covered. As a 'nearly as good' alternative, or if the tree is not easily climbed, a delta loop of the type used in Fig 12.18 may be pushed up into it from ground level or the top of a ladder.

4. In the years since this book was first published, the delta loop in one or other of its many forms has in the author's experience emerged as an overall 'best buy', providing the best answer to more problems than any other type of

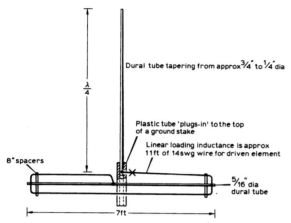

Fig 11.19. Constructional details of 14MHz monopole with short, inductively loaded counterpoise. It may be fed with 50Ω coaxial cable at point X (outer to counterpoise) but do not expect an SWR of less than about two unless additional impedance transformation is used. Alternatively the feeder may be connected through a balun to a series-tuned triangular coupling coil placed in the angle at X

element. This applies particularly to multiband operation as featured in Chapters 5, 7 and 12, much of this material being equally applicable to single elements. Supported by a pair of fishing rods it can often provide more height than could be achieved by any other means, though in this form it lacks the simplicity or low visual impact of the inverted-V. For suspending *between* trees or masts use a 'squashed' delta loop as in Fig 11.1(b), (f), or 11.13(g).

5. If vertical polarisation is favoured and two supports are available, the inverted ground plane, Fig 11.11(b), can be recommended. This can also be used as a horizontal λ/2 dipole or a top-loaded ground-plane antenna at half the frequency.

6. A vertical monopole based on Fig 11.12(a), as shown in Fig 11.19 which includes dimensions found by experiment, though mutual coupling of the feeder (see p44) may be preferable. Outstanding features of this antenna are ease of erection and adjustment when installed close to ground level and restricted to monoband operation, but about 3dB improvement can be expected from an increase of base height to at least λ/6, and multiband operation may be feasible along the lines of Fig 11.17(c). For a given mean height as measured to the centre of gravity of the current

distribution, performance can be reckoned as identical to that of a vertical dipole provided no current is allowed to flow on the outer of the coaxial feeder.

7. Last but not least, the G5RV antenna remains an excellent choice for a general-purpose antenna. The arguments in its favour would appear to be considerably strengthened by getting rid of the impedance discontinuities in the manner which has been described.

If operation is restricted to one or two bands some other antennas qualify for nomination as 'best buys'. These include the delta-matched inverted-V; the two-band delta loops of Fig 11.8; short end-loaded elements such as Fig 11.1(j) or (m); symmetrically end-loaded elements such as Fig 11.1(g) or (i) in wire form mounted vertically and slung between poles; and the 'top-hat loaded' quad loop of Fig 11.5(d), which allows an antenna to be accommodated in the shortest possible span without significant loss of efficiency or bandwidth.

References

[1] 'Invisible antennas', T J Gordon, W6RVQ, *QST* November 1965, p87.
[2] *The ARRL Antenna Book,* 13th edn, ARRL, 1974, p265.
[3] H R Habig, K8ANV, *The ARRL Antenna Anthology,* ARRL, 1978, p84.
[4] *CQ* May 1976.
[5] *Wire Antennas,* W I Orr, W6SAI, Radio Publications Inc, 1972, p127.
[6] 'Shunt feeding towers for operation on the lower amateur frequencies', B A Boothe, W9UCW, *The ARRL Antenna Anthology,* ARRL, 1978, p34.
[7] 'A new multiband quad antenna', W Boldt, DJ4VM, *Ham Radio* August 1969.
[8] 'Aerial masts and rotation systems', R Thornton and W H Allen, *Radio Communication* August 1972.
[9] *The ARRL Antenna Book,* 12th edn, ARRL, 1970, p276.
[10] 'The G5RV antenna – up to date', Louis Varney, G5RV, *Radio Communication* July 1984.
[11] 'Two-element HF beams', Les Moxon, G6XN, *Ham Radio* May 1987.
[12] 'Ground planes, radial systems and asymmetric dipoles', *The ARRL Antenna Compendium,* Vol 3, ARRL, 1993.
[13] *Amateur Radio Techniques,* 7th edn, Pat Hawker, G3VA, RSGB, 1980, p270.

Chapter 12

Horizontal beams

The choice of horizontal beams is almost unlimited but two types of rotary beam, the three-element trapped Yagi and the two- or three-element quad, seem to have a clear lead in the popularity stakes. Despite this, the reader who has persevered with Chapters 5 and 7 will not expect further consideration of triband trapped beams, and the quad does not emerge as the wisest choice for a rotary beam since it poses major problems of weight, windage and visual impact. Nevertheless, it must be admitted that in terms of signal strength the shortcomings of trapped beams add up to something less than the average differences between locations, by no means all the big DX signals come from beams without traps, and for large numbers of amateurs who need to buy a multiband antenna 'off the shelf' the only current alternative is the three-band quad. Some traps and some types of trapped beam appear to be much more reliable than others, and if it is essential to purchase a proprietary article it would be wise to seek the experience of other amateurs at club meetings or over the air.

These lines were written for the first edition, prior to release of the WARC bands, but there has been little new development. Trapped beams providing acceptable coverage of five or six bands are hard to imagine, stacking poses other problems, and alternatives such as the log-periodic antenna involve large structures beyond the means of most of us. However, the new bands are narrow and, unless something is done to improve reception and restrict emissions wherever possible to wanted directions, the future prospects are not encouraging. In Chapters 5 and 7 attention was drawn to arrangements based on the use of resonant feeders, not only for tackling this problem but also for achieving small size combined with high efficiency, deep nulls and low visual profile.

To these ends a number of practical arrangements are featured later in this chapter. These are 'no compromise' antennas, based on arrangements in regular use by the author over a period of many years and backed by strong preferences even for monoband operation which was the sole requirement over a considerable period. Advantages, in addition to deep steerable nulls, have included instantaneous beam reversal, continuous monitoring of performance and, by switching between two antennas, all-round coverage without incurring the high cost, delays and unreliability of beam rotators. This does not imply any absence of problems and, with five or six bands to cover, the in-shack tuning, switching, and matching arrangements can look extremely complicated, even though the underlying system is basically simple. Inevitably a single coaxial feeder coming into the shack is much neater and simpler to deal with than a pair of resonant lines, but it is arguably better to have the complications in the shack rather than 50ft up in the air and, as outlined in Chapters 4 and 5, new and simpler procedures have now been developed.

It is recognised that these features will not coincide with everyone's needs or preferences, neither are they all dependent on resonant feeders, and requirements for one-, two- or three-band beams will remain as long as there are old rigs around or amateurs who prefer to specialise. Most of the arrangements featured in the earlier edition have been retained, though later experience has suggested some changes; interaction between stacked elements can take subtle forms, and cases of tracking have caused the use of polythene insulation to be approached with greater caution. On the other hand, nylon fishing-line, despite some defects, has emerged as the solution to a lot of problems since it is almost invisible, strong and capable of accommodating a great deal of stretch as well as being an excellent insulator. In general, particularly for the amateur with limited means at his disposal, elements with dual resonances (ie two-band elements) can be graded as 'easy', three-band elements as 'very difficult' and four-band elements as 'virtually impossible without compromising performance', though skilful use of dual resonances combined with stacking should result in satisfactory performance on three or four bands.

The selection of beams for inclusion in this chapter is a personal choice seeking to cater for a wide diversity of practical needs, each antenna being visualised as a possible 'best solution' to some practical problem. Inevitably a lot of excellent ideas will have been overlooked, but much else has been rejected because it derives its main substance from assumptions or observations at variance with established principles or good practice.

Readers who have persevered with earlier chapters should find little difficulty in identifying the 'good' and the 'bad', and on this basis the quad antenna invites rejection in view of typical performance claims which 'ride roughshod' over the rules relating radiation resistance, mutual resistance and antenna current, as well as denying the normal relationships between unit gain, stacking gain, and stacking distance. These claims are also in direct conflict with the experience of the author and others as set out in Chapter 5; nevertheless, faced with the insistence of unbiased observers that quads often give good results where Yagis do not, one needs to look around for explanations which for consistency with natural laws need to exclude the the prevailing tendency to regard square $\lambda/4$ loops as stacked pairs of dipoles.

The most obvious one is the 'periscope effect' which seems to have escaped the attention of everyone except possibly neighbours into whose view the top of the quad may well be obtruding. The significance of this is likely to be lost on the quad owner who will be well aware that it is average height that matters but, if the extra height to the top of a loop lifts it clear of obstructions, it may be not only the neighbour but also the DX station that only sees the top. In this case up to 3dB improvement can be expected from getting rid of the lower part of the loop, ie by converting the loop into a short dipole, so that more power is radiated into space and less into the obstruction.

Exit the quad? Well, maybe not quite, since (to be fair) antenna problems are rarely as simple as this, and the height theory is still unproven. To complete the record, major disadvantages of quads include the visual impact added to high windage and a poor reputation for survival in strong winds.

On the other hand, the important multiband properties of quad loops, particularly in the DJ4VM form (pp139, 187), have been largely ignored and other advantages include the existence of more-or-less critical coupling between elements without the need for special measures like bending the elements. For this reason, added to the higher value of R and easier access to tuning points, optimum adjustments are achieved more frequently in practice. A further advantage, important in some countries, is virtual immunity to rain static, though this is one of several (p179) that it shares with loops in general.

Points to be noted in choosing a beam include the following:

1. Although many amateurs have been able to erect 'full-sized' three-element or four-element rotary Yagis such as Fig 12.1, the difficulties escalate rather rapidly with increasing size. The use of large fixed beams is recommended if there is plenty of space available, combined with a special interest in one (or a small number) of fixed directions as further discussed in Chapter 14.

2. Full-sized elements can be reduced in length by about one-third as in Fig 12.2 with almost no change in any aspect of performance. The only real advantage of retaining the full length lies in the possibility of extra gain at the second-harmonic frequency.

3. Requirements for 'smallest possible' beams arise because of limited space, or to reduce visual impact including that of supporting structures which need to be sturdily built to withstand the weight and windage of large beams. Ultimate possibilities for size reduction are represented

by Figs 12.12 and 12.29 which provide gains of about −2dB relative to typical full-sized arrays.

4. To be in the 'best possible' category, a beam needs to be instantaneously reversible to reduce time wasted in beam rotation and for added convenience in net operation.

5. Size can be reduced if arrangements are made to allow fine tuning of elements from the shack.

6. It should ideally be possible to establish different directional patterns for transmission and reception according to the needs of the moment.

7. Keeping the size as small as possible may enable height to be increased, thereby obtaining better performance than would be possible with a larger beam.

8. There are obvious advantages, including the possibility of large cost savings, from the use of beam-direction switching rather than rotation. For all-round coverage (albeit with reduced performance in some directions) at least two reversible beams are required. Fixed beams tend also to be more easily concealed.

9. For the achievement of efficient multiband operation, the advantages of resonant feeder systems should not be overlooked, particularly when used in conjunction with improved designs of element.

10. In this chapter the lower-frequency bands are not specifically considered since in most cases requirements will best be met by vertical arrays for DX with horizontal dipoles for shorter ranges. However, the smaller beams described here can be readily adapted for use on 7 or 10MHz, and should give a good account of themselves at heights upwards of 40ft (12m) or over sloping ground.

The beams to be described are of nine main types.

(a) The Yagi of Fig 12.1(a), having three full-sized (or equivalent) elements based on Figs 5.24 and 5.25, but with the suggested addition of capacitors to form linear resonators (shown dotted) to provide operation on at least one extra band [1, 2].

(b) The basic two-element dipole array derived from Fig 5.17(f) or (i) which can provide coverage up to three bands: see Fig 12.2. (a) can be erected as an inverted-V whereas (b), which is more suitable for vertical beams, can be closely identified with the VK2ABQ array shown in its original three-band 14/21/28MHz form by Fig 12.3. This shows its derivation from a single quad loop and is included largely for its historical interest in view of later improvements. These are all basically similar and by carefully controlled spacing between the ends it is possible to achieve critical coupling, equal currents, and theoretically infinite front/back ratio. Two feeders are advised to permit precise tuning and instantaneous beam reversal from the shack. Despite the greatly reduced space occupied by most of these arrays, the first two are equal in gain and only slightly inferior in bandwidth to full-sized two-element monoband beams which are therefore not advocated.

(c) The miniature two-element monoband (or possibly two-band) Yagi using end-loading by folding, Fig 5.29, with

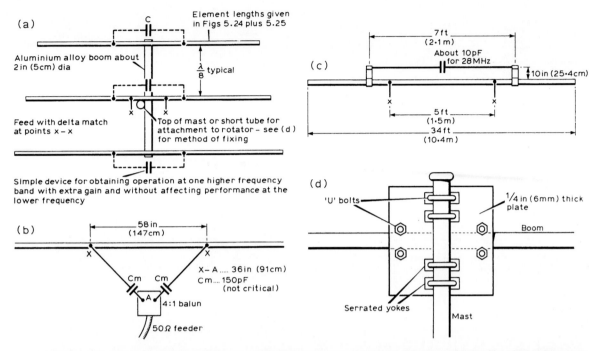

Fig 12.1. Full-size three-element beam based on Figs 5.24 and 5.25. For two-band operation with increased gain at the higher frequency, linear resonators may be used as shown dotted. Typical designs for 14MHz use 1.5in (38mm) diameter alloy tubing, tapering in three or four sections to 0.5in (13mm) but smaller diameters may be used for higher frequencies or with cord bracing. Open-wire feeder is recommended but (b) shows a delta match suitable for use with 50Ω coaxial line. Points of connection for 600Ω should be slightly further apart. Dimensions of linear resonator for 14/28MHz are shown at (c); the capacitor has no effect at 14MHz but for 21MHz it has to be roughly doubled and element lengths must be reduced 2–5%. For arrays without bracing the boom should have an outside diameter of about 2in (5cm) and wall thickness of 0.2in (5mm). One method of attaching elements to the boom and the boom to the mast is shown at (d), taken from the **ARRL Antenna Book**

neutralisation of the excess coupling produced by loading; this also uses two feeders for remote fine tuning and beam reversal [5, 6].

(d) Three-element compact beams with end-loaded and/or bent elements.

(e) The miniature top-hat loaded quad as devised by G3YDX, Fig 12.15. Two-band operation is possible by the use of traps as patented by G3IMX.

(f) Fixed arrays using loops with resonant lines in accordance with Figs 11.13(d), (e) or (f) or the DJ4VM quad: Fig 11.13(h).

(g) Small delta-loop arrays, elements based on Figs 7.6 and 12.17, with resonant feeders if multiband operation is required.

(h) Dipole arrays with resonant feeders. Due to wider frequency coverage and more gain at the higher frequencies, dipoles are preferred to delta loops if it is feasible to use element lengths of about 1.2λ at the shortest wavelength.

(i) The log-Yagi, a large monoband array of outstanding performance.

Fig 12.4 draws attention to the possibility of using very light structures braced with polythene cord as an alternative to conventional methods of construction. Similar ideas can be used for a wide variety of beams, including the VK2ABQ array [3], which in any case uses a somewhat similar mechanical principle. Suitable materials include bamboo, glassfibre and aluminium alloy tubing, depending on whether a particular structural member is or can conveniently be used also as part of the radiating system. This tends to be a desirable goal from the point of view of economy, weight, windage and visual impact. The design aims are as follows:

(a) to arrive at a reasonably stable mechanical structure based as far as possible on the beam elements themselves, although this is not practicable in the case of the VK2ABQ and its derivatives;

(b) To obtain multiband operation without loss of effective aperture at the higher frequencies or having to complicate the physical structure.

If the basic structure is that of a three-element beam for the lowest frequency, it becomes possible to use long end-loaded wire elements for the higher frequencies, and because these have relatively high radiation resistances the wire can be thin so that it is easily supported by the cords and visual impact is minimal. Fig 12.5(a) shows a suitable wire element resonating at 28 and 21MHz; ignoring the capacitor, the length of wire is 3λ/2 on 28MHz, the middle λ/2 being folded so that

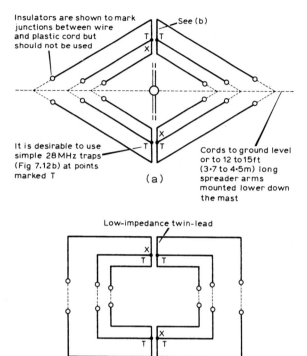

Insulators are shown to mark junctions between wire and plastic cord but should not be used

See (b)

It is desirable to use simple 28MHz traps (Fig 7.12b) at points marked T

(a)

Cords to ground level or to 12 to 15ft (3·7 to 4·5m) long spreader arms mounted lower down the mast

Low-impedance twin-lead

(b)

Fig 12.2. Multiband dipole arrays. Elements are connected in parallel using low-impedance twin-lead, and spacing between adjacent ends is adjusted to ensure equal currents in conjunction with correct phasing; (a) can be erected as an inverted-V and (b) is basically similar to the VK2ABQ array, Fig 12.3. Total wire lengths for 14MHz are approximately 35ft 6in (10.8m) with a spacing between ends of 12–15in (30–38cm), these dimensions being scaled down for higher frequencies in the appropriate ratio. Both may be fed at X with 50Ω cable and 1:1 balun. Use similar feeders for each set of elements. Preferred system uses 1:4 bal-bal transformer into 300 or 600Ω line (not plastic); open-wire line is used in multiples of 20m, terminating in a 4:1 balun plus coaxial line for the remainder of the feeder run

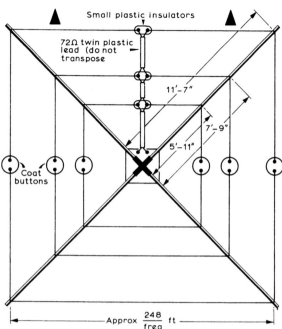

Small plastic insulators

72Ω twin plastic lead (do not transpose

11'–7"

7'–9"

5'–11"

Coat buttons

Approx $\dfrac{248}{\text{freq}}$ ft

Fig 12.3. The VK2ABQ beam for 14/21/28MHz seen looking down on the array. The dimensions are attributable to G3FRB

earlier types of beam, but to cover the new developments this chapter has been considerably extended, and the lessons

there is little radiation from it. In some cases the other two half-waves may be optimally spaced, giving a gain of 3dB for a single element, though this will be somewhat reduced in the case of a beam or if the element has to be folded to fit into a smaller space, as for example in Fig 12.5(b). The capacitor is added at a point where the current is zero on 28MHz so that operation on this band is unaffected, its value being adjusted to tune out the inductive reactance of the outer arms of the dipole, together with that of the stub at 21MHz.

What has thus far been described is a basic set of building blocks from which the design of beam antennas can be tailored to fit individual requirements.

Of the various options featured in Fig 11.13, (f) has been found particularly attractive and, after featuring in several new developments has emerged as, so far, the only type of beam element to meet the requirements for efficient operation on five or six bands without the need for some sort of massive structure. This does not deny an important continuing role to

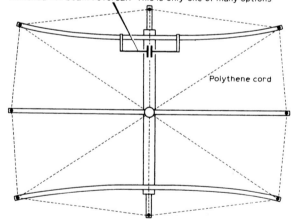

Linear resonator increases electrical length of reflector and can be switched for beam reversal. This is only one of many options

Polythene cord

Fig 12.4. Lightweight three-element array braced by polythene or nylon cord as shown dotted. The diagonals are secured to a light 3ft (1m) mast extension and the boom is extended slightly to provide 'bowstring' anchorage for the outer elements. Additional sets of ties can be used if necessary. The cords can support very thin wire (eg 19swg/1mm) elements for the higher frequencies, this being acceptable in view of the relatively high values of radiation resistance. In this way full use can be made at the higher frequencies of the available aperture. Element lengths are as for Fig 12.1 except that for beam reversal both parasitic elements are tuned as directors, C being then switched in to tune one or the other as a reflector

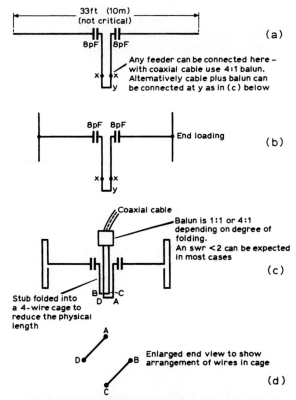

Fig 12.5. Two-band (21/28MHz) element suitable for use in conjunction with Fig 12.4. In the case of 28MHz the capacitors are located at a current node and thus have no effect, but at 21MHz they are suitably placed for tuning out the inductive reactance of the shortened 1λ element. The basic element is shown at (a), while (b) and (c) show various ways in which this can be end-loaded and/or folded for fitting into a smaller space. At (c) the fold forms a four-wire cage 4ft (1.2m) long; this is shown end-on, looking towards the element, at (d). Values of capacitors will depend on the amount of folding

learnt in this context from the application to beams of resonant feeder systems have been applied also to larger arrays.

Full-sized beams

For one-band or two-band operation the recommended design is in accordance with Fig 12.1, sizes of tubing for self-supporting elements being as given in Fig 19.1. There are various options based on Figs 5.24 and 5.25 but it is probably best to aim for the lower right-hand corner of Fig 5.24 which provides a gain of just over 6dB and a radiation resistance of around 20Ω. This region of the chart corresponds to rather long reflectors (+40Ω to +50Ω reactance) and directors which are rather shorter than optimum (−30Ω to −40Ω) from the point of view of gain. It results in reasonable bandwidth and constructional tolerances as well as good back-to-front ratio. As explained earlier (p94), it is very difficult in practice to realise much of the additional 1.5dB gain which is theoretically possible with three elements.

For multiband operation there is no reason in principle

why several beams should not be stacked on the same boom, provided precautions (p132) are taken to prevent the elements for one band resonating in or near other bands. Optimum performance at the higher frequencies will be obtained by making the elements as long as possible in conjunction with suitable tuning devices. Unfortunately, with self-supporting elements this adds greatly to the weight which is almost proportional to the number of bands. Linear resonators, as shown dotted in Fig 12.1, overcome this to the extent of allowing each element to operate on two bands and, if the requirement is for two bands only, this is a preferred method (p134). Adjustment of capacitance is critical, being roughly equivalent to the more usual length adjustment which it replaces. Three-band operation by this means requires the more elaborate resonator shown in Fig 7.15(b), though as an alternative relays may be used to switch the capacitors [2].

On the other hand, for the amateur prepared to embark on relatively uncharted waters, the cord technique just described opens up interesting prospects for much lighter and cheaper arrays and, by the use of the capacitively-stretched two-band wire element (Fig 12.5), a relatively simple and foolproof answer to the problem of three-band operation. It would be acceptable to retain the linear-resonator system for two-band operation and use the wire elements for one band only, except that insertion of capacitors in the wire element is much easier than construction of the linear resonator. It also has the advantage of not exacting a penalty in terms of bandwidth, which is appreciable in the case of linear resonators at the second harmonic frequency and, in the case of traps, at all of the frequencies.

It is recommended that elements should be insulated from the boom since only a small amount of asymmetry is required for enough current to flow along the boom to upset the radiation pattern. Due to the longer boom the effect is worse with three elements than two, and the problem is further exaggerated by harmonic operation of elements owing to the presence of relatively large RF voltages in the vicinity of the boom. Insulation from the boom is not necessarily a cure since some capacitive coupling to it is unavoidable, and it remains important to ensure symmetry which is one reason for not recommending the gamma match. Another is an experimental finding, admittedly not fully explained, that bandwidth was improved by some two or three times when a delta match was substituted for a gamma match. This was an isolated incident and may not apply generally, but the asymmetry of the gamma match is obvious to the eye and it is possible to imagine circumstances in which this definitely would cause trouble as described in Chapter 4, p53.

For those requiring the best possible monoband beam and able to contemplate the use of a long boom of the order of 0.4λ, the log-Yagi [4] of Fig 12.6 may be a better choice than the usual addition of another director to an array such as Fig 12.1(a). Dimensional details are given in Table 12.1 for tubing elements of about 7in (22mm) average diameter and will probably need some modification for use with wire elements. The feedpoint impedance is 37Ω. The four close-spaced elements or 'log cell' are in effect a short segment of

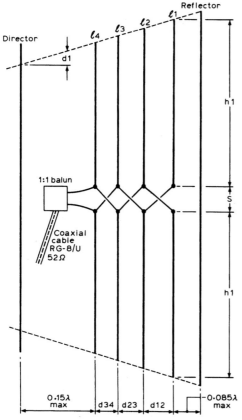

Fig 12.6. Layout of the log-Yagi array *(ARRL Antenna Anthology)*

a log-periodic array, such as the one described in Chapter 14, and provide additional gain as well as greater bandwidth.

Three-element compact beams

Fig 12.7(a) shows one method of reducing the length of an element with virtually no effect on operation at its fundamental resonance. Each tip of a λ/2 dipole is removed and replaced by a slightly longer vertical length, about 2.2 to 3 vertical feet (0.8–0.9m) being required for each 2ft (0.6m) removed. The length of a 14MHz driven element can be reduced from 33ft (10m) to 24ft (7.3m) by using 4in (6mm) diameter vertical

Table 12.1. Log-Yagi array dimensions [4]

Element	Length (ft)	Spacing (ft)
Reflector	36.4	6.0 (ref to l_1)
l_1	35.14	3.51 (d_{12})
l_2	33.27	3.32 (d_{23})
l_3	31.49	3.14 (d_{34})
l_4	29.81	10.57 (l_4 to dir)
Director	32.2	

1ft = 0.3048m

rods 5½–7ft (1.7–2.1m) in length, depending on diameters of tubing used for the radiating portion and effects due to linear resonators or other tuning and matching devices which may be required in the centre of the element. With this type of loading the radiation resistance is only slightly reduced, from 73Ω to 60Ω (Fig 3.12), which is barely significant. The gain of one element at the second harmonic frequency is reduced from 1.9dB to about 1.4dB, so even in this respect the effect is quite small. The process can be carried slightly further but with increasing length of the loading rods the structure rapidly becomes heavy and cumbersome.

Depending on the length of the loading rods a small amount of inductive loading can be accepted without much drop in performance; how far one should be prepared to go in this direction is a matter of opinion. Fig 12.7(b) is recommended as a lower size limit for this type of loading since there is already a drop of about 1dB in effective gain, and if it is necessary to reduce size still further equally good or better results can be obtained from two elements.

A better method [6] of arriving at a size of 17ft (5.2m) square is shown in Fig 12.8, though in this case there is a fairly critical lower limit to the size and fewer alternative options. In this case the full 24ft (7.3m) length is retained for the driven element which forms the diagonal of the square, parasitic elements for each band being hung round it.

Despite excellent gain, this beam had relatively poor front/back ratio and the major disadvantages of being neither reversible nor remotely tuneable. Fig 12.9 was in all respects superior, but Fig 12.8 has been retained as a possible source of inspiration for anyone needing a small 'flat' beam, ie one with zero extent in the vertical plane. The driven element would require to be full length, the boom being envisaged as a pair of fishing rods, and the turning circle radius, λ/4, would be about 20% less than for an equivalent array of conventional

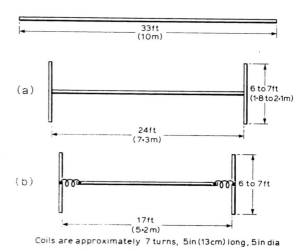

Fig 12.7. End-loaded elements for compact beams. Element lengths can be reduced as shown at (a) without significant effect on any aspect of performance. Further reduction is possible as shown at (b), subject to a loss in gain of about 1dB and some reduction in bandwidth

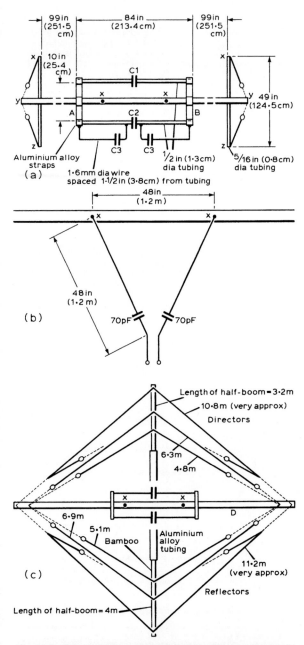

Fig 12.8. Compact three-element beam. Driven element is constructed from 1¼in (32mm) diam tubing, tapering to 0.5in (13mm). The feeder is connected at XX using delta match as shown at (b). The end-loading rods shown at (a) are also used to provide anchoring points x, y, z for the ends of the parasitic elements. 'Bowstrings' attached to the loading rods provide additional loading and counteract the pull of the parasitic elements. The plan view, (c), shows the layout of the parasitic elements. Approximate values of capacitors C1, C2, C3 are 10pF, 20pF and 12pF respectively, short 'whiskers' of open-wire line being connected across them to provide fine tuning. To avoid overcoupling it was found necessary to use relatively wide spacing in the case of the 14MHz reflector. Approximate wire lengths are indicated for the parasitic elements *(Ham Radio)*

design. Such an antenna could be seen as a three-element version of the VK2ABQ, which would be the better choice in the event of an even smaller turning circle being required.

Fig 12.9 shows an experimental antenna which, though fitting within a 12ft (3.7m) radius turning circle, provided the most facilities and 'equal best' performance of any of the author's antennas so far until blown down in a severe storm. Based on Fig 12.8, it makes fuller use of the available turning circle and provides the additional (though optional) feature of instantaneous beam reversal by means of relays. Mechanically the design follows the general features of Fig 12.4 but with a driven element identical to that of Fig 12.8. The other tubing elements, which operate respectively as directors for 21 and 28MHz, can be loaded by vertical rods to keep them within the 24ft (7.3m) diameter of turning circle or allowed to project slightly outside it. The 14MHz reflector and director are wire elements hung around the perimeter of the turning circle and, since their radiation resistance is relatively low, the wire should not be thinner than 14swg (2mm).

Beam reversal is effected by means of short-circuited stubs in the case of 14MHz, but an interesting situation arose in the case of 21 and 28MHz – it was found that whereas large currents flowed in directors, reflector elements had little effect. This is the exact opposite of what happens in the case of the quad, being due presumably to the collinear as opposed to broadside configuration of the driven element. It was judged to be equally acceptable, and on this basis it seemed unnecessary to bother with reflectors. The parasitic elements were series-tuned for operation as directors at 28MHz, having first adjusted their length to provide director operation on 21MHz when the relay contacts were closed. At any given time one pair only of relay contacts is closed and the beam fires in one direction on 21MHz and the opposite way on 28MHz. To some extent the 21MHz director operates as a reflector on 28MHz but, as in the case of a director fitted to a quad, the benefit from this is marginal.

Two-element rotary beams

A two-element beam may be constructed on the lines of Fig 12.1 merely by omitting one element, in which case the somewhat unconventional measure of bending the ends inwards to achieve critical coupling and improved front/back ratio should be adopted as explained in Chapter 5. For monoband operation this offers the advantages of improved bandwidth, simpler construction and perhaps neater appearance than the arrangements shown in Fig 12.2, though it is considerably heavier and more expensive. Two-band operation is achieved easily and three-band operation is also possible by the use of linear resonators as already described. Nevertheless, if the user is prepared to go to a structure of this size, a three-element beam may offer better receiving performance. If this is felt to be too ambitious, the modified VK2ABQ array described below can be recommended since it is almost as good, extremely light and inexpensive, and achieves operation on two or three bands with maximum simplicity and fewest problems.

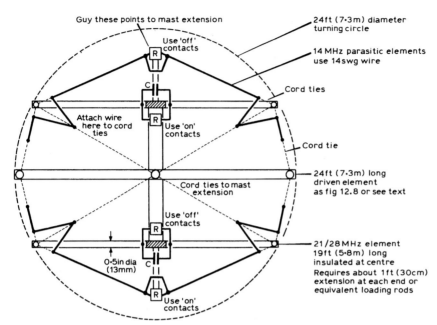

Fig 12.9. Reversible version of three-element compact three-band beam. With relay contacts closed, a short parasitic element acts as a director for 21MHz; with the contacts open it is series-tuned to operate as a director for 28MHz. Compared with Fig 12.8, fuller use of the available turning circle provides better bandwidth and a closer approach to optimum design on 14MHz. R denotes relays; on 14MHz one of the reflector stubs is shorted. On 21MHz director operation is obtained by shorting out a capacitor, on 28MHz an unshorted capacitor tunes the element as a director and shorting a capacitor provides a slight reflector action. Back contacts used on one pair of relays, front on the other; beam direction is reversed on 21 relative to 28MHz. All relays are energised in parallel. Total boom length is 19ft (5.8m). Wire length total for 14MHz parasitic elements is 32ft (9.8m) plus 40in (1m) for the reflector stubs. Value of C is approx 15pF (calculated) inclusive of insulator which needs to be of high quality; length of dural angle carrying four stand-off insulators suggested

Alternatively the constructional principles of Fig 12.4 may be applied to shortened end-loaded elements to produce the electrical equivalent of the modified VK2ABQ.

Referring to Fig 12.2(b), there are many different constructional possibilities but the author was fortunate in obtaining a rotary clothes line of rectangular shape, based on 4ft (1.2m) tubes which were extended by 8ft (2.4m) bamboo garden canes to the required length of 12ft (3.7m) and wired as shown in Fig 12.10. It is important that the aluminium tubing should be short enough not to have any resonance in the wanted range of frequencies, and the bamboos should be given several protective coats of polyurethane varnish or wrapped with insulating tape. It will be noticed that the shape is rectangular, in contrast to the square shape of the VK2ABQ array, Fig 12.2(c). This was done to arrive at the optimum spacing and required no increase in length of the spider arms, the perimeter of a rectangle being only very slightly greater than that of a square for side ratios up to about two; any excess wire was easily accommodated by tucking in the corners as described below. The author used two sets of cord ties, one linking the tips of the bamboos and also guying them back to a light 4ft (1.2m) mast extension and a duplicate set in the position of the 21MHz elements.

The centres of the elements were attached to an additional support (not shown) and the ends were fixed to the side cords in the positions indicated. The wire was secured along the cord at frequent intervals by wrapping with a few turns of thin wire. This stopped about 8in (20cm) short of the ends of the bamboo, the slack at the corners being taken up by bending it into a U shape and attaching it to the radial cords going to the top of the mast. Spacers made of strips cut from plastic tubing were found desirable about a foot from the end of the U.

The dimensions indicated in the diagram are not critical but shape differences can result in small changes in the

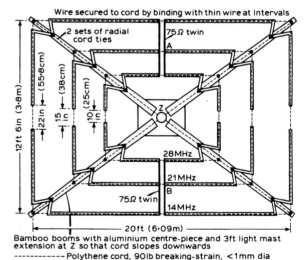

Fig 12.10. Two-element beam based on Fig 12.2(b). Spider arms may consist of 4ft (1.2m) lengths of dural tube extended by carefully-selected 8ft (2.4m) bamboo garden canes bound with insulating tape. Traps as Fig 7.12(b) are desirable in the 21MHz elements. See Fig 12.2(b) for details of feed. Note the method of attaching the corners of the elements to the polythene cords, avoiding direct contact with the bamboo. The amount of wire in the corner folds is not critical and these can be used for taking in any slack. The total length of each wire is about 35ft (10.7m) for 14MHz, 23ft (7m) for 21MHz, and 17ft (5.2m) for 28MHz but can vary with the size and shape of the corner folds

Two-element beam based on Fig 12.10 for 14MHz but using stretched and folded elements similar to Fig 12.5(c) for 21/28MHz. Note the very close spacing between adjacent ends of the higher-frequency elements. Old TV line-output tubes were used as high-Q (vacuum) capacitors but later measurements suggest that short lengths of coaxial cable should be satisfactory if adequately sealed. The 14MHz elements are delta-matched to 600Ω lines which also feed the 21/28MHz elements via pairs of 14MHz traps; the method of matching at 21/28MHz is similar to that of Fig 11.12(e) with a stub length of 22in (55cm). A separate photo shows enlarged details of the corners of the 14MHz elements

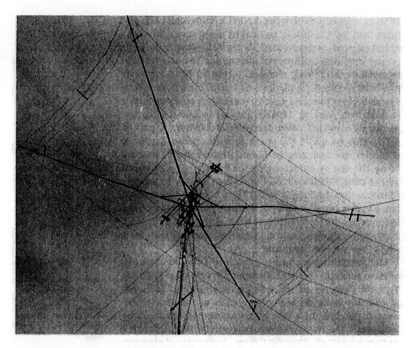

overall length required, and it is advisable to allow a bit of extra length with the ends bent back as necessary and the wires only loosely secured until adjustments have been made. If desired, the cord can be removed, leaving only the radial ties and the short insulating sections at the corners. The 28MHz elements can be added without the need for additional cords, except for insulation at the corners where the U sections (being relatively short) can be allowed to hang down. The use of 28MHz traps in the 21MHz elements as shown in Fig 7.12 has been found necessary to overcome critical tuning, poor front-to-back ratio and narrow bandwidth on 28MHz. Even with the traps it is difficult to avoid some loss of directivity over at least part of the 28MHz band and the possibility of extending this treatment to additional bands is no longer envisaged.

Values are not critical but traps should be tuned by applying a few watts of power at the frequency to be trapped and adjusting the spacing between the wires for equal currents, or (since the currents flow in opposite directions) for zero current when the probe is held half-way between the wires. The mid-position can be judged well enough by eye and a check of the 21MHz elements just beyond the traps should now indicate zero current. If one feels uneasy about possible losses the relative currents in the traps and the 28MHz element can be roughly estimated using the probe – the increase in total loss as a percentage can then be calculated, making use if necessary of the usual I^2R formula to obtain the relative powers. An example of this procedure will be found on p282 and in the present case the extra loss was an estimated 0.016dB only.

With the close spacings involved in covering 10, 18 and

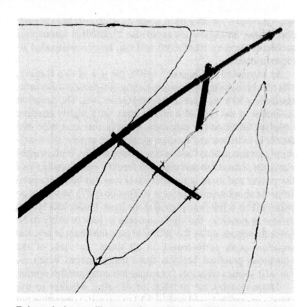

Enlarged view to illustrate the tucking-in of the corners of the 14MHz elements of the array shown in the adjoining photograph. The folds provide loading and are readily adjustable, thus providing considerable freedom as regards element sizes, shapes and spacings. Spacers, obtained by lengthwise cutting of short lengths of plastic pipe, are used to maintain the shape of the folds which (as may be inferred from the picture) is not critical! This method allows the wire to be kept well away from wet bamboo but it remains nevertheless advisable to give the bamboo several coats of polyurethane varnish. The method has other applications and can, for example, be used to allow tubing elements to support folded wire elements for a lower frequency band.

24MHz, interactions between dipoles become quite compli-cated, and the alternative method of using relays to open-circuit elements as required (p133) can be recommended with greater confidence. However, the author has successfully replaced the 21/28MHz elements of Fig 12.10 by a pair of two-band elements on the lines of Fig 12.5(c), both sets of elements being matched directly to 600Ω. A common feeder is used with pairs of 14MHz traps to isolate the higher-frequency elements when operating at 14MHz. A pair of ATUs plus baluns in the shack provide remote tuning of reflectors and matching to the transmitter, beam reversal being effected by interchanging the feeders. At a height of 48ft (14.6m) this is currently providing slightly better per-formance than the quad at 38ft (11.6m) which it has replaced but, had they been available at the time, the relays described in Chapter 7 (p133) would have been used in lieu of the four traps which are bulky and suspected of responsibility for a slight 'wet weather' problem.

One practical point to have emerged from this and one other experiment has been the need for very tight coupling between elements of the type pictured in Fig 12.5, due presumably to the relatively large value of radiation resist-ance. In the case of (c) a compromise was possible covering both bands; this required spacings of only an inch (2.5cm) or so over a length of about 8in (20cm). In the case of elements of the type shown in Fig 12.5(a) a spacing of about 6in (15cm) was required over lengths of some 2–3ft (0.6–0.9m) at each end. These arrangements avoid the 21/28MHz interaction problem, improve bandwidth and can be recommended to experimenters.

As explained in Chapter 5 (p87), the use of two feeders, one of which is used for remote tuning of a parasitic element, results in a 50% increase in the total feeder loss. The situation is similar in the case of a driven array with highly reactive coupling between the elements, since in this case also one feeder is matched and handles most of the power, the maxi-mum currents in both feeders being comparable. With straight elements spaced λ/8 and matched feeders, each handles half the power and there is no additional loss but beam reversal from the shack results in a large mismatch (p87), so we are no better off! It is felt that, provided the basic feeder loss is kept as low as possible, the slight increase in loss is likely to be more than made up by the ability to tune the beam *in situ* and maintain peak performance at all times. In view of the enormous practical benefits from instantaneous beam re-versal it seems a great pity not to take advantage of this option.

There remains the problem of deciding whether to use driven operation based on Fig 5.13 or parasitic operation but there is no need for hasty decisions since usually the same components can be used for both purposes. In practice the parasitic mode has proved more convenient with near-critical coupling and just as good, though there may be trouble with some feeder lengths unless the remote tuning arrangements are adapted to suit. In the driven case it is important to connect the elements in antiphase as with the W8JK array, so that the recommended phase difference of 157° is obtained by a 23° shift from the 180° condition. Whichever method is used,

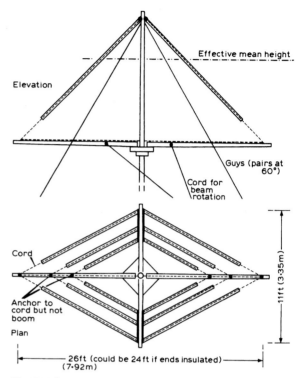

Fig 12.11. Inverted-V equivalent for Fig 12.10

adjustment should preferably be for a null on a bearing of about 140° and *not* the reciprocal of the beam heading (p156).

Fig 12.11 illustrates the inverted-V equivalent of Fig 12.10; note that only two arms lower down plus one spreader at the top are needed. Careful disposition of guys etc allows sufficient rotation by means of two cords.

Phasing of separate beams

Assuming beams in accordance with Figs 12.1, 12.4 or 12.9, the easiest method of obtaining additional gain is probably to erect two beams and phase them together rather than use a longer boom with more elements. This provides a gain of 3dB whereas gain increases only very slowly with increasing boom length, and with larger and heavier beams it may be necessary to settle for reduced heights. The technical prob-lems are discussed in Chapter 6, p113, and Fig 6.14 shows the recommended method of phasing. Alternatively, the reso-nance method (Fig 5.21) can be used to provide continuous adjustment of phase, but it has the disadvantage that large phase shifts may be needed and this results in variations of load impedance which need to be compensated.

The objections previously raised to the use of lines as in Fig 6.14 arose from mutual coupling between beam elements, whereas the scheme now under discussion rests on the as-sumption that the beams are far enough apart for mutual coupling to be ignored so that the antennas constitute a pair of independent matched loads. The phasing requirements in this case can be readily calculated from the line lengths and velocity factor, steps of 60° being small enough since this results in a worst error of 30° only; this reduces the gain to just under 2dB though a close approach to 3dB is obtainable for nearly all directions. These phasing steps are best achieved in the form of three positions with phase reversals as shown, the method of use being to find the position giving least signal and then reverse the phase of one antenna. For all-band 14–28MHz operation at least six steps are required, since 60° steps at 28MHz become 30° only at 14MHz.

Very small beams

Requirements for very small beams arise from such obvious reasons as lack of space or the difficulty of providing an adequate support for large ones. There is also the need for small size in order to minimise visual impact and hence the risk of objections by neighbours; under this heading there is also the possibility that, if the beam is made small enough and the best choice is made from the available design options, the uninitiated will be unable to distinguish it from a television antenna! Now that the use of VHF for television in the UK has been discontinued this has become much more difficult to achieve. A monoband beam for 24 or 28MHz bearing some resemblance to an antenna for the FM band should be feasible, though it might result in acute frustration during sunspot minimum periods. For the 24MHz band, this could be as little as 6ft (1.8m) square, based on Fig 12.13 but using for the end-loading whatever combination of vertical or horizontal rods and thin wires was judged least likely to offend the eyes of possible objectors. In Japan TV antennas are often gaily painted in a variety of colours, an idea which might be worth importing – but consult the neighbours first! The best form of disguise is probably to use a genuine (fringe area) TV antenna to support a pair of thin wire elements as described in Chapter 15. On the other hand, the smaller the beam, the better the chance of fitting into a confined space for concealment or otherwise.

Fig 12.12 gives design details of the author's first serious venture into the minibeam field, the overall dimensions being slightly greater than might appear from the diagram since the elements were tensioned between the six arms of a spider which projected beyond the corners and included two additional arms to counter the inward pull along the centre line. This beam at 55ft (16.8m) was at least as good as a quad at 45ft (13.7m), but could only be properly tested in dry weather – this was due to a tuning shift of about 200kHz when it was wet which took it below the 14MHz band, the bamboo being untreated. At this time only a single feeder was in use and so the tuning error could not be corrected.

Adjustment was carried out at a height of about 8ft (2.4m), tuning the reflector for maximum back-to-front ratio and comparing the currents in the two elements. The current in the reflector being higher than that in the driven element, the neutralising capacitor was increased in small steps, retuning the reflector each time by bending the wire ends, and eventually

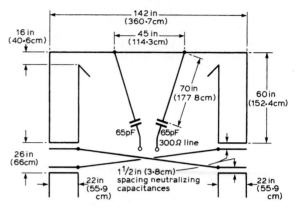

Fig 12.12. Practical design details for small beam based on Fig 5.29(a). The elements are identical with a total wire length of 37.3ft (11.37m). For initial adjustment one element without its feeder may be tuned as a parasitic reflector. The driven element can then be adjusted for an optimum match and the reflector made identical with it, thereafter being tuned remotely using its own feeder, though a check should be made to ensure this does not degrade the performance. The elements and neutralising capacitors may use 14–16swg (1.6–2mm) bare copper wire, but a much lighter gauge can be used for the delta match and the neutralising wires. The spider projects beyond the elements which are suspended by short lengths of polythene cord *(Ham Radio)*

achieving current equality and sharp nulls. The tuning of the driven element was adjusted as necessary to maintain a reasonable value of SWR but was fairly non-critical, exhibiting the flat response typical of slightly overcoupled circuits. A useful bandwidth of about 200kHz was achieved, the gain being 1dB down at one edge and the front-to-back ratio down to 8dB at the other [6].

With two feeders either driven or parasitic operation can be used exactly as described above in the context of Fig 12.2. In this case the reflector should be made identical with the driven element, and interchangeability of the elements should be verified before erection. Due to the highly capacitive nature of the coupling it is essential to tune a parasitic element as a reflector, not a director, and with driven operation SWR is unimportant in the case of the reflecting element.

This method of construction is inexpensive, light and simple, and because the beam is reversible about 130° of rotation is adequate. This can be achieved by the means of two cords attached to points about 2–3ft (0.6–0.9m) each side of centre on suitable spider arms. Some reinforcement such as a short stiff piece of wood or aluminium alloy tubing may be needed between the points of attachment.

Fig 12.13 shows a neater version [6] using metal tubing for the radiating portions of the elements, the vertical rods at the ends acting mainly as brackets for supporting the wire zigzags. About 16ft (4.9m) of wire was needed in each zigzag, and to avoid the need for heavy-gauge elements the ends were guyed back bowstring-fashion to short extensions of the boom. Two open-wire feedlines were used and Fig 12.14 shows typical performance with parasitic operation of the reflector, a front-to-back ratio better than 20dB being obtainable over a bandwidth of 50kHz. This could be shifted to any part of the band

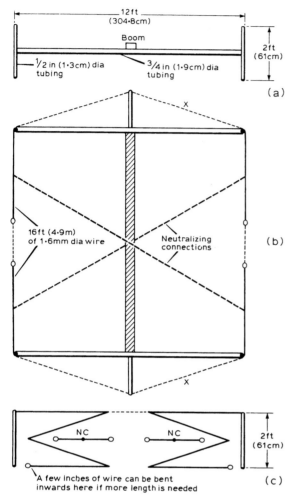

Fig 12.13. Based on Fig 5.29(b), this shows construction details of a 10ft (3m) square beam for 14MHz. The front, plan and side views are shown as (a), (b), and (c) respectively. In (b) the 'bowstring' principle is used to counter the pull of the loading wires and allow the use of lightweight elements. Each neutralising capacitor, as shown in (c), is about 1.9ft (58cm) long. If more loading is required, additional wire can be added as indicated in (c) (Ham Radio)

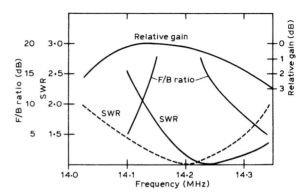

Fig 12.14. Typical performance of the 10ft (3m) square beam. Measurements (solid line) were made with the beam at a height of 7ft (2.1m) and the reflector tuned for 14.2MHz. The dotted curve shows the improvement in SWR after adding 4in (10cm) to each end of both elements and retuning the reflector for best front/back ratio at each frequency. Note that the gain curve shows decibels down relative to best performance (Ham Radio)

by using the phasing-line components rearranged as a tuned circuit. Originally 300Ω feeders were used with 4:1 baluns in the shack to bring the impedance down to 75Ω but, due to wet weather and weathering effects (which proved disastrous), a change was made to 600Ω lines of resonant length, no other alterations being made in the system.

Further reduction in the area occupied by the elements would be possible by extending the vertical rods, increasing the length of loading wires and accepting some reduction in performance, but it is doubtful whether in practical terms much would be gained by this and, if the main need is to reduce the diameter of the turning circle, the capacitively loaded quad (p207) is a better proposition. For significantly reduced visual impact it is necessary either to go to a higher

frequency or use loading coils, with inevitable penalties in terms of efficiency and bandwidth.

A third design of minibeam [6] used 11ft (3.4m) elements for 14MHz and a third central element for 21/28MHz which helped to support the loading wires, three-band operation being achieved by a combination of linear-resonator type traps and stacking of additional parasitic elements. Performance on 14MHz was at least as good as with the earlier designs and good DX contacts were obtained on 21 and 28MHz, but there were several bandwidth and coupling problems, and in overcoming them the design became more and more complicated. Although none of the difficulties were insuperable, it had ultimately to be accepted that *efficient* multibanding is far from easy when beam size is reduced to the minimum, despite the fact that the frequencies to be added are higher than the fundamental so that one might expect size to be less of a problem. As a monoband design this arrangement has a possible merit to the extent that there are no vertical projections, and there is no problem in using the central member with some end-loading as a dipole for 21, 24 or 28MHz.

At this point it is useful to bring a number of threads together. The parallel-dipole idea has already been helpful in the search for efficient methods of multibanding, and closely resembles the multiband counterpoise used for the grounding of vertical antennas (p171), except that in the latter case resonating and radiating functions have been kept separate. However, this is *almost* what has happened in the case of Fig 12.13! The loading wires are very near self-resonance and the radiator, being shorter and of much larger diameter than the wires, possesses a relatively small impedance. In other words, the tuning and radiating functions are very nearly separated in this case also. In this way one can use either two sets of λ/4 wires or a pair of multiband counterpoises (as in Fig 11.17) connected by a short length of larger-diameter tubing which supplies the radiating function.

This appears also to be the operative principle of some commercial designs including mobile antennas; these commercial designs suffer from the criticisms which have been levelled against the use of small capacitive hats working in conjunction with large inductances (p98). However, this fault is unavoidable in the case of mobile antennas (p252) and the objections do not apply to *large* hats working with *small* inductances, or to λ/4 resonators which are more or less equivalent.

The capacity hat loaded mini-quad

This is in a slightly different category to the other small beams, being of much greater extent in the vertical plane, but if this is acceptable it offers the most satisfactory specification and provides the smallest possible diameter of turning circle. The recommended design is due to G3YDX [7] and his description follows.

"For spreaders, 8ft (2.4m) bamboo canes liberally coated with varnish were used and these were attached to the boom in the usual double-X arrangement. A 6ft (1.8m) length of 1 by 1 by ¹/₈in (25 by 25 by 3mm) dural angle was sawn into 18in (46cm) lengths, drilled to accept 1in (2.5cm) car exhaust clamps, and the canes firmly attached with adhesive tape reinforced with light wire to prevent it from being undone by rain and wind. Jubilee clips could be used for this application but they are expensive and tend to crush the bamboo if not carefully fitted. The spiders thus produced could accommodate about 10ft 6in (3.2m) of wire per side, compared with 11ft 8in (3.55m) per side for a *full-sized* 21MHz quad.

Trials were undertaken to build one element for resonance tests. Because the sides are a lot shorter than 12ft (3.7m), the arrangement shown in Fig 12.15(a) gave resonance at too high a frequency, but eventually, after cutting and trying, and some bending (a GDO helps), the sizes shown in Fig 12.15(b) resulted in resonance with the element in the air. Tested against a ground plane, the single-element loop did not appear to have any significant advantage, apart from possessing a deep null in the plane of the element. This null could only cope with a small proportion of the inevitable interference on the band.

When the element was raised to its operating height the resonant frequency increased by some 150kHz. Constructors are advised to bear this effect in mind, as it will vary with the surroundings of the antenna. In the author's case the element was built parallel to, and about 8ft (2.4m) from the ground. When raised, the boom height was 30ft (9.1m).

The next step was to build a parasitic reflector of the same size as the driven element, but with a stub added; the boom was an 8ft 6in (2.6m) length of 1in (2.5cm) outside diameter 16swg (1.6mm) alloy tube obtained to match. Because of the reduction in impedance expected due to the smaller loop size, to some two-fifths the impedance of the full-sized quad, the addition of a parasitic element would result in a change of feedpoint impedance to below limits where acceptable direct match to coaxial feeder could be achieved. A gamma match was used to match the line to the array; 16swg (1.6mm) wire with about 1.5in (3.8cm) spacing and a receiving-type 100pF variable capacitor being used. The length of the gamma section was adjusted for 14,050kHz with the array near to the ground to take into account the correction factor found necessary in the single-element tests. A gamma section length of 3ft (0.9m) was about right.

The mast was walked up on the back of the house, and the resonant frequency was found to be about 14,190kHz. The next job was the stub tuning. Due to a minor constructional difference in the reflector, no stub was required for what seemed to be the best front/back ratio. The author suggests that anyone constructing this array should test both elements for resonance rather than copy the dimensions from one to the other. In this small design the odd half-inch is critical.

There are, however, some provisos which should be mentioned.

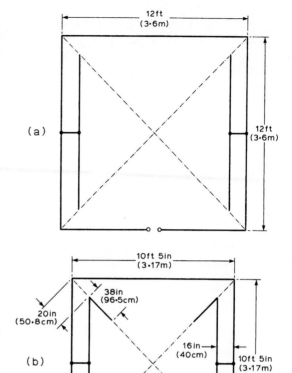

(a)

(b)

Fig 12.15. Miniature quad array with 'top-hat' loading due to G3YDX. (a) Starting point for design; (b) final version

1. Because of the reduction in size, the SWR bandwidth of the array is reduced. This is illustrated in Fig 12.16. It should be noted that the array has a 2:1 SWR bandwidth of about 200kHz, which is a distinct improvement over some well-known miniature beams available commercially at what seem astounding prices. The array will work on the CW end of the band with a reduction of directivity, and an ATU is recommended because on 14,025kHz the SWR is above 3:1. Obviously bandwidth will increase as loop size increases.

2. The gain will not be as good as that of a full-sized quad due to the reduced element size, but in fact miniaturisation will only reduce it by some 0.5dB, which is hardly noticeable on the air. Front/back ratio seems to equal that of a full-sized quad; this suggests that an even smaller element may be useful for receive only.

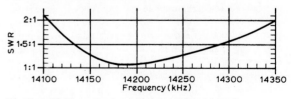

Fig 12.16. Miniature quad – variation of SWR with frequency

3. It is important that the elements are tuned very carefully or disappointing results may ensue."

Fixed beams

As a new amateur the author was equally interested in all available frequency bands and all directions, but after a time the interest in collecting QSL cards, working new countries, and taking part in world-wide DX contests wore off. Instead of rarely working the same station twice, most contacts are now with old friends in a small number of directions, concentrating on one or two frequencies and times of day which happen to be best for this purpose. Exceptions include a certain amount of antenna testing but it has for the most part been possible to combine even this with regular operation over the long path to Australasia. This occupies as much time as can readily be spared for operating and it is clear that many other amateurs find themselves in a similar position, in which case needs are usually best served by fixed arrays with their many advantages such as lower cost, less visual impact, and in some cases higher gain. Others may find their hands forced in this direction by necessity or, if they happen for example to be living on a steep hillside, may find that they do so well in one particular direction that it quickly absorbs the whole of their interest.

Loop arrays

The author's antenna experiments have usually resulted in possession of at least one beam, rotary or otherwise, capable of meeting normal operating requirements, and repeatedly over 25 years he found himself returning to the fixed reversible quad based on two or three loops similar to those shown in Figs 11.4, 11.13(d) and 11.13(e). Originally this approach was adopted as providing the best type of beam for mounting in trees as discussed earlier (pp169, 179), although in this case there was no need for concealment – it just happened to be the easiest way of obtaining the necessary height. Later other supports were used but many of the advantages remained.

In view of earlier discussion the reader may be surprised by the reference to three loops, but it was difficult to shake off the feeling that there *ought* to and just possibly *might* be some advantage, and it makes beam reversal somewhat simpler. At one time, two reed relays were used to make the changes from reflector to director, taking advantage of the relatively low current in the case of quad directors. Another advantage of three elements when each has its own feeder is that if one breaks there are two left and, subject to minor changes at ground level, there is little effect on performance!

In the case of fixed beams the mechanical considerations are relatively less unfavourable to the quad since there is no need for a heavy spider. The top corners can be carried by a lightweight spreader and when a mast is used as a support the corners can be pulled out in much the same way as the ends of an inverted-V.

With a reversible quad centred on VK2 good results were obtained in most directions excluding polar paths and the greater part of Africa. As a 'fill in' for these directions a single

delta loop had for several years given a good account of itself on 14 and 21MHz, in spite of being undersized (60ft (18.3m) of wire in the loop) and almost completely buried in a tree. On the strength of this a two-element full-sized version was erected as a second antenna for Australia.

Though solidly constructed, well clear of branches and intended to be permanent, this had a very short life due to unusual wintry conditions which turned the top conductor into a thick rope of ice that proved too heavy for the supporting arms. This was before the delta loop had been officially invented and the corner supports must have been considerably stronger than the tubing normally specified. Conditions were very exceptional for the UK but this does seem to indicate a serious weakness of full-size 14MHz delta loops for areas liable to experience severe winters.

Prior to this disaster the delta loop had been successfully phased with the 'tree quad' to form a high-gain array, the two beams being identical in performance. Loop spacing in such systems should be about 11ft (3.4m) for operation on 14 and 21MHz, or 8ft (2.4m) if it is required in addition to operate the system as a bi-square at 28MHz, although this results in some overcoupling at 14MHz if there are no losses. There is, however, no need to worry if (as tends to happen with tree mounting) it is difficult to achieve accurate symmetry.

The use of resonant feeders as described in the last chapter allows useful radiation to be obtained over all of the HF bands, except that for 1.8MHz and 3.5MHz it is necessary to operate loops plus feeders as a vertical system. For 7MHz there is a choice of (a) operating loops plus feeders as a vertical dipole, (b) using the outer elements of a three-element array as a two-element vertical beam, or (c) using the loops (preferably in parallel) as horizontal radiators. Beam operation at harmonic frequencies is discussed on p123.

Collinear arrays

Prior to becoming interested in the quad, the author had for many years been using collinear pairs backed by reflectors. Two such arrays erected at a height of some 17ft (5.2m) above a 20° slope to the west and phased together (one of them about 60ft (18.3m) in front of the other) gave excellent results. This might be expected in view of the estimated gain of 9dB relative to free-space propagation for a radiation angle of *zero* degrees. This may sound like a large and ambitious array but in fact covered an area of only one-sixth of an acre (0.07ha), such as many amateurs have at their disposal, and this area could have been further reduced.

The low height rendered this system much easier to erect than even the simplest of horizontal beams capable of reasonable performance over flat ground. The arrays were invisible to neighbours; design, construction and adjustment being made very simple by virtue of the high value of radiation resistance typical of collinear arrays. This example is illuminating for anyone lucky enough to have steeply sloping ground since it demonstrates how easily this can be exploited to achieve exciting results.

Arrays such as this over flat ground are of little use without several very tall masts and thus of limited interest to the amateur. It is in any case better to split a 1λ collinear array into two separate λ/2 arrays since this allows the beam to be swung through a fairly wide angle by appropriate phasing of two halves, otherwise the azimuth coverage is very restricted (Fig 6.3).

Large Yagi arrays

A long Yagi array probably makes the best use of the opportunities in the case of a long narrow garden sloping in a wanted direction and, unless there are plenty of trees around, the best method of construction might be as a set of inverted-V elements suspended from a catenary. One or two intermediate supports may be needed. Data for long Yagi arrays with thin-wire elements at HF is in short supply but director lengths of 0.45λ and spacings of 0.3–0.35λ would appear to be a good starting point. A length of 0.49λ and spacing of 0.2λ is suitable for the reflector. Adjustment of directors in 6in (15cm) steps based on DX reports with another station acting as a yardstick is suggested. Performance data will be found in Chapter 5, p104. The log-periodic array (p242) may also be worth considering in this context. Alternatively, in the case of flat ground and restricted height, Yagi arrays using short loaded vertical elements (Chapter 11) offer the best prospects.

Two-element dipole arrays

Two-element arrays based on Fig 12.2(a) have many advantages as detailed below and will often be preferred to quad arrays, being relatively inexpensive and easy to erect. In their inverted-V form they represent the ultimate in lightness, simplicity of construction and low cost, as well as providing the easiest means of gaining all-important height. Mounted horizontally between two supports, a two-element wire beam can be made reversible by employing two feeders as described earlier or, if a single feeder is used, reversed mechanically by means of two cords attached to the centre of the reflector. One hangs straight down whereas the other is taken over the top and hangs down on the opposite side. By releasing the cord that hangs straight down and pulling on the other one, the beam can easily be 'flopped over' so that the position of the element and the beam direction is reversed.

Horizontal dipoles can, as already indicated, be constrained into almost any shape within reason and, whereas the VK2ABQ or modified VK2ABQ format is ideal for a rotary beam, the inverted-V configuration is more useful for fixed beams, the spreader being fixed to the top of a mast before erection or hauled up by a rope over a pulley. The apex angle should not be less than 90° and, if there is enough ground space, the ends of the central cord can be brought within reach of the ground and used to walk the beam round into any direction. Otherwise the direction may be fixed and, failing suitable trees, chimneys or other supports, one or more auxiliary masts employed. A further alternative based on Fig 12.11 requires only a single support with, for 14MHz, a 24ft (7.3m) spreader which can be rotated through 120° or so, assuming a suitable arrangement of guy-wires.

In principle two beams can be mounted at right-angles, one below the other, on a single mast to provide switched selection of four directions, in which case it is absolutely essential to detune the one not in use. This is possible by suitable termination of unused feeders but may need a certain amount of skill and patience. Similar remarks apply to quad- or delta-loop arrays.

There is difficulty in tuning an inverted-V beam before erection because the requirement for access to the centres usually means that the ends have to be brought very close to the ground, which lowers the resonant frequency (p117). It is best to lay out each element in turn horizontally (just within reach) for checking resonance. To establish correct coupling between the elements, the ends should if possible be attached to long cords which can be manipulated from ground level with the beam *in situ*. The use of two feeders is recommended so that the reflector can be tuned for maximum rejection of signals or minimum field strength on a bearing of −140°.

Three-element inverted-V arrays are feasible but are more difficult to support; if it is possible to erect three elements at height *h* it is usually possible to erect two elements at height 1.12*h* which is enough to neutralise any gain advantage, although in some cases three elements may result in a lower average level of interference (pp154–156) as discussed in Chapter 9.

Small delta loop (SDL) arrays

Fig 12.17 compares a conventional 'full-size' delta loop element with a small delta loop which proved to be the prototype for a long series of developments, culminating in two novel types of beam element capable of a close approach on five or six bands to the performance of typical monobanders. An advantage of the full-sized delta loop compared with the quad is an increase in effective height which exceeds that of the mast by about 0.14λ, but its size renders it top heavy, in many cases difficult to handle and, added to problems of insulation at the lower corner where high voltages would exist at some frequencies, unsuitable for multiband operation. In some climates icing can also be a problem.

Multiband versions shown in Figs 12.18–21 are aimed at placing the lowest-frequency current zeros in the middle of

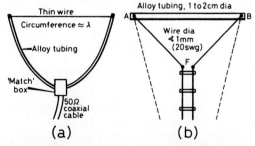

Fig 12.17. Delta loop – two versions compared. (a) Classic form: features include extra height but only suitable as monobander. (b) Small version for 'pushing up anywhere' (including trees). AB is 18–25ft, ABFA is 40–60ft for multiband operation (14–28MHz). For monoband operation, AB is 0.25–0.35λ and sides can be brought down steeply as shown dotted, provided AF is less than 0.3λ

the sides (Fig 12.20, point C) so that all the radiation comes from the top section AB, thereby maximising the effective height, though the position of C is not critical. AC, BC, can therefore be regarded as end-loading and perform the same function as the bent-across ends of the VK2ABQ elements, Fig 12.10, although the construction is in general more convenient. Both arrangements give rise to some radiation in endwise directions, though in the case of the SDL this disappears at certain frequencies in accordance with Fig 7.5. As shown in Fig 12.17, the SDL prototype is a monoband element which is how it was first conceived, the object being to resume regular VK contacts as quickly as possible from a new QTH. It was found a simple matter to push a pair of loops up into the branches of a tree at a height of some 30ft, the ends of the stubs being readily accessible from a ladder for tuning and matching.

Ease of construction and manipulation in a cluttered environment are outstanding features of this type of antenna. All one needs is a suitable tree, any climbing problems being overcome (at a cost small compared with that of commercial antennas) by enlisting the services of a tree-surgeon. There may be no need for the ladder either, since the stubs can (for example) be extended to ground level for matching and thence to the shack for beam reversal and deep-nulling in accordance with earlier recommendations. Alternatively a mast or chimney can be used instead of the tree.

Compared with all-wire loops featured later, the use of tubing for the top portion reduces losses (if any), improves bandwidth and can improve matching, values of R (as seen at the feedpoint) being increased by up to 30% due to marginal involvement of the ITL principle (p89). On the other hand, the larger the ratio of conductor diameters, the more side wire is needed to bring the top to resonance so that point C moves closer to the bottom corner; with the loop as shown C is found about 18in above centre and, allowing for the impedance transformation, this is roughly correct, giving an R of about 60Ω. If AB is reduced to 20ft, C is pushed down to within 4ft of D, and R drops from a wire-loop value of 45Ω to about 25Ω.

For monoband operation, in contrast, the loop can be increased up to and beyond quad size with no direct adverse effect on performance other than through the reduction of effective height as discussed earlier. However, the main advantages of SDL arrays are strictly size-related and include operation over a wide range of frequencies as illustrated by Figs 7.4 and 7.5; lightweight methods of construction yielding effective heights considerably in excess of the mast height; and exceptional versatility extending to many different types of construction, including 'invisible' arrays featured in Chapter 15.

Assisting in these objectives, the 90° loop has emerged as an optimum choice, a relatively large value of R at its fundamental resonance or 'main design frequency' f_m being attributable to its incipient resemblance to a folded dipole which fortunately stops short of dragging R down to zero at $2f_m$. It will be seen from the graphs that at all frequencies within the limits imposed by Fig 7.5 this shape yields R values as good, and at the lower frequencies better than, the

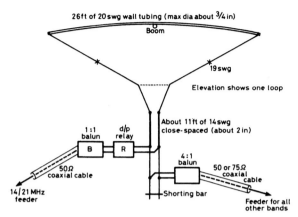

Fig 12.18. Multiband beam element based on Fig 12.17(b). This uses 26ft of tubing as the radiating element. On 14MHz all radiation is from the tubing, ie from the highest part of the antenna

alternatives, making it an important step in the search for a small beam element capable of operating over the widest possible range of frequencies.

The use of matched feeder systems is feasible subject to the 'two bands easy, three bands difficult' rule-of-thumb stated in Chapter 7, and Fig 12.18 shows an example which gave a good account of itself on the air. This could obviously have been extended by means of resonant feeders to include the WARC bands had these been available at the time, and it would appear to be a simple matter on this basis to convert existing trapped tribanders for coverage of additional bands and improved performance on the old ones by dropping wires down from the ends of elements as suggested in Fig 12.19. Trouble with guy ropes or other obstructions could be overcome by routeing the new feeders via a 10 or 12ft 'fishing rod'

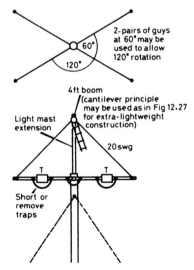

Fig 12.19. Suggested conversion of existing tribander to 'all band' array. One element only shown

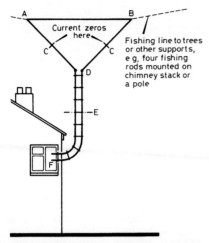

Fig 12.20. Basic SDL array. Sketch shows one element mounted directly above shack with short feeder. Loop ABCD is brought to resonance by the stub DE which can be continued into shack, or 300Ω line can be patched in at E as in Fig 7.6(b)

mast extension. 600Ω line can be substituted and, if used for the outer elements, these can be used as a two-element beam for 10MHz subject to some restrictions in respect of feeder length and performance as discussed on pp214, 217.

There are several practical points to be noted. When two elements are used efficiently, little benefit is to be expected from a third element except at the top end of, say, an octave frequency range (eg 28MHz) where the size of the antenna takes on a larger aspect and, unless 10MHz is required, only two adjacent elements need to be treated. The director should, however, be left 'as is' unless it is desired to exercise the beam-reversal option. Commercial 300Ω line operating at high SWR requires readjustment of the ATU whilst getting wet or drying out (p293), and is liable to damage if used in conjunction with the 10MHz option except at low power levels.

The small delta loops described thus far have been based on the use of tubing, but important advantages have accrued from the use of wire elements such as Fig 12.20(a) which can, for example, be held up by fishing rods to achieve effective heights of up to 15ft in excess of the mast height. As will be clear from Chapters 5 and 7, design problems centre primarily on the 'lowest' frequency or rather what has been defined as the 'main design frequency' (MDF), in view of the possibility in certain circumstances of pressing the antenna into service on an even lower frequency band (p85).

At the MDF one is faced with the difficult task of trying to make the antenna as small as possible, in order to realise a lot of advantages without sacrificing anything of importance. The difficulties are compounded by the fact that the MDF is likely to be the most popular DX band so that, in view of the competition, compromises are least likely to be acceptable. In addition it is at the lowest frequency that antenna height, from the propagation aspect, is most important; this ties in well with the SDL philosophy which aims to maximise height at

the MDF, accepting that at higher frequencies the effective mean height is slightly reduced by radiation from the lower portions of the loops. Fig 12.21 gives details of a practical design based on Fig 12.20 which serves also to demonstrate the process of evolution from the VK2ABQ array.

Some of the methods for optimising performance at the MDF have to be discounted on grounds of creating problems at higher frequencies, leaving a total of four methods deserving of further discussion, as follows.

1. Rewiring only

Do nothing, apart from wiring each loop directly back to the shack in the form of 600Ω line as in Fig 12.20 which is based on Fig 7.6(a). The impedance discontinuity at D steps down the value of R as seen by the feeder to about half, but this may be acceptable if the feeder is short enough.

There could be a nearly ideal situation in the case of a first-floor shack with the antenna directly above it. This assumes an effective antenna height not exceeding about 40ft, in which case DE will be no more than 3 or 4ft, allowing resonance to be restored at the MDF by series capacitance just inside the shack. Above this height, the increasing length of DE means the presence of large RF voltages in or close to the shack which could lead to TVI and other problems, though subject to good feeder balance the author has experienced no trouble on this score. On the other hand, one of the main attractions of this arrangement, apart from its simplicity, is the option of being able to reduce or eliminate visual impact by the use of very thin wire without compromising efficiency. To achieve this with Fig 12.20 means that stub lengths must be kept short, as demonstrated by the following calculation.

Using 20swg copper wire the total loss resistance for a pair of equal-current resonant loops is 7Ω. Squeezing in the bottom corners of the loops to arrive at the right-angled delta

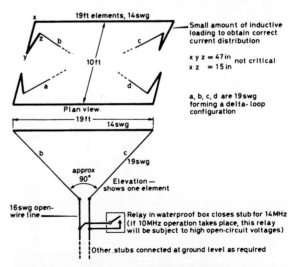

Fig 12.21. An example of compact G6XN multiband all-wire beam based on the VK2ABQ form of construction. Main constructional details are similar to Fig 12.10 (see photograph)

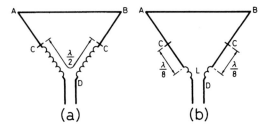

Fig 12.22. Two methods of resonating small delta loops. (a) Helically loaded λ/2 dipole CDC has roughly the same Z_0 as CABC so that the impedance seen by feeder is roughly equal to radiation resistance R. (b) λ/8 line CD results in an impedance $2R/Z_0$ at lower corner so that, putting $\omega L = Z_0$, the feeder sees a resistance $2R$. This method provides a useful impedance step-up of 2, but L can cause problems at 18 or 21MHz where the loop is nearly self-resonant. It helps to wind it in the form of short helices forming part of CD

shape with the recommended circumference of 0.75λ results (Fig 7.4) in a radiation resistance for a single loop of 64Ω or about 50Ω for the driven element of a two-element parasitic array with typical spacing and phasing; this gives an efficiency ratio of 50/57 or 88%, a loss of 0.57dB which (to keep matters in perspective) is about the same as the loss in 30ft of RG-58 coaxial feeder. Thus far, as may have been noticed, the unfortunate impedance transformation which causes the feeder to see only half the true value of R has been ignored but there is no need to re-work the example since by using 14swg for the feeder its loss resistance is also halved and, with luck, this part of the antenna is out of sight so that visual impact problems continue to be avoided. Increasing DE to λ/2 will double the losses or, without the increase in wire diameter, increase them to nearly 2dB.

An alternative is to use 300Ω line for DE as in Fig 7.6(b). Assuming open-wire construction and 14swg, this has little effect on losses but improves bandwidth (Table 7.2), and avoids the complications of further impedance transformation inside the shack where the use of 300Ω line is preferable (p63). The effect of such choices on operation at higher frequencies can be gauged from Table 7.2.

2. Resonant loop method
Fig 12.22 shows three ways of bringing the SDL to resonance at the MDF, originally conceived in the context of the impedance-transforming loops described below. Applied to simple loops, the advantage lies in avoiding the impedance step-down at D and, in case (b), replacing this by a step-up of a similar amount, sufficient to permit the use of long (2λ) feedlines.

This arrangement came into use as a result of storm damage to the ITL array, Fig 7.6(g), the twin-wire loops having been replaced as a temporary measure by single strands of 20swg. This incident, with further repercussions, is featured in Chapter 7 (p127). A major limitation of this method arises from the flow of large currents through the inductance L on both 18 and 21MHz; this can result in high values of SWR, the problem being accentuated in the case of single-wire loops although, as explained in Chapter 7, it was

found to be mitigated in the present instance by the 'distributed' nature of the loading inductance which was wound over a 2ft length of 1in tubing. In comparison with the ITL arrangement, bandwidth on 14MHz was roughly halved but numerous 'on the air' comparisons with another station acting as yardstick failed to reveal any signal-strength differences, the theoretical loss (less than 1dB) being too small to manifest itself.

3. Impedance-transforming loop (ITL) arrays
These solve the matching problem at the MDF without unduly hindering operation at the higher frequencies. The price paid for this is greater complexity, since the Z_0 of the top half-wavelength of each loop has to be reduced by using at least two well-spaced wires in parallel and the remainder of the loop rendered self-resonant by some form of inductive loading, keeping its Z_0 as high as possible. Fig 12.23(a) and the photograph, p220, give details of an ITL array used over a period of some years [11, 12], culminating in the incident related above, and (b) is a modified design in line with the latest thinking; this features the right-angled delta shape, and use of the largest loop size (0.85λ) compatible with requirements for 28MHz reduces the amount of inductive loading so that increases of SWR at 18 and 21MHz are kept to a minimum. It also results in a large-enough value of R, about 20Ω, to allow operation as a beam on 10MHz as described below. Measured performance data for this and other SDL arrays will be found in [11].

It is important to distinguish between inductive loading used in this manner and more-familiar arrangements in which the loading inductances replace substantial portions of the radiating system with a catastrophic effect on R. The difference is that in the present case, as in that of radials (p43), the loaded conductors are not primarily concerned with the radiating process. Note, however, that in addition to functioning as a λ/4 transformer the lower dipole of Fig 12.23(b) has the task of neutralising the radiation from AC and BC, and to this end both the current, which is reduced by the impedance ratio, and the current distribution, which is sinusoidal, must be taken into account. Fortunately these two factors nearly cancel each other, and further simplification arises from a tendency for different methods of loading to increase both C and L by the same amount so that Z_0 tends to stay in the region of 1000 to 1100Ω. As an alternative to the helical loading shown in Fig 12.23(b) planar loading, Fig 17.9(b), can be strongly recommended for operation below the MDF due to its lower losses, though Z_0 figures have yet to be determined. With likely values for the radiator impedance not much in excess of 500Ω (Table 7.1) the multiband properties of elements such as Fig 12.23(b) can be quickly and easily evaluated by means of the Smith chart, along the lines of the following example.

The half-length of top at 14MHz is 0.175λ and each side 0.25λ. This allows for the lower dipole a physical half-length also of 0.175λ but this is inductively loaded to an equivalent length of 0.25λ. From Fig 7.4 we have 110Ω for R, but the figure for a beam will be slightly less, let us say (to keep the

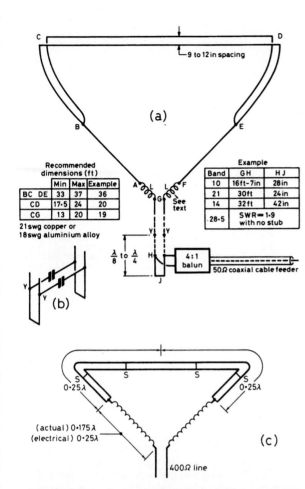

Recommended dimensions (ft)

	Min	Max	Example
BC DE	33	37	36
CD	17·5	24	20
CG	13	20	19

21 swg copper or
18 swg aluminium alloy

Example

Band	GH	HJ
10	16ft-7in	28in
21	30ft	24in
14	32ft	42in
28·5	SWR= 1·9 with no stub	

Fig 12.23. (a) Mark IV (ITL) version of the Claw, one of many options. Small capacitors as at (b) can be used between feedlines to improve coupling and null depth on some bands. In-shack tuning arrangements in line with Fig 4.54 are now preferred, with coupling adjusted by taping together the lower ends of the 300Ω extension lines. Series-matching capacitors close to the antenna were used for operation on 10MHz. (c) Impedance transforming loop beam element, 'ideal version'. Z_0 data for wires in parallel can be obtained from Table 7.1. For strict compliance with the conditions of Table 12.2, aluminium wire 16–18swg, spaced 12in, may be used. For 14MHz about 60ft of 20swg copper will be required for helices. For the 400Ω line, 16swg spaced 1in is suitable. Shorts at S to be spaced not more than 13ft. Wire spacing can be reduced to 3in and any feeder impedance from 300–600Ω used with little adverse effect

figures simple but of the right order) 100Ω. Assuming for the loop a Z_0 of 500Ω and turning to p214 we enter the chart, Fig 12.24, at A and proceed 0.25λ round the 0.2 circle to B where $Z = 5 + 0j$; normalising for 1000Ω takes us to C and proceeding another λ/4 we arrive at D to find $Z = 0.4$, ie 400Ω, which means that the bottom corner of the loop would present a perfect match to 400Ω line. This result follows directly from the impedance ratio, so use of the chart was unnecessary except to demonstrate the basic simplicity of a method capable of resolving much more complex problems with

Table 12.2

Band (MHz)	ITL, SWR in 400Ω feeder, Z_0 (top) = 500Ω	Single-wire loop, 20swg. SWR in 400Ω feeder	Constant-Z_0 system: 600Ω. 0.85λ loop	Constant-Z_0 system: 600Ω. 0.75λ loop
10	30	85	30	–
14	1.0	8	6 (no stub)	9.3
18	4.5	2.9	2.4	3
21	4.1	4	1.6	2
25	2.6	5.4	1.6	1.5
28	1.4	6.2	2.2	1.6

almost equal ease, though for the moment its use will be confined to finding out what happens on other bands.

At 21MHz the line lengths are 0.375λ and $R = 370Ω$; this takes us from E on the 0.74 circle to the point F where $Z = 1 - 0.3j$, which normalises to $0.5 - 0.15j$ at G, a distance of −0.03λ on the 0.48 circle. Adding 0.375λ we arrive at H where $Z = 1 - 0.8j$. Normalising to 400Ω gives $2.5 - 2j$, ie point J, giving an SWR of 4.1 which is still satisfactory. Proceeding similarly for the other three bands leads to the completion of Table 12.2, which includes figures for the CIL system, showing in both cases a marked improvement over those for simple loops which are included for comparison, though all three systems are viable if feeder lengths are not excessive. Though rather similar to examples presented in Chapter 7, these differ to the extent of being geared specifically to the task of developing the 'ideal' beam element. This has included an increase in span from 21 to 24ft which imparts a slight bias in favour of the lower frequencies and should not be exceeded. The advantages of going to the larger size are subtle, for example the need to readjust the ATU or retune the reflector will arise less frequently; one will be able to incorporate more commercial 300Ω line in the feeder system without being bothered by 'wet-dry' effects; bamboo is more likely to be satisfactory over a longer period of time without overhaul or with less-efficient waterproofing; and much more of the same ilk. On the other hand, rather more substantial benefits can be expected if it is desired to operate on 10MHz where gain performance within 2dB of a monoband beam can be expected subject to the measures recommended below.

4. Constant-Z_0 systems

As explained on p128, these are aimed at securing most of the advantages of the ITL systems with less complexity, though two-wire loops are needed in this case also. The essential feature is a combination of antenna and feeder having the same value of Z_0 throughout, which in principle ensures that resonances are in strict harmonic relationship (p37) and eliminates mismatches caused by 'wrong way' transformer action at the feedpoint or elsewhere along the system. With the loop illustrated in Fig 12.25 the radiation resistance is sufficiently well matched on each band to the 600Ω value of Z_0, though the match to 300Ω is better and can be achieved for the non-WARC bands by a transition to the lower impedance

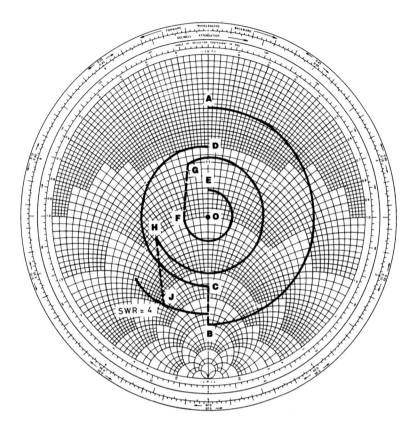

Fig 12.24. Application of Smith chart to the ITL. On 14MHz, starting from A (top centre), we arrive at D (bottom corner). If we choose a feeder Z of 400Ω, D normalises to O, ie an SWR of 1.0 in the feeder. Corresponding points on 21MHz are E to J. It is assumed that the feeder impedance has been chosen on the basis of the 14MHz example, so the final step on 21MHz has to be normalisation to the same value, 400Ω, ie point J which lies on the SWR = 4 circle

as illustrated. This makes the SWR worse at 24MHz and 18MHz (the 'worst case') though it should remain within acceptance limits. Figures for two loop sizes (500Ω line) are included in Table 12.3. In practice harmonic ratios continue to exhibit considerable scatter, but this is to be expected unless the 'rule of thumb' which relies merely on the use of two wires in parallel is replaced by something more accurate.

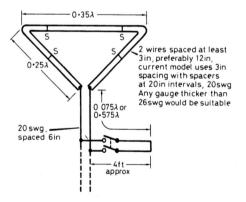

Fig 12.25. Constant-Z_0 version of Fig 12.23(b). Switched stub improves bandwidth on 14MHz (the MDF), eg if system length above the stub equals the feeder length below it, bandwidth is doubled. (Not needed with short feeders.)

Measures to reduce the Z_0 of the radiating portion of the antenna system help in two ways since, apart from lower values of SWR, the RF voltages are reduced, allowing smaller tuning and matching components to be used as well as reducing the likelihood of problems due to 'RF in the shack'. This also greatly improves the prospects for remote tuning or band-switching by components mounted in the antenna, thereby enabling it to be fed with low-impedance line.

At the lowest useful frequency for any small loop or dipole beam element there will be a large SWR which can, in principle, be corrected by using a relay for the attachment of a suitable stub or other matching device. In practice, with resonant feeders, this may be impracticable due to very high RF voltages existing at the relay at some other frequency. By eliminating impedance discontinuities, assuming a typical ratio of 2:1, safe operating power levels can be increased by a factor of 4.

Operation below the MDF

Several of the ITL arrangements described above have been successfully tested half-an-octave below the MDF, to the extent that no difficulty has been experienced in making DX contacts on 10MHz with 14MHz beams, and the 21MHz version described below was fully evaluated on 14MHz by exclusive use over a period of several months for the author's regular VK contacts, with G6BZ providing a constant reference signal. On this basis the reduction in effective gain attributable to the small size was about 2dB, in good agreement with the estimated losses. Front-to-back ratios were typically in excess of 20dB.

Such operation is not without its hazards, with baluns, switches, ATUs and 300Ω feeders all being potentially at risk from high voltages and currents. For serious use at the lower frequency, two-wire loops (ITL or constant-Z_0) are highly desirable, and feeders must be short unless a matching device can be inserted close to the antenna, an arrangement used successfully on 10MHz but unsuitable for 14MHz because of the narrow bandwidth which necessitates in-shack retuning if the frequency is changed by more than a small amount. It is advisable also to increase wire sizes and, although this applies more particularly to feeders, tuning stubs and loading coils or sections, it inevitably places extra demands on the supporting structure.

Construction of SDL arrays

SDL arrays may be hung from spreaders, supported spider's web fashion from trees or other supports by means of nylon fishing line as in Fig 12.26, or held up by fishing rods angled upwards and outwards from the top of a mast as shown in the photograph, the angles being set to ensure that the wires are kept under tension since flexing leads very quickly to breakage.

Known from its appearance as the 'Claw', this has been the mainstay of operation from G6XN for many years during which it has undergone a number of design changes. As illustrated the loop design conforms to Fig 12.23(a); the arms consist of fishing-rod blanks with the tips cut back to about 0.25in diameter, the lower ends being extended to give a total length of 19ft by means of 6ft lengths of 1in diameter glassfibre tube which happened to be available, though other materials can be used if wires are kept well clear of metalwork or poor insulators such as wet bamboo. To avoid RF excitation of the supporting structure at 28MHz, metalwork should not extend more than about 5ft from the mast.

The rods are plugged into sockets (about 7in) attached to the mast with the help of short lengths of alloy 'angle' held in place with exhaust clamps. Points 6ft out along the arms are guyed back to a 5ft lightweight mast extension and to the ends of a boom of about the same length aligned with the beam heading, using ¾in diameter alloy tube for both items. The 'boom' also supports the feeders, together with the bottom corners of the loops for which a spacing of about 4ft has been found suitable though it may be varied for adjustment of coupling. The angle between adjacent arms is set with the help of rods extending 2ft out from the mast, and cord ties are used between points about 4ft down from the tips to give a top spacing of 10ft.

Regrettably, any reader expecting to find a drawing of this will have to be disappointed for several reasons: it is extremely difficult to draw, and the details could be improved to the extent that any reader reasonably competent in such matters should be able to evolve better ones, with the above description as a starting point.

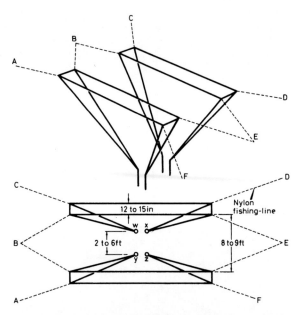

Fig 12.26. SDL array supported by nylon fishing line. Use of CIL principle reduces visibility and improves performance. Use any wire gauge not finer than 26swg. Tapered side spacings may improve performance at the higher frequencies and help to maintain Z_0 constant. For supports, anything goes! To start the ideas rolling, A, B, C could be points on the boom of a large TV or FM antenna, and the antenna could slope down towards extended fence posts DEF with w, x, y, z dangling over the shack window. Spacing wx–yz is 2–6ft approx but may need to be adjustable so the corners should be left free to slide through nylon loops

For those less gifted there is an easier, though less elegant, alternative as shown in Fig 12.27. This is simpler than it looks, consisting of a very light extension mast carrying an ultra-lightweight but well-braced top boom which has virtually no weight to support other than its own. Four 12ft spider arms attached to a median position on the mast extension hold up the top corners of 0.75λ SDL elements, and a 4ft long lower boom attached to the mast holds the lower corners of the loops and the feeders. This is the version of the SDL shown in Fig 7.6(b) and the two-element beam has been in use throughout the last winter, its performance being well up to the standard set by its predecessors, and for a total weight of 8½lb it provides the equivalent of an 8ft mast extension, though the mechanical design still awaits the test of time. It has also for some of us the major advantage of being easy to handle in a cluttered environment, unlike the Claw which (in common with the traditional forms of delta-loop construction) is extremely top-heavy, making it dangerous to handle on top of a ladder, though the central mast extension means that this problem is not too difficult to overcome with the help of a gin-pole.

Given a clear space for erection and a mast with suitable tilting or luffing provisions, the Claw still remains for the author a preferred option but, having none of these things, its use as a test-bed for the 'constant-Z_0' idea posed something of

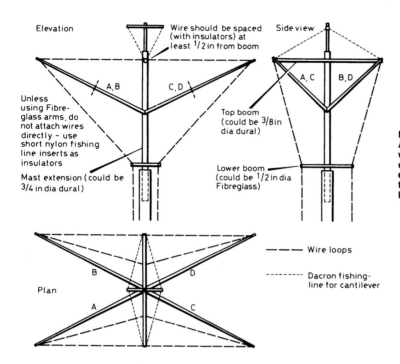

Fig 12.27. Constructional details of SDL array. A, B, C, D are spider arms (fishing rods, well-wrapped bamboo – can be partly metal but only inwards from the dotted lines marked on elevation). Details of attachment of spider arms to mast not shown (could be secured to short lengths of angle held to mast by U-clamps)

a problem. A new 'piecemeal' method of erection was evolved but, though finally successful, demanded a plentiful supply of calm weather as well as patience, both in short supply. There was one disappointment; being possessed of a set of four 19ft 'fishing rods' there was no way of changing over to the (now preferred) right-angled delta shape, short of an act of vandalism, the new T-type design (Fig 12.27) being in this respect much more flexible. Nevertheless the system, though somewhat dishevelled, is now working well.

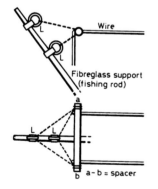

Fig 12.28. Equalising tension in paired wires of ITL or CIL. Nylon line, two looped lengths as shown dotted, is free to slide through loops, rings or insulators L

As the Claw construction is unusual it is encouraging to record the survival of the single-wire elements (20swg) in one of the areas worst hit by the storms of January 1990, though breakages have occurred in the case of two-wire elements due to difficulty in ensuring that both wires were kept under tension. The method of attachment shown in Fig 12.10 has been devised to try and overcome this problem. Two other

wire breakages have occurred, one due to corrosion and neither of them to the type of construction. The hurricane of November 1987, though it brought down a large beech tree which damaged the house, left the antenna in place and still in one piece but upside down and held by its strings! The spigot holding it to the mast, consisting of a short length of very thin-walled alloy tubing (fitted in some moment of aberration), had stripped and all the wires had disappeared, but otherwise the antenna (not being a quad) was as good as new and easily rewired.

It should be noted that in the case of the Claw it is not possible to specify exactly the shape of the sides, and as described above (equilateral, 0.85λ) the loop size is larger than ideally recommended for 28MHz. It is instructive also to consider what would have been the effect of changing to the preferred right-angled delta shape without altering the loop circumference; the length of top is increased to 24ft and its height decreased by about 4ft, but 28MHz needs should now be adequately met and at 14MHz R (single loop) is increased from 65 to 110Ω. This rise is due unfortunately to radiation from the lower part of the loop, and drags the mean height down by a further 2ft to a total of about 8ft above the mast height. A change to the T form should result in lighter construction, allowing some increase of mast height for restoration of the status quo.

Fig 12.29 illustrates the 'Miniclaw'. This is the version designed for an MDF of 21MHz and cited above to illustrate the possibility of operation at lower frequencies, though using it on 14MHz had not been part of the original intention. Apart from the obvious attractions of an even smaller size, the original goals included better directivity on 28MHz combined

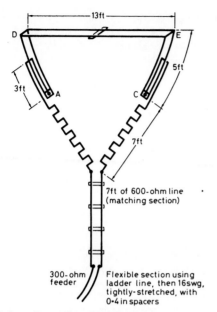

Fig 12.29. A smaller version of the Claw antenna

Diagram labels:
13ft
D
E
5ft
3ft
A
C
7ft
7ft of 600-ohm line (matching section)
300-ohm feeder
Flexible section using ladder line, then 16swg, tightly-stretched, with 0·4 in spacers

with full efficiency on 18MHz where the rather low estimated R value of 34Ω inspired the inclusion of loading stubs at A and C. The stubs improve the current distribution on the lower frequency bands, losses being further reduced by using a much heavier gauge of wire (14swg) for the lower dipole ABC. Use of this beam on 14MHz at a few minutes notice as a substitute for the Claw (one element of which had finally succumbed to rough treatment due to one corner being grabbed by an adjacent tree) provided an impressive demonstration of the virtues of resonant feeder systems, though it is easy in this respect to press one's luck too far. The two pairs of feeders coming into the shack from the Miniclaw, being of exactly the right length for operating it as a two-turn loop on the 3.5MHz band, presented an irresistible challenge and resulted in some good contacts which, with an estimated ERP of 15W, was fully to be expected. The question of what was happening to the other 385W remained unasked until next morning on 14MHz, when one element was found to have an open-circuit in what would normally have been the least likely place, ie close to 'top dead centre'. This was where maximum current would have occurred on 3.5MHz, and inspection revealed that both wires (18swg aluminium alloy) had *fused*, which was probably an 'all-time first' but hopefully also a 'last', so please, reader, be warned!

Application of resonant feeders to dipole arrays

Possibly by now some readers may have been persuaded that the SDL, in one of its many forms, is the answer to all beam problems. Others undoubtedly will remain convinced that the 'bigger the better' whilst the truth, for those whose hands are not tied by legal restrictions or lack of resources, falls somewhere in between. A dipole array which is shortened or folded to fit into the space required by an SDL array is, for five-band operation, a non-starter, but if instead the length is increased to some 42–44ft, each element becomes an 'extended double-Zepp', providing 3dB of extra gain on 28MHz, and in addition continues to function as an efficient 'no problems' beam element all the way down to 10MHz. There is in fact no need to stop at 10MHz but for 7MHz, if efficiency is not to be sacrificed, matching must be arranged close to the elements and there may be problems in locating or devising suitable remote-switching devices. There is, however, no intrinsic difficulty, provided power is not applied during the switching operation which, on the basis of the UK licence (400W PEP) would limit the voltage to about 1200 (14MHz) and the current to 5A (7MHz). To benefit fully from these options it is essential to have three elements, of which the two outer ones only are used on 7 and 10MHz. The spacing should be λ/8 on 14MHz as in Fig 20.2. If only two elements are used, the ends should be pulled in to within about 2 or 3ft of each other (by means of nylon fishing line) in order to equalise currents and reduce the effective spacing at the higher frequencies as described on p129.

Constant-Z_0 operation is possible also in the case of dipoles with single conductors, but for strict compliance with the conditions requires an average diameter of at least ¾in for the elements of a rotary beam in conjunction with 700Ω feeder, eg 20swg, spaced 6in. Figures for 600Ω feeder have been included in Table 12.2 and will be seen to fall well short of straining resources to the limit. It may well be better to use thicker feeder wire, allowing SWR to rise in some instances in order to improve bandwidth at the lowest frequency.

A further advantage of dipole elements is the virtual absence of pattern break-up so long as the 44ft dimension is not exceeded. Like SDL elements they can also be suspended between trees or other supports by means of nylon fishing line, in which case the constant-Z_0 feature can be achieved by using pairs of wires spaced about 6 to 12in for the horizontal spans.

Other large arrays using resonant feeders

Mention has already been made of the DJ4VM quad, and the double-delta, Fig 12.30, is a similar arrangement based on the SDL concept; apart from the multiband aspects this bears some resemblance to the 9M2CP double delta [9, 10]. In each case, excluding the quad at 14MHz, some 2–4dB of additional gain can be expected, with the double-delta providing this on 14MHz also, due to the wider spacing between the two horizontal sides. However, due to the reduction in mean height, these gains are unlikely to be realised in practice without a big mast or a steep ground slope. In both cases there is little sideways radiation, though operation below 14MHz is not normally to be recommended.

The adjustment and testing of arrays based on resonant feeders

Major virtues of these antennas include ease of adjustment followed by more-or-less continuous monitoring as a feature

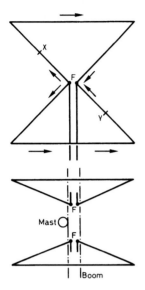

Fig 12.30. Double-delta array. Note similarity to the DJ4VM quad, but construction is simpler. Patterns and gain should be almost identical with the DJ4VM for same overall loop size. Note similarity also to the 9M2CP double-delta, eg at the fundamental frequency I = 0 at X and Y so FX, FY can be omitted

only one element is affected and both directions of fire should always be checked. In the case of loops DC continuity checks can be particularly valuable, especially if there are a lot of joins in the system and one is able to make accurate measurements of low resistance.

Faulty weatherproofing of components is another possible source of trouble but with large values of SWR some change of velocity factor is to be expected in wet weather, even if one is not using slotted 300Ω line which, as related elsewhere (p293), is liable to rather large changes during periods of getting wet or drying out. One other phenomenon that may be found puzzling is lack of T/R reciprocity when observing deep nulls; this is due to pick-up on wiring which, due for example to the switching-in of a linear, may be slightly different for the two conditions.

Assuming then that all is well, routine monitoring may consist of:

(a) The continued observance of deep nulls during reception.

(b) Observation of SWR for both beam directions. Ignore changes like 1.1 to 1.3 but if, despite previous good equalisation, SWR goes up from 1 to 2 there could be a fault such as a twisted feeder, in which case insulation (if any) on wires may break down when power is applied. There may even be some 'innocent' explanation like wire stretch, but any lack of symmetry can be a nuisance since it is not then possible to check (or demonstrate) the quality of the F/B ratio by a simple reversal of beam direction.

(c) Checking of DC resistances from time to time or if a fault is suspected.

Indoor beams

Before embarking on an indoor beam the section on indoor antennas in the last chapter (p192) and the indoor environment (p172) should be consulted. Even if there is room for a small beam it may be better to stick to a single element, at least for transmission, since in the case of the beam there will usually be increased losses and a greater risk of RF voltages getting into the mains wiring (p193). A beam, even if it does provide useful gain, may not be rotatable and for all-round coverage it might then be better for example to use two dipoles at right-angles. It may even be possible to erect two beams at right-angles but if these are close together the one not in use must be open-circuited.

Assuming sufficient space, the desirability or otherwise of a beam can probably be resolved only by experiment, and in this respect indoor beams have a number of advantages since usually they are readily accessible, can be adjusted in situ, and do not require weatherproofing.

The chances of success are obviously much greater the higher the frequency and, given a space of at least 7ft (2.1m) diameter and 5ft (1.5m) high, a small quad based on Fig 12.15 is the best choice for 28MHz, leaving its competitors a long way behind by virtue of its much larger radiation resistance and smaller diameter of turning circle. At 14MHz the

of normal use, though problems can arise in the initial stages. The following discussion assumes the use of two feeders which are interchangeable for beam reversal by means of a switch or relay, and that all reasonable precautions have been taken to ensure that the elements are identical and the feeders non-radiating. It also assumes the provision of remote tuning by means such as those illustrated in Fig 4.53.

All being well, the reflector tuning can be set approximately to the signal frequency by means of a GDO, after which it should be possible by slightly varying its tuning to obtain deep nulls on most signals coming from back directions. Switching to transmit and adjusting the ATU in the normal way will mean that the station should now be fully operational. If deep nulls are not obtained, try tuning the reflector whilst observing the SWR; if it shoots up to 4 or 5 this suggests serious overcoupling, and close inspection of the antenna may suggest a reason such as ends or corners of elements nearly touching, or feeders spaced by distances less than several times the spacing between wires. If there are points of high RF voltage in the shack, make sure that this is not where you have put the beam-reversing switch or relay. If, on the other hand, the SWR meter hardly moves, the problem is undercoupling, and if it is easy for example to alter the antenna (eg to bring ends closer together), this should be tried.

The possibility of adjusting coupling by lapping 300Ω feeders together in the shack may be the easy way out but can complicate band changing. (Note, however, that if the effect on SWR of tuning the reflector is considerably less on the highest frequency bands, this is to be expected in view of the wider spacing). Excessive losses may be a cause of 'undercoupling' and a likely explanation could be feeder imbalance. In one bad case the trouble was traced to coupling between the reflector line and a feeder going to another antenna, and nulls can also be upset by reflections from other antennas. In the event of such problems arising it may be that possibilities are likely to be limited in most cases to the VK2ABQ or one of its derivatives. Fig 12.10 is a strong candidate unless space is sufficient to accommodate something on the lines of Fig 12.9. It must again be strongly emphasised that some form of phased array is essential, the W8JK being the worst possible antenna for indoor use due to its exceptionally low radiation resistance.

For a given type of element in a specified position relative to any surrounding lossy materials, it should be recalled (p100) that two are always better than one, subject to the provision that, if they are lossy, both must be driven or the coupling between them must be increased. This could mean, for example, that a beam on the lines of Fig 12.12 does not have to be neutralised but, if losses are due to the proximity of a wet roof, they will be highly variable and it is best to neutralise for fine weather, relying in all conditions on phasing by the method of Fig 5.21.

If losses are high it may be that a much more efficient design of element could be used if it is only necessary to fit one into the given space. In this case it should be possible to use a separate small active element (p156) for improving reception, although this is a field wide open to the experimenter seeking to break new ground.

Conclusions and recommendations

As in the case of the last chapter it seems appropriate to conclude with the author's selection of 'best buys'.

1. The author's first choice now has to be one of the SDL arrays, since these are small, efficient, and available in a wide range of shapes, sizes and means-of-support, so that they can be tailored to fit most requirements. However, they owe much [8] to their near relative the VK2ABQ antenna, which many will find a good choice for at least one-band or two-band operation. The small 90° delta loop is distinguished by relatively large values of radiation resistance and, for a loop, comparative freedom from pattern break-up, making it an ideal choice for multibanding by the use of resonant feeders. On the other hand, for those who dislike open-wire line and are prepared to settle for two-band (or possibly three-band if relays are used) operation, they can be matched into coaxial cable (eg as in Fig 12.18). A possible disadvantage up to the time of writing is the 'experimental' status of some of the mechanical designs, though there are clearly no insuperable problems. It is a feature of all these arrays that they provide near-optimum performance for transmission and (aided by some exercise of skill on the part of the operator) very deep nulls 'off the back'. Their particular merit lies in the fact that these advantages are obtained for a minimum of cost, weight, and windage and with a turning-circle diameter little more than half that of a normal full-size three-element Yagi. In many cases low visual impact is another important 'plus', and in general, it is difficult to achieve better performance without being prepared to erect some comparatively large structure, though

sometimes if suitable supports (trees, etc) are available wire dipole arrays such as the 'wire' version of Fig 20.2 may be a better choice. As well as the arrays featured in this chapter attention is drawn also to the two 'invisible' SDL arrays in Chapter 15.

2. For DX operation on the 14–28MHz bands, a strong preference now exists for pairs of SDL elements exploiting the constant-Z_0 principle as in Figs 12.25 or 7.24, though choice may be influenced by special circumstances such as sloping ground, the ability to erect large towers, and sundry restrictions or special interests.

3. Fig 12.10 in monoband form is the type of beam which can be recommended with most confidence to those without previous experience, though one or two additional bands should not present much of a problem, particularly if relays are used to open-circuit the 21MHz elements during operation on 28MHz.

4. For those who already have a three-element Yagi or the means of supporting one, Fig 12.1 provides the basis for an antenna having broader bandwidths (leading to greater operational convenience) and at the higher frequencies about 2dB more gain than option 1. Operation on at least two bands is possible by means of linear resonators. The constructional method of Fig 12.5 saves weight and windage, and allows the use of separate wire elements for 28MHz or two-band wire elements (eg Fig 12.6) for 21/28MHz.

5. For mounting in trees, pairs of quad elements with resonant feeders may be used as fixed reversible beams. The use of open-wire feeders simplifies multiband operation, the arguments presented in Chapter 11 (p179) being applicable in this case also. Similarly, for mounting between poles or trees, 'squashed' delta loops are recommended; in this case the ends should be brought in towards a common anchoring point, a separation of about 3ft (0.9m) probably being about right for 14MHz. This should, however, be checked by observing relative currents at the bottom end of the resonant lines or, if the parallel-connected high-impedance matched line in Fig 11.13(f) is used, just above the feedpoints. For mounting in trees attention has been drawn to Fig 12.17(b) which can be a much easier alternative, though if equally buried in branches and foliage any losses in the tree will be worse because R is lower; on the other hand, the tips of the elements are more likely to be clear of foliage, and for the same effective height the top corner of the quad loops have to be higher by about 0.17λ which adds greatly to any difficulties. Pursuing the search for a 'best' antenna, it has been the author's 'on the air' impression that exceptional performance owes more to location than anything else or, failing that, a big antenna such as a rhombic, and sometimes both! Short of this, consistently outstanding performance at 14MHz and above (though often linked to mast heights of 100ft and large monoband arrays) includes instances of two-element beams, one at least of which was an 'equal current' array, as deduced from its front/back ratio. Examples of arrays which in the author's

The Claw antenna. Small delta-loop elements are held up by glassfibre arms angled upwards and outwards from the masthead. Bottom corners are brought down to a short boom where they are attached to open-wire feeders. Spacing of the top wires is set to 10ft by cord ties (not visible). The span is 20ft and with all the radiation coming from the top the height gain (14MHz) is 13ft. Loop types used have included single wire (Fig 12.22(b)), ITL (Fig 12.23) and constant-Z_0 (Fig 12.25), as in the photo

recollections 'never produce a poor signal' (admittedly not a scientific method of assessment) include, in addition to some commercial monoband Yagis, the log-Yagi of Fig 12.6.

Cases to which these recommendations are not applicable are 'special', in the sense that each needs to be considered in the light of earlier discussion, though, given a requirement for the smallest possible turning circle, Fig 12.15 is the obvious choice.

The author feels considerable doubt as to whether a strong case can often be made out for more than three elements in the case of rotary beams at 'ordinary' heights.

As will be evident from Chapter 5, a six-element beam on a 50ft (15m) boom at 50ft is no better than three elements on a 16ft (4.9m) boom at about 65ft (20m) or, except in regard to the *average* interference level, a phased pair of two-element beams at 50ft. Even if considerations of size, weight and cost are ignored, those with experience of switched beam reversal may well regard this possibility as an overriding advantage of two-element and three-element beams.

It should be stressed that many of the constructional ideas employed in this chapter are still in the embryo stage or by way of suggestions for experimenters interested in trying out new ideas. Advice at all times has to be 'safety first' and the reader, after taking due note of p311, should (a) avoid quads in exposed locations and (b) seek advice from reference [13], particularly in an exposed location or if any hazards are involved.

References

[1] *Radio Communication Handbook,* 5th edn, Vol 2, RSGB, 1977, p12.75.
[2] 'The disappearing inductance, a new trick and some better beams', L A Moxon, *Radio Communication* April/May 1977, pp284–289 and 364–367.
[3] F Caton, VK2ABQ/G3ONC, *Electronics Australia* October 1973.
[4] 'The log-Yagi array', P D Rhodes and J R Painter, *The ARRL Antenna Anthology,* ARRL, 1978, p49.
[5] 'Technical Topics', *Radio Communication* February 1977 and June 1978.
[6] 'High performance small beams', L A Moxon, *Ham Radio* March 1979.
[7] 'Practical design for a top-hat loaded 14MHz miniquad', R G D Stone, G3YDX, *Radio Communication* October 1976.
[8] 'All-band beam antennas', Les Moxon, *Radio Communication* July 1991.
[9] 'The 9M2CP Z-Beam', 'Technical Topics', *Radio Communication* August 1971.
[10] *Radio Communication Handbook,* 5th edn, RSGB, 1977, p12.50.
[11] 'Two-element HF beams', Les Moxon, *Ham Radio* May 1987.
[12] 'Technical Topics', *Radio Communication* January 1987, p27.
[13] *Physical Design of Yagi Antennas,* Dave Leeson, W6QHS, ARRL, 1992.

Chapter 13

Vertical beams

It will be clear to the reader from earlier chapters that vertical antennas have major virtues as well as some awkward vices. Some of these differences are further emphasised in the case of beams, and the task in this chapter is to show how the merits of vertical arrays may be exploited to the best advantage.

For the higher-frequency bands, vertical antennas with their 'feet on the ground' are easy to erect and normally provide much better performance than horizontal antennas at a low mean height. On the other hand, a horizontal antenna at 40–50ft (12–15m) will usually give significantly better performance than a vertical one having the same gain, but in some cases a relatively elaborate low-height vertical array will be found easier to erect and will give as good or better DX performance. The low height has many attendant advantages since the elements are accessible for adjustment and there is no major mechanical engineering involved.

For a given gain a vertical beam is normally much broader in azimuth than a horizontal beam, thus making it easy to obtain omnidirectional coverage by beam switching, and a broad beam is considered to be in itself an advantage rather than otherwise. At any given time the area of interest may subtend an angle of up to 90° or so. If the beam is narrower than this there will certainly be less risk of interference from other stations in the same distant area but such interference can usually be avoided if frequencies are checked before using them, whereas too narrow a beam will result in contacts being missed. On the other hand, the relatively narrow beamwidth in the vertical plane reduces both short-skip interference and noise from outer space.

One of the biggest problems with vertical elements is to prevent them interacting electrically or mechanically with supporting structures. To avoid electrical losses there are three main methods:

(a) The use of self-supporting elements.

(b) Suspending the vertical elements from catenaries which can also be used to provide capacitive loading at one or both ends.

(c) Arranging that the elements 'billow out' from the supporting mast so that they are well clear of it for most of their length. Metal masts and guys are best avoided but it should be possible for problems to be overcome by methods described on p193.

There remains the general problem of feeding vertical antennas so that power is not lost due to earth currents or feeder radiation. The requirements laid down in earlier chapters are modified in the case of beams only to the extent that radiation resistances tend to be lower, so that any losses which are allowed to occur in the earth connection will become proportionately greater.

In principle any of the single radiators described in Chapter 11 may be used as beam elements, though it is difficult in general with close-spaced elements to use ground planes consisting of three or more $\lambda/4$ radials. This is because adjacent sets of wires (or at least their respective near fields) get entangled but, given the advantages of short radials with a common loading coil as set out in Chapters 4 and 8, this is a problem which should no longer arise.

To avoid losses due to ground currents, the obvious requirement is to ensure that the antenna current is able to find its way back to the source without flowing through the ground, a requirement which is met in the case of a centre-fed element but, in the case of a base-fed 'monopole' with a set of radials, imposes a minimum height condition in line with Fig 6.25, p120. Alternatively, with a high-impedance feed, such as Fig 13.5(d), the ground current is usually small enough to ensure that the losses are negligible.

With vertical antennas the provision of end-loading by means of horizontal wires is a relatively simple matter; alternatively one can use asymmetrical dipole (eg 'ground-plane' type) elements such as Fig 11.19. Depending on site conditions, this may or may not result in a good low-angle radiating system, but there will be the prospect of 3dB improvement if the antenna can be raised to a height of about 0.3λ, as measured to the 'centre-of-gravity' of its current distribution, so that each element with its image resembles a collinear pair.

Further increase in height may be of little or no benefit but, given the right circumstances, signals may compare favourably with those from much more ambitious arrays; moreover, as so little height is needed the chance may exist of deploying relatively large numbers of elements in ways which would be unthinkable in the case of horizontal beams. On the other hand, problem areas include the prevention of feeder radiation and multiband operation.

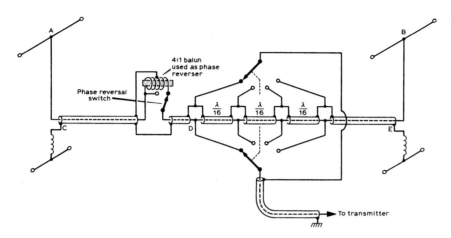

Fig 13.1. Phased pair of vertical antennas. Each step on the phasing switch alters the relative phase by 45°. The bifilar (balun-type) transformer provides phase reversal so that a total of eight phasing steps of 45° (relative) is available. Electrical lengths of CD, DE, are equal. The figure shows vertical monopoles working against artificial earths but a similar arrangement can be devised for any pair of antennas. The counterpoises should be at least 1–2m above ground [1] for negligible losses due to earth currents

Phased verticals

The best-known type of vertical array consists of two or more 'ordinary' vertical antennas, which can be of almost any type and are usually widely spaced, in which case mutual impedance is not a factor of major importance. In this case it is a simple matter by means of phasing lines (ie suitable lengths of feeder) to feed them in such a way that the radiation is additive in some wanted direction and, with adjustable lines, the alternative possibility exists of nulling out interfering signals. The antennas do not have to be identical, and it has been pointed out [8] that quite a wide variety of vertical structures can be pressed into service, though to obtain useful gain they need to be of comparable performance as discussed on p113. Methods of phasing are illustrated in Figs 5.19, 5.21, 13.1 and 13.4.

Beams using elements 'designed for the job' are featured in the following pages.

Two-element arrays

Fig 13.1 shows the 'simplest possible' two-element array. Wire elements and counterpoises are shown as being perhaps the easiest and cheapest if suitable supports (eg trees, chimneys) are available, but most other types of element are suitable. With wide separation of the elements and correct phasing the gain is 3dB for all directions; the adjustment is by altering the relative lengths of the two feeders and, with four switch positions plus a reversing switch as shown, the worst phase error is 22.5°, corresponding to a drop in gain of 0.7dB. This can be reduced to 0.17dB by doubling the number of switch positions. Each feeder should be accurately matched at the antenna.

A 4:1 balun transformer is used as a phase-reversing device but alternatively it would be possible to switch in an extra $\lambda/2$ of feeder or merely to have twice as many positions (same line lengths between them) on the phasing switch. The balun is preferred since it is cheaper and more compact than the extra cable, particularly for the lower-frequency bands, and a separate reversing switch is more convenient because

the easiest method of adjustment is to find a null and then reverse the phase of one element.

With reduced spacing between the elements the possible gain increases to 5dB along the line of the elements, but at the same time shrinks to only just over 0dB at right-angles to this, being 4.6dB and 1.1dB respectively for a spacing of 0.25λ. For spacings less than about 0.35λ, phasing lines used in this way usually result in unequal currents as explained on p90, and a lumped network of the type shown in Fig 5.21 is preferable.

Even with wide spacing, one result of paralleling the feeders will be to present a mismatch at the transmitter and if necessary a separate pi-network can be used to correct this. For simple in- or out-of-phase operation the antenna may be designed to have an impedance $Z_0/\sqrt{2}$ or $\sqrt{2} Z_0$ so that, if the feeders are even or odd multiples respectively of $\lambda/2$, the transmitter sees an impedance equal to Z_0. With close-spacing and phasing by the method of Fig 5.21, the impedance varies with phase angle and use of an ATU is advisable, the feeder lengths being made equal to a multiple of $\lambda/2$.

The elements need not be identical and for the lower-frequency bands various assortments of antennas, towers and mast can be pressed into service as described on p136. With this type of array there is little benefit to be obtained from spacings much less than $\lambda/8$, and even then the gain is only along the line of the array. Even with this restriction the possibility of useful gain even on 'top band' exists for some locations.

The VK2ABQ antenna, either in its basic form (Fig 12.3) or using V-shaped elements, is suitable for use in the vertical position since it meets the 'billowing out' requirement without demanding excessive height. Two could be mounted at right-angles for all-round coverage but there is little point in view of better ways of using four such elements as described below. From 90° to 120° of rotation is possible with suitable arrangements of four guys, which is more than adequate if the beam is reversible. Half-wave elements may also be fed at their lower ends using the modified Zepp feed or a tuning unit as shown in Figs 13.2(a) and (b), though a coaxial end-feed similar to that featured in Fig 13.9 is recommended as it offers

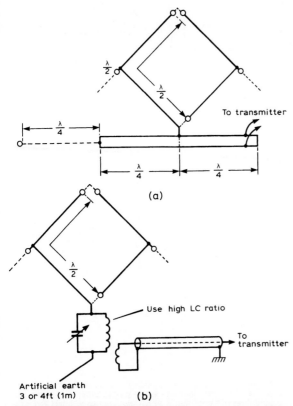

Fig 13.2. The two λ/2 elements of (a) or (b) may be suspended from a single pole. At (a) the modified (G6CJ) Zepp feed is used and either an open-wire feeder or coaxial feeder with 4:1 balun may be connected as shown. An artificial earth such as the λ/4 wire shown dotted may be advisable. At (b) a high LC ratio (eg 25pF at 14MHz) is desirable. The length of the artificial-earth wire is not critical. Matching is adjusted by movement of the coupling coil

a number of advantages, especially in respect of bandwidth. A 1:1 balun provides the antiphase voltages, and the elements share a common two-radial ground plane or counterpoise.

Three radiators spaced in the region of 0.15 to 0.35λ may be used two at a time or grouped so that two are used in parallel to form one of the elements; this allows direction to be switched in 60° steps and makes available a gain fairly close to 4dB for any direction. In both of these cases the beam remains effectively a two-element system.

Beams with three or more elements

The phasing of three or more wide-spaced elements (or separate antennas) is feasible, providing a gain equal to the number of elements (p23) if all are fed with equal power. The effect of unequal power division has already been analysed for two elements (p113) and shown to have little effect for quite large ratios, provided the elements are of equal performance. The easiest way to share power between elements or groups of elements is by splitting it equally, eg power is

shared equally between, say, elements 1 and 2. We thus have a group of two elements out of a set of three, one of which is left over, so that with further equal division of power, half the total goes to 3 and half to 1 + 2; in other words, 1 and 2 each receive only a quarter of the power. This reduces the gain from 4.77dB to 4.61dB, a negligible difference, so that there is no urgent need to resort to the complexity of more accurate power division.

If a number of scattered elements are co-ordinated in this way the overall pattern is likely to vary greatly with the beam heading, and large lobes in unwanted directions can be expected. Large arrays can in general be spaced and phased to provide either maximum gain or minimum sidelobes, but amateur requirements are more likely to be met by closely spaced groups of elements and, given sufficient space, up to four such groups spaced well apart from each other. Beyond this size the cost per decibel is escalating rapidly, particularly in terms of space, labour and complexity.

A number of groupings of up to four closely spaced elements have been subjected elsewhere to a computer study [2] which established a clear margin of superiority for an arrangement forming the basis for Fig 13.3(a); this shows what is in effect a three-element array, a pair at opposite corners of the λ/4 square being used in parallel as the main radiator and the other two operating as a reflector and director respectively. The recommendations require equal currents in all four elements with phase differences of minus and plus 110° respectively from the driven element, but there is some doubt as to whether this specification could be met adequately with parasitic operation of the elements.

The use of four separate feeders allows (a) beam directions to be switched instantaneously without using relays, and (b) either remote tuning of parasitic elements or the setting-up of correct operating conditions for driven operation by means of phasing and matching devices located in the shack, including the possibility of setting up different patterns for transmission and reception.

Fig 13.4 suggests two methods of achieving the correct phases and amplitudes, one based on the lumped-constant phasing line of Fig 5.21 and the other on switched lengths of feeder cable in conjunction with variable couplings in the common tuning unit for adjustment of amplitudes. Phase and amplitude adjustments are interdependent in both cases, this being an intrinsic feature of close-spaced beams; this causes problems which escalate rapidly with the number of elements and imposes major demands on the skill of the operator.

Of the two alternatives, (a) provides more flexibility and precision but may be difficult to adjust in practice. Parasitic operation is simplest and should be acceptable provided the currents in all four elements are equal within 20% or so. The computer results predict a gain of 6.4dB with back and minor lobes not exceeding −24.4dB compared with the forward field. The beamwidth is just under 90° so that with a switched beam a loss of nearly an average S-unit can be expected in the worst directions, though the gain exceeds 5dB over a total of some 240°.

Most of the drop in signal for the 45° directions can be

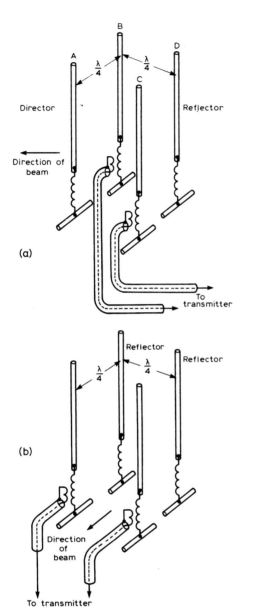

Fig 13.3. (a) Three-element Yagi making optimum use of four λ/4 elements. BC are fed with equal currents in the same phase, A and D being respectively advanced and retarded by 60° from the antiphase condition. For best performance the currents should be approximately equal in all four elements. Artificial earths have been substituted for the extensive systems of ground radials assumed in the reference, but the principles should be equally applicable to all types of element, including those of Fig 13.2, assuming correct amplitudes and phases. Computed gain from reference [2] is 6.4dB and suppression of back radiation is 18dB or better for all angles. If only one direction is required the elements may be rearranged in line as a four-element Yagi to obtain slightly better gain and directivity. (b) Alternative two-element configuration analogous to quad antenna. Gain is reduced to 5.1dB but the 45° shift in direction means that by using both alternatives 5dB gain can be obtained even in the worst directions

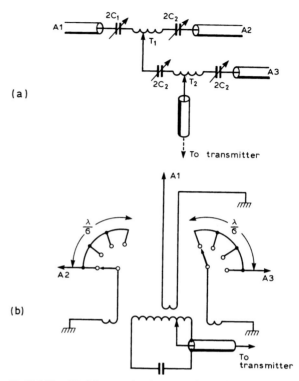

Fig 13.4. Simplified diagram showing two methods of power sharing and phase adjustment for three antennas or elements. (a) uses two resonant lines; C1 determines power ratio between 1 and 2 and C2 between (1 + 2) and 3. Taps provide phase adjustment. At (b) variable-length lines are provided for phase adjustment and amplitudes are adjusted by varying the couplings; to simplify the diagram switching is shown for one pole only, but both poles must be switched as in Fig 13.1 and unused portions of lines disconnected. Phase reversal is obtained by changing over the leads to the coupling coils

avoided by switching to a different configuration, Fig 13.3(b); in this case adjacent elements are paired and the array becomes almost the exact equivalent of a two-element vertically polarised cubical quad having an element spacing of λ/4. This changes the beam heading by 45° and from the computer results the gain becomes 5.1dB with 16.6dB discrimination against all back and minor lobes. Though not as good as before, this performance is still acceptable by most standards. Changing to a different configuration for the intermediate direction complicates not only the switching but also the phasing and matching systems, though only to the extent of requiring an eight-position switch and denuding the junk-box of a few more components.

From arguments presented in earlier chapters one might expect a spacing of 0.25λ to be excessive. This tends to be confirmed by figures for 0.167λ spacing which show an improvement of 0.2dB in gain and 4dB in discrimination, though the author of the reference considers the extra gain will probably be offset due to the larger currents. This seems open to doubt (unless possibly there are large earth losses) in view of performance figures established in Chapter 5 for

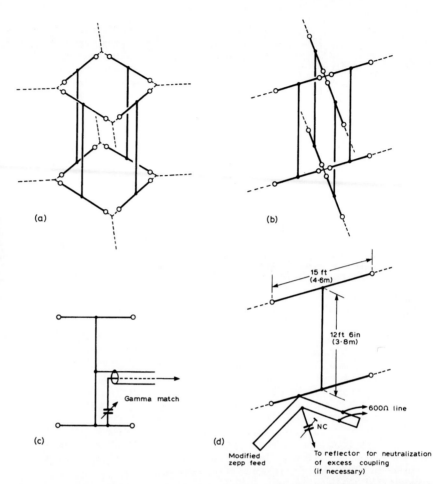

Fig 13.5. (a) and (b) show two ways of supporting short end-loaded vertical dipole elements. Sufficient loading can be accommodated in case (a) for a vertical dimension of about 0.18λ, and some further reduction in height is possible in case (b). (c) and (d) show two methods of feed and typical dimensions for 14MHz are given at (d). The Zepp feed is the same as for Fig 13.2(a) but it is worth noting that the feed does not have to be attached to the end of the radiator; connected as shown here it may provide a better match or improved bandwidth or both. Various connections are possible but two-element operation analogous to Fig 13.3(b) is recommended. Adjacent ends should be connected in parallel and share a common feeder

close spacings in the case of horizontal elements, even small ones with low radiation resistances; the more important point to emerge, however, is that *spacing is non-critical*. Even for a spacing of 0.333λ the gain only drops to 5.6dB, and for very close spacings the basic geometrical principles featured in earlier chapters must be assumed applicable; in effect gain and directivity remain unchanged *in principle* down to zero spacing, long before which losses or bandwidth become unacceptable.

It is reasonably certain that an array of this type could be erected in a very small space, provided it is not too closely surrounded by buildings etc. As in the case of horizontal arrays with comparable element spacings, it is evident that such arrays can be designed to operate efficiently at a number of frequencies spaced over a bandwidth of at least one octave, subject to the limitations of the individual elements which can make use of one or other of the multibanding methods described in earlier chapters.

It is believed that the systems just described come close to being optimum designs of vertical array; it is likely a number of amateur requirements can best be met by two, three or four such groups suitably phased. Many variations on these themes

are possible and Fig 13.5 shows two ways of constructing an efficient low-cost array using very short end-loaded dipoles supported catenary fashion from four light poles. For a 14MHz array, 15ft (4.6m) bamboo canes would be adequate except that antenna wires at about knee height above the lawn tend to be unpopular (even if they fail to cause RF burns).

In the case of monopoles, earth losses can be reduced and gain improved by increases in base height up to about 0.2λ. Fig 13.5(c) shows a form of gamma match which has been used successfully with a long Yagi array composed of similar elements. One suggestion is that coaxial feedlines should be brought away at right-angles into the centre of the array, then bunched together and brought out midway between two of the elements, preferably keeping them horizontal in order to minimise possible coupling between elements and feedlines. The usual precautions against feeder radiation (p53) should in any case be observed.

Fig 13.6 shows a 'monopole' variant of this arrangement likely to be more convenient; with a substantial amount of end-loading the current distribution is relatively uniform and the 2:1 advantage in terms of radiation resistance of dipoles over ground-based monopoles (p119) largely disappears so

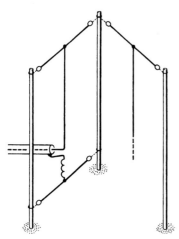

Fig 13.6. This shows part of a monopole version of Fig 13.5, allowing even more reduction in physical height. The elements may be inverted to increase the effective height and can be fed as at Fig 13.9(a)

that a series-tuned 0.34λ monopole could be roughly equated to a 0.5λ dipole. A simple low-cost version of this can be based on the use of a single feeder with plugs and sockets or clips for pairing the elements or making them into directors or reflectors as required, but to achieve the convenience of switched beam headings it is necessary either to use four feeders or for example a Ledex-type switch.

Manual operation is possible also in the case of dipoles whose lower ends are accessible; in this case the modified Zepp feed may be used (p49) in conjunction with Fig 13.5(b) but switching at high-voltage points is difficult but, for a switched system, Fig 13.6 is preferred to Fig 13.5. Any accessible points of high RF voltage must of course be well protected from accidental contact.

The above systems are all by way of suggestions inspired by the computer study in conjunction with practical experience of some of the types òf elements described, and it is believed they should be near-optimum systems, a number of amateur requirements being best met by two, three, or four of such four-element groups suitably spaced and phased together.

A 4 × 4 system with group spacing upwards of 0.8λ could be expected to provide some 11–12dB of gain, thereby more than making up for the deficiencies of vertical polarisation (at least for 14MHz) as compared with good conventional horizontal rotary beams at heights of 40–50ft (12–15m). The height required for the vertical array is dictated largely by the need to prevent accidental contact with the lower wires of the system, though this also helps in other respects. Good results on 14MHz could be expected with a height of about 6ft (1.8m) plus, say, 1–2ft (0.3–0.6m) clearance for the counterpoises, though a loss of some 2–4dB might accrue from (a) extra ground losses and (b) the smaller array factor for the antenna plus its image. Unipole operation with T-shaped elements and an inductively loaded counterpoise is assumed as in Fig 13.6.

One practical point to be noted is the risk of overcoupling

when the ends of elements are brought close together as in Figs 13.5 and 13.6. A modest degree of overcoupling can be taken care of automatically with all elements driven, but with parasitic operation there is an optimum coupling. This will usually not be the same for a director as for a reflector, though a reasonable compromise in the case of a three-element reversible beam should be possible. If coupling is excessive the top-loading wires can usually be reduced by at least 20% without ill-effect, except the need for a small loading coil at the top of the vertical wire in order to restore resonance. Alternatively for monoband operation it may be sufficient to increase the spacing somewhat, though it should not exceed λ/3. The remaining method is neutralisation (p99) which is very simple in some cases, eg Fig 13.5(b) with lower-end Zepp feed as shown at (d), since the 'hot' ends are all brought to the same point and an antiphase voltage is available from the opposite side of the open feedline.

The above principles have also been applied to some vertical arrays based on the quad. These offer a number of advantages and form the subject of the next section, but reference should first be made to one other type of array which uses a ring of switched elements. This has appeared in various forms such as the 'QH' (quick-heading) beam illustrated in Fig 13.7. Eight beam headings are obtained by switching any single or any adjacent pair of parasitic elements to act as directors. The reference [3] from which this diagram was taken quotes a gain of 6.5dB but states that 'its construction is, however, somewhat complicated'.

This need not be the case and in one version, designed (though never quite completed) by the author, the parasitic elements were arranged as in Fig 13.5, the driven element being supported in the centre of the ring by cords from the four

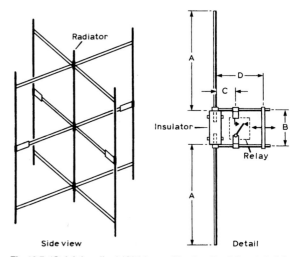

Fig 13.7. 'Quick-heading' (QH) beam. The length of the stub D is adjusted to provide reflector operation of each element in the outer ring and length C is adjusted so that closing of the relay contacts results in director action. By converting any one element or adjacent pair of elements into directors, eight beam headings are obtained at intervals of 45°. B is not critical. See Table 13.1 for dimensions. (Antennenbuch)

Table 13.1. Dimensions for QH-beam [3]

Band (MHz)	Radiator length	Distance of radiator from parasitic elements (all lengths in cm)	A	B	C	D
14	1027	253	460	10	40	90
21	686	170	307	7	27	60
28	512	126	230	5	20	45

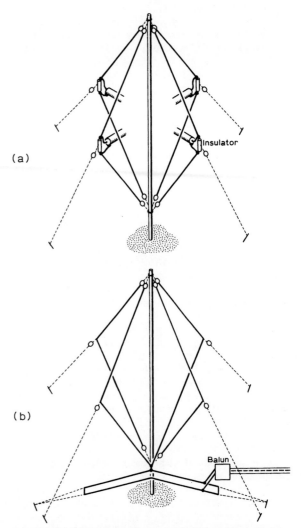

(a)

(b)

corners which also carried wire crosses for end-loading. Lower-end Zepp feed was intended, and such an arrangement is attractive since directional switching from the shack is obtained with only one feeder and four relays, though it lacks some of the sophistication of the four-feeder system. One can also have a 'poor man's version' without relays, assuming access to the lower ends of the parasitic elements so that lengths can be altered manually.

From inspection there seems no obvious reason to expect four parasitic elements to show a marked advantage over three. The case of a triangular group of three elements with a fourth in the middle was included in the computer study quoted earlier, and found to be little better than three elements on their own which had a gain of 4.35dB and a front/back ration of 10.45dB. Although the cases are not precisely comparable, it seems likely that the 'pig in the middle' arrangements (at their best) waste one element, but some readers may find the idea sufficiently attractive to be worth pursuing.

The half-loop vertical array

The author has long been intrigued by the idea of integrating a high-gain beam antenna with the guy-wire system so that the mast and the antenna support each other, but some partial solutions of this problem using horizontal polarisation fell a long way short of the main objectives. These included the possibility of using much less substantial structures which have little visual impact, are easy to erect, are light enough to cause no damage even if they blow down, and are unlikely to require planning consent. This goal has now been largely achieved by the use of vertical arrays consisting of four half-loops mutually at right-angles and suspended from a single pole: Fig 13.8. As an additional feature the beam is intended to be switchable in any direction. With all these advantages the observed loss of one S-unit compared with a horizontal beam at 40ft (12m) (p164) may be thought a small price to pay. If the user is prepared to dispense with remote beam switching or is able to devise a satisfactory switch for use at points of high RF voltage, the arrangement shown at (b) is preferred. There is in this case no need to support the weight of feeders and a much more slender mast structure is possible; this uses the same method of feed as Fig 13.2(a).

An attempt to realise similar objectives has been described by UA3IAR [4] who uses a pair of horizontally polarised diamond-shaped quad loops at right-angles. These are supported by a single mast so that the sides act as guy wires, and looking down from above one sees an X configuration.

Fig 13.8. This array uses four vertical half-loops suspended from a single pole, with the top portions of the loops forming part of the guy-wire system. In the preferred arrangement, diagonally opposite pairs are fed in phase as the driven element, the other two elements being tuned as reflector and director. The equivalent quad configuration, analogous to Fig 13.3(b), may also be used. For 360° directional switching the four feeders may be brought into the shack or a 'switchbox' may be mounted on the mast. The arrangements shown in Fig 13.2(a) and (b) can also be adapted, assuming access to the lower end and the use of plug-and-socket connections

Inevitably this suffers from the disadvantages of X-beams in general (p95) and, referring to Fig 5.4, the shape of the published radiation pattern suggests a phase-angle ratio φ/φ_0 of 1.8, corresponding to a gain of only 3dB. If it is necessary to lose an S-point anyway, it seems to the author that given the choice one might as well combine it with the advantages of low height and, incidentally, vastly greater reductions of rear and minor lobes, assuming the results of the computer study [2] to be applicable despite the bends in the elements.

The basic problems with X-beams are low radiation resistance and large dips in the radiation pattern with zero front/back ratio for the 45° directions as explained in Chapter 5. Both of these are avoided by changing to vertical polarisation as in Fig 13.8 since maximum current is now in the middle (or perhaps one should say at the side corners) where separation is maximum. Although each quarter-loop on its own produces radiation in all three planes, on considering the whole of each element one finds that everything cancels except the wanted vertical components. What we now have is virtually identical with the 'second choice' (quad-like) configuration for the four vertical elements which emerged in the course of the earlier discussion.

In the case of the vertically polarised quad there is no need for the elements to be joined at the top corner; insulating the top ends of all four wires leaves one free to connect the bottom ends so that either the quad configuration can be retained or an attempt made to simulate the optimum Yagi configuration of the computer study referred to earlier. Both configurations were used successfully with no observable difference in terms of signal strength. However, because it uses pairs of wires in parallel for both elements, the quad is much superior in respect of bandwidth, a fact initially obscured by the narrow bandwidth of the Zepp feed.

Tested over a long period as a direct replacement for a horizontally polarised quad at the same height (40ft), the array shown in Fig 13.8(b) was found to be down on average by one 'average' S-point (3 to 4dB), the variability of results, plus-or-minus one S-point, being typical of comparisons between horizontal and vertical antennas. The most interesting feature, however, was the fact that *when brought down almost to ground level the performance of the vertical antenna remained equally good.*

The possibility of efficient beams needing nothing more than a fishing rod tied to a fence post for support was an exciting prospect, especially as two such arrays suitably phased should suffice for recovery of the lost S-unit and would not require planning consent, but there were some problems. These arise in the case of Fig 13.8(b) as a result of high RF voltages at the lower ends of the elements which make it difficult to switch them for beam rotation. Accidental contact must be prevented and disposing of the stub can be difficult. On the other hand (a) requires large quantities of coaxial cable, some of which would have to be supported by something stronger than a fishing rod whilst a lot more will be exposed to strong RF fields.

Some readers have successfully tackled these problems but the situation has been completely transformed by the advent of the '*nearly* zero-length' single-wire feed [9, 10]. This is explained on p47, and Fig 13.9 illustrates its application to the present problem. Moving a short distance upwards along each element, a point is found where the radiation resistance equals the Z_0 of the wire, the large value of inductive reactance associated with it being tuned out by a small series capacitance. In this case (21MHz) it is about 9pF, the impedance for the two wires in parallel being stepped down from an estimated 6000Ω to about 300. This allows

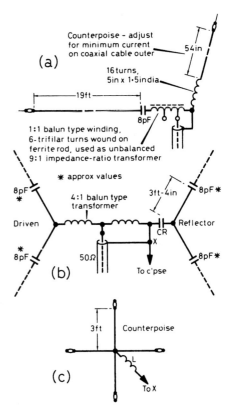

Fig 13.9. (a) Basic 'zero length' single-wire feeder system using short resonant counterpoise. The 'zero length' is between the transformer and the capacitor. By making it finite as at (b), the capacitor, together with the high voltage on the far side of it, is pushed away from the junction so that the wires can be switched as in Fig 13.10. (b) Application of (a) to a single-pole-mounted, switchable, four-quadrant, directional 21MHz array based on Fig 13.8 but using short, matched single-wire lines to keep high RF voltages away from the switching. CR tunes reflector by resonating with the single-wire feeders (which in the reflector case are 'inductive connections to ground' so the inductance has to be removed). (c) Counterpoise details. Four radials (each 3ft long) are used for reasons of symmetry. L is eight turns, 2.75in diameter, 6in long, wound over fishing rod extension

four-quadrant directional switching to be achieved by means of a pair of ordinary double-pole reversing relays as shown in Fig 13.10, though switching should not be attempted with RF power applied.

In the first test of this system (14MHz) the change in SWR over a 2% band was barely detectable and the front/back ratio remained in excess of 30dB over more than 100kHz. The use of two widely spaced wires in parallel almost doubles the bandwidth and, although this has been halved by the bending of the wires, the Q for a single element with a wire diameter of only 1mm comes to about 14 which is very acceptable. Moreover, viewing the wires in parallel (for ease of calculation) the radiation resistance is about 40Ω and the losses 0.9Ω (pp9, 26), giving an efficiency of 97.8%, so that if necessary much thinner wire could be used before the drop in performance becomes noticeable. The effective spacing between elements

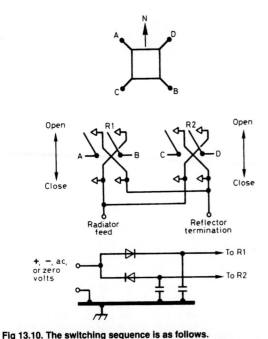

Fig 13.10. The switching sequence is as follows.
R1, R2 both open, BD driven, so beam heading EAST
R1 closed, R2 open, AD driven, so beam heading NORTH
R1 open, R2 closed, BC driven, so beam heading SOUTH
R1, R2 both closed, AC driven, so beam heading WEST
Note that relay wires need to be well bypassed and filtered; also that there is the possibility of two-wire control for four directions as shown below

is about 0.16λ and, when tuning for maximum 'nominal' front/back ratio, the losses, though nearly doubled when allowance is made for operation as a beam, are still very small. Radiation resistance (though now the total for the two elements) is much the same as before, from which can be deduced a signal loss of only 0.5dB for a wire gauge of 30swg, making this an excellent basis for an 'invisible' antenna.

Further advantages of the new method include the 'pushing out of reach' of high RF voltages since these now only appear in full strength on the upper side of the capacitors, though except with low powers accidental contact still needs to be prevented. Another aspect of this is reduced coupling, to the extent of correcting an overcoupling tendency previously experienced with the quad configuration.

In order not to raise unduly the hopes of others similarly handicapped by light sandy soil and a heavily wooded environment, it has to be said that the results quoted earlier were obtained in fairly open farming country with heavy clay soil and, for low-angle propagation, the relative performance of vertical antennas has been consistently about 6dB worse than at the earlier location. This underscores the advice to carry out tests (p164) and and casts doubt on the oft-repeated assertion that 'vertical antennas are good low-angle radiators'. This depends on the environment but in a location such as the one just described the most-flattering description would perhaps be 'good *medium-angle* radiators with a useful DX potential

so long as the required radiation angle is average or above'. This is illustrated by the following experience with the switched 14MHz version of the Fig 13.9 array. This disclosed the existence of a small but interesting horizontally polarised *low-angle mode*, associated with low antenna heights.

The mode is bidirectional at right-angles to the vertical beam and comes about as demonstrated by Fig 13.11. It will be seen that, if one considers the top and bottom halves of the antenna separately, there is a small horizontal component resulting from the phase difference between reflector and driven elements which tends to produce a figure-of-8 pattern at right angles to the main beam. The 'top' and 'bottom' contributions should cancel each other but, if the height and the angle of radiation are low enough, the 'bottom' is less effective than the 'top' so cancellation is incomplete.

An accurate analysis of this mode would be difficult and time-consuming, but from inspection an advantage of about 16dB has been 'guesstimated' in favour of the vertical mode so this must have been propagating very badly indeed to account for an apparent switch-over to the horizontal mode which occurred on two or three occasions towards the end of long path openings to VK! This manifested itself in the form of stronger signals when the beam was switched to north or south, although the westerly heading had been best earlier in the contact. It should perhaps be added that these openings had almost certainly been prolonged and inefficient propagation from G6XN greatly assisted by a large rhombic at the VK end of the path. Using vertical and horizontal test antennas the two modes were clearly identifiable in the case of the ground-wave, the horizontal component being fairly strong, though the difference was not quantifiable. To conclude this account it should perhaps be stressed that the relatively poor low-angle performance is a feature of the location, not the antenna. There are lots of much better locations around but also worse ones, and horizontal modes are not affected.

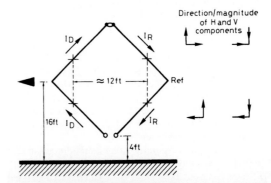

Fig 13.11. Side view of array with equal currents I_D, I_R, analysed into H and V components. The distance x, y between 'centres of gravity' of the current distributions is $\lambda/6$ (approx) so for zero signal in the back direction we have $I_R = -I_D \angle 60°$. Note that in free space the upper horizontal components are cancelled by the lower ones, but the height to 'centres of gravity' of the current distributions is 20ft and only 12ft respectively, so assuming F is proportional to height, the cancellation is only 60% complete for the above example (f = 14MHz). Rough estimates suggest a 14dB advantage for the vertical mode for the same efficiency of propagation (typical height assumed)

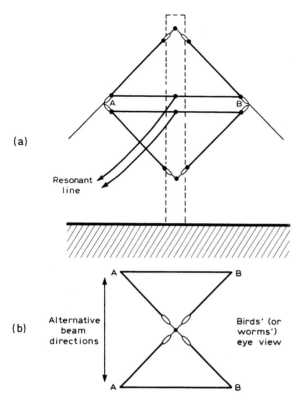

(a)

Resonant line

(b)

A   B
Alternative beam directions

Birds' (or worms') eye view

A   B

Fig 13.12. Arrangement based on DJ4VM quad is completely symmetrical, multiband operation being achieved by the use of resonant feeders. For satisfactory performance at the higher frequencies it is essential to use the 'quad' configuration, ie the half-loops must be paired as at (b). The length of the feedlines AB is not critical and they may be routed via a switch box (or anchoring points) located near the mast

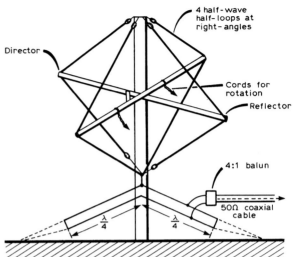

4 half-wave half-loops at right-angles

Director

Cords for rotation

Reflector

4:1 balun

50Ω coaxial cable

$\frac{\lambda}{4}$ $\frac{\lambda}{4}$

Fig 13.13. Rotatable array using four vertically polarised half-loops similar to those of Fig 13.2(a). The optimum configuration of Figs 13.3(a) and 13.9 is applicable in this case also, lower-end Zepp feed being more convenient for rotation. Dimensions of Fig 13.2(a) are applicable and any type of feeder may be used. For 14MHz the balun should be located 40in (102cm) from the end of the stub. Driven elements are 33ft (10.1m). Reflector and director lengths typically 31ft (9.4m) and 34ft (10.4m) respectively but should be found by experiment

Yagi arrays with short end-loaded elements

Elements of the type used in Figs 13.5 and 13.6 can be used to form long Yagi arrays as in Fig 13.14 or added to arrays such as those just described to provide increased gain in a particular direction, or more than one direction provided elements not in use are thrown out of resonance. Good results have been obtained on 7MHz over the long path from the UK to Australia using up to six elements suspended from one or two catenaries, the lower ends being at times only a foot or so and never more than 6ft (1.8m) from the ground. The basic element size was 25ft (7.6m) for the vertical portion and 30ft (9.1m) for the horizontal loading sections, one or both of the lower arms being bent back or the vertical portion reefed in to obtain director action. Best results were obtained with the director elements shortened so that the currents decreased by about 30% from each element to the one in front, the spacing being λ/4.

It was the role of this antenna to be used exclusively for maintaining good long-path communication with VK during three sunspot minimum periods, being rolled up and stored away as soon as 14MHz conditions returned to normal. Each time the configuration was different, though favouring the use of directors, and with two or more of these the reflector if used was almost 'dead' so that it made little or no contribution to the forward field. The design was empirical, bearing little resemblance to one produced by G0GSF who used a computer to take the guesswork out of it [11], ending up with the two-element design illustrated in Fig 13.15 and the computed

With arrays such as Figs 13.8 and 13.9 symmetry is important for cancellation of the unwanted modes. On the other hand, Fig 13.12, derived from the DJ4VM type of quad (p187), is less critical in this respect but involves more weight and windage so that a stronger support is needed. Advantages of this antenna include the realisation of 3–4dB of extra gain at 28MHz, assuming a fundamental resonance of 14MHz.

Fig 13.13 shows a rotatable arrangement which is cheap and simple to implement but requires the use of what is in effect an ordinary quad spider, though the four arms can be of lighter-than-usual construction.

A fully rotatable array requires either a support substantial enough not to need guy wires or, following a suggestion by G6BZ, hanging from the centre of a catenary suspended between two large trees or a house and a tree.

In some cases mechanical rotation may be preferred to the greater complexity of switching, and has the further merit of avoiding the dips in performance (up to 2dB) in between the beam headings. Replacement of the Zepp by coaxial feed as in Fig 13.9 is strongly recommended, and options include the use of two feeders for beam reversal, possibly with remote tuning of the reflector, though this has yet to be investigated.

Fig 13.14. Vertical Yagi array using short end-loaded elements. Height is not critical, no drop-off in performance being noticed even with 'sag' to within 1ft (30cm) of the ground. The reflector and director are tuneable by adjusting the length of the verticals or the span of the lower horizontal wires. Alternative sets of dimensions for driven elements and reflectors are available from Fig 13.16. Alternative feeder systems which have been used successfully include those of Figs 13.5(c) and (d). Additional directors may be used to fill whatever space is available; the optimum spacing for such additions is probably about 0.35λ.

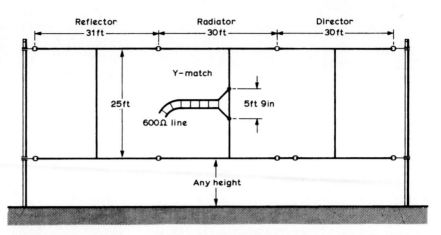

relationship between element dimensions shown in Fig 13.16. This indicates considerable latitude in respect of element shape, inclusive of the dimensions shown in Fig 13.14. For Fig 13.15, the computed gain and front-to-back ratio is given by Fig 13.17, and Fig 13.18 shows his recommended matching circuit, though this might have to be modified somewhat to suit a different set of dimensions.

The antenna is envisaged as a "simple wire-element Yagi with shortened elements hanging vertically from light nylon line", the elements being "light, almost invisible, and their wind loading minimal". He comments on the excellent

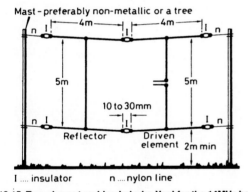

Fig 13.15. Two-element end-loaded wire Yagi for the 14MHz band

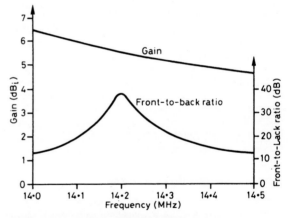

Fig 13.17. Computed gain and front-to-back ratio of the two-element end-loaded wire Yagi for the 14MHz band

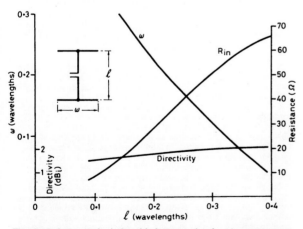

Fig 13.16. Computed relationship between *l* and *w* at resonance as well as the variation in the input resistance and directivity of the end-loaded dipole

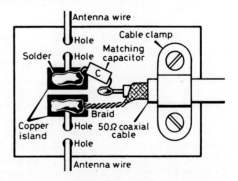

Fig 13.18. Single-sided glassfibre PCB at the feedpoint, potted in silicone rubber. C is 220pF for the 14MHz band

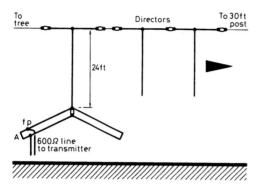

Fig 13.19. Inverted ground-plane array

matching, with a VSWR bandwidth in excess of 350kHz, and the excellent radiating performance which provided regular contact with ZS using 50W of SSB.

Compared with Figs 13.8–13.13 this is more modest in its height demands and also has the advantage of being able to use widely available supports such as trees and chimneys. On the other hand, in its original long-Yagi form this could be particularly useful to someone with a long narrow strip of ground and severe height restrictions, though a seven-element 14MHz array scaled from the 7MHz design was disappointing to the extent of being 2–3 S-points down (at the good location) into VK compared with a typical horizontal array. Into South America the drop was only one S-point, however, and a computer study would no doubt improve matters.

Fig 13.19 shows another vertical wire beam which was tested successfully despite the very short matching stub, performance being comparable with that of Fig 13.8. This would become much more attractive end-fed with coaxial cable (Fig 13.9), matching data being obtainable from Fig 4.29 using a rough 'guesstimate' of *R* based on Fig 2.5.

Asymmetrical dipole arrays

Attention was drawn in Chapter 4 to the disadvantages of using λ/4 radials, a major advantage of using much shorter ones being the ease with which antennas constructed in this way, such as Figs 11.12 or 11.19, can be pressed into service as beam elements (Fig 13.20). This is believed to be the simplest possible method of constructing a beam antenna; they can be used in the face of severe height restrictions, and provide a simpler basis for evolving multiband and directionally switched arrays since these functions can be provided by tuning units at ground level. An interesting aspect is the portability of the elements complete with their ground systems, such that one could even dismantle a directionally switched, three-element array and re-erect it, say, as a five-element Yagi in some fixed direction in less time than it takes to rotate the average horizontal beam! Similarly, there is little effort involved if they have to be taken down when not in use. With this type of parasitic element there seem to be no ground losses, due presumably to the distributed nature of the signal injection which does not demand a return path to the ground.

A disadvantage of monopoles and the reason why compared with the dipoles of Figs 13.14 or 13.15 they have to be a second choice is a loss of some 2–3dB in performance. assuming the base to be at a convenient height such as 3 or 4ft (0.9–1.2m). This is because the antenna with its image resembles a single dipole rather than a collinear pair, thus broadening the pattern in the vertical plane and reducing the gain. This can be overcome by raising the base height to some 12ft (3.7m) or so but dipole arrays then become relatively more attractive, except possibly in respect of direction switching and multiband operation.

The drop in average performance of vertical beams compared with horizontal beams at 35–40ft (11–12m) only emerged clearly from tests over a period of time, being roughly 4dB for the dipole and 7dB for the low-height monopole arrays, the differences being extremely variable.

Multiband beams

The DJ4VM quad described earlier is probably the best choice if the necessary conditions can be met and, since a

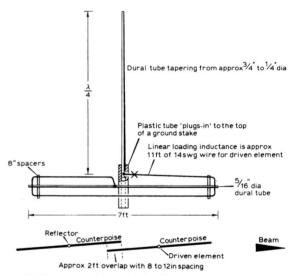

Fig 13.20. (a) Constructional details of monopole with short inductively loaded counterpoise. The antenna may be fed with 50Ω coaxial cable at point X (outer to counterpoise) but do not expect an SWR of less than about two unless additional impedance transformation is used. Alternatively the feeder may be connected through a balun to a series-tuned triangular coupling unit placed in the angle at X. (b) Plan view of two-element array; the only critical dimension is that of the driven element, the lower end of which should be at earth potential to minimise coupling into the feeder. A director may be added; satisfactory results were obtained with the director and reflector resonated at 14.8 and 13.9MHz respectively, the reflector and driven element counterpoise rods being increased in length to 10ft (3m) and swivelled towards each other so as to make the reflector current equal to that in the driven element. Linear loading can be used as in Fig 11.19 but for the driven element the author has also used four 40in (102cm) radials with a five-turn loading coil, 3in (76mm) diameter and 2in (15mm) long, overwound with a single-turn coupling coil. For directional switching the driven element may be surrounded by at least four parasitic elements, and relays used to short-circuit part of the loading inductances

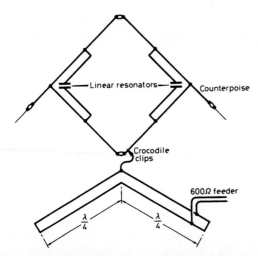

Fig 13.21. Multiband form of the basic vertically polarised element, showing method of feeding and use of counterpoise on 28MHz. Note that two crocodile clips are required in order to drive two adjacent vertical members in phase. Switching of capacitors (not shown) is required for 21/28MHz

lower height may be acceptable, it is easier to recommend than the standard quad with its poor reputation for survival, the extra gain on 28MHz being an important bonus.

Multibanding is generally more difficult with vertical antennas, particularly beams, since each pole of an asymmetrical radiator needs different treatment and balanced feeders, which are only recommended if they can be run more-or-less at right-angles to the radiator, get in the way of beam rotation.

There are various single-element multiband verticals on the market as well as possibilities for the constructor, and if enough space is available any of these can be used as the basis for phased arrays as explained earlier. Beyond this there are various dual-resonance possibilities, and Fig 13.21 (though only one wire of each element is visible) represents a triband version of Fig 13.8(b) which was successfully tested [12]. As illustrated by Fig 13.22, this exploits the principle of tapered spacing described on p129, and it should be noted that the counterpoises (which can be short and inductively loaded) are needed only for 28MHz where a ground reference has to be provided so that the resonators can operate as phase inverters. In this case there is no alternative to the Zepp feed except a base tuner, though the possibility of devising a dual-resonance version of Fig 13.11 is not excluded. For stable tuning the resonators must be rigid, spacers at 6 or 8in intervals being suggested.

Dual-resonant 'ground-plane' type elements based on 'optimised' traps (p131), linear resonators or some other form of base tuner can be recommended, subject to duplication or retuning of the radials. Equalisation of coupling on all bands may call for some ingenuity but, in one's favour, any length of radial less than $\lambda/4$ can be used on any band and probably, more often than not, the feedpoint and radials will be within reach.

For coverage of all bands from 28 to 14MHz, and possibly 10MHz, it should be possible for a fixed array to use SDL elements (p126) taped onto (or supported bowstring fashion by) fishing rods or glassfibre poles, the height required being a minimum of 17ft (20ft or more preferred) plus some ground clearance. A method of rotation has been worked out based on a 10ft radius semicircle of sockets supported by fence posts as shown in Fig 13.23; by plugging the 'fishing rods' into the appropriate sockets the beam can be rotated in 60° steps. Alternatively it should be possible (using four elements) to employ remote switching, subject to ensuring that elements not in use are adequately detuned; there will, however, be rather high voltages at the switch on 18 and 21MHz unless using two-wire loops as featured in Fig 7.6(f). This is helpful in other ways, since for the same losses the wire diameter can be halved.

Log-periodic arrays

One solution to the problem of multiband operation would be to stack three separate Yagi arrays covering 14, 21 and 28MHz directly in front instead of alongside or on top of each other. This increases the overall length but using four stacks it would be possible to obtain in this way 360° coverage with an average gain of nearly 6dB. A single fairly high support would be needed, surrounded by four shorter ones at a distance of about $\lambda/2$ at the lowest frequency.

Thus far the reader will be on familiar ground, though he may well ask, 'why not stack the beams concentrically?' Less space is needed, but to take advantage of this the outer ring of supports must be so much higher that it is almost certainly better to use more space if it is available. It must next be asked whether the arrangements just described are in fact the best way of using the space; this would almost certainly have been the case prior to the invention of log-periodic arrays which are one of the topics for consideration in the next chapter.

Though somewhat similar in appearance, the log-periodic antenna is in fact a major breakthrough since it provides about the same gain, and in addition can readily provide continuous

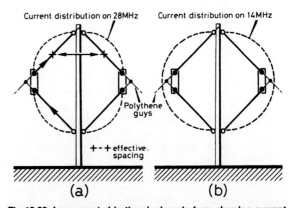

Fig 13.22. Loop erected in the single-pole form showing current distribution on 28 and 14MHz, and indicating how the effective spacing is automatically reduced on 28MHz. The feeder arrangement is not shown

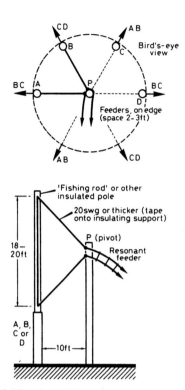

Fig 13.23. Multiband rotatable vertical array based on two SDL elements for a lowest band (MDF) of 14MHz. PABCDP is the required ground area. Four fence posts in a semicircle provide three reversible beam positions, giving all-round coverage in 60° steps. Lettered arrows indicate beam directions for corresponding posts

coverage of the entire frequency spectrum from 14–28MHz. This means that the 18 and 24MHz bands are automatically included with no need for special dispositions and, within the individual frequency bands, there are no bandwidth worries. For optimum design rather more elements (at least 12) are needed in the log-periodic case but by further increasing the number the frequency range may be extended. Alternatively the gain may be increased by as much as 2dB, but this narrows the beam by some 25% so that more arrays are needed for omnidirectional coverage, an alternative option being acceptance of inferior performance in a few directions.

The log-periodic array described on p242 can be erected vertically for this application, assuming a central pole height of at least 40ft (12m) and about 28ft (8.5m) for the outer ring. Before embarking on such a project consideration should be given to using a set of three two- or three-element reversible horizontal arrays arranged at 120° intervals around the same central pole; this should give appreciably better DX performance besides using a lot less wire and one less outer pole! The log-periodic array provides in some respects a much neater solution, but for unequivocal justification of its use in this application emphasis must again be placed on the low-height possibilities which the above example has failed to realise.

For keeping height to a minimum, monopole arrays offer

the best prospects; the earthing problem can be resolved by using separate two-radial ground planes for each element, but with a total of perhaps 12 elements for coverage of one octave the amount of wire needed is rather large, and the numerous radial wires, however useful they may be as part of the antenna system, are not an asset to the garden. As an alternative the use of (a) short counterpoise earths with loading coils (Fig 13.1) and (b) top-loading wires forming part of the catenary as in Fig 13.14 is suggested. Lengthening the array would allow the length of the loading wires to be increased, and the possibility exists of achieving a height of 10ft (3m) or less for a length of 120ft (37m) or so before the drop in performance becomes serious, provided suitable amplitudes and phase angles are maintained.

Uncertainty arises from the lack of simple explanations or formulae for log-periodic antennas which take into account the mutual couplings that play a vital role and will be considerably influenced by measures such as those just described. Nevertheless, there is evidence from the literature of a great deal of design latitude, and experiments with Fig 13.24 as a starting point may lead to a workable design. In the possible event of overcoupling this should be controllable by shortening the top loads and introducing some loading inductance at the top of the vertical wires, but this is a new field not recommended to the novice. Design formulae for straight elements will be found in the next chapter.

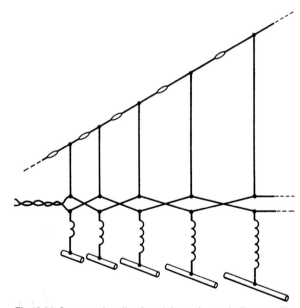

Fig 13.24. Suggested outline for miniature log-periodic array. The design principles outlined on p242 should be valid in respect of spacings and relative (electrical) lengths. The artificial grounds should be resonant at the same frequencies as the vertical wires, reactances of 500Ω being suitable. If the rods are allowed to swivel or are replaced by wires capable of being pegged to run in any direction, it should be possible to realise some control of the coupling between elements. Some inductive top-loading may be used if necessary. Note that the left-hand supporting pole can be very short

Trees and vertical beams

It is known that tree trunks can have a serious effect on vertical elements up to distances of at least a few feet, but up to the moment of writing it has not been established whether this excludes the use of trees for supporting beams such as Fig 13.8 which 'billow out' from their supports. It is also known that (a) a single row of trees at a distance of 50ft (15m) or so from a vertical antenna has negligible effect; (b) attenuation of vertically polarised waves through thick woodland occurs as discussed in Chapter 10. Arising from this it was suggested that radiation free from ground reflections might be obtained by erecting a vertical antenna just above tree-top level. This idea is easier to conceive than to implement; any readers with large woodland areas on or adjacent to their property who might like to try it out would be well advised to experiment with a simple monopole such as Fig 11.10(a) in the first instance. This could be checked at ground level for DX performance in comparison with a horizontal reference antenna and then raised above the tree tops, perhaps by using successive extensions on the principle of a chimney sweep's brush and choosing a period of calm weather!

Another method of erection, capable of being used for a beam if the trial proves a success, is shown in Fig 19.11. It is assumed that the house is in a clearing at the edge of the wood or that it is at least possible to clear a rectangular space to fit the antenna. The block and tackle is attached to a point on the tree trunk which is accessible by ladder or climbing, and if necessary the antenna support may also be secured at a higher point by means of a strategically placed projection which can be used to carry a rope over a suitable branch. Guys, even though not needed for support, will probably be needed for manoeuvring the mast into position.

Depending on height, layout and the construction of the support it may be necessary to use more than one elementary block-and-tackle. This method depends for its feasibility on the layout of the tree branches but was used successfully to erect a miniature beam above a 50ft (15m) high tree, though there were problems with open-wire feeders getting entangled in branches. This is one case where coaxial feeder is recommended rather than open-wire line.

Despite the few extra feet of support needed, a beam on the lines of Fig 13.2(a) but end-fed in accordance with Fig 13.9 in place of the Zepp feed, is recommended in preference to any of the end-loaded wire beams which require additional supports. These will be found very difficult to erect because of interference by intervening tree branches, and the problem of ensuring survival under severe storm conditions is also less likely to be resolved. One half of the array shown in Fig 13.3(b), probably with some top-loading, might also be suitable.

Radiation from closely spaced pairs of sources in opposite phase

Several of the antennas featured in this chapter are symmetrically loaded with horizontal wires or T-pieces. In such cases,

including also the use of long counterpoise wires or two-radial ground planes, it would be reasonable to expect some radiation from these parts of the system resulting in loss of power in the wanted modes. To investigate this, the problem was modelled on similar lines to the treatment of dipoles on p9, from which the ratio of power in an unwanted mode to that in the wanted mode was found to be approximately

$$P_u/P_w = t^4/4h^2$$

where t is half the length, in wavelengths, of a symmetrical loading wire or the length of one radial in the case of a two-radial ground plane, and h is the length of the radiator. Using this it is easy to demonstrate that appreciable loss is possible only in very extreme cases; consider for example a 13ft (4m) vertical at 3.5MHz with a 130ft (39.6m) counterpoise and a top load which needs to be nearly as long as the counterpoise. In order not to complicate the example, the two long wires are assumed to be at right-angles so that interaction between them is minimal: we have $h = 0.05$, $t = 0.25$ and $P_u/P_w = 0.39$ for the counterpoise and similarly for the top load. Strictly speaking, the formula should be corrected to take account of the sinusoidal current distributions in the long wires, but it will be seen that even in this very extreme case the total of the unwanted radiation is at most roughly comparable with the wanted radiation.

The loss decreases very rapidly with improvement in element shape and for a 25ft (7.6m) dipole loaded by 65ft (19.8m) at each end the loss is only 1.2% or about 0.01 of a S-unit! This is still a fairly extreme case and it seems very difficult to envisage a practical situation in which any symmetrical arrangement of loading wires or artificial earths would have a significant effect on gain or directivity.

Discussion and recommendations

A survey of the different types of antenna used by UK stations has been reported by VK3OM [7]. Out of the 147 stations worked over the long path, 56 were using horizontal beams and 36 some form of vertical antenna, *but there was not a single vertical beam*. This is a very remarkable finding, given the author's conclusion that vertical beams can often be nearly as good as the average horizontal beam at 14MHz but do not have to be put in the air, cost very little, are easily and quickly constructed, have few maintenance problems and are much less likely to lead to difficulties with neighbours or planning authorities.

In seeking the reasons for this one finds that vertical antennas have a reputation for being inefficient and noisy, there are *no* published designs of vertical beam which the author would care to recommend for 14MHz or above, and most of the amateur reference books insist on extensive systems of buried wires requiring a big investment in themselves, to say nothing of the purchase of several adjoining properties! The only alternative, according to the references, would appear to be the use of ground planes consisting of three or four $\lambda/4$ radials and suitable only for single-element monopole antennas. It is true there are some vertical dipole arrays described in the literature but here again one comes up against the unwarranted assumption that the dipoles have to be straight. This means that instead of being the easiest of all types of beam to support, since it needs only a single pole with no superstructure, the vertical array is reduced to being in most cases a non-starter.

If vertical beams are to have a fair chance it is essential to make sure that energy is not radiated from the feeder or allowed to get into the mains wiring, and this should take care of many possible sources of noise pick-up. This is particularly important, since the most frequent criticism of vertical antennas seems to be the amount of noise picked up, whereas one writer faced with this problem [6] found that the answer lay in using a screened loop, the method of its connection to the receiver being important; in other words the problem was nothing to do with vertical polarisation as such. This article should be consulted in the event that anyone is still bothered with excessive noise after taking the precautions indicated here, but it is impossible to say at this stage whether there is a residue of insoluble problems under this heading.

The choice of beam element can probably be narrowed down to centre-fed or end-fed dipoles, monopoles operating against short end-loaded counterpoises, and possibly loop arrays such as the DJ4VM quad.

Easy methods of erecting dipoles usually involve some form of shortening, and the arrangement of four right-angled elements hanging down from a single pole as in Fig 13.10, is recommended as a 'best buy', provided one can tolerate a pole height of at least 28ft (8.5m) for 14MHz. Note, however, that the support can be extremely slender (eg using 8ft by 1in (2.4m by 13mm) bamboo garden canes or fishing rods for at least the top section) since the antenna itself constitutes a large part of the guy-wire system. Possible compromises include 90° rotation using the arrangement of Fig 13.13 in conjunction with beam reversal, which requires only the use of stubs with relays for short-circuiting them in the centre of the parasitic elements.

Wire beams using short end-loaded vertical dipole or monopole elements are recommended as a 'best buy' for DX operation on the lower-frequency bands, a height of 30ft (9m) or so being sufficient for a two-element or three-element monopole array at 3.5MHz. It should be noted that short end-loaded dipoles and the recommended monopole designs are strictly equivalent for a given mean height reckoned to the 'centre of gravity' of the current distribution, ie the centre of a dipole or roughly $\lambda/12$ from the base of a monopole. Performance with vertical polarisation is affected by ground constants as discussed in Chapter 10, and the figures quoted above relate to the author's location, the ground being nearly flat farming land with heavy clay soil and no nearby obstructions.

It may be asked, 'why not use a typical horizontal beam in the vertical position?' The problem here is the one of electrical and mechanical interaction between the beam and its support as mentioned earlier. The author has, however, made tests with a horizontal beam in the early stages of erection, the mast being nearly horizontal and the beam rotated into a vertical position just clear of the ground, results being comparable with those for the dipole array described above. Quads have also been used successfully by a number of amateurs but require feeding at a side corner which tends to be inconvenient. The author has also successfully used an arrangement based on the DJ4VM type of quad, Fig 13.12(a).

The 'best buys' in their monoband form should present little difficulty even to the inexperienced, but electrically-rotatable vertical beams are an area of development which has hitherto been much neglected. The SDL array has only just emerged as a possible solution, and among other ideas the monopole approach based on 'electrotator' principles (plus, say, the use of linear resonators for multibanding) should be relatively straightforward. Even so, to 'do everything' by remote switching may require a separate set of four relays per band plus additional relays for band changing, adding up to quite a large total! In the case of a ground-based monopole system, horizontal arrays have a bigger start at the higher frequencies and to reduce this lead the whole of the 14MHz element or an equivalent length with appropriate tuning should be used in each case. Multibanding by means of linear resonators employing switched capacitors in weatherproof boxes is one suggestion, since in principle there should be no insuperable difficulty in accommodating all bands from 14–28MHz, including 18 and 24MHz but, as in the case of horizontal beams, the use of resonant feeders applied to loop elements (eg Figs 13.12 or 13.23) is likely to be less demanding.

This field is strongly recommended to the experimenter looking for a new challenge with good prospects. The possibilities are wide-ranging and the author has presented no more than a selection of those which seem most promising.

Further to highlight the possibilities of vertical arrays as well as some of the problems, consider the following scenario. An amateur receives a generous but unwanted present of a six-element rotary beam; unwanted because he has nowhere to put it. Being reluctant to hurt the feelings of the donor by failing to put it to good use, he finds himself in a dilemma until (after reading this chapter and Chapter 5) the solution becomes obvious: cutting the elements in half, they can be used to form four separate three-element vertical monopole arrays, each having a gain of 6dB compared with 9.5dB for the original, for which a boom length of 1λ has been assumed. Cut into four pieces, the boom provides the counterpoises. Suitably spaced and phased the four ground-based Yagis provide a gain of 12dB and the DX signal should be roughly equivalent to that from the original beam, supposing this to have been erected at a height of 30ft (9m). There remains the problem of beam rotation but, armed with the complete works of Heath Robinson and a good assortment of ropes and pulleys, there should be no problem in devising a solution making use of the beam rotator supplied with the antenna. An alternative method, based on the principle of running round in small circles with an element in each hand is, however, better for the figure and (if one is young and fit enough) probably quicker!

References

[1] *Antenna Theory and Design,* Vol 2, H P Williams, Pitman, London, 1966, p73.

[2] 'Simple arrays of vertical antenna elements', *The ARRL Antenna Anthology,* ARRL, 1978, p114. (Based on article by J L Lawson, W2PV, *QST* March 1971.)

[3] *Antennenbuch,* K Rothamel, Telekosmos Verlag, Stuttgart, 1968, p179.

[4] 'Quad with switchable polar diagram', L Vsevolzhskii, UA3IAR, *Radio* (USSR) No 6, 1978, pp18–19. See also 'Technical Topics', *Radio Communication* October 1978 *et seq.*

[5] *Radio Communication Handbook,* Vol 2, 5th edn, RSGB, 1977, p12.67.

[6] 'Beat the noise with a "Scoop Loop"', *The ARRL Antenna Anthology,* ARRL, 1978, p76. Material on presented in *QST* by Ben Vester, K3BC. 'Technical Topics', *Radio Communication* September 1980, p90.

[8] 'Short antennas for the lower frequencies', Yardley Beers, W0JF, *QST* September 1970.

[9] 'End feeding a Windom and related topics', 'Technical Topics', *Radio Communication* May 1991, p29.

[10] 'Ground planes, radial systems and asymmetric dipoles', *The ARRL Antenna Compendium,* Vol 3, ARRL, 1993.

[11] 'Designing end-loaded HF wire Yagis', Brian Austin, G0GSF/ZS6BKW, *Radio Communication* September 1989, p44.

[12] *Amateur Radio Techniques,* Pat Hawker, G3VA, 7th edn, RSGB, 1980, p333.

'rays

The arrays described in earlier chapters bear little resemblance to the large rhombic, curtain or log-periodic arrays often used by commercial services. For the most part these are highly sophisticated systems requiring a large amount of real estate and of relatively little direct interest to amateurs; nevertheless, the amateur with a one-acre (0.4ha) field at his disposal may be wondering just how large a rhombic has to be in order to provide a worthwhile gain compared with antennas described in earlier chapters. A number of log-periodic arrays have been successfully constructed by amateurs and interest in them has been further stimulated by additional frequency allocations. Small V-beams are often used by amateurs with plenty of space at their disposal but the echelon version of them, though much easier to accommodate, seems to have received little attention as does also the capacitively stretched long wire which has interesting possibilities even when confined to a medium-sized garden.

The long single wire

This requires a very long length to provide gain comparable even with that of a close-spaced beam and is of interest mainly as a building brick for V- and rhombic systems. The gain and directive properties of single wires are summarised in Table 14.1 from reference [5].

V- and rhombic antennas are formed from single wires disposed in such a way that main lobes of radiation coincide; thus a V-antenna might consist of two 4λ wires fed out of phase with an apex angle of $2 \times 26° = 52°$, and would provide a gain of $3.3 + 3 = 6.3$dB. This is comparable with that of a three-element or four-element close-spaced Yagi but with the disadvantage that the direction is fixed and the angles of coverage very restricted.

Termination of a wire in its characteristic impedance results in a unidirectional pattern as explained on p109 but has little effect on gain. Methods of feeding and terminating long single-wire antennas are shown in Fig 14.1. The resonant length for long wires is given approximately by

$$l = (n - 0.05)λ/2$$

where n = the required number of half-wavelengths.

Sloping wire antennas are frequently used and many different arrangements are possible. The radiation pattern should be visualised as a cone surrounding the wires in accordance with the angles given in the table; seen end-on, the sloping wire looks vertical and polarisation is therefore vertical but becomes mainly horizontal as one moves to the side, while still remaining within the cone. For a height of 50ft (15m) and 3λ of wire at 14MHz, the slope of the wire is 14° which puts the endwise lobe at an angle of 16° above the horizon. At a radiation angle of 6° there is a loss of about 3dB which exactly neutralises the gain, the total coverage in azimuth being about 75°. For the horizontal directions (after allowing for ground reflections), gain is likely to be about 3dB better than this or roughly equal to a dipole at 35ft (11m). The attractiveness of such a system derives from its simplicity and the low visual impact, assuming a suitable tree or tall building for supporting the antenna and a long enough garden, in this case over 200ft (60m). For such a span the wire needs to be fairly strong and it would usually be better if possible to use it for supporting a delta loop (at the top) plus (at a lower point) a three-element wide-spaced vertical (end-loaded) Yagi; between them these would provide coverage of four directions with gain in both cases roughly equal to that

Table 14.1. Properties of long wire radiators

Length (λ)	Angle of main lobe to wire	Gain of main lobe over half-wave dipole (dB)	Radiation resistance (ohms)
1	54° (90°)	0.4	90
1.5	42°	1.0	100
2	36° (58°)	1.5	110
2.5	33°	1.8	115
3	30° (46°)	2.3	120
4	26° (39°)	3.3	130
5	22° (35°)	4.2	140
6	20° (31°)	5.0	147
8	18° (26°)	6.4	153
10	16° (23°)	7.4	160

The number of complete conical lobes (see Fig 6.4) is equal to the number of half-waves in the antenna. The main lobe is the one nearest to the direction of the wire, and the figures in this table give its direction and gain. When a multiple 1λ antenna is centre-fed the pattern is like that of one half, but with more gain in the main lobe. The angles in brackets correspond to this case. When the antenna is terminated or self-terminating, the radiation resistance is 30 to 50% greater and the main lobe slightly nearer to the wire.

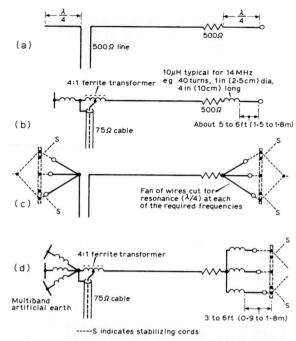

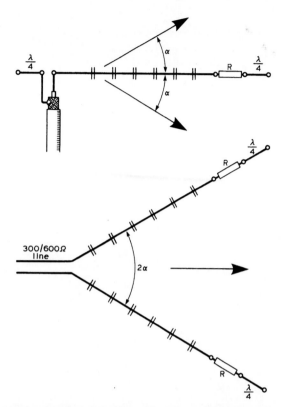

Fig 14.1. Methods of feeding and terminating long single-wire antennas. Artificial earths are used at each end, the radiation resistance being high enough to mask any losses in loading coils such as those shown at (b) and (d). Capacitive hats similar to those used in mobile work (p252) or even smaller should be usable. Artificial earths are not broadband but their use makes the whole of the available span available for gain purposes. The baluns shown at (d) allow the antenna to be fed with coaxial line, all artificial earths being individually self-resonant. The arrangement at (a), though the one usually recommended, is unlikely to achieve good feeder balance

Fig 14.2. 'Stretched' long wires with resistive terminations. The angle α depends only on the stretch factor n, and the gain is proportional to length being 3dB less for a single wire. The figures in Table 14.2 are typical, and for a stretch factor of 4 at 14MHz the wire length is 132ft (40.2m) broken with 43pF capacitors at intervals of 5ft 6in (1.68m). For a single wire the method of feed shown at (b) in Fig 14.1 should provide a better match and less risk of feeder radiation

of a horizontal beam at 25ft (8m). Spreaders could be used to turn the delta loop into a two-element beam but mechanical and visual impact problems may then arise.

Better single-wire performance may be achieved by capacitive stretching (p110), in which case the 200ft (60m) wire can be turned into the equivalent of a four-element or five-element collinear array with 7dB gain but a rather narrow pattern at right-angles to the wire. It is found that if such a wire is terminated in its characteristic impedance (as in Fig 14.2) the lobes are pushed forwards and this provides about 7dB of gain at 75° to the wire for a 'stretch factor' of 4. One method of construction is to use 80Ω twin lead, forming the capacitors by cutting the conductors alternately to leave overlapping sections. The antenna is broadband so that dimensions are not unduly critical, and harmonic operation is possible.

Rhombic antennas

The most efficient way of using a one-acre (0.4ha) plot for a transmitting antenna would be to fill it with dipoles as in Fig 14.3(a). This would provide a gain about equal to the number of elements, ie 14.8dB at 14MHz with perhaps another 3dB

if each dipole is backed by a reflector. This arrangement is singularly unattractive and the rhombic array, Fig 14.3(b), fitting into the same space is of much more interest; apart from being a lot neater it requires only four poles instead of 10, substantially less antenna wire and several times less antenna-plus-feeder wire. With some manipulation of ropes, terminating resistors and feedpoints it can be switched to provide a choice of four directions, with a good chance of being able to put a useful sidelobe in most of the other directions that may be needed.

With the design optimised for maximum radiation in the

Table 14.2. 'Stretched' long-wire antenna data

Length λ	n	α (deg)	R (ohms)	Gain (for Vee array) (dB)
1.5	2	60	300	5
2.0	3	70	200	6
3.0	4	75	150	10

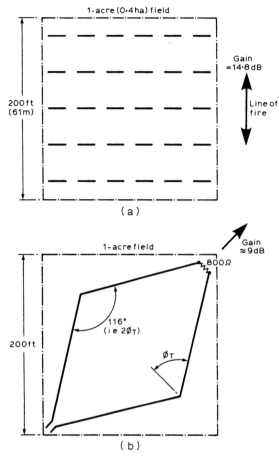

Fig 14.3. Two ways of trying to get as much gain as possible from a one-acre (0.4ha) field. The dipoles at (a) are assumed to be connected to a network of feedlines arranged so that the radiation adds up in phase for the directions at right-angles to the dipoles. The rhombic at (b) provides less gain but is a great deal less obtrusive. Details include the definition of tilt angle φ_T

plane of the array (zero angle of radiation in the vertical plane) the angles are as shown and the leg length is 2.5λ, giving a gain of 9dB over a λ/2 dipole, though this could be up to 3dB greater for reception due to noise absorbed in the terminating resistance (p153). Terminated long-wire antennas such as this are inherently broadband and unlike dipole arrays can be used over a band of an octave or more, though the design is only correct at one frequency and several decibels may be lost at, say, 28MHz by optimising the design for 14MHz. Front-to-back ratio depends on leg length but may be optimised by adjustment of terminating resistance to obtain high values in all cases. The terminating resistance should be non-inductive and capable of dissipating at least a third of the transmitter power, the optimum value being around 800Ω.

Fig 14.4 shows the variation of gain with leg length for zero wave angle [2] and it will be seen that the gain is increased by 3dB each time the leg length is doubled; for this wave angle

the required apex angles are double the values given in Table 14.1. It is more usual, but less convenient for the present purpose, to refer to the 'tilt' angle which is half the corner angle, and equal to 90° minus the angles from the table. Leg lengths greater than 6λ are not recommended [2] because the beam is then so narrow that performance is greatly affected by the small changes in arrival angle (or optimum launch angle) which are typical of DX signals.

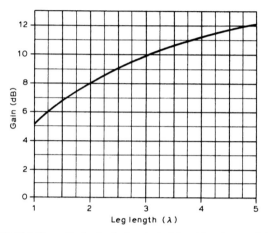

Fig 14.4. Theoretical gain of a terminated rhombic antenna relative to that of a λ/2 dipole in free space (ARRL Antenna Book)

It is common commercial practice to design for a wave angle somewhat above the horizon but in general this is not recommended in view of the stress placed earlier (p16) on the use of the lowest possible angle of radiation for long-haul DX. If it were possible to differentiate between the direct wave and the ground-reflected wave, this could alter the position somewhat but, with typical beamwidths (free-space) of 20–40° and required radiation angles of 6° or less, very little discrimination is possible. Thus even the rhombic with its relatively narrow beamwidths is no exception to the rule that for all practical purposes the effect of the ground is independent of the type of antenna. Nevertheless, despite the emphasis placed on this rule in earlier chapters, it is usually possible with the help of the rhombic, a hilltop and knowledge of Fresnel zones (p166) to conceive a situation which defeats it. Thus in Fig 14.5 a cone of rays 20° wide emanates from the point P; for an antenna height of 50ft (15m) and a required angle of radiation of 5.7° the distance to the geometrical reflection point is 500ft (152m) but the Fresnel zone extends outwards from 86ft (26m). However, beyond 300ft (90m) the grounds drops away so that the greater part of the zone is lost; the remainder, though not illuminated by the 20° cone, would respond fully to the 60° beam from a typical Yagi. However, most of the zone is lost in any case and the reflection coefficient will be fairly small.

This example is unrealistic to the extent that in practice one does not get a 20° beam from a point source and the radiation from one half of the rhombic will illuminate all or part of the

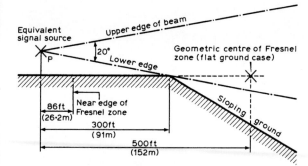

Fig 14.5. Illustrating possible loss of ground reflection if vertical beamwidth is sufficiently narrow. To demonstrate the principle it is assumed that the antenna can be represented by an equivalent point source at P. If the beam is replaced by a dipole or a small Yagi array the reflected wave, though reduced in amplitude, reappears due to illumination of the foreground

near zone, thus further reducing the small advantage of the large array. The example is very much oversimplified but answers an obvious question. It further emphasises the basic rule that *under normal conditions* the effect of ground is independent of the type of antenna; it seems nevertheless worth recording that (in a situation not unlike that just described) one Australian station was able to put a consistently strong signal into the UK during 'difficult' sunspot minimum periods, including many times when no other VK signals were audible. Although the example indicates a possible tendency, it falls well short of explaining the observed performance, which in the light of all the evidence has to be attributed to the combination of a large antenna with the hill-top location and not to either alone.

Two-wire systems

From earlier mention of the V-beam it may be felt that the gain is not too impressive, having regard to the amount of space occupied. The V may, however, be backed by a reflector at a distance of any odd multiple of λ/4 to obtain a further gain of 3dB; it now occupies less space than the rhombic for a given gain, although bandwidth is restricted by the spacing requirement and additional poles are required. Both of these problems may be overcome by the arrangement shown in Fig 14.6, the reflector being mounted a short distance above or below the radiator; with each of its arms shortened by λ/2 the reflector is effectively moved back by λ/4, thus achieving the correct spacing [3]. Front-to-back ratio may be further improved if desired by terminations as shown in Fig 14.1(a), and for multiband operation traps may be acceptable since the radiation resistance is fairly large. In this last case termination is practicable only at the highest frequency but a simpler method might be to retain the arrangement of Fig 14.6, displacing the reflector mechanically as required.

The echelon antenna [4] is equivalent to the V but requires much less space. In Fig 14.7 the wires are displaced, so that the line AB joining any pair of corresponding points is at right-angles to the direction YY which corresponds to the

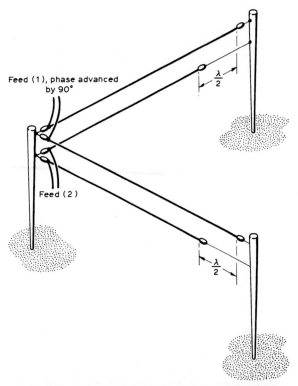

Fig 14.6. Addition of reflector to V-beam without additional poles or spreaders. One V is mounted a short distance below the other, making the legs shorter by λ/2 to give an effective mean displacement of λ/4. The V with the longer legs is fed with a signal advanced in phase by 90° to obtain a unidirectional pattern

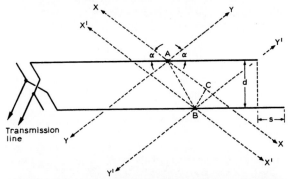

Fig 14.7. The echelon antenna; though equivalent to the V, this requires much less space. The two long parallel wires are spaced a distance *d* and staggered by the amount S. As shown, radiation takes place along the lines XX whereas the fields at a distant point along YY will cancel. If the wires are fed in phase, radiation takes place along YY. The spacing *d* and the amount S are given by

$$d = \frac{492 \sin \alpha}{f \sin 2\alpha}$$

$$S = \frac{492 \cos \alpha}{f \sin 2\alpha}$$

where α is the angle of maximum radiation from a single wire (Table 14.1). *d* and S are in feet and *f* in megahertz *(ARRL Antenna Book)*

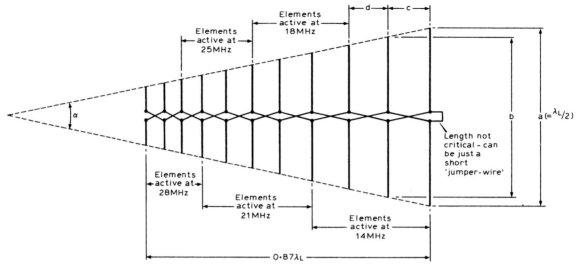

Fig 14.8. Typical log-periodic array. The ratios *b/a* = *d/c* are identical for all adjacent pairs of elements. As shown the frequency range is one octave but this can be extended in either direction by adding more elements according to the same basic rule. At any given frequency within the band there are three or four elements contributing appreciably to the radiation, and performance is comparable with that of a three-element Yagi

appropriate angle of propagation from Table 14.1. Since the wires are fed in opposite phase there is no propagation along this line. For the other pair of directions there is an effective separation distance AC between the wires so that the signal is not cancelled, and if AC = λ/2 the fields are directly additive. The wires may be terminated as in Fig 14.1 or 14.2 to obtain a unidirectional pattern and harmonic operation should be possible, though no record has been found of its use hitherto; it is true that the optimum geometry is frequency dependent, but this applies equally to rhombic and V-antennas. At the second harmonic the angle a is roughly halved so that YY is no longer quite at right-angles to AB, and AC (though not halved as one would like) is reduced sufficiently to ensure a much bigger field along the line XX than along YY. For such operation the choice lies between acceptance of a compromise or use of the supporting halyards for adjustment of *S* and possibly *d*.

If the position of one wire is adjustable by ropes over pulleys and each wire is fed separately via a phasing unit, near-optimum gain should be realisable for any frequency, any spacing between wires (if not too close), and along either of the lines XX, YY.

The effect of close spacing has apparently not been investigated for either the echelon or the V-plus-reflector.

Stacked dipole arrays

Having rejected the idea of filling the one-acre field with dipoles one might perhaps still consider, say, a row of five multiband dipoles backed by reflectors along one edge. This would yield a gain of at least 11dB, or rather more than the rhombic, though average front/back ratio would not be as good and the arrangement lacks aesthetic appeal.

Broadside and end-fire arrays of vertical dipoles with fields adding in phase provide almost identical gain for the same length but the optimum spacing is 5λ/8 and 3λ/8 respectively, so that a lot more elements are needed in the end-fire case which includes long Yagi arrays. The 3λ/8 spacing, as well as being near-optimum, is also a critical value which should not be exceeded and applies both to Yagi and driven arrays; the gain is 11dB for a length of 4λ and is more or less proportional to length. In the broadside case an additional 3dB can be obtained by the use of reflectors and in the end-fire case more gain can be obtained by increased phase shift, thereby to some extent invoking the supergain principle. The 11dB figure is about 1.5dB higher than that given by the 'gain equals *n*' rule based on λ/2 spacing of elements; actually gain exceeds *n* by 3dB in the simple broadside case and is roughly equal to *n* for the end-fire case. This means that with optimum spacings there is, perhaps not surprisingly, a beneficial effect rather than otherwise from the mutual couplings.

Log-periodic arrays

Log-periodic arrays are found in a wide variety of forms, shapes and sizes but Fig 14.8 represents those of most interest to the amateur. Typically, for any frequency within a specified range there is a group of elements near enough to resonance to take part in the radiating process, all such groups having identical proportions so that the gain is the same throughout the band. The signal travels along the array, ignoring the shorter elements (which present large capacitive reactances) until it encounters the right group of elements. Beyond the λ/2 element the current decreases rapidly with the feeder looking into a highly inductive reactance.

The ratio *b/a* = *d/c* = τ for any pair of adjacent elements or spaces, this and the apex angle (α) being the basic design parameters of the system [6, 7]. The longest element is made equal to 492/*f*, ie approximately λ/2 at the lowest frequency f_L, and the length of the array should be as long as conveniently possible, though this is not critical – a reasonable compromise is given by τ = 0.9, spaces between elements being made equal to one-tenth the length of the longer element. This value of τ gives the smoothest radiation pattern; lower τ means fewer active elements and lower gain, whereas increasing τ to, say, 0.95 produces more back lobes, requires twice as much wire, and increases gain by at most 1dB. About 1.6dB extra gain is possible if the spacing and array length is increased (ie (α reduced) by a factor of three.

A simplified design procedure is as follows:

1. Draw to scale the longest element and a centre line representing the length available plus a small amount, eg about 50% if coverage is restricted to one octave, since the HF end of the 'possible' array is not needed. Complete the triangle as in Fig 14.8.
2. Fill in further elements, making each one 10% shorter than the previous one (ie τ = 0.9) until the element length is λ/2 at the *highest* frequency. Continue for a further three elements.

This fixes the dimensions. Since the active elements are only three or four in number and closely spaced, additive gain is not possible, and as for other close-spaced arrays the connections must be crossed over as shown.

Calculation of matching impedance and of the number of active elements is complicated but inspection of many published designs confirms that usually three or four elements can be assumed active, subject to the sort of design conditions likely to be imposed. It appears also that a good-enough match (better than 2:1 SWR) can usually be obtained using 50Ω coaxial line with a 4:1 balun. Alternatively 600Ω line may be used with an ATU. The array shown in Fig 14.8 may also be erected in vertical form; in this case a single post surrounded by a ring of much shorter ones can be used to support a number of antennas for coverage of all directions.

For a vertical array with top-loaded elements as in Fig 13.5 the spacing needs to be increased in order to accommodate a useful amount of loading without the risk of overcoupling. If it is increased by 40% it should be possible to use top loads of at least 0.1λ, thus reducing the required length of vertical monopole elements from 0.25λ to about 0.17λ or a maximum of 12ft (3.7m) for coverage of 14–30MHz. In practice it should be satisfactory to check *one* element with a GDO to ensure equivalence with a straight element, the rest of the array being designed by appropriate applications of the factor τ to *all* dimensions.

Also of possible interest is the log-periodic inverted-V antenna. Assuming sufficient lateral space for stringing out their ends, the centres of the elements can be supported by a catenary running between two supports. Similar design considerations apply and, although windage may be considerable, there is no feeder drag to put excessive strain on the masts.

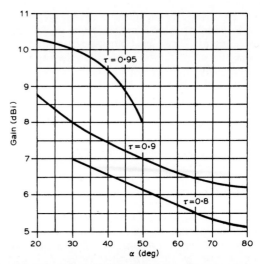

Fig 14.9. Gain of log-periodic array as a function of the design parameters τ **and** α **relative to an isotropic source**

If end-loading is not required the angle α in Fig 14.8 may be increased to 45°, thereby reducing the array length from 60ft to 26ft (18.2 to 7.9m) before practical difficulties become apparent. This decreases the gain relative to a dipole from 6.5dB to 4.8dB, and a comparable rotary array has been described [8] using 12 elements, the boom length being 26.5ft (8.1m), coverage 13–30MHz, and total weight 116lb (52.6kg). A comparable three-element or four-element Yagi would have more gain, be very much lighter and have lower wind loading as well as less visual impact on the neighbourhood, so that clearly a price must be paid for the wide bandwidth. On the other hand, a vertical wire beam with dimensions adapted from Fig 14.8 but using monopole elements based on Fig 13.24 could be arranged to cover 10–30MHz, assuming *L* is 60ft (18.3m) and a pole height of 30ft (9m) without (or 24ft (7.3m) with) end-loading.

There is some discrepancy between references in regard to gain figures, and if consulting other sources the reader is likely to be confused by conflicting definitions of α, which in references [7] and [8] is *half* the apex angle, and τ which in reference [6] is not *b/a* but *(b/a)²*. The former definition has been used in references [7] and [8], and also by this author in view of its more obvious physical relevance in the amateur context. Gain is shown in Fig 14.9 as a function of τ and α, using figures taken from reference [6].

Discussion and conclusions

Exceptional signals are often attributed to the use of a large array such as a rhombic but, theoretically at least, the performance could usually be equalled or exceeded by the use of a small number of three-element arrays suitably spaced and phased as discussed on pp113 and 121; thus rhombics with leg lengths of 2.5λ and 5λ can be expected to equal the performance of groupings of two and four close-spaced arrays respectively, the required spacings being of the order of 3λ/4. Much less space is needed for the stacked arrays, which have the major advantages that they can be pointed in any direction and deployed according to the needs of the moment, eg four could be used for instantaneous switching between four directions (eight if reversible) instead of being phased to provide maximum gain in a given direction. The advantages of the rhombic lie in its relative simplicity and broad bandwidth.

Long Yagi arrays have not been considered separately in this chapter since the main essentials were covered in Chapter 5 and arrays of short end-loaded elements were discussed in Chapter 13. In general, the long Yagi makes better use of space than the rhombic but has the disadvantage that gain increases rather more slowly with increase of length as demonstrated by Fig 5.34. Like the rhombic, the log-periodic array provides broad bandwidth with a 'minimum of fuss' but at the price of increased weight, windage, and space occupancy for a given gain as compared with a typical Yagi array.

On the other hand, efficient use of a large area for coverage of all directions with horizontal polarisation poses formidable problems.

References

[1] 'Loaded wire aerials', F C Charman, G6CJ, *RSGB Bulletin* July 1961.
[2] *The ARRL Antenna Book,* 13th edn, ARRL, 1974, p175.
[3] *Radio Engineers Handbook,* F E Terman, McGraw-Hill, 1943, p808.
[4] *The ARRL Antenna Book,* 12th edn, ARRL, 1970, p174.
[5] *Radio Communication Handbook, Vol 2,* 5th edn, RSGB, 1977, p12.59.
[6] *Antenna Theory and Design,* H P Williams, Pitman, 1966, p484.
[7] *The ARRL Antenna Book,* 13th edn, ARRL, 1974, p160.
[8] 'The log-periodic dipole array', Peter D Rhodes, K4EWG, *QST* November 1973.

Chapter 15

Invisible antennas

Planning regulations or restrictive covenants may prohibit the erection of the desired antenna system, or even of any kind of antenna, and dwellers in high-rise buildings have particularly difficult problems. In interpreting regulations there tend to be large areas of uncertainty which are best resolved by common sense and goodwill, but it helps if the antenna is designed to attract as little notice as possible – few of us are so isolated from our neighbours that we need give no thought to its appearance which is often of much greater importance than its electrical qualities. For this reason visual impact has been featured among the basic characteristics of antenna systems discussed in Chapters 11–14 and we return to these topics in Chapter 20.

In this chapter an attempt is made to offer a few solutions for those cases where the erection of a visible antenna is expressly forbidden or ill advised. One answer of course is the indoor antenna, which has already been discussed in some detail, but this does not help the dweller in a steel-framed apartment block and is a serious hardship to anyone living in a bungalow unless they are lucky enough to have a steep ground slope or are not interested in DX. For outdoor antennas there are basically two possibilities: (a) concealment and (b) disguise.

If suitable supports are available the use of thin wires held up by nylon fishing line can provide a very simple and easy solution of the problem. Fig 15.1 illustrates a typical situation as described [5] by G0DLN. Despite excellent DX performance the portion DE resulted in some TVI and (one must suppose) some loss, though with a suitable ATU its multiband properties should be excellent and one can conceive of many variations depending on the space and means of support available. His final version, Figs 15.2 and 15.3, gets rid of DE

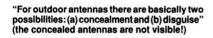

"For outdoor antennas there are basically two possibilities: (a) concealment and (b) disguise" (the concealed antennas are not visible!)

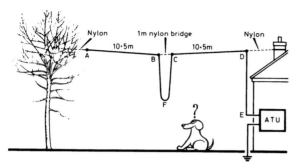

Fig 15.1. Invisible end-fed collinear array devised by G0DLN. The necessary phase-reversal is provided by the loop BFC. The use of monofilament nylon fishing line ensures low visibility and excellent insulation. The addition of insulators contributes nothing except weight, windage, and extra complication. (This applies to visible antennas as well.)

and results in fewer losses, less noise, and the elimination of TVI, though in less favourable circumstances the matching circuit might constitute a visible feature. Even in this form, operation was found to be possible on 3.5, 21, and 28MHz, though a reduction in C1 was necessary for best results at the higher frequencies.

G0DLN points out that a span of 27m could be used to achieve the equivalent of the extended double Zepp (ie 2 × 5/8λ), alternatively shortening is possible by bending the ends over to fit the available space, with suitable adjustment of phasing-loop length. Additional points to be noted are the gain of 3dB with the longer length (though this narrows the radiation pattern and restricts the area coverage) and the possibility of using the new method of end-feeding illustrated in Fig 4.28. This will improve bandwidth and, in the case of an upstairs shack adjacent to the end of the antenna, might allow the end to be hauled inwards in order to change the value and position of the matching capacitor for operation on a number of other bands including 7MHz.

An apartment dweller located near the top of a high-rise building may be quite well placed since he has plenty of height with which to offset the low efficiency of a small antenna such as a mobile whip. Harry Bourne, later ZL1OI, found himself in just such a situation while stationed in

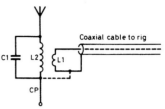

Fig 15.3. Matching circuit for Mk 2 version of the collinear array; see text for alternative

Washington, DC, USA, and reports using a mobile whip for all five bands mounted on the balcony railing and sloping at 45° to the horizontal [1]. During the day it was inside the balcony, with a concrete floor, concrete roof and steel-framed building just behind it, thus forming a box with a slot in one side, Fig 15.4. At night he used a rotator to swing the antenna over the side into the clear and could then work worldwide with no trouble, but even in daytime it could be swung over the side for a few minutes without attracting attention. The steel railings were used as the ground plane except on 3.5MHz where a counterpoise wire was run under the carpet indoors.

A somewhat similar arrangement has been used to lift an antenna off a flat roof [2], and it occurs to the author that in some cases a dipole such as Fig 15.5 could be folded back against the building and raised by cords or a beam rotation unit at suitable times. It would require some experiment to determine a minimum size for the arms and careful painting to match the building. Theoretically, at a height of 80ft (24.4m) the DX performance should equal that of a three-element monoband beam at 40ft (12.2m), and with luck the attenuation through the building would provide a good back-to-front ratio. Given this kind of performance, a single direction and frequency (if well chosen) can provide a lot of DX interest but, since the user has the big advantage of living on top of his mast, as it were, with ready access to the antenna, band changing should not prove too difficult.

Even the bungalow dweller need not give up hope, in view of the description in Chapter 13 of beams using 6ft (1.8m) elements hanging from a catenary. This provides very much more efficient end-loading than is achievable in the case of,

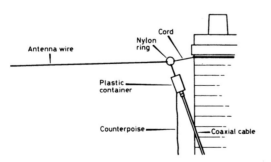

Fig 15.2. This is a Mk 2 version of Fig 15.1; the plastic container houses the matching section shown in Fig 15.3. The counterpoise, which effectively prevents feeder radiation, is allowed to hang down vertically

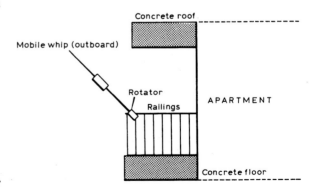

Fig 15.4. Use of mobile antenna for operation from an apartment block. Beam rotator swings the antenna out of sight when not in use, eg during the daytime

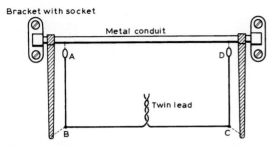

Fig 15.5. Retractable antenna suggested for use from an upper floor of an apartment block. Visual profile is low but with sufficient height the performance could equal that of the average suburban beam. Antenna could be a centre-fed bent dipole as shown or an end-fed wire. For best results AB, DC should be at least 0.08λ. BC may be reduced to as little as 0.14λ by additional folding of the ends, eg as in Fig 11.1(j)

say, a mobile whip, and has the further advantage that it can be effectively disguised if necessary by actual use as a washing line! For all-round coverage by beam switching the elements can be arranged in a neat square formation based on Figs 13.5 or 13.6, of which neighbours may well be envious. However, it must be noted that vertical antennas in close proximity to a building cannot be expected to fire efficiently through it.

In the case of taller houses other possibilities arise; for example, an end-fed wire trailed over the ridge of the roof should give good results at least in dry weather, but if it can clear the roof by a few inches this would be a help. Alternatively the use of the outer conductor of a length of coaxial cable will reduce the characteristic impedance and hence the dielectric losses. Two or three suitably spaced elements can be used as a fixed reversible beam along the direction of the roof ridge, remembering that if there are significant losses all elements must be driven, not parasitic.

Other possibilities include the use of guttering, lightning conductors or flagpoles in ways which will no doubt suggest themselves to readers of earlier chapters. The need for efficient earthing of the transmitter (p193), and any other steps such as harmonic filters which may be necessary to prevent TVI or stereo breakthrough, must be stressed since an amateur who may be treading delicate ground needs, above all, good relations with his neighbours.

If TV antennas are permitted more possibilities unfold themselves. A TV antenna erected as high as possible can be used, either complete with feeder as a vertical on any band (with the help where necessary of linear-resonator-type traps clipped across or coupled into portions of the down lead, as discussed on p192), or to support a thin-wire antenna such as an inverted-V or end-fed long wire (inverted-L). It appears from one account [3] that there is no need to use anything thinner than 28awg (30swg or 0.3mm), and that this is just thick enough to be satisfactory as regards possible breakage by birds, although experience might be different in other areas and circumstances. Even 36awg (38swg or 0.15mm) was satisfactory for performance, and invisible to the naked eye at distances greater than 15ft (4.5m).

Further to this, there is the possibility of disguising a beam as a television antenna. In the UK it has been officially stated that TV and FM broadcast receiving antennas do not need planning permission; in other words, they are regarded as part of the general residential scene and not affecting the general character of a property.

Planning permission is also not required in the UK for an antenna attached to the house, provided it does not project above the highest part of the roof or beyond the forwardmost part of any wall of the dwelling which fronts on a highway. The height restriction is unhelpful and it will probably be better in general to take advantage of the TV or FM antenna concession. The largest TV antennas advertised for use in the UK have boom lengths of about 11ft which is more than adequate for a fixed 14MHz array, 8ft being a recommended minimum and 6ft probably just acceptable. Assuming the antenna to be mounted on a chimney the beam could consist of a pair of inverted-V wire elements trailed out to points on the guttering, the ends of the roof ridge, or more-distant supports such as trees or fences. For 14MHz elements the wire ends should be brought in towards each other for optimisation of coupling as explained on p79, and this may mean that only two end supports are required. For a gain of 4dB the radiation resistance (90° apex angle) would be 15Ω per element, and from Fig 3.10 the loss resistance using 24swg (0.6m) wire (which might well not be noticed) would be 2.9Ω, a loss of 0.77dB only.

The use of pairs of wires in parallel improves bandwidth, and the halving of current in each wire allows the wire diameter also to be halved if the increased risk of breakage is acceptable; on the other hand, unless 'pushed to extremes' an increase of wire diameter to 20swg is recommended. There is no need for insulators since excellent insulation and virtually zero visibility can be achieved by the use of monofilament nylon fishing line as shown in Fig 15.6 which illustrates an SDL alternative to Fig 15.10 which is suitable for multiband operation as described on pp124, 125. For reversible beams the elements, each with its own feeder, should be identical but, if interest is restricted to one direction and deep-nulling not important, the reflector can be fixed-tuned.

The TV antenna concession may be no help in the face of some restrictive covenants but this need be no cause for despair. For example, Fig 15.7, though (as illustrated) strictly

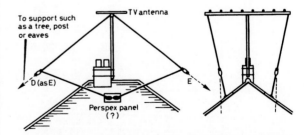

Fig 15.6. Small delta loop (SDL) array hanging down from boom of TV antenna. Multiband operation is possible as described in Chapter 13 but requires resonant feeders to be brought down through (or into) the roof space

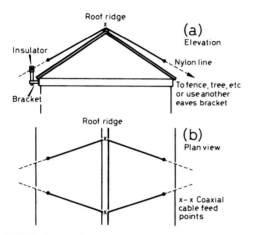

Fig 15.7. Dipoles used as beam elements may consist of wires trailed over a roof ridge, and can be fed with coaxial cable led away at right-angles either along the ridge or down into the roof-space. At (b) the centres can be positioned by means of fishing line trailed along the ridge. At (a) the ends are shown fixed in two different ways to illustrate alternatives. In this case, also Fig 15.10, multiband operation should be feasible if the dipoles can be formed into loops by trailing wires through the roof space

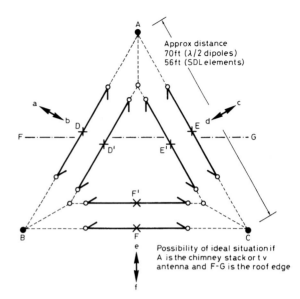

Fig 15.9. 'Spiders web' array requiring only three supports. This is switchable in 60° steps. Reversible beams AB, BC, AC fire in directions ab, cd, ef respectively

monoband since no RF voltage can be tolerated at its centre, may be only marginally worse than 15.10(a).

There are other possibilities. Fig 15.8 shows three types of element culled from Chapters 11 and 12 which, if three suitable supports are available, can be erected spider's web fashion as shown in Fig 15.9 using only thin wire and fishing line to provide all-round coverage by beam switching, as well as in simpler configurations. For 21MHz or higher the vertical array of Fig 13.9 and 13.10 requires only a single fishing rod mounted on a fencing post and, since the wires can be as thin as desired, should not attract adverse attention.

In the case of Fig 15.9 the use of small delta-loop elements requires less area and greatly reduces the strain on supports. For example, using pairs of 26swg wires the weight of each element is 2oz and, allowing a 1ft sag, the total pull on each support is of the order of 4lb only. In the case of the dipole elements calculations are more difficult but one can arrive at a comparable figure by considering only the weight of the

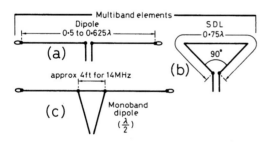

Fig 15.8. Suggested 'invisible' elements for arrays such as Fig 15.9, giving all-round coverage by directional switching; (a) and (b) are multiband elements described in detail in Chapter 13 and (c) is a Y-matched dipole suitable for a relatively simple monoband system

outer ring feeders. The layout will usually be dictated by the environment, the example marked on the figure being a favourable situation which allows the lower corners of two of the loop pairs to be brought in to junction boxes just under the eaves. If the shack is ideally located, eg half-way between D and E, 300Ω feeder may be used, or if necessary 'invisible' 600Ω line could be constructed using 32 or 34swg conductors spaced about 1in (2.5cm). To achieve exact symmetry small projections will be required from the eaves but this may be unnecessary, The third beam, BC, is more difficult since even if an invisible support can be contrived for the feedpoints the equalisation of line lengths may be awkward and, opting for a simpler life, it may be decided to settle for two beams at right-angles and accept an appreciable drop in performance (in a few directions only).

To avoid undue complication in the shack, beam selection will need to be carried out at the point of entry so that the same multibanding arrangements can be used for all directions. The use of multiple wires for the elements, by invoking the constant-Z_0 principle (p126), reduces RF voltages and eases the switching problem but on some bands it may be necessary to detune elements not in use.

Every care must of course be taken to make sure that any wire liable to break in a storm or due to impact by birds cannot come into contact with electric cables or constitute a hazard to traffic or passers-by. In some cases it may be best to slope the wires down to the rear of the building, accepting some loss of height. Alternative suggestions are presented in Fig 15.10. Fig 15.10(b) avoids the need for a spreader but the height loss may be serious.

Trees (where available) often provide a simple answer to the problem of concealment and a study of Chapters 11 and

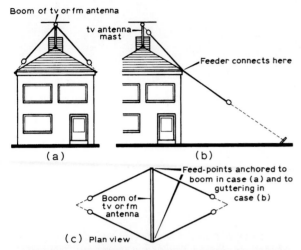

Fig 15.10. Two-element beams using thin-wire dipoles. Wire should not be thinner than 24swg (0.5mm). At (a) the boom of a TV or FM antenna is used as the spreader for an inverted-V beam, extended if necessary to provide at least 10ft (3m) spacing at 14MHz or 7ft (2.1m) at 21MHz. The two feeders may each be 50Ω with balun and brought down alongside the TV/FM feeder. At (b) the ends of the wire elements are both brought in to the pole, allowing a separation of about 8in (20cm), and the centres are attached to points 10–12ft (3–4m) apart on the guttering, the lower ends being also spaced 8in and strung out to a tree or small post retaining as much height as possible. (c) Bird's-eye view

12 should provide the reader with plenty of encouragement, assuming that a reasonable height can be achieved. The possibility of using a low tree to conceal a vertical antenna needs further assessment as does the possibility of using trees themselves as antennas; this is achieved [4] by feeding energy

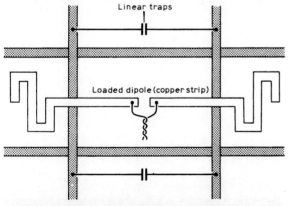

Fig 15.11. Part of a metal grid such as a steel framework. For RF the rectangle may in principle be isolated from the rest of the structure by linear traps. In principle the rectangle may be resonant at a desired frequency and can then be excited with an additional coupling loop or delta match. Success would, however, be more likely with a separate resonant element as shown, relying on the traps to prevent current flowing in horizontal members of the framework. Broad copper strips should be used to reduce losses in walls etc. The success (if any) of this will depend on being able to locate the framework, and on how close to it one can get. For operation at low heights the polarisation should be vertical

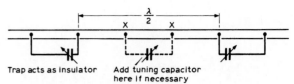

Fig 15.12. Conversion of any long metal conductor into a λ/2 dipole. Traps may be satisfactory if mutually coupled as in Fig 11.18(a), but direct connection as shown is likely to result in better efficiency. Feeder may consist of a 50Ω coaxial line connected to XX via a 4:1 balun. The traps should be as long as possible, up to about λ/4, and should if possible be constructed with flat strip or large diameter tubing, though wire should be satisfactory provided the traps are not too short. Spacing, particularly if wire is used, should be as wide as possible up to at least 1ft (30cm)

into the tree via a toroidal coil wrapped around the trunk. The system has been found "particularly useful in wet jungles", efficiencies of "up to 22dB better than a conventional whip antenna" being reported. Few other details are given but the principle can be applied to other objects and it is claimed that "whenever an environment detrimentally loads a regular whip, we can couple a transmitter or receiver into the environment and make it work well as a substitute".

Requirements for short-range and medium-range communication on all bands are probably best met by an end-fed long thin wire with some folding over of the far end if necessary. Attention must be given to proper tensioning (p178) and correct feeding (pp41–42).

Requirements under the present heading vary widely as do the possibilities for meeting them, and it is hoped that the few ideas presented here, even where not directly applicable, may at least provide encouragement in the search for solutions so that situations which may at first seem hopeless are construed rather as a challenge. It may be impossible, at least without causing TVI, to excite the steel frame of a building, but reference [4] reports some success even in this unlikely context, and other solutions are not necessarily ruled out. For example, given access to the frame it would be possible *in principle* (with or without making direct connections) to use the linear resonators of Fig 11.18 to mark off a section for use as in Fig 15.11, where they act as insulators. The same principle can be applied (with rather more confidence) to sections of drainpipe, guttering, or plumbing as in Fig 15.12. Such methods are more likely to succeed at the higher frequencies in view of the relatively small value of the inductances which are involved.

References

[1] Material presented by H K Bourne in *CQ*.
[2] *Wire Antennas*, W I Orr, W6SAI, and Stuart D Cowan, W2LX, Radio Publications Inc, 1972, p139.
[3] 'Invisible antennas', T J Gordon, W6RVQ, *QST* November 1965, p87.
[4] 'It's a tree . . . a pole . . . a man; No! a short range HF antenna', *Electronic Design* 20 December 1973.
[5] 'An invisible DX antenna for 14MHz', Del Arthur, G0DLN, *Radio Communication* October 1987.

Chapter 16

Mobile and portable antennas

Signals from mobile stations are usually weaker than those from fixed stations, even after allowing for possible power differences. This is usually taken for granted and it might be thought absurd to question the acceptance of anything so obvious; nevertheless, pursuing the themes of equality between antenna systems (Chapter 3) and the differences between horizontal and vertical polarisation (Chapter 10), the performance of a mobile station on the higher bands might be expected to equal that obtained with the same rig and a horizontal dipole at 30ft (9.1m).

There are in fact two reasons why the mobile antenna is 'down' in performance and one of these does not apply at the higher frequencies, while the other is somewhat obscure. The first arises because height is typically limited to around 8ft (2.4m), or effectively a bit less than this taking into account partial screening by the car body, and it is mechanically impracticable to rely on efficient methods of end-loading except at the highest frequencies. One is therefore forced, for 14MHz and lower frequencies, to break the rules laid down in Chapter 5 in the course of the search for efficient elements for small beams.

The second problem is that of the ground connection which is usually composed of the capacitance to the ground of the car body. Though difficult to analyse or even describe precisely, there must be some loss since the car body breaks the rules for counterpoise earths, ie that they must be low loss and sufficiently clear of the ground to provide a return path for the antenna current without forcing it to flow through 'lossy' ground. In other words, it should be possible to regard the counterpoise as the lower half of a dipole rather than as a ground connection, the 'car body' earth being in fact an unknown quantity somewhere between the two extremes.

The antenna is normally vertical with loading coils at the centre or base, and a 'capacitive hat' is often added at the top of the antenna. Base-loading is in general much less efficient, whereas the desirability of a capacitive hat *in terms of radiation efficiency* is proved by the complaints of 'excessive Q' (or insufficient bandwidth) which often result from its use!

To get this in perspective consider the situation illustrated in Fig 16.1. As a rough approximation one can regard the current distribution as triangular over a distance not exceeding $\lambda/8$ inwards from one end of a dipole or monopole, and uniform over at least $\lambda/16$ outwards from a point of maximum

current. If part of the end section is replaced by a 'capacitive hat' it is the inner part of the triangle which is retained.

These current distributions are shown in the diagrams and it will be clear that the field strength produced will be as if the current I flowed through lengths $h/2$, $3h/4$ and $7h/8$ respectively. From the squares of these currents the radiation resistances are in the ratio 1, 2.25 and 3.063. It will be found that at the lower frequencies the inductance of the antenna below the coil is negligible compared with the required loading inductance. If this equals L in case (a), we require $2L$ in case (b) and in case (c), since eb = h, it is again equal to L. Since the value of L has little effect on the best obtainable coil Q, which is likely to be of the order of 300 in each case, the coil loss resistances R_c are given respectively by $\omega L/300$, $\omega L/150$, and $\omega L/300$. It is necessary also to assume an earth-loss resistance (unknown) of R_e which is the same in all three cases.

From inspection of Fig 16.2 it is found that the proportion

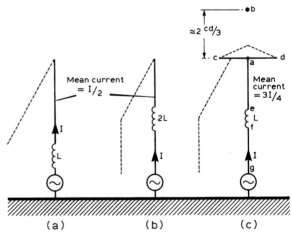

Fig 16.1. Alternative methods of loading a mobile antenna. The height *h* of the radiator is assumed to be the same in each case, and the shape of the current distribution is shown by dotted lines. At (c) a hypothetical increase in height ab = ae has been replaced by horizontal loading cd which leaves the current distribution below a unaffected. The length of cd is roughly equal to 1.5 ab. The value of L is doubled in case (b) since the length of wire above it, and hence the capacitance, is halved

of power radiated is given by $R/(R + R_c + R_e)$ but at low frequencies R is only a fraction of an ohm and very much less than R_c or R_e so that the efficiency becomes $R/(R_c + R_e)$ approximately. The capacitance of an 8ft (2.4m) whip is in the region of 30pF so that at 3.5MHz we have for case (a) $\omega L = 1/\omega C$ = 1600Ω, R_c = 5.3Ω and a value of 10Ω is often assumed for R_e. For case (b), R is multiplied by 2.25 and R_c by 2, and for case (c) R is multiplied by 3.06. The efficiencies (relative) are 0.06, 0.11 and 0.2 so that centre-loading is 2.6dB better than base-loading, and the top hat gives a further improvement of 2.6dB.

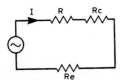

Fig 16.2. Estimation of efficiency of mobile antenna, R = radiation resistance, R_c = loading coil resistance, R_e = earth losses. The antenna is assumed to be resonant

It may be of interest to note that with $R_e = 0$ these ratios become 0.5dB and 4.35dB respectively so that the improvement due to centre-loading comes about mainly because of the earth resistance. Without this, the rise in R_c largely offsets the improvement in R. The overall Q is given by $\omega L/(R_c + R_e)$, ie 105, 78 and 105 respectively, the 2.6dB improvement in case (c) compared with (b) being obtained at the price of a 26% reduction in bandwidth.

The situation is slightly different at 14MHz because the inductance of the lower portion of the antenna is no longer negligible compared with L and the current in the centre of the antenna is some 13% less than at the base. The reactance above the coil is 400, 800 and 400Ω respectively but the lower half of the antenna contributes about 200Ω of inductive reactance in cases (b) and (c), so that $\omega L = 400, 600$ and 200Ω respectively. Corresponding values of R_c (ohms) are 1.33, 2.0 $\times (0.87)^2$ and $0.67 \times (0.87)^2$, these being the values referred to the feedpoint for comparison with R, the factors in brackets serving to take account of the sinusoidal current distribution. The radiation resistance in case (a), from Fig 3.12, is 5.5Ω and the factors for cases (b) and (c) are approximately as before, so that (again taking R_e as 10Ω) the efficiency is 33, 52 and 62% respectively. The improvement from centre-loading is 2dB and the further advantage from the capacitive hat is only 0.8dB. With R_e removed, the top hat would reduce the coil losses by four but these are small enough for the improvement in overall performance to be negligible.

At 28MHz the antenna is self-resonant and losses are even less. One might expect this to be reflected in impressive performance but, for DX communication as compared with 14MHz, an average fixed station will be obtaining an extra 6dB or so of height gain from its horizontal antenna and the mobile station can expect to be relatively down by some 9–10dB.

Radiation resistance is proportional to f^2 and, for heights of

$\lambda/8$ or less, also to h^2. The 8ft (2.4m) base-loaded whip has a radiation resistance at 3.5MHz of only $5.5/16 = 0.34\Omega$ and the efficiency is therefore 0.34/15.64 or 2.2% only, rising to 6.6% for case (c).

Fig 16.3 shows another common form of mobile antenna, the helical whip. A 3.5MHz helix might consist of about $\lambda/4$ of 14swg (2mm) wire wound on an 8ft (2.4m) rod of 1in (25mm) diameter. From Fig 3.10 the HF resistance is 0.8Ω and, assuming a sinusoidal current distribution, the radiation resistance may be obtained directly from the height of the whip relative to that of a $\lambda/4$ monopole, ie it is equal to $(4h/\lambda)^2$ $\times 36\Omega$, giving an efficiency of 3.6% compared with 4% for the centre-loaded whip without a capacitive hat. Both systems can be improved by a hat, and there seems little to choose between them. The helix can be somewhat improved by tapering, ie using thicker wire and wider spacing for the lower portion.

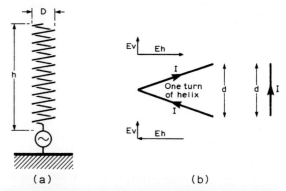

Fig 16.3. Helical whip. (a) shows schematically a vertical helix and (b) is an enlarged view of one turn showing the horizontal and vertical fields produced by each half-turn as seen by a distant observer. The horizontal components cancel; the vertical ones add to produce the equivalent of a current I flowing through a distance d equal to the pitch of the turn as shown on the right. The losses are increased compared with those in a straight conductor of the same wire diameter in the ratio $\pi D/d$, or rather more unless the turns are spaced by several times the wire diameter

It is important to appreciate that coiling of the wire has no effect on radiation resistance, except indirectly by changing somewhat the shape of the current distribution as in the above example. The reason for this can be appreciated from inspection of Fig 16.3(b); each turn of the helix appears to the observer as a zigzag and, following the rules explained in Chapter 2, the field produced in the vertical plane is proportional to the extent of these wires in the vertical plane, the horizontal components being cancelled. As a corollary to this it follows that loading coils cannot contribute in themselves to the radiation resistance, though their length must be included in reckoning the total height of the antenna.

Due to differences in car bodies and mounting positions, no precise dimensions can be given and each installation must be tuned *in situ*. The position of the coil is not critical; moving it to the middle of the top half at 3.5MHz requires L and therefore R_c to be doubled, but increases R in the ratio $(7/6)^2$

Table 16.1. Inductance values, efficiencies, and overall bandwidth for 8ft (2.4m) centre-loaded whip without top-loading

Frequency (MHz)	1.8	3.6	7.05	10	14.2	18	21.3	25	28.5
Inductance (µH)	582	142	35.5	17	7.24	4	2.1		0
Radiation resistance (Ω)	0.2	0.8	3	6	12	17	21	28	36
Efficiency (Q = 100) (per cent)	0.26	1.9	10	22	42		62		
Efficiency (Q = 300) (per cent)	0.62	3.7	16	30	50	60	66	73	78
Overall bandwidth (Q = 100) (kHz)	21	48	124		490		1420		
Overall bandwidth (Q = 300) (kHz)	9	24.5	78		417		1290		

and reduces the efficiency by 10%. There is therefore a loss in signal strength of 0.4dB, though there could be a slight additional loss due to the self-capacitance of the coil which could be approaching self-resonance. Assuming a stray capacitance of 1.5pF, which is probably equal to about 20% of the total tuning capacitance, this increases the current in L by 20% but reduces the required value of L by the same amount, so that there is a net increase of 20% in the effective value of R_c. This results in a signal loss of 0.3dB.

The capacitance of a short whip antenna ($<\lambda/8$) can be reckoned as roughly 3.4pF/ft (11.2pF/m). This assumes an average diameter of 0.5in (13mm) and is a bit on the low side for longer lengths but, subject to normal practical constraints, differences of more than 15% are unlikely. Such figures can in any case be used only as rough guidelines in view of the many other variables as already indicated.

Table 16.1 shows approximate values of loading inductance required for the various bands on the basis of the above figures for C and, at the higher frequencies, due allowance for the inductive reactance of the lower half of the antenna. A value of 10Ω is assumed for R_c.

Table 16.1 may be scaled for other lengths of whip, eg for a 12ft (3.7m) whip the 21MHz column applies at 14MHz, subject to maintaining unchanged the coil reactance and the overall Q. In other words, the inductance for 14MHz becomes $2.1 \times 1.5 = 3.15µH$ and the bandwidth ($Q = 100$) becomes 1420/1.5 = 947kHz. For maximum Q the coil size should be as large as possible but it is not critical. Weather protection tends to degrade the Q but is necessary if there is any chance of moisture being trapped between turns. The use of a long coil with self-supporting turns should avoid this but it is possible only at the high frequencies; too long a winding degrades the Q and a diameter of 3in (7.5cm) with a length of 6in (15cm) is a reasonable compromise. Coil turns may be obtained from Table 16.2, using the fact that inductance is proportional to the square of the number of turns.

For multiband operation the best method is to change the coil since it would appear that any attempt at variable tuning must result in some loss, particularly if a capacitor is used as this 'works' by increasing the current in the coil; typically, if I is doubled L is halved and losses doubled.

To obtain maximum benefit from use of a hat it should be as large as possible, so that its removal or reduction as a means of band changing is not acceptable, except perhaps at the HF end of the range where efficiency is still moderately high even without the hat.

Top-loading

A 3ft (0.9m) horizontal bar as in Fig 16.1(c) is not the most convenient method of top-loading, a 'skeleton' disc, Fig 16.4, being generally favoured [1]. For a solid disc the capacitance in picofarads is roughly equal to 0.9 times the diameter in inches (0.36 times the diameter in centimetres) and the skeleton disc is only slightly less. To obtain the required capacitance of 13.5pF a disc diameter of 15in (38cm) with at least four spokes should be satisfactory. Alternatively, for a cylinder having a length equal to the diameter [2] the capacitance in picofarads is equal to twice the diameter in inches (0.8 times the diameter in centimetres). To obtain the greatest possible loading effect for a given length of conductor this should be curled round or bent over, leaving the end free as in the case of the miniature beam elements (p205). The increased loading is due in part to the introduction of an inductive component, but this is relatively low loss and some overall improvement might be expected, though this idea is still only an idea for the experimenter.

One effect of top-loading which may be advantageous mechanically is that it allows the loading coil to be mounted if necessary in a lower position. The tendency in this direction

Table 16.2. Inductance values, efficiencies and overall bandwidth for 8ft (2.4m) centre-loaded whip with 7pF top-loading capacitance ($R_e = 10Ω$)

Frequency (MHz)	1.8	3.6	7.05	10	14.2	18
Inductance (µH)	287	67	16.8	7	2.6	0
Radiation resistance (Ω)	0.27	1.09	4.1	8.3	16.3	27
Efficiency (Q = 200) (%)	1.3	6.8	24.7	43	60	72
Overall bandwidth (kHz)	11.5	37	141	450	934	
Coil turns, 3in (7.6cm) diam, 6in (15.2cm) long	98	47	24	15	9	

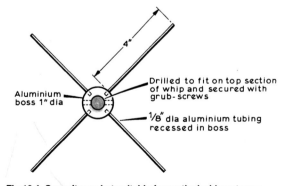

Fig 16.4. Capacitance hat suitable for vertical whip antenna

4"

Aluminium boss 1" dia

Drilled to fit on top section of whip and secured with grub-screws

1/8" dia aluminium tubing recessed in boss

is evident if one thinks of an extreme case in which the amount of top-loading is so large that it results in uniform current in the vertical portion of the antenna. Further loading, even if placed at the base, then has no effect on the radiation resistance.

To take a more practical example, assume an 8ft (2.4m) whip with the loading coil at the top and surrounded by a cylinder of 8in (20cm) length and diameter; the current distribution is virtually uniform, thus increasing the radiation resistance by four compared with Fig 16.1(a), ie to 1.36Ω at 3.5MHz. The capacitance is 16pF so that $L = 129\mu H$ (total) or $125\mu H$ for the coil. The coil resistance ($Q = 300$) comes to 9.16Ω and the radiation efficiency is 1.36/20.52 or 6.6%, ie very slightly worse than the previous example in which the coil was placed half-way down. Next consider base-loading, but since the coil no longer has to be supported, let it be supposed that the cylinder can be increased to 14in (35.6cm) length and diameter; this doubles C, thereby halving L and R, but the current is now non-uniform to the extent that the radiation resistance factor is 2.25 (as for Fig 16.1(b)) instead of 4. The efficiency is therefore 0.8/15.4 or 5.2%, which is slightly worse, being 1.5dB down in terms of signal level compared with the original figure of 6.8% efficiency for centre- plus top-loading, but still 3.74dB up compared with simple base-loading.

There is of course an exact optimum position for the loading coil, but the optimum is extremely flat, especially (as we have just seen) if top-loading is also used, and there is unlikely to be much advantage in departing from the centre position for the loading coil. Table 16.2 provides design data for top-loading in accordance with Figs 16.1(c) or 16.4(b). The whip will be roughly self-resonant at 21MHz and for higher frequencies it will be necessary to reduce the amount of top-loading.

Coil construction

Nylon or PTFE is recommended for coil formers and the wire gauge should be chosen so that the spacing between turns is not less than 0.6 times the wire diameter. Self-supporting air-spaced coils are preferable at the higher frequencies and can be wound with $^3/_{16}$in (5mm) or $^1/_4$in (6mm) diameter copper tubing. Mechanical fixings can be devised using, for example, wing nuts to allow interchange of coils plus the top sections; however, tapped coils may be used for greater convenience if some slight drop in efficiency is accepted at the higher frequencies. One method of coil assembly [1] is shown in Fig 16.5. Loading coils should be protected from moisture and this can be done by means of shields cut from old polythene bottles.

Earth resistance

Despite the crucial role of earth resistance and the capacitance to ground of the car body. there are few data available for these quantities, the 10Ω resistance assumed in the above calculations being a value which happens to be consistent

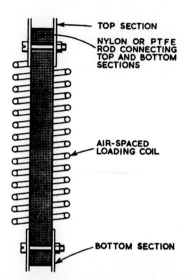

Fig 16.5. Loading coil assembly. An insulated rod is inserted into the bore of the whip above and below the coil, and runs through the centre of the coil. The rod must have good insulating properties and mechanical strength, PTFE or nylon being the most suitable materials

with some measurements at 4MHz [3]. As the main source of loss it is worth looking into more closely, and from inspection of Fig 16.6 it looks as if R_e ought to be reducible by mounting the antenna directly above the centre of the car roof. The RF return circuit from the antenna is partly by capacitance directly to the car body (mainly the roof), and partly by capacitance to ground in series with the capacitance to ground of the car body *via the resistance of the ground. It is this second path which must account for the whole of the unavoidable losses.*

A major improvement would result if this lossy path could be short-circuited and it would appear from inspection of Fig 16.6(a) and (b) that this objective might be largely achieved by mounting the antenna in the centre of the car roof. Further to encourage the RF current to take the shortest path back to the transmitter, the base of the antenna could be surrounded by two or three tuned radials mounted a few inches above the roof. The antenna could then be isolated from the car body by parallel tuning of the capacitance between the body and the radials as shown in Fig 16.6(c) and (d) thereby, at least in principle, removing most of R_e. However, owing to the resistance of the loading coil this is unlikely to help much at the lower frequencies, and a better course in this case might be to series-tune the car body with a suitable inductance so that it acts like the lower half of a dipole. This should add to the radiation resistance, and thus to some extent offset the reduction in length of the radiating element which is likely to be part of the price paid for roof mounting.

A possible source of earth resistance is poor electrical contact between different portions of the car body and, if for example the antenna is mounted on a wing or bumper, it is advisable to check the DC resistance between this, the chassis and other large areas of metal such as the roof. Up to the time

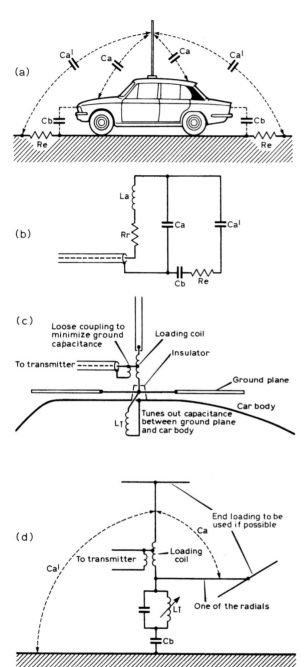

Fig 16.6. Reduction of earth losses. (a) analyses the problem in terms of the relevant capacitances and resistances, the equivalent circuit being shown at (b), and the simplest approach requires that everything possible should be done to reduce C_a' relative to C_a by careful positioning. (c) is an attempt to remove earth losses almost completely. The antenna plus radials can be regarded as a loaded dipole, the 'outer' of the feeder being joined to the point of minimum RF potential on the loading coil (four radials preferred though one may be enough). The capacitance between the radials and car body may be tuned out by L_T, the equivalent circuit being shown at (d)

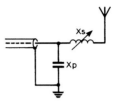

Fig 16.7. L-match. X_p is determined as shown in Fig 16.8; use of this value ensures that a match can be achieved by tuning the antenna slightly low

of writing Fig 16.6(c) and (d) is an untried idea, the discussion of it being aimed at providing further insight and forestalling any temptation to dismiss R_e (prematurely) as an insoluble problem.

Matching

Matching between the mobile antenna and the transmitter is probably best achieved by means of an L network, Fig 16.7. For the examples given earlier the total resistance R of the antenna is very roughly 20Ω in all cases, since reduction in radiation resistance is accompanied by increases in coil resistance and a constant figure of 10Ω has been assumed for R_e.

By tuning the antenna 'slightly long' a reactance $+X_s$ is caused to appear in series with R_a and this is equivalent to a parallel combination of resistance R_a' and reactance X_p. For matching, X_s is chosen so that $R_a' = Z_0$ and the resulting value of X_p is then tuned out by a parallel reactance $-X_p$. This can be done very easily with the Smith chart; referring to Fig 16.8, moving half-way round the circle from any point P corresponding to $(R_a + jX_s)$ brings us to a point P', the coordinates of which are equal to $1/R_a'$ and $1/X_p$. For this exercise one uses the 'normalised' values of R_a and X_s obtained by dividing Z_0 into the actual quantities, and the answer is interpreted via the reverse process of multiplying by Z_0, as explained in Chapter 4.

For matching to 50Ω the normalised R_a is 0.4, and going from P to P' must be done so that, starting from a point on the $R = 0.4$ circle and proceeding on a straight line via O, we arrive on the $R = 1.0$ circle in such a way that OP is equal to OP'. Laying a transparent ruler across the chart, it is easy to find a position such that intercepts with the $R = 0.4$ and $R = 1.0$ circles are equidistant from the centre as shown. Corresponding reactance values read from scales round the edge are $X_s = 0.5$ and $1/X_p = -1.25$. The last figure is the most interesting one since it tells us that if $R_a = 20Ω$ a capacitive reactance of 50/125 (ie 40Ω) will provide a perfect match subject to adjustment of antenna length, size of capacitive hat or loading inductance, whichever is most convenient. Since X_s is slightly greater than R_a, the amount of detuning required to effect the matching will be just over half the bandwidth figures given in the tables.

The corresponding capacitance values are given in Table 16.3. It will usually be sufficient to select the nearest convenient values. In cases where the antenna is nearly self-resonant,

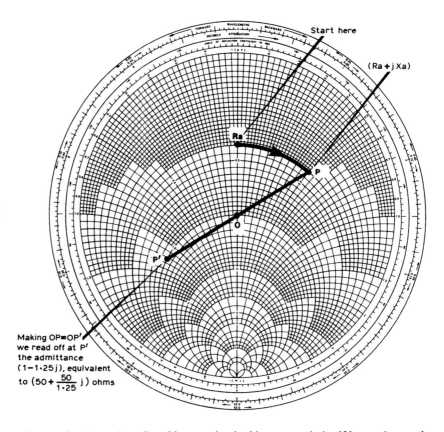

Fig 16.8. Use of Smith chart to determine X_p. Given that $R = 0.4Z_0$, points are found on the 0.4 and 1.0 resistance circles such that OP = OP', all three points being in a straight line. This gives the value of X_p and also of X_s, though this latter value is found in practice by tuning for minimum SWR after connecting the right value of X_p

Making OP=OP'
we read off at P'
the admittance
(1−1·25 j), equivalent
to $(50 + \frac{50}{1·25}$ j) ohms

eg for 24 or 28MHz, the radiation resistance plus the earth resistance should provide a reasonable match to 50Ω feeder without the use of a capacitor, though the antenna length or loading must be adjusted for resonance.

If a base-loading coil is used, matching may also be carried out by tapping the inner conductor of the coaxial feeder onto a suitable point on the coil.

The antenna may be tuned approximately by using a GDO, the feeder being preferably short-circuited which will place the frequency slightly on the low side as indicated earlier. After arriving at the right size of loading coil with as much capacitive loading as possible, final trimming may be carried out for minimum SWR using whichever method is most convenient. If it is not possible to obtain a satisfactory SWR, this may be due to values of R_e or coil Q different from those assumed in the above calculations and a different capacitance should be tried.

Portable antennas

Some of the antennas described in earlier chapters lend themselves better than others to 'fixed-portable' and field-day activities but broadly similar considerations apply and there is felt to be no need for further elaboration. The situation is however rather different if discussions are limited to antennas which are 'portable' in the strict sense, that is to say capable of being carried on foot for appreciable distances.

Portable operation in this case can in itself be a unique and fascinating hobby, especially if topographical features are exploited for low-power DX as outlined in Chapter 10.

The ideal portable antenna in most cases is the inverted-V dipole (Fig 16.9), 18–22swg (0.7–1.2mm) copper wire being suitable. Since the apex angle can usually be made large so that the ends are not too close to the ground, the length formula on p176 can be used. The feeder can be short and the power is low so that lighter grades of 75Ω twin-lead or 72Ω coaxial cable (though less efficient) are quite suitable, the use of a balun being advisable at the bottom or top respectively. Suitable baluns can be extremely small, lightweight, and easily constructed (p56).

It is usually desirable for DX work to use as much height and as large an apex angle as possible, for example 20–25ft (6.1–7.6m) and a base-line several times the length of the dipole but, when making use of a really steep ground slope, even lower heights down to 10ft (3m) or so can sometimes be equally effective. On the other hand, it has at times been found more convenient to string the dipole horizontally between trees. At other times the dipole has been rigged between

Table 16.3. Values of matching capacitance assuming R_a = 20Ω

Frequencies (MHz)	1.8	3.6	7.05	10	14.2	21.3
Capacitance (pF)	2212	1106	564	400	280	186

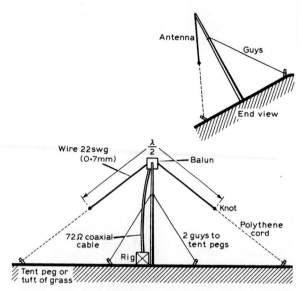

Fig 16.9. Inverted-V dipole over steep ground slope as used by the author for numerous antipodal and other DX contacts with very low power. Average time for erection is about 15min

projections near a cliff top, for example rocks or tufts of heather, a 10ft (3m) 'clothes prop' being used to push the centre of the dipole out over the edge. On other occasions a stone attached to polythene cord has been thrown over a tree branch and used to haul up the centre of the dipole, the ends being attached to 50–100ft (15–30m) lengths of thin polythene cord or nylon fishing-line (no other insulation needed) and strung out to whatever anchorage happened to be available. Even a tuft of grass serves if there is nothing better, though the anchorage should be as high and as far away as conveniently possible.

Alternatively a mast can often be improvised from bits of wood that are lying around, for example drift wood on the sea shore. On one occasion the author used a dipole stretched across a ravine, though reliance on natural features can be somewhat restrictive. The advantages of carrying one's own mast around are considerable, and a 20–24ft (6–7m) mast suitable for use in the sort of weather conditions conducive to portable operation can be constructed from tapered 4ft (1.2m) lengths of bamboo with short pieces of aluminium tubing pushed over one end to form a socket for the next section. For use on steep ground slopes two guys are sufficient and in some cases the mast can merely lean against a fence, tied loosely to a post. Such a mast need weigh no more than a camera tripod and is easily carried.

It takes only a few minutes to rig such an antenna and results will be much more interesting than anything likely to be achieved with the more usual vertical whip unless one is specialising in seashore or 'at sea' locations.

The reasons for this will be obvious from Chapter 10, and for general use the author considers there is no sensible alternative to a light thin-wire dipole with long strings attached,

which can be rolled up to fit into a pocket and erected in one of the ways just described. Such an antenna, erected at heights upwards of 10ft (3m) above a ground slope of 30° or more, is capable of reliable worldwide voice communication with radiated powers of the order of 1W. The comparison between a home location with 400W PEP, plus a three-element beam, and portable operation with 1W may be estimated roughly as follows:

Home station

Power advantage	26dB
Gain of beam	6dB
	32dB

From this, depending on the wave angle and antenna height, it may be necessary to deduct some loss due to the reflected wave, probably 2–3dB.

Portable station (worst case)

Gain from foreground reflection	6dB
Advantage of home station	25dB

The following comparison roughly summarises the author's experience of Australian contacts on 14MHz:

Home station report (typical from best stations)
  = S9 + 10dB
Portable stations report (typical)
  = S5, ie 26dB down in line with the above prediction, allowing 4dB per S-unit.

Portable stations (predicted for best case, see p138)

Extra gain from distant reflection	6dB
Extra low-angle gain (typical)	10dB
Portable station report (best actual)	= S9

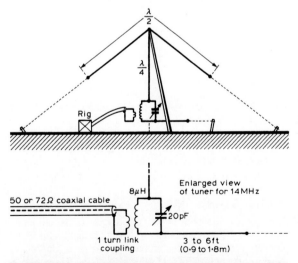

Fig 16.10. Method of rearranging the inverted-V to provide vertical polarisation for experiments over sea water. The balun should be short-circuited, the feeder being cut to a length of about 15–20ft (4.5–6m) for 14MHz and the system end-fed by the same method as the 'odd bit of wire' (p42) with Fig 4.30 as a suggested alternative

In line with this a long-path contact (GM–VK) between ideal locations was held down to 25mW [4].

The use of a reflector is open to consideration but in this case the wire diameter must be increased and, unless use can be made of trees or other natural supports, a heavier mast or two masts must be carried.

The use of a monopole (or more accurately perhaps, asymmetrical dipole) along the lines of Fig 16.10 is recommended for exploiting the possibilities of low-angle propagation with vertical polarisation over sea water . This should be erected as high and as close to the sea as possible, though height is only of secondary importance.

For short-range or medium-range working the dipole may be erected over flat ground, but DX possibilities on 14MHz are then very limited unless several watts of CW or well-processed SSB are available and the antenna can be raised to a height of at least $3\lambda/4$ which of course is much easier.

References

[1] *Radio Communication Handbook,* Vol 2, 5th edn, RSGB, 1977, pp14.10–14.12.
[2] *The ARRL Antenna Book,* 13th edn, ARRL, 1974, p62.
[3] *The ARRL Antenna Book,* 12th edn, ARRL, 1970, p293.
[4] 'HF antennae and propagation modes in relation to the amateur service', L A Moxon, *IEE Conference on Antennas and Propagation*, 28–30 November 1978 (see summary in *Radio Communiciation* May 1979).

Chapter 17

Small antennas

Inspired by a recent upsurge of interest in very small transmitting antennas, this chapter takes a critical look at three different approaches to the problem, endorsing the view that it is possible to construct efficient antennas much smaller than has generally been considered necessary, though the principles need to be clearly understood and rules strictly observed.

The primary concern when reducing the size of an antenna is to keep the radiation resistance R as high and the losses R_l as low as possible, R being strictly governed by the dimensions and varying as the square of dipole length and the fourth power of the loop diameter, or inversely as the square and fourth powers of λ respectively. This means that loops have much lower values of R but, offsetting this, they also have much lower loss resistances, though this makes them much more sensitive to losses arising from poor construction.

Size reduction in the case of dipoles is restricted mainly by losses in loading coils, whereas the very high Q of loops demands a high standard of mechanical precision as well as imposing a fundamental limit due to cutting of sidebands in the case of the lower-frequency bands. The loading of dipoles must (as far as possible) be capacitive, but in designing 'smallest possible' antennas this normally has to be supplemented by inductive loading. Losses can be reduced by increasing the diameter of conductors, and good construction becomes increasingly important as elements gets shorter.

Sources of loss include poor insulation, bad joins between conductors, and lack of symmetry which may be responsible for radiation from feeders. End-loading, if in close proximity to wet brickwork, may well be counter-productive due to the increased capacitance and higher voltages, and generally size reduction will tend to demand greater clearance from surrounding objects.

In the case of a short end-loaded dipole, the current distribution is virtually uniform for a length of about 0.1λ or less (Fig 2.5) and below this R is inversely proportional to the square of the length; in contrast to this, loops operate on the basis of antiphased sources separated by the loop diameter, thereby invoking an additional inverse-square law. These relationships are governed by the fundamental laws of physics and, despite sensational claims that appear from time to time, there is no way they can be circumvented. It is also to be noted that a very short dipole radiator forms only a small part of the circuit needed for establishing resonance so that the loss resistance is constant, bandwidth being directly proportional to the sum of the two resistances. It follows from this that, in the limit, there is an inverse-square relation between bandwidth and efficiency, and claims of wide bandwidth allied to high efficiency should in general be discounted in the case of reduced-size antennas.

It will be evident from Chapter 11 that the number of ways a single radiating element can be folded and loaded to fit it into spaces of various sizes and shapes is almost unlimited, though some methods are better than others. The recommended options in the earlier chapter can be expected to give almost identical performance in like circumstances apart from some trade-offs between size and bandwidth but in many cases, especially at the lower frequencies, even the smallest is much too large for fitting into an available space.

Since excellent contacts, including DX, can be regularly achieved with small fractions of the licensed power, there is plenty of scope for compromises such as the mobile antennas covered in Chapter 16. These can also be used for fixed installations, though freed from the constraints of mobile operation many other options become available and a major new development [1, 2] has been the upsurge of interest in small transmitting loops.

Although these have been around since early days, their merits have been overlooked on account of the narrow bandwidth, a typical instance of mistaking means to an end for the end itself which in this case is the ability to move frequency without impediment. As already demonstrated in the case of beams, small size requires remote tuning and this brings with it other important advantages. Likewise, because of their very high Q, tunable loops can play an important role in the suppression of spurious responses and overloading by strong signals.

Unfortunately, since bandwidth in some cases may be no greater than the width of a single SSB channel, tuning devices have to meet very high standards of mechanical precision as well as electrical quality. This places a severe strain on amateur ingenuity and resources, though many have tackled these problems successfully and commercial products, though inevitably expensive, are also available.

Loops are commonly considered as responding to magnetic fields and dipoles to electric fields, but this can be highly misleading since all antennas respond to both fields, and it is

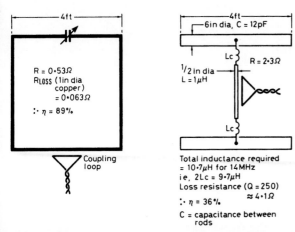

R = 0·53Ω
Rloss (1in dia
copper)
= 0·063Ω
∴ η = 89%

Coupling loop

─6in dia, C = 12pF

Lc
R = 2·3Ω

½ in dia
L = 1μH

Lc

Total inductance required
= 10·7μH for 14MHz
ie, 2Lc = 9·7μH
Loss resistance (Q = 250)
≈ 4·1Ω
∴ η = 36%

C = capacitance between rods

Fig 17.1. Comparison of loop with dipole for 'attempted best' designs fitting into a space of 4 × 4ft. Note that in the limit (ie at low efficiencies) $\eta \propto f^{3.5}$ for loop (see text) and f^3 for dipole since $R \propto f^4$ and $R_{loss} \propto f$

interesting to note that the radiation resistance of the loop in Fig 11.3 can be worked out correctly either by the usual loop formula:

$$R = 31,200 \ (A/\lambda^2)^2$$

or by treating the loop as two pairs of antiphase-connected dipoles at right-angles (in effect, as a pair of very small W8JK beams – nothing could be more 'electric' than these), adding the radiation resistances determined in accordance with Fig 3.4 using the method of calculation described on p81. This method was successfully used to determine which of two apparently different loop formulae had given the correct answer! As a demonstration of principle this was no less impressive for having been occasioned by a careless slip on the part of the author.

That said, there are a number of important practical differences which Fig 17.1 seeks to demonstrate by means of loops and dipoles, each designed to make the best possible use of the same small space, subject to keeping within the limits of what is reasonably practicable. As will be seen later, this is not quite fair to either of them since a circular loop shape is optimum and the dipole would be better as a rectangle. As illustrated the dipole follows conventional lines by using as much end-loading as possible; this is not enough in itself and has to be supplemented by loading inductance which is placed at the ends of the radiator, thereby ensuring a uniform current distribution and the largest possible value of R.

The essential design features of loops are likely to be less familiar to most readers and need to be explained in greater detail. After obtaining R from the above formula, the next thing we need to know is the loss resistance from Fig 3.10; this is proportional to $\sqrt{f}$ so that with $R \propto f^4$ we find on nearing the useful limit that efficiency is decreasing as $f^{3.5}$.

The need to minimise RF resistance makes it necessary to use copper tube of the largest possible diameter, in practice about 1in because of difficulty in bending larger sizes added

to the law of diminishing returns. There should be no joins except (unavoidably) at the ends since solder, especially when corroded, is a likely source of RF resistance, and further to reduce losses the capacitor must be well constructed with no moving contacts. Also, because of very high voltages, 'lossy objects' of all kinds (including the ground and, not least, the operator) must be kept at a distance! This applies also to the sides of the loop since, although the voltage between side-centres is only half that across the capacitor, it will still be large.

The feed normally uses a small coupling loop at the bottom of the main loop, and the tuning motor cables can be taken up the centre of the supporting mast which can be plastic or preferably glassfibre.

A loop circumference of 0.25–0.3λ at the highest frequency is recommended, except that at 29MHz loops larger than 0.25λ have been found difficult to tune. These figures are in line with the references, and it may be of interest also to relate them to the SDL curves, Figs 7.4 and 7.5, which indicate roughly equal amplitudes for the two orthogonal modes of radiation at a circumference of just under 0.5λ. This can be interpreted as a DX signal loss of 3dB, making 0.5λ a 'worst' loop size. Going the other way, a circumference of 0.25λ at 28MHz translates into a loss of only 3dB at 14MHz and about 7dB at 10MHz, but in view of the rapid decrease of bandwidth and efficiency, added to escalation of voltage across an expensive capacitor, restriction of frequency range to one octave [1] would appear to be good advice.

To this must be added the importance of ensuring symmetry and checking for possible RF currents on the feeder or motor control wires (which must be screened as well as effectively bypassed at the motor) in accordance with the recommendations of Chapter 4. If helpful the braids could be grounded by means of short loaded counterpoises (p54) at right-angles to the plane of the loop. They should also be bonded to any metal supporting mast.

Figs 17.2 to 17.5 give the main constructional details [1] of a loop for 14 to 29MHz, apart from the tuning capacitor and motor which will depend on the contents of the reader's junk box, his success in tracking down 'surplus' components, the size of his bank balance, or whether he really needs to cover five (or more) bands! A problem which appears to have caused some difficulty is the bending of large-diameter (22mm) copper pipe, but this can be achieved quite easily [1] by filling with dry sand which should be pressed down firmly while continuously shaking the pipe. After sealing the ends this can be bent around a circular object of correct size. One way to avoid the bending problem might be to use, for example, two ½in diameter tubes in parallel; I1ARZ advises that this has been tried with good results, but considers the difficulty of co-ordinating multiple loops to be greater than the bending of 1in tube. Against this, there could be possibilities of saving weight and cost (given that RF resistance is proportional to surface area) and the idea seems worth placing on record; it is suggested that conductors be spaced by several times their diameter, and currents should be equalised within 5–10% with the help of a current probe.

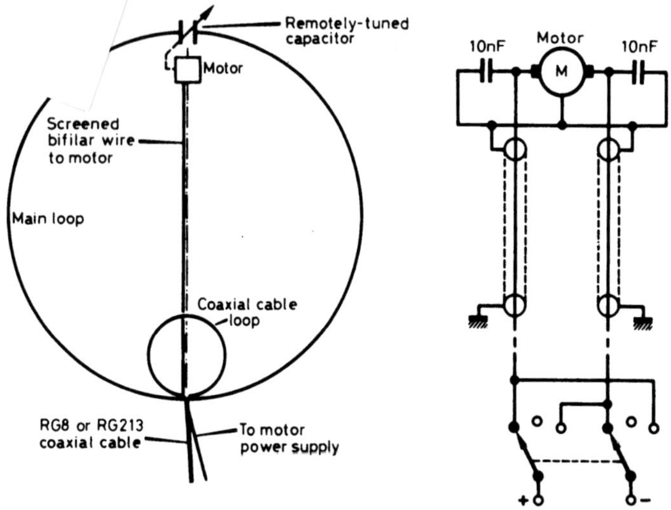

Fig 17.2. Schematic diagram of the loop antenna plus the tuning motor connections

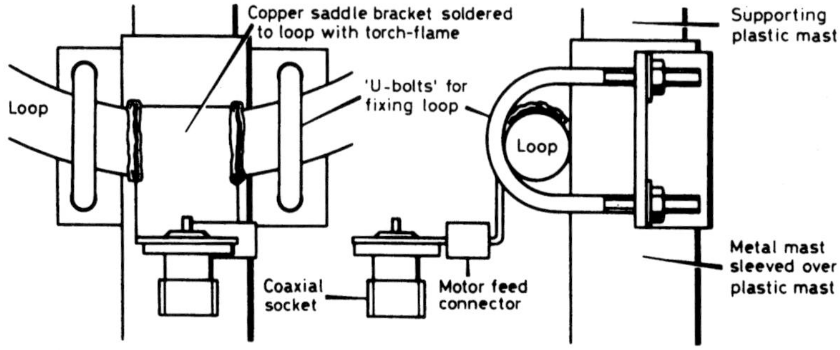

Remotely-tuned capacitor
Motor
10nF   Motor   10nF
M
Screened bifilar wire to motor
Main loop
Coaxial cable loop
RG8 or RG213 coaxial cable
To motor power supply
+   −

Fig 17.3. Details of the bottom of the loop – from the front

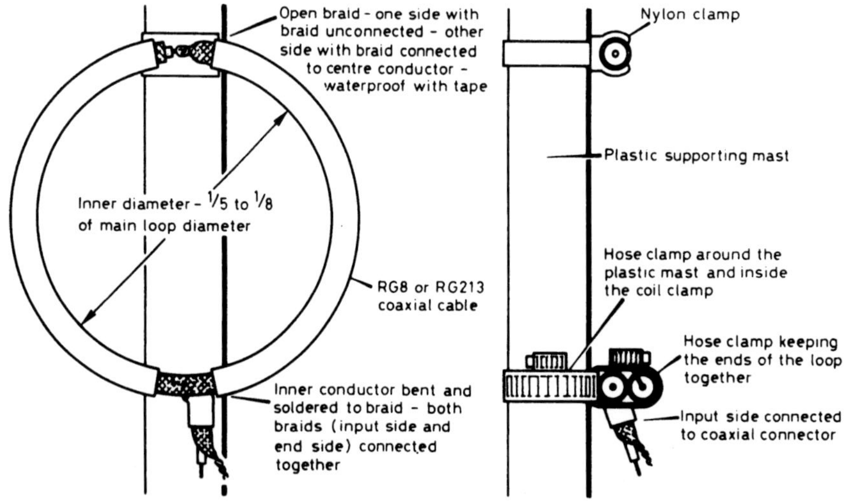

Copper saddle bracket soldered to loop with torch-flame
Supporting plastic mast
Loop
'U-bolts' for fixing loop
Loop
Metal mast sleeved over plastic mast
Coaxial socket
Motor feed connector

Fig 17.4. Construction of the coaxial feed loop

Open braid – one side with braid unconnected – other side with braid connected to centre conductor – waterproof with tape
Nylon clamp
Plastic supporting mast
Inner diameter – ⅕ to ⅛ of main loop diameter
RG8 or RG213 coaxial cable
Hose clamp around the plastic mast and inside the coil clamp
Hose clamp keeping the ends of the loop together
Inner conductor bent and soldered to braid – both braids (input side and end side) connected together
Input side connected to coaxial connector

For coverage of one octave (using 1 in tubing) an efficiency of 50% can be expected at the lowest frequency and, for a half-octave, this can be increased to 80%; these figures are for circular loops and, because of the reduced area, decrease to 34% and 70% respectively for the same length of tubing formed into a square loop. For a monoband loop 5ft in diameter an efficiency in excess of 90% at 14MHz can be expected, and Fig 17.6 shows how this varies with frequency. Fig 17.7 shows how efficiencies corresponding to those in Fig 17.6 vary with the conductor diameter. and in line with this

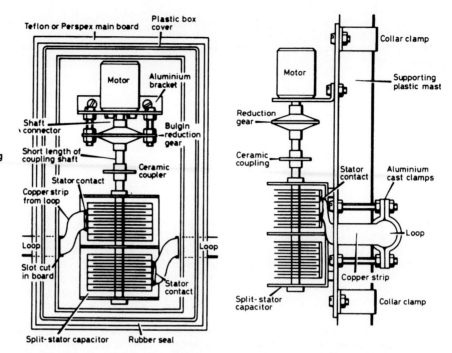

Fig 17.5. Two views of the tuning board

I1ARZ reports favourably on loops formed from RG-213 coaxial cable using the outer braid only. The author is indebted to I1ARZ also for information that in the monoband case fine tuning is possible by means of a coil wound on a toroid core which is threaded onto the bottom of the loop; this coil is connected by coaxial cable to a similar coil in the shack, series-tuned by a large variable capacitor. In this way it is possible for narrow-band operation to avoid the problems of remote tuning with very-high-voltage variable capacitors.

For further advice and suggestions the references should be consulted. It is encouraging to note that the small loop seems now to be firmly established as a 'no compromise' transmitting antenna. Further to this, reference [1] points out

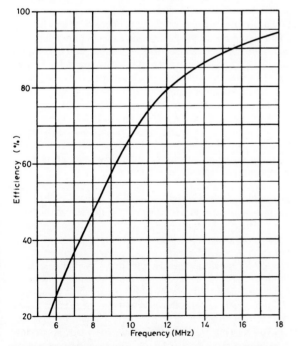

Fig 17.6. Variation of efficiency with frequency for 5ft diameter circular copper loop. Conductor diameter = 1in (may be difficult to tune above 14.5MHz)

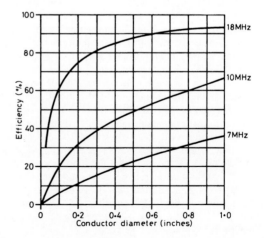

Fig 17.7. Variation of efficiency with conductor diameter for 5ft diameter circular copper loop

that it performs well indoors, but also draws attention to the potential hazard of prolonged exposure to strong magnetic RF fields, though the degree of risk is still an unresolved question.

Small loops seem to be acquiring an enviable reputation for 'working well close to ground' and the author's experience with parasitic ground-plane elements (p232) suggests a possible explanation since in both cases current is able to flow between the terminals of the 'equivalent generator' without necessarily flowing through the ground. In the case of the loop the path is a series-resonant circuit of extremely high Q and therefore low impedance. On the other hand, if the top and bottom of the loop are visualised as very short horizontal dipoles, some ground losses are to be expected (p116), in which case they should be reduced by means of a ground screen under the loop.

Indirect confirmation of this can be inferred from claims that such screens act as 'reflectors', though as will be evident from Chapter 10 reflections occur elsewhere and involve much larger areas. A more likely explanation (assuming low height) would be the reduction of ground losses.

As an example, extrapolating from Fig 6.19, a loss figure for a $\lambda/16$ square loop at ground level can be estimated from the relative lengths of conductor at zero height, recalling that a $\lambda/2$ dipole is equivalent to a λ/π dipole carrying a uniform current. This yields a resistance of $(\pi/16)^2 \times 80 = 3\Omega$. For a loop of this area $R = 0.48\Omega$ and for the loop away from ground at 14MHz we have $R_1 = 0.13\Omega$. It follows that if all the loss can be removed by using a conductive mat to provide a low-resistance path for currents induced in the adjacent ground, efficiency can be increased from 13% to 79%.

Figures for different heights and circular loops are difficult to calculate, but the loss will decrease very rapidly with height, and division by a factor somewhere between 10 and 100 can be expected for a circular loop at a height equal to its diameter.

There appears to be some confusion also about directivity and gain, in which respects it will by now come as no surprise to readers that 'small loops' (at the upper end of the recommended frequency range) differ little in respect of gain from other small radiators of sizes up to and including that of a quad element, though they are *not* usable as close-spaced beam elements; it will also be noticed that the radiation pattern is omnidirectional in the plane of a loop but 'cos θ' at right-angles, whereas the opposite applies in the case of dipoles and ground-plane antennas. In free space it would be impossible to determine from the radiation pattern which type of antenna is being used to produce it, and at a height of 0.3λ the antenna with its image constitute a collinear pair providing 3dB of gain in both cases. At ground level the loop, especially if rotatable, should be more effective for discriminating against local noise sources, while the lack of vertical directivity makes it equally suitable for DX and short-skip communication; on the debit side, short-skip QRM from the wanted direction or its reciprocal will be worse.

Returning now to Fig 17.1(b), the capacitance between two parallel conductors remote from ground is given [8] by:

$$C \approx 3.7/(\log 2D/d) \quad \text{pF/ft}$$

where D is the spacing and d the diameter. The inductance of a straight round conductor is:

$$L \approx 0.005(2.3 \log 4l/d - 1) \quad \text{microhenrys}$$

where l is the length, d the diameter, and all dimensions are in inches. These formulae give the values marked on the diagram, and it will be noticed that resonance at 14MHz requires an added inductance of 11µH which at a Q of 250 will introduce 3.7Ω of loss. This results in an efficiency of 40% compared with 83% for the loop, though increasing the dipole length by 50% brings its efficiency up to 67%, ie it is down on the loop by only 1dB and the capacitance could be nearly doubled by using two conductors at right-angles. The respective bandwidths are 77kHz for the dipole and 17kHz for the loop.

We can do much better also with the loop, since the square shape is inefficient, having been introduced for the sole purpose of trying to compare like with like; note that the same length of conductor bent into a circle provides 27% of additional area which increases R by a factor of 1.62. The loop is perceived as an ideal antenna for small spaces and low or moderate heights, massive construction and the need for precision engineering being factors to its disadvantage.

The small dipole, on the other hand, is a kind of 'poor relation', with monoband operation a serious limitation; however, it is much more versatile and can be constructed in wire form for fitting into spaces of different shapes and sizes as suggested in Fig 17.8. Note that if, for example, it were to find itself in a long narrow space, the amount of end-loading could be increased, the loading inductances eliminated, and the loss resistance reduced to less than an ohm (12swg) or about 0.15Ω if one could afford 0.5in copper tube, loss by radiation from the end-loading being of the same order. Since R is about 0.8Ω this suggests the possibility of efficient radiation at 14MHz from a vertical dipole only 2ft in extent; loss by radiation from the end-loading would be negligible on the assumption of perfect balance, though this seems highly unlikely. Although because of the nature of the loading the description 'small' no longer fits, this example helps to demonstrate a wide range of options.

Subject to the continued assumption of uniform current distribution (achieved by end-loading) there is clearly no distinction to be made, for a given radiator length, between symmetrical and asymmetrical dipoles (eg 'ground-plane' antennas) except for the greater risk in the latter case of feeder radiation due to imbalance.

Fig 17.9 shows another useful form of small dipole based on either helical loading, as commonly used in mobile work, or planar loading, an idea for which the author is indebted to VK5HA. In these cases the current distribution is sinusoidal and the radiation resistance assuming a length l is given by $(2l/\lambda)^2 \times 80$. Of these, the helix is neater but less efficient since it requires a much greater length of wire, and to get enough onto the former usually requires a smaller gauge. The planar dipole shown at (c), though only about 11ft long for 14MHz,

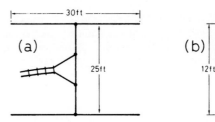

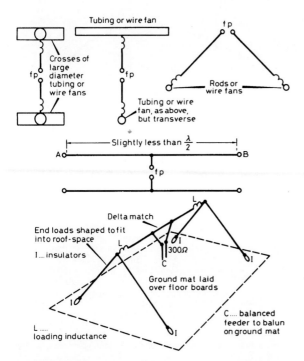

Fig 17.8. Small dipoles for odd spaces. Any of these *might* benefit from a ground mat

Fig 17.10. Capacitively loaded dipoles. (a) Dimensions for 7MHz but could be scaled to fit into 7ft square for 28MHz (see Figs 13.14, 13.15, 13.16). (b) Total wire length 37ft 3in for 14MHz (based on miniature beam element, Fig 12.13)

0.15λ and height or width of 0.075λ, though any increase in these dimensions could be used to advantage, with one of the arrangements described in Chapter 11 possibly becoming more appropriate.

A suitable space, which might consist for example of a backyard, a flat roof, the area between two chimney stacks, or an attic, may be used to accommodate a short end-loaded radiator such as Fig 17.10(a) or (b) or, if space is very tight, one of the options in Fig 17.11. In each case the dipole may be fed symmetrically, or off-centre as in Fig 17.12 where in one case the use of top-end feed ensures the absence of losses

has a very low visual profile and an estimated efficiency of about 80%.

Small dipoles and the real environment

Neither of the antennas featured in Fig 17.1 scores well on visual profile but a circular loop would appear to have a decided 'edge' in cases where both height and width are severely restricted. On the other hand, the simplicity, low cost and ease of construction of wire dipoles (vertical as well as horizontal) makes them the more attractive subject to sufficient space being available. For a 'full gain' antenna this could mean a rectangle with a minimum length of the order of

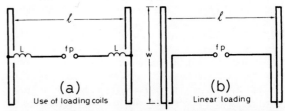

Fig 17.11. Capacitive loading with additional inductive loading. In both cases, $R \approx (2l/\lambda)^2 \times 160$. In case (a), l can be as short as desired, except that losses in L increase and R decreases as l is reduced. In case (b) there is a lower limit to l, depending on w

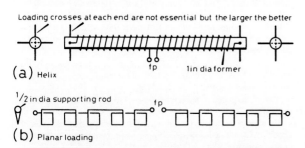

Fig 17.9. Loaded dipoles. For 14MHz about 40ft of wire is required at (b) and 50–60ft for (a). Dimensions are not critical as they must be finalised by trial and error. The two halves of the helix may be wound in the same or opposite directions. Maximum length for (b) is about 11ft. Suggested wire gauge is 16swg, at least four loops per side, taped to glassfibre rod

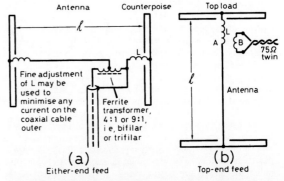

Fig 17.12. Asymmetric dipoles. Note that the antenna and counterpoise or top load *must* be individually resonated. In both cases R, l, the capacitive hats and the total inductance between them are assumed to be identical. In (b) coupling coil must be carefully positioned (close to A) to minimise any out-of-balance indicated by probe held 1in from feeder. It may help to join A to the centre (B) of the coupling coil, or to wind a few turns of feeder (well spaced) on to a ferrite rod or ring

due to ground currents as can be inferred from p120, though in this respect centre-feed should be equally effective. In the case of vertical antennas the top-loading, base-loading, or both, may with advantage be replaced by sets of four radials in place of the single pairs shown. Note that R is the same in all cases for a given length due to the uniform current distribution.

Reference [7] makes interesting reading for further insight into the relative merits of loops and dipoles for use in small spaces, tending to favour dipoles rather than loops especially in 'crawl spaces' where, though the vertical dimension is restricted, relatively long horizontal runs capable of use for the provision of good 'capacity top hats' may exist. Tighter coupling into surrounding energy absorbers (due to the very large associated RF currents) is also seen as a disadvantage of loops.

The 'hula-hoop' antenna

This antenna, Fig 17.13, also known as the DDRR or 'directional-discontinuity ring radiator', is surrounded by an intriguing air of mystery which is accentuated by bringing together a number of threads as related below. Though announced some 30 years ago [3] as a 'coming trend', capable of reducing antenna heights from 60ft to 2ft, it has made little impact on the amateur scene, though the original prescription continues to be featured in amateur reference books, eg [4] which refers readers also to an excellent theoretical study (of early date) explaining why the vertical dimension needs to be greatly increased [5]; this points out that, in the case of a 40m antenna, increasing height from 1ft to 3½ft and using copper for the resonator and ground screen in place of the high RF-loss steel and chicken-wire currently in vogue increases efficiency from 2.75% to a rather more useful 25.8%, the increase of R with height being roughly square law.

Apart from this digression the 'hula hoop' story unfolds as follows, starting with a description of the original antenna as set out by Pat Hawker, G3VA [6].

"A revolutionary approach which may allow us eventually to forget high masts or towers is foreshadowed in 'Hula hoop antennas: a coming trend' by J M Boyer in *Electronics* (11 January 1963), an article aimed primarily at commercial stations. This exciting new concept suggests that an antenna only about *2ft high* can give a performance comparable to that of a full λ/4 high 60ft antenna, a height saving of some 30 times. Imagine an effective DX antenna some 4ft high for 1.8MHz, down to 3½in high for 28MHz!

In the past it has been shown that when vertical antenna height is reduced by electrically loading the element (as for example in mobile rigs) efficiency deteriorates pretty rapidly. But in this new system, which is termed a 'leaky waveguide radiator', it is claimed that circumferential aperture is substituted for the lost height of the antenna.

This particular 'hula hoop' has no connection with an earlier amateur antenna of the same name. In general appearance it resembles the popular halo but the loop extends right round (see Fig 17.13) and the whole system is tuned against the ground plane earth by C rather like a λ/4 Marconi. Basically it is explained as 'circular array with a λ/4 conductor conductively joined to the top of a 2.5° high

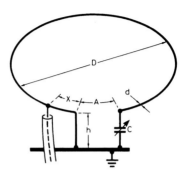

Fig 17.13. Dimensions given by W4MIP for the W6UYH Northrop 'hula hoop' DDRR antenna.

Band	D	H	d	A	X	C1
160m	36ft	48in	5in	18in	12in	100pF
80m	18ft	24in	5in	12in	6in	100pF
40m	9ft	12in	2½in	6in	3in	75pF
20m	4ft 6in	6in	1in	3in	1½in	50pF
15m	3ft 4in	4½in	½in	2in	1in	35pF
10m	2ft 3in	3in	½in	2in	¾in	25pF

where *D* is diameter of loop, *H* is height above ground plane, *d* is tube diameter (two band), *A* is gap, *X* is feedpoint. *C* must have a very high voltage rating – about 4kV for 100W

vertical element and bent round in the horizontal plane at this height to form a circle.'

In the article all dimensions are given in terms of electrical degrees (90° equals an electrical quarter-wave). As stated the vertical section is only about 2.5°, and the circular conductor has a diameter less than 28°. The feedpoint dimension X depends upon the feeder impedance and it is stated that it can be adjusted for lines of 36–500Ω. By varying C1 a given antenna can be tuned over a frequency range of 2:1 (thus in theory making possible use on two adjacent bands) without exceeding a feeder standing wave ratio of 2:1, although its efficiency would appear to fall off sharply.

A snag is that with the hula hoop an extremely efficient ground plane is required, preferably a solid circular sheet of copper or aluminium (provided that this is prevented from becoming oxidised). This ground plane should have a diameter some 25% larger than the antenna ring.

A 2ft high model KM2XOP (an American experimental station) supported on a circular ring of insulators was tested against 110ft and 68ft high radiators all using the same ground plane. At 4MHz ($h = 2.88°$, $D = 26.28°$) the loss compared with a 68ft tower was less than 3dB (½ S-unit). At 2MHz the same antenna was only 1.44° high, 12.9° diameter and compared with a 110ft tower represented a loss of about 2–2½ S-points. The ground plane, however, consisted of no less than 90 λ/2 radials.

A mobile model for 26.5 to 31MHz, 27in in diameter and only 3½in above the vehicle roof which formed the ground plane, is reported to have performed better than a λ/4 whip.

The dimensions given under Fig 17.13 are those suggested by W4MIP in *CQ*.

By using a thick loop (as shown in the table) operation is possible, says W4MIP, on two bands; for single-band operation a much thinner loop is possible.

Because of the requirement for an extremely good ground plane, this antenna is probably of most use in its mobile application."

Radiation is variously described as coming from the horizontal and vertical portions of the DDRR, but in fact comes from

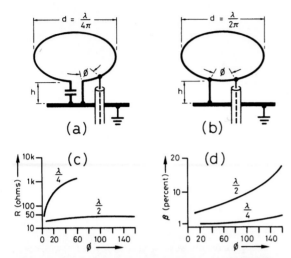

Fig 17.14. (a) The λ/4 'hula hoop' DDRR antenna. (b) λ/2 closed loop. (c) Resonance impedance versus feedpoint angle. (d) Bandwidth versus feedpoint angle

both as analysed in [5]. Careful inspection shows that it is in fact a top-loaded vertical, radiation directly upwards from the nearly-λ/4 top being incompletely suppressed by bending it into a circle whereas [5] radiation from the vertical is partially cancelled by antiphase radiation from the leads to the capacitor. This requires a close approach to resonance so that the value of capacitance is held to the minimum needed for tuning purposes. An unexplained feature is the failure to bend the loop into a figure-of-eight, an obvious step which would cancel most of the unwanted upwards radiation and halve the area occupied. In this form it offers interesting possibilities for an antenna of exceptionally low profile and reasonable efficiency.

Shortly after publication of the original DDRR design, a λ/2 version was proposed as illustrated in Fig 17.14; this offers a number of advantages, though in view of larger size (10ft, diameter for 14MHz) this qualifies only marginally for inclusion in the present chapter. G3VA reports on this as follows [6]:

"The quad 'hoop' is basically one wavelength in perimeter. The original Boyer (W6UYH) DDRR hula hoop was resonated to λ/4 by the capacitor at the free end. This suggests that there might be an intermediate λ/2 form of loop – and delving into the literature has produced evidence (*Electronics Letters* September 1965) that this has been recognised. An Italian group then pointed out that, compared with the Boyer λ/4 'less known is the λ/4 closed-loop antenna which has quite a different and, in some ways, better performance'. Fig 17.14 shows the basic differences between the hula hoop and the λ/4 closed loop.

The information given by the Italians (including various plots of impedance and radiation characteristics) seems to indicate that the λ/2 system may have considerable advantages for amateur experimentation: the bandwidth of the λ/2 system can be up to 10 times that of the λ/4 system, thus allowing a band to be covered without

retuning; the feedpoint impedance remains roughly 50Ω for φ angles from about 20° to 160° (making for easy matching and providing a simple means of finally resonating the loop to the required centre frequency); feedpoint impedance and resonance frequency can also be varied by changing *h*.

The λ/2 closed loop should prove far less critical in adjustment, and – with a good ground plane – should give omnidirectional radiation at reasonable vertical angles. A suggested value for φ for 50Ω coaxial feed would be roughly 100° and *h*/λ about 5%. The letter suggests that there could be many applications, particularly for mobile work, of such loops (the original work was at 400MHz)."

In this case the radiation is horizontally polarised, and despite the apparent lack of further recognition (or the all-too-familiar extravagant claims) the possibilities are interesting. Long ago, when curves showing the variation of *R* with height for horizontal antennas invariably assumed perfect ground, the author nurtured the idea that below a height of about λ/8 there ought to be no further drop in signal strength because the antenna and its image could be regarded as a close-spaced beam; in this case halving the spacing would divide *R* by 4, double the current, and compensate for the drop in height.

The reason why this does not happen is the sharp rise in ground losses shown in Figs 6.17 and 6.19. The last figure, however, also shows that the losses can be prevented by means of a ground screen, and it has been established (eg in the case of the DDRR antenna as noted above) that for small antennas close to ground the screen does not have to be much larger than the antenna. From Fig 6.19 the value of *R* for a λ/2 dipole at a height of 0.05λ above an adequate ground screen (in a typical case) is 8Ω, implying a gain of about 10dB to set off against a height loss of 20dB compared with the same dipole at a height of λ/2. In practical terms this should work out as a very useful DX capability at 14MHz with a horizontal antenna only waist high. In the case of the λ/2 hula hoop, efficiency has been found difficult to estimate, but a 0.23λ magnetic loop, arranged horizontally, would require a much smaller ground screen and should be almost as good as the λ/2 dipole.

References

[1] 'Electrically tunable HF loop', Roberto Craighero, I1ARZ, *Radio Communication* February 1989.

[2] *The ARRL Antenna Book*, 15th edn, ARRL, 1988, Chapter 6, pp5-9 to 5-16.

[3] 'Hula hoop antennas, a coming trend', J M Boyer, *Electronics* 11 January 1963.

[4] *The ARRL Antenna Book*, 15th edn, ARRL, 1988, p6-9.

[5] 'Study of the DDRR antenna', Robert B Dome, W2WAM, *QST* July 1972.

[6] *Amateur Radio Techniques*, 7th edn, Pat Hawker, G3VA, RSGB, 1980, pp272, 288.

[7] 'Secret antennas', R Silberstein, W0YBF, *Radio Communication* September 1989, p52.

[8] *Radio Engineers Handbook*, F E Terman, McGraw-Hill, 1943, pp49 and 119.

8

Making the antenna work

Ideally, it should be possible for an antenna to be made up according to instructions, erected, connected to the transmitter and guaranteed to work without imposing any further tasks on the operator. To achieve this, however, a number of conditions must be satisfied, as follows:

(a) The antenna must be designed to present a specified load impedance to the transmitter.

(b) The transmitter must be pre-tuned to work into the above impedance, either by the operator using the appropriate 'dummy load', or by the manufacturer who presets all the adjustments before it leaves the factory on the basis of some commonly used impedance, such as 50Ω, to which the antenna must also conform.

(c) Differences between the environment assumed in designing the antenna and that in which it is installed must be negligible. This means any effect on antenna impedance must be within the tolerances allowable at the transmitter, eg an SWR better than 1.05 as specified for the author's FT75.

(d) The antenna must experience no significant changes between the design or adjustment process and the final erection; this places a serious handicap on anyone whose experimental efforts tend, like those of the author, to find themselves lying in the grass and repeatedly tripped over on their way from the tune-up position to the end of the mast. In the case of a commercial design the manufacturer, the carrier and the recipient *may* take every precaution, and the purchaser's confidence may or may not be justified. On the other hand, when an antenna is built from published data, even though this has been obtained from two or more sources cross-checked with one another, there is no more than a fair chance that it will work well enough to be incapable of improvement; this leaves a likelihood that adjustment will be needed or desirable and the user may be unaware of this.

In some cases, eg mobile antennas as we have just seen, final adjustments *have* to be carried out *in situ;* moreover, this book has been addressed in particular to experimenters looking for something which is either better than the antenna designs currently available 'off the shelf', or more closely tailored to their personal requirements. This has included the presentation of ideas, many of which are still in the experimental

stage, and such constructional data as may be available does not have behind it the weight of experience enjoyed by well-established designs such as the quad. Yet, even with this latter antenna, poor results are often obtained at the first attempt due to the reflector being tuned too low.

It may be worth also recording the author's personal experience with design data for Yagi antennas from two sources; when IBA TV transmissions first started from London the author, being in a fringe area, decided to try a double Yagi with five elements in each 'bay'. There was no picture and (aurally) the vision signal was weak though the sound signal (lower in frequency) was of usable strength. It was recalled that some weeks earlier it had been necessary to shorten the directors of a vertical wire Yagi for 14MHz by more than a foot (30cm), though at the time it was thought this might have been due to neglecting the effect of insulators. On the strength of this, armed with the requisite ladders and a hacksaw, 0.5in (13mm) was removed from all the directors; on returning to the TV set, a perfect picture was found on the screen.

In contrast to this experience, a three-element 14MHz Yagi designed from the data in Fig 5.25 worked perfectly. Nevertheless, the author's reluctance to guarantee such information can perhaps be appreciated; instead the reader may expect to be told how to adjust and check antennas so as to be assured that they are in fact working correctly.

Against this background it is not difficult to appreciate the benefits of resonant feeders which allow all adjustments to be carried out in the shack using the equipment normally available, with the recommended addition of a GDO. The necessary tests in the case of beam antennas have been described in Chapter 12, though even in this case additional measurements based on local test signals can be of value.

Simple antennas

In a few cases, such as the $\lambda/2$ horizontal dipole, standard length formulae can be used with reasonable confidence, though (at the very least) some form of antenna current indicator is needed for tuning the transmitter.

The simple indicator shown in Fig 18.1 was used in the author's first portable rig, which was operated with powers in the region of 0.25–1.0W, and it can of course be adapted for

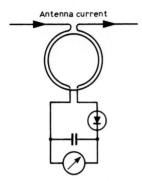

Fig 18.1. Simple current indicator. A loop of 1in (2.5cm) diameter has a reactance of only 4Ω at 14MHz and will have negligible effect on matching

higher powers by reducing the loop sizes and the meter sensitivity.

Alternatively, an SWR bridge (p274) can be used as the RF indicator and this is strongly advised since it provides other important functions. Assuming the use of coaxial feeder, it affords the simplest indication of correct matching and is a valuable tool for correcting a mismatch should this be necessary. Regardless of the type of antenna or feeder system, it allows an ATU or other matching device to be adjusted so that a sufficiently good match is presented to the transmitter. It can also be roughly calibrated by the method described on p274 as a power meter for confirming that the transmitter is giving its rated output, whereas the simple current meter establishes merely that the transmitter is giving whatever maximum output it happens to be capable of producing at that moment. In principle the simple indicator can also be calibrated in terms of RF power, but only if the antenna impedance is known and can be assumed not to vary.

Antennas can usually be tuned satisfactorily at a convenient height of 6ft (2m) or so, allowing for an upward shift in frequency of 1–1½% when they are raised to their full height. In the case of single-element antennas, correct operation can usually be secured by first tuning them approximately to resonance with a grid dip oscillator (GDO); after this the feeder should be connected and any variables in the matching system adjusted simultaneously with the tuning of the element, so as to obtain minimum SWR.

When making observations on a driven element with a GDO, the feeder must *always* be disconnected since otherwise what is being measured is the resonance, not of the antenna itself, but of a complex system consisting of antenna plus feeder plus whatever unknown impedance is presented to the feeder by the transmitter or ATU. In the case of a centre-fed antenna correct resonance will be obtained with the feeder short-circuited, but with a T- or delta match the feeder must be physically removed and this will result in a slight shift in the effective resonance of the system.

Loops or V-shaped elements may be tuned in a horizontal position. It is important in the case of a V that the ends should not be allowed to trail in such a way that they are much closer to the ground than its centre since this can lower the resonance by several per cent. The SWR meter should be placed at the antenna, partly because this is the centre of operations, but also because the SWR will be reduced by any losses in the feeder and readings may also be affected by currents induced in the outer conductor of the line, a situation which is more difficult to avoid with the antenna near ground.

Special problems exist in the case of asymmetrical dipoles since, as explained on p41, if a dipole is fed off-centre then each pole must be individually resonant. If one pole is of resonant length the other can in the first instance be tuned against it by means of a GDO, but the adjustment may be inexact due to mutual coupling between the poles so that it needs to be finalised by tuning the loaded side of the dipole (or even both) for minimum current on the outer of a coaxial feeder. If neither side is resonant, each side may be initially tuned against a λ/4 wire cut to the right length and erected temporarily for the purpose, but when the halves are joined it may be found that the resonant frequency is displaced by up to 2 or 3%. Again the same treatment is applicable, but it will almost certainly be necessary to adjust both sides and, since balance can only be 'perfect' at one frequency, imbalance will be observable at others if a sensitive meter is in use.

The question then arises as to how much imbalance can be tolerated. This can probably be judged only by results, eg whether TVI or noise are made worse or signal strength reduced when frequency is altered, or preferably an equivalent imbalance introduced at a fixed frequency, in which case any decrease in efficiency can be determined by observing the change (if any) of current induced in another antenna.

A very similar situation occurs when the top and bottom dipoles of an impedance-transforming loop (p126) are tuned individually and then joined, but this is of little consequence as the system is symmetrical and exact resonance not essential to its proper functioning.

Even a simple antenna can acquire faults which are not immediately obvious. For example, suppose the wire used for a portable antenna, being thin and subjected to a lot of flexing, breaks in the course of erection; a twisted join allows operation to proceed, but may then be forgotten until after corrosion has set in. If a balun is used it should be tested before use and particular care taken to ensure that it is connected correctly. Most such faults can be avoided by inspection in the case of a portable antenna (Chapter 16) but the coaxial or 300Ω twin feeder of a permanent installation can deteriorate without this being obvious.

Breakdown can occur in a balun, though this is unusual when working with low impedances; on the other hand, operation *may* be perfectly satisfactory *without* a balun – until the feeder length is changed, due perhaps to a rearrangement of the shack.

Assuming reasonable precautions such as careful attention to symmetry, weatherproofing of any vulnerable components, and observance of any necessary precautions against feeder radiation (p53), there is not much else to go wrong. However, an 'invisible' (thin wire) antenna could stretch under severe tension, eg under storm conditions if anchored to a swaying tree without due safeguards. Also, if there is more than one antenna at a given location, each should be suspected of upsetting the other 'until proved innocent' or unless adequate precautions have been taken (pp269, 270).

The adjustment and testing of two-element beam antennas

The findings reported in Chapter 5 cast doubt on traditional methods for the adjustment of two-element beams since the main objective now includes equalisation of current amplitudes by adjustment of coupling, which has to be achieved simultaneously with correct phasing, though in practice it may be sufficient to fix either the tuning or the coupling and vary the other. These adjustments rigorously determine the radiation pattern and gain; conversely, observation of the radiation pattern can be used as the test of whether the amplitudes and phases are correct, the design objective being based on Figs 5.4 and 5.7.

Usually a parasitic element is best used as a reflector although there are exceptions (p201). Ideally both elements should be self-resonant but close inspection of Fig 5.3 points to the desirability of tuning slightly low to secure the widest possible range of adjustment for QSY, nulling or insurance against maladjustment. The parasitic element is then tuned for minimum response on a signal in the selected null direction, eg 140° relative to the beam heading as recommended on p156. The use of a field-strength meter in accordance with Fig 18.2 is one option. However, invoking the principle of reciprocity, there are important advantages in replacing the detector by a low-power transmitter, which can for example be a crystal oscillator powered by a couple of nicad batteries (2.5V) and feeding into the test antenna through an attenuator. A main advantage of this is the much greater sensitivity of the receiver in the rig, which makes it possible to operate with very low power levels and thereby reduce 'spectrum pollution'.

For adjusting conventional beam antennas near ground, the receiver output from a CW signal can be wired to a meter at the test position, the AGC being switched out of circuit, though this will not guarantee correct operation at normal height and needs to be supplemented by measurement of directional pattern after erection. This can be done from the shack, an oscilloscope being the ideal indicator. Measurements at low height can be useful for checking symmetry, but only if there is no feeder radiation and elements remain strictly parallel with the ground as well as clear of other objects. Use of the CW mode avoids complications arising from the non-linearity of AM detectors at low levels, though care must still be taken to avoid receiver saturation at high signal levels. Whatever the type of beam, in-shack observations will help to disclose problems caused for example by screening or reflections from other antennas. Whether a remote signal source or a field-strength meter is used, adequate precautions are needed to prevent RF pick-up on, or radiation from, control leads as described later in this chapter.

The relative currents in the elements may be checked as described on p279, aiming for at least 20% undercoupling if

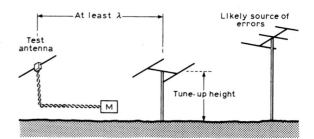

Fig 18.2. Use of field-strength meter. A test antenna having the same polarisation as the beam under test incorporates a diode detector with a meter for indicating the rectified current. The meter is wired back to a convenient position adjacent to the antenna under test. A separation of 1λ should suffice for providing an accurate indication of the null directions, but care must be taken to avoid reflections from surrounding objects such as another beam as shown on the right

adjustments are made within reach of the ground, though this figure may be modified by experience. Ultimately the correctness of coupling needs to be judged by the depth of nulls and the directions in which the deepest nulls are obtained in the course of normal operation. On the other hand, a steady signal for initial tests is extremely helpful. This may well be difficult without the help of another amateur station well within ground-wave range and similarly polarised because, although a separation of λ is adequate for determining null directions, it needs to be increased to at least 3λ if seeking to establish null depths in excess of 20dB. Likely adjustments include the spacing between ends of dipoles or bottom corners of delta loops, increase or decrease of coupling by the overlapping of tuning stubs, adjusting the spacing between adjacent ends of VK2ABQ-type elements and, if resonant feeders are used, coupling between lines in the shack. After any adjustment of spacing or neutralising, the reflector tuning should be rechecked and the whole process repeated if necessary. The driven element should then be matched as described above for a single element.

The reflector is likely now to be identical with the driven element; it should be made so and given its own separate feeder which can be used for remote fine tuning, the two feeders being interchangeable for beam reversal as recommended in earlier chapters; this applies equally to driven arrays if these are a preferred option (p90). Among other advantages, beam reversal provides an immediate audible check of correct operation, though possibilities of asymmetry can arise and the check needs to be made for *both* directions of fire. An antenna can often work well despite detuning of the driven element so that, if a two-element beam is working well to the west with a sharp null to the east, this is no proof that there will be gain to the *east* if the beam is reversed by an interchange of feeders. It is even possible there could still be gain to the west and a minimum to the east unless the two elements with their feeders are identical.

The reason for first tuning *one* of the elements as a reflector may seem obscure, since eventually both are required to be identical and matched to the feeder. The matching process must, however, take due account of the impedance transferred into the driven element from the other element *when this has the correct current flowing in it*. The easiest method of establishing this is the one just described though, provided both elements are *nearly* correct, it is possible to drive them both as described on p92. In this case the SWR meter should be placed in the feeder handling most of the power, ie the forward element if the mutual coupling is capacitive or the rear element if the coupling is inductive as explained on p83. The other feeder has relatively little work to do, whether it is being used for remote tuning of a parasitic element or as part of a two-driven-element system, and identical results should be obtainable.

At this point it may be recalled that with straight λ/2 dipole elements spaced λ/8 the mutual coupling is resistive and both feeders of a driven system handle the same amount of power, so that the above argument might appear to be invalidated. Note, however, that this case has been excluded by insisting on correct operation as a parasitic array before the second feeder is connected; because the coupling is resistive the currents *cannot* be equal and to make them equal reactance *must* be introduced. This in itself provides more or less the required phase shift so that, assuming the correct choice has been made of reflector or director operation (reflector in the case of quad), one feeder becomes 'idle' and dissipates comparatively little power whether connected to the transmitter or not.

It might be thought simpler to retain straight elements with λ/8 spacing, so that the coupling is resistive, and match the two driven elements individually. This is the apparent basis of several published antenna designs, except that in most cases matching appears to have been assumed despite the lack of any provision for achieving it. *Individual* matching (as explained in Chapter 5) is in fact quite a difficult process, largely because it has to take into account the very different reactances transferred from the leading element into the lagging element and vice versa. This can in principle be compensated by means of matching devices at the antenna but it then becomes impossible to reverse the beam efficiently by any means available in the shack. A compromise is possible by resonating each of the elements individually with a GDO in the absence of the other, and accepting a mismatch to each separate feeder of the order of 2.5 to 3.0 SWR for both directions of fire. The transmitter will, however, 'see' a resistive match in both cases, the reactances contributed by the individual feeders being equal and opposite.

It may be that the reader has not been impressed by the advantages claimed earlier for instantaneous beam reversal, in which case the adjustment procedure described above can be halted after the reflector has been tuned and, if possible, the currents equalised. The resulting improvement in front/back ratio will, however, be realisable over only a small part of the band in the absence of the remote tuning made possible by provision of a second feeder.

Disregarding losses, the placing of a deep null in the chosen direction results in a gain which is given precisely by Fig 5.5, since the directional pattern depends only on the relative phases and amplitudes of the currents, and it is the phase difference alone which fixes the direction of the null. The depth of nulls depends only on the current ratio; it is infinite if the currents are equal and in typical cases the gain is not seriously affected until the null depth drops to less than 12dB. The direction of nulls may be translated into the equivalent phase difference by means of Fig 5.5 or 5.7.

It is best to aim for over- rather than undercoupling, since operation is then less critical. In the case of a two-feeder system a simple test for overcoupling can be made after erection by adding resistance to the reflector; if it is found possible in this way to *increase* the depth of nulls, this indicates overcoupling. If the improvement is large, eg from 10dB to 20dB, this suggests severe overcoupling with possibly some adverse effect on gain as well as directivity.

Losses, their detection and prevention

For the determination of losses it is helpful to start by obtaining the lowest possible value of SWR and avoid making frequency changes since otherwise the losses may be aggravated or meter readings made more difficult to interpret. Losses can occur in several ways, as follows:

(a) *Ordinary resistance (I^2R) losses.* Loss resistance and radiation resistance are both easily calculable or read from charts (pp26, 27), and relative currents can be observed at tune-up height with a current probe (p279), so that, provided there are no faulty joins, the losses in each part of the antenna can be readily estimated and added together. Any suspected joint can be checked by short-circuiting. An example of this procedure will be found on p282.

(b) *Feeder loss.* This can be checked using a dummy load and an SWR meter, or any form of RF current meter which can be roughly calibrated. Of these indicators, the SWR meter is preferred since it reveals any mismatch between the feeder and load, and allows it to be corrected. A simple measurement of feeder insertion loss can then be made as shown in Fig 18.3. If the loss exceeds the specification for the feeder this is almost certainly due to effects of ageing or ingress of moisture and the feeder will have to be changed.

(c) *Losses or dispersion of energy in unwanted directions due to feeder radiation* (p52). The current probe (p279) should be used to check for current on the outer of a coaxial feeder or on the centre line of a twin feeder but this is not necessarily conclusive. With the antenna at tune-up height the power flow should be checked at *both* ends of the feeder and the difference should not exceed the loss measured in the previous test. This is still not conclusive either way, but if there is excessive loss one should look for some (usually obvious) cause of asymmetry. If the SWR is much better at the transmitter than at the antenna this is cause for suspicion. Try a deliberate mismatch at the antenna; if there is little change in SWR at the transmitter, be even more suspicious. Coaxial feeder used

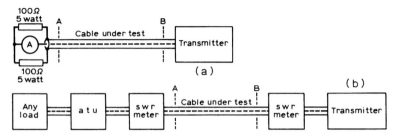

Fig 18.3. Measurement of feeder loss. In case (a) the transmitter drive is set to give an output level of about 5–15W, and the dummy load on the left incorporates an ammeter which can be as shown in Fig 18.1; alternatively an SWR meter may be used as the indicator. The power or current is observed using first a short lead between A and B, which is then replaced by the feeder under test, the loss being observable directly since there should be no change in the loading of the transmitter. (b) shows a more rigorous method using two meters and allowing the use of any load resistance. Instead of replacing the cable the two meters may be interchanged, or a single meter may be used, moving it from one end to the other of the line. Many variations of these methods are possible. For temporary connections there is no need to use plugs and sockets, ordinary plastic strip mains connectors being suitable if leads are kept short

for this test must be the permanent one, not shortened, and it should be brought away at right-angles to the elements but, if using open-wire line, there may be difficulties in achieving this with the antenna at low height. If the beam is satisfactory with coaxial feeder, open-wire line can be substituted prior to erection and will usually result in lower losses.

(d) *Losses, or dispersion of energy in unwanted directions, due to radiation from a metal boom or even the mast.* Radiation from the boom will show up as poor front-to-side ratio for at least one of the endwise directions, and also as asymmetry of the main lobe. Make sure that maximum response coincides with pointing the antenna in the wanted direction. If the effect is present or suspected, look for some cause of asymmetry; also test with the probe for current flowing in the boom. Radiation from the horizontal (or vertical if the antenna is vertical) portion of a feeder can also cause asymmetry, and there could be vertically polarised radiation from the mast or vertical portion of feeder. This will cause asymmetry if the measuring antenna also has a vertical component but otherwise may not reveal itself, so that a thorough check should perhaps also include use of a vertically polarised test antenna.

The contingency is, however, fairly remote if adequate care has been taken to prevent feeder radiation and the mast is either non-resonant or fully symmetrical with respect to the antenna. On one occasion the elimination of boom current resulted in a symmetrical main lobe but strong radiation off the ends was still registered by the field-strength meter. This was traced to the antenna being at low height and the support not quite straight, so that (in the end-on position *only*) one end of the elements was closer to the ground! Asymmetry is less likely to occur if the centre of the elements is at earth potential as in monoband or trapped-dipole arrays, and is reduced if the elements are insulated from the boom. Owing to the residual capacitance this is not always a complete cure; in such cases a symmetrical feed, eg a delta or T-match (not a gamma match) is essential.

(e) *Screening by other antennas or overhead wires;* refer to discussion on p277. Useful antenna measurements can be impossible unless other antennas in the vicinity are (or can be made) end-on, open-circuited (all elements), or lowered. A quad loop open-circuited for horizontal polarisation still responds to vertical polarisation and vice

versa. One beam 100ft (30m) in front of another can screen to the extent of one to three S-units. When working with vertical antennas, any nearby masts, feeders, guy wires or other vertical conductors should be checked by GDO (p273) to ensure that there are no resonances close to the frequency of interest. If there are, and it is not possible to fit insulators, the linear resonator trick (p193) may be tried.

Tuning and checking beams with three or more elements

In this case there is no simple way of relating gain to the directivity pattern, though a reasonable estimate should be obtainable by plotting the directivity pattern in the horizontal plane and for Yagi arrays dividing this by cos θ to obtain a 'guesstimate' of the vertical pattern. Noting the two 3dB beamwidths α_1, α_2, and expressing them in radians (ie degrees ÷ 57), the gain in decibels is given by

$$G_{dB} = \left(10 \log \frac{16}{\alpha_1 \alpha_2} - 2.1 \right)$$

Adjustment is difficult unless a field-strength meter can be placed at a sufficient distance, the meter leads being run to the antenna position as described on p276. In general, the reflector should be tuned for minimum signal 'off the back' and directors for maximum forward gain, repeating the process as necessary. If field-strength measurement is not practicable it may be possible to arrange for a steady ground-wave signal, eg from another local station, *which must be using the same polarisation as the antenna under test.* This condition applies equally to test antennas used for field-strength measurements.

If the antenna has been purchased or carefully constructed in accordance with Figs 5.24, 5.25, observations at tune-up height should be used as a rough check only and disregarded unless badly out. If the antenna appears to be tuned low by some 1–2%, this is normal and should correct itself, more or less, when the antenna is raised to 30–50ft (9–15m). If the antenna is unsatisfactory when tested *in situ,* a careful record should be made of directional patterns, both at the ends and centre of each band, and rechecked after the antenna has been returned to a tune-up position. This will enable correct allowances to be made for the height difference in the course of any subsequent adjustments.

The ultimate test

The ultimate criterion of performance in the case of antennas, as of most other devices, is how well they do their job. This is often the only test method open to the user lacking sophisticated and usually expensive test equipment, and applies especially to the assessment of antenna gain. This, as mentioned earlier and further explained on p277, is virtually impossible to measure in the present context.

There are right and wrong methods of assessing the 'job performance' of an antenna and a number of possible pitfalls. Comparisons with other stations on the basis of DX signal reports are usually satisfactory when the other stations are within ground-wave range, and often in the case of much greater separations, particularly if large numbers of reports are averaged over a considerable period. It is desirable if possible to find as a yardstick some other station where the conditions are maintained reasonably constant, and long-range chordal-hop paths such as UK–Australia or South Africa are much more useful than, say, transatlantic paths which are subject to multimode propagation. Due to interference between, say, two- and three-hop modes, transatlantic paths also exhibit considerable fading which is not synchronised between different stations, even when these are quite close to each other.

When checking a new antenna against its predecessor, a number of comparative signal reports averaged over periods of a week or more are desirable and, of course, the more the better. If reports are consistently 'down' compared with several other stations using similar powers, antenna heights, antenna gains and equipment, this is legitimate cause for concern, though it may be due to some environmental factor (Chapter 10). Tests should be made in more than one direction before suspecting a fault in the antenna or other equipment. Allowance can be made if necessary for differences in power, though this should be equalised if possible – it can be reckoned as a guide (for flat sites) that DX field strength should be proportional to antenna height; this can however be invalidated by environmental factors as explained in Chapter 10.

Some descriptions of antennas include gain estimates based on signal reports, assuming for example 6dB per S-point as formally defined, though in practice the *average* bears little resemblance to this, being closer to 3 or 4dB – some commercial S-meters are indeed known to be calibrated on a 4dB basis. The attempt to standardise on 6dB per S-unit is nevertheless achieving some success, and this in the author's personal opinion is unfortunate since 6dB is a very big step, whereas differences as small as 1½ to 2dB can be reliably

perceived to the extent that most stations asked, while reporting little difference, think that the first (or second) antenna is slightly better. Unfortunately, due to the current escalation of the S-point there is no longer an international language adequate for such reporting, although the 'half S-point' is widely used and seems to be understood by most operators, at least in the form "your signals are Q5, S5 to 6". In the event of a reported difference of say one S-unit, one simple way to determine the number of decibels is to switch out the linear amplifier. The effect will probably be reported as a drop of two S-units and this can be compared with the known power difference which is likely to be in the region of 6dB.

If a second antenna is available as a yardstick this is a useful situation *provided* interaction between them is not allowed to influence the results. Usually, if antennas are spaced by at least 3λ/4 at roughly the same height and at least one of them is end-on to the other, there should not be much problem, but if one is in front of the other a separation of several wavelengths may be needed. If resonant feeders are used there is no difficulty in detuning the antenna (or element) by suitably placed short-circuits (ideally at voltage points on the lines), and the ends of an inverted-V can usually be slackened off so that the wires drop down vertically.

Single-element antennas can in principle be detuned via their feedline, and it may be sufficient merely to open- or short-circuit this, but with appreciable line loss there could be a problem. Parasitic elements of rotary beams are not usually accessible for detuning but the beams can be rotated to an end-on position. In the case of the two-element, two-feeder designs recommended in these pages, it should also be possible to detune each element by finding conditions which result in little or no current in a feeder if the other element is energised. Vertically polarised *dipole or monopole* antennas should not interact with horizontal antennas unless very close, but complete loops have circular symmetry and can respond to any polarisation.

If disabling or rotating one antenna has no effect on the other as judged from signal reports, preferably with the help of another station acting as yardstick so that instantaneous comparisons are possible, each antenna may be used as a yardstick for the other, and usually either of them can be replaced for investigation of a third. For example, one of the first two antennas could be a reference dipole such as an inverted-V, requiring only a light temporary support, and the third antenna might be a new beam which it is required to evaluate against its predecessor.

In using this procedure some caution is needed insofar as a dipole may 'see' reflections that are not seen by the beam, and it would certainly be preferable to use a beam for the reference antenna. However, the author has found comparisons using dipoles are useful provided all antennas are at the same height and the reference is not moved. *It is, however, essential for all results to be checked against 'common sense' and if there is any doubt the test set-up should be the prime suspect.* If height is varied comparisons between a beam and a dipole will not stay the same, if only due to the changes in radiation resistance of the dipole as depicted in Fig 6.17, any corresponding variations in the case of a beam being much less.

Comparisons are greatly facilitated if it is possible to switch rapidly between antennas, and usually more or less any standard-sized rotary switch, or a relay with short leads, adequate contact area and good insulation, can be pressed into service, any mismatch being compensated by an ATU (p60). *At least one ATU is necessary unless both antennas are very accurately matched;* this is because any change in antenna impedance 'seen' by the transmitter and not corrected by retuning will result in a difference in radiated power – and possibly 'splatter'! It will be recalled that a 2:1 limit on SWR can involve as much as a *four* to one change in impedance, and this is a very large difference in loading of the transmitter.

It is often advised that tests should be made on a 'steady' carrier, not a voice signal, but the author dissents from this *provided the speech is held at a fairly constant level by an efficient RF processing system.* This is because fading is largely selective, ie it does not take place simultaneously at all frequencies in the passband, so that useful averaging tends to occur if the whole passband is used. Incidentally, it is worth noting that S-meter readings are the result of an averaging process which is different from that which takes place in the ear, and therefore different for processed and unprocessed signals. This may need to be taken into account when assessing signal reports relative to other stations.

Test equipment

It has been shown that adjustment and checking of antennas can be carried out with very little equipment. One could manage with even less, except that this would be a foolish economy in view of the advantage to be derived from the acquisition of an SWR bridge and a GDO. Even if purchased, these items involve comparatively little outlay, and the remainder of the essential instrumentation consists of little more than an assortment of diode detectors and at least one sensitive meter. As we shall now see, there are few constructional problems, though measurements are beset by a varied assortment of problems and pitfalls to which the reader needs to be fully alerted.

The grid dip oscillator (GDO)

The term 'grid dip oscillator' (abbreviated to GDO) is convenient and lingers in use, though the original valve devices have been mainly superseded by the much more convenient transistor versions [1] such as Fig 18.4. The principle is very simple: when the oscillator is tuned to the same frequency as the circuit under test, some of its power is absorbed in the test circuit so that the voltage across L1 is reduced and this reduces the gate current or, in the case of a valve oscillator, the grid current. In the case of a bipolar transistor oscillator the emitter RF voltage may be applied through a capacitive potential divider to a rectifier and DC amplifier [2].

The resonant frequency of any tuned circuit L1, C1 may therefore be found by varying the tuning of the GDO until a

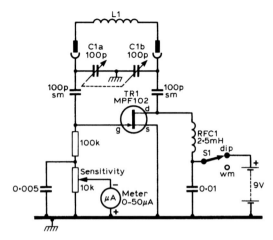

Fig 18.4. FET source-dipper suitable for use from 1.5 to 50MHz (ARRL Radio Amateur's Handbook)

dip is observed on the meter, and an antenna, being a form of tuned circuit, might be expected to have a similar effect on the GDO. According to several of the author's informants this does not happen, thereby leaving them with something of a problem. The reason for this is not far to seek, since the coils normally specified for use in a GDO are only 1in or less in diameter and can hardly be expected to couple to any appreciable extent into, say, a 33ft (10m) length of 1in (2.5cm) tubing or a 133ft (40m) long wire.

Fortunately there is a simple and very effective way out of this difficulty, as shown in Fig 18.6. The bipolar dip oscillator shown in Fig 18.5, though slightly more complicated [2], has been found particularly suitable for HF antenna work in view of its outstanding sensitivity, due probably to careful design of the feedback network (as explained in the reference) and to the DC-amplified meter circuitry. Modifications, taking advantage of the restricted frequency range, include reduction of supply voltage to 2.5 (a much more convenient value), use of a fixed value for CF, and miniature 'no frills' construction which reduces the capacitive coupling and to some extent the risk of exciting unwanted modes. It is best to locate the tuning capacitor at the end of a paddle with all the other components hung round it, and use an insulated extension shaft. A tuning scale is optional, assuming availability of a frequency counter. Full coverage was achieved from 1.5 to 60MHz (with accurate read-out from the counter) in steps of just over one octave, using a supply of only 2V. The usual absorption wavemeter facility is not provided because it is far better to use the instrument in its 'active' mode for this purpose. Even very weak harmonics can be detected by noting the swing, up as well as down, on the meter as one tunes through them, and there is much less risk of destroying transistors. For most applications there is no need to stabilise supply voltage, but good stability can be achieved by deriving the supply voltage from a pair of nicad batteries.

In the case of Fig 18.5 a single-turn, right-angled, triangular loop with an 8in (20cm) base was used for 14–30MHz.

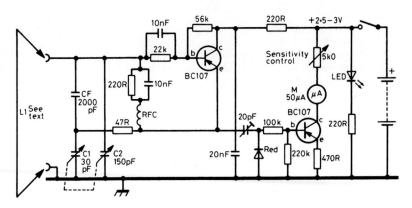

Fig 18.5. Dip oscillator for HF antenna work based on reference [2]. Tuning capacitor C1, C2, as commonly fitted to AM/FM receiver, with the two small sections in parallel for C, largest section for C2. RFC to have large reactance compared with CF at lowest frequency, eg 5–10μH. Transistor types not critical. For L, C measurements etc, L1 can be replaced with small coils if desired. If L1 is lost, use any bit of wire that happens to be lying around!

Two turns the same size were used for 7–15MHz and four turns for 3.5–7.5MHz. Depending on the value of tuning capacitors, the range covered may be slightly less on the lower bands owing to the self-capacitance of the coil. There is no difficulty in extending the range except that this tends to make the scale rather cramped at the HF end.

For the GDO of Fig 18.4 a larger coil is required; two turns with a 12in (30cm) base should be suitable for 14–30MHz but there should be no difficulty in adapting the design to suit any twin variable capacitor of 40–200pF capacitance that happens to be lying around in the junk box. The smaller values, however, provide increased coupling and some transistors may not oscillate with the larger values. Users of existing GDOs have found no difficulty in finding the correct size of loop, but as a guide a single turn as shown in Fig 18.6 is roughly equivalent to six turns spaced out to occupy a 7/8in (22mm) length on a former of 7in diameter. The author is indebted to G3JKF for pointing out that sensitivity can be further improved by using the ear rather than a meter as the indicator; this requires the addition of a modulator and audio amplifier.

It might be thought that loops as illustrated could be easily distorted, thus upsetting the calibration, but considerable mishandling is possible if frequency errors of 1 or 2% are acceptable. In general, even if the loop is squashed and then pulled out again so that it 'looks right', the calibration will

usually be found to have remained 'spot on', or near enough, but the use of heavy-gauge hard-drawn copper (or even brass strip) should be satisfactory if greater precision is desired.

Other difficulties arise in applying the GDO to antenna measurements as a result of (a) the large number of different ways a wave can wrap itself round a metal structure and (b) multiple resonances due to interaction between elements, particularly in the case of multiband beams. In checking the resonant frequency of a beam element other elements should be removed or detuned in some way, eg by the temporary attachment of an extra 3 or 4ft (1m) of wire to each end. Such attachments should be varied in length, checking that this has no effect on the resonance under observation, which in this case can be taken as almost certainly genuine.

Fig 18.7(a) shows some of the unorthodox ways in which a wave can wrap itself around a 'plumber's delight' beam structure; any of these modes should be identifiable by coupling the GDO into the boom and they are not excited in practice provided the feed system is symmetrical. Usually the

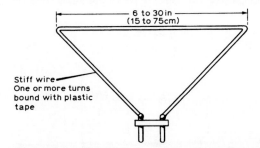

Fig 18.6. Large-area GDO coil for antenna measurements. A single 8in (20cm) turn was used to cover 14–30MHz with a GDO based on reference [2], but two turns 12in (30cm) wide would be required for the capacitance value shown in Fig 18.4. The coil shape is not critical except that it must have one long flat side, and the design can be readily adapted to suit any GDO

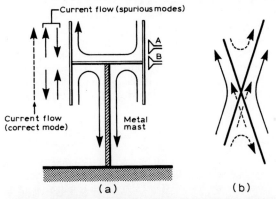

Fig 18.7. (a) Spurious resonances detected by GDO; the beam is of "plumber's delight' construction, ie the elements are electrically bonded to the boom and the boom to the mast. Note the "unauthorised' ways in which a wave can wrap itself round the structure; a GDO at A responds to all three modes but at B, with careful positioning, the unwanted modes should cancel. The elements can be either horizontal or vertical. (b) shows a two-band dipole for which there are two wanted modes (solid arrows) and two slightly different unwanted modes (dotted); for clarity the angle between the wires is exaggerated

correct mode can be identified because its frequency is known approximately and it is the only one near enough to the observed frequency to be plausible. If the elements include resonators the situation can become quite complicated, though usually still capable of being resolved by common sense. Due to capacitance across the insulation, resonances which involve the boom may be only shifted, not removed, by insulating the element from the boom.

Fig 18.7(b) illustrates how spurious resonances, not relevant to practical operation but liable to show up with the GDO, can occur in the case of a multiband dipole. The use of traps can lead to further problems in the interpretation of GDO measurements. In the case of a driven element many resonances will be observed if a long feeder is connected and (as pointed out earlier) this must be removed or short-circuited, whichever is most appropriate.

Provided these limitations are understood and appreciated the GDO is an extremely useful tool for the adjustment of antenna systems, although (as already explained) completion of the matching process usually requires the use of an SWR meter.

The GDO provides a simple means for the measurement of inductance or capacitance, the unknown L or C being connected across a known C or L, the resonant frequency observed and the 'unknown' calculated from the usual resonance formula or appropriate chart. For most purposes the 'known C' can be any close-tolerance capacitor of suitable value, and for a 'known L' the author finds it convenient to remember the inductance formula for single-layer windings:

$$L_{(\mu H)} = Fn^2d$$

where d is the diameter in inches, n the number of turns and the shape factor F is 0.017 (or roughly 1/60) for a 1:1 ratio of length to diameter. However, it should be noted that, in the case of very small inductances or capacitances, errors arise due to lead inductance and stray capacitance, including the self-capacitance of the coil.

One little-known problem which the author has encountered with a dip oscillator has been locking by strong signals injected from the antenna under test; this is fortunately rare, the effect being easily recognisable from the very critical tuning with the meter needle swinging up as well as down from its usual position.

The SWR meter

There are two types of SWR meter, the reflectometer shown in Fig 18.8 which is highly frequency dependent, and the 'reflected power meter' (Fig 18.9) which is independent of frequency and can be designed to read forward power subject to correct termination. In Fig 18.9 currents flowing in the inner conductor of a transmission line induce waves in the adjacent lines *but in the opposite direction,* this being a fundamental property of coupled lines. Thus the forward wave results in a wave travelling in the lower line cd towards the terminating resistor R, where it is absorbed so that no power is reflected back to the detector, whereas the backward

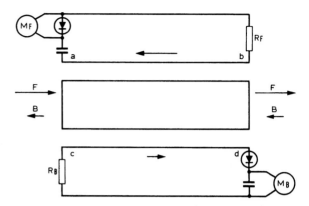

Fig 18.8. Reflectometer: currents flowing in the centre conductor of a transmission line induce currents which flow in opposite directions in the adjacent lines. The instrument is encased in a metal box which provides the outer conductor of the central line; to avoid an impedance discontinuity when the instrument is inserted in 50Ω line the central conductor may be a strip about 1in (2.5cm) wide mounted about ¼in (6mm) above the base of the box

wave sends a signal in the direction from c to d where it registers on the meter M_B. Similarly the forward wave, not the backward wave, registers on M_F, subject in both cases to suitable termination of the auxiliary line.

The majority of SWR meters currently in use are of this type and incorporate sensitivity controls, a single meter being used in many cases with a switch to read forward or backward power. A full analysis of the operation is quite complicated but, bearing in mind that a current I in any conductor induces a voltage $j\omega MI$ in a second conductor where M is the mutual inductance between them, one might expect the sensitivity to be proportional to frequency and this is about how it works out. Apart from this drawback readings can be badly upset if 'antenna current' is allowed to flow in the transmission line, ie errors can be expected under the same conditions which result in feeder radiation. To check for this an extra length, say $\lambda/8$, of feeder may be inserted on the *antenna* side of the SWR bridge; if there is no change in SWR reading there is probably nothing to worry about.

Many readers will already possess meters of this kind.

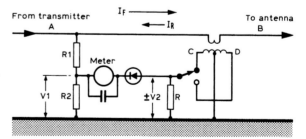

Fig 18.9. Reflected power meter, illustrating principles as explained in text. Ideally two meters are used to provide simultaneous observation of forward and reflected power. L_t is the total inductance of the winding CD and M is the mutual inductance between the windings

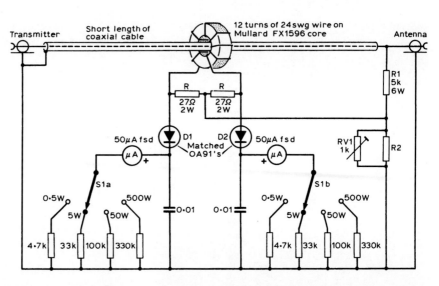

Fig 18.10. Circuit of frequency-independent directional wattmeter with four ranges corresponding to FSD of 0.5, 5, 50, and 500W in 50Ω lines. The value of R2 (including RV1 if fitted) should be 220Ω. For 75Ω systems R2 is 150Ω and the calibration is different. The outer of the coaxial cable acts as an electrostatic screen between the centre conductor and the secondary winding of the transformer; the cable length is unimportant *(Radio Communication Handbook)*

Despite the above defects, plus a tendency to be extremely inaccurate for SWR greater than 2 or 3, they are usually adequate for their main purpose and can be left permanently in circuit. Calibrated by methods described later, they can also be used as sub-standard power meters, remembering that a given calibration holds for one frequency only. They are inexpensive to buy and easy to construct; in contrast, the SWR bridges advertised as power meters can be quite expensive but have the big advantage of being independent of frequency. For the constructor they are equally inexpensive and even easier to build since the slightly esoteric process of achieving correct dimensions and proper matching for the secondary lines is replaced by a straightforward bridge-balancing operation; in view of this the reflectometer will not be described in further detail.

Automatic instruments which provide an accurate reading of SWR independent of power level from about 2W upwards are available commercially. These make it possible for an ATU to be reset very quickly even on a voice signal, a particularly valuable feature when working with reflectors tunable from the shack in view of the changes in SWR which may result, for example, if the null direction is altered in order to get rid of QRM. It is also a great time-saver in antenna work generally as it avoids the need for resetting the SWR meter when changing bands or altering power levels.

The principle of the power meter is illustrated by Fig 18.9. A reading of 'zero reflected power' indicates balance between the voltages V_1 and V_2 which are derived as follows. V is the voltage across the line but (except at very low power levels) it is too large for the present purpose, and a potential divider is used to produce the smaller voltage V_1 which is required to equal the voltage developed across R as a result of the current I_F or I_R flowing through the primary of the transformer. Depending on which way round the secondary winding is connected, V_2 will be in or out of phase with V_1 so that if $I = 0$ the voltage across the meter is $V_1 - V_2$ for one position of the switch and $V_1 + V_2$ for the other, ie zero and $2V_1$

respectively if the bridge is balanced. For a wave travelling in the opposite direction, the readings are reversed and the bridge should be perfectly symmetrical with respect to forward and backward power. The inductance of the transformer primary is small enough for any voltage drop across it to be ignored, so that A and B are at the same RF potential.

The potential divider can be resistive, capacitive or inductive and, although a resistive divider as shown might be expected to absorb some power, this amounts typically to only 1% (0.04dB) in the case illustrated. The reactance of the secondary winding must be large compared with R to ensure correct phasing, the voltage induced in the secondary being given by $j\omega MI$, and the secondary current by $j\omega MI/(R + j\omega L_s)$ so that the voltage across R is equal to IRM/L_s provided R is small enough compared with ωL_s. The phase shift is given in radians by $R/\omega L_s$ and, for a 'residual' SWR reading of 1.05 at 3.5MHz, values of $R = 10\Omega$, $L_s = 9\mu H$ would be suitable. At a frequency somewhat higher than 30MHz accuracy will be affected by stray capacitance, and it is important for such bridges to be well screened against the influence of possible stray RF fields.

Fig 18.10 is a practical design taken from reference [3]. The circuit uses a current transformer in which the low resistance at the secondary is split into two equal parts. The centre connection is taken to the voltage sampling network so that the sum and difference voltages are available at the ends of the transformer secondary winding.

Layout of the sampling circuit is fairly critical. The input and output sockets should be a few inches apart and connected together with a short length of coaxial cable. The coaxial outer must be earthed at one end only so that it acts as an electrostatic screen between the primary and secondary windings of the toroidal transformer. The layout of the sensing circuits in a similar instrument is shown in the photograph.

The primary of the toroidal transformer is formed by simply threading a ferrite ring on to the coaxial cable. Twelve

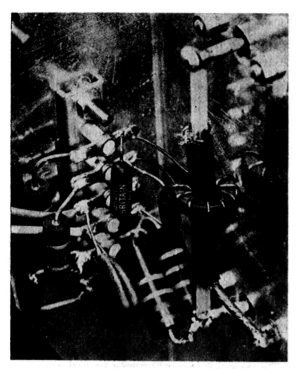

View of the sensing circuits of the frequency-independent directional wattmeter

turns of 24swg (0.6mm) enamelled wire, equally spaced around the entire circumference of the ring, form the secondary winding. The ferrite material should maintain a high permeability over the frequency range to be used; suitable ferrite rings are the Mullard FX1596 or FX3852.

Other components in the sampling circuits should have the shortest possible leads. R1 and R2 should be non-inductive carbon types. For powers above about 100W, R1 can consist of several 2W carbon resistors in parallel. RV1 should be a miniature skeleton potentiometer to keep stray reactance to a minimum. The detector diodes D1 and D2 should be matched point-contact types with a PIV rating of about 50V. OA79 and OA91 diodes are suitable. The current transformer resistors should be matched to 5%.

The ratio of the sampling resistors R1 and R2 is determined by the sensitivity of the current sensing circuit. As the two sampling voltages must be equal in magnitude under matched conditions, RV1 provides a fine adjustment of the ratio.

Accurate calibration requires a transmitter and an RF voltmeter. The wattmeter is calibrated by feeding power through the meter into a dummy load of correct impedance. RV1 is adjusted for minimum reflected power indication and the power scale calibrated according to the RF voltage appearing across the load. The reflected power meter is calibrated by reversing the connections to the coaxial line.

This instrument has full-scale deflections of 0.5, 5, 50 and 500W selected by the range switches. These should not be ganged since the reflected power will normally be much less than the forward power.

Germanium diodes as specified are essential if an instrument is to be used at low power levels, otherwise silicon diodes may be substituted. If an RF ammeter is available it may be used instead of a voltmeter, except that its range may be rather more restricted.

The main problem area is likely to be the dummy load since accurate loads suitable for high power levels are quite expensive, but it is a simple matter for calibration purposes to make use of the antenna itself. First a low-power load must be constructed using, say, five selected 270Ω 1W carbon resistors in parallel, keeping the connections as short as possible; this is used for setting up the power meter at the 5W level. The antenna may then be connected via a matching unit which is adjusted to give unity SWR, and the antenna plus matching unit can thereafter be used as a matched load for any required power level.

As an alternative to using a voltmeter or ammeter, a simple and accurate method of calibration is possible with the help of a lamp load and photo-electric exposure meter. Having first balanced the bridge by means of RV1 at roughly the power level which it is required to measure, the antenna is replaced by a load consisting of one or more lamps adding up to the required wattage. The resistance of the lamp load varies with the power level but it is not too difficult to adjust the tuning unit and the controls on the transmitter so that full lamp brilliance and an SWR reading of unity are obtained simultaneously. 'Full brilliance' can be judged by eye, more or less, if a mains-energised lamp is available for comparison but, using the exposure meter, the lamps can be pre-calibrated in terms of exposure reading and this makes for greater accuracy and convenience. Assuming accurate calibration of a single point, it is a simple matter to calibrate the rest of the scale, given any type of RF indicator known to have a linear characteristic such as an oscilloscope; thus if 400W produces 4cm deflection, 1cm will represent 400/16 or 25W.

For very low power levels, eg less than 1W, increased sensitivity is obtainable if the feedline is looped round the core to form a complete turn instead of being taken straight through the centre of the toroid.

For the adjustment and testing of antennas it is desirable to work at low power levels but, before an antenna is erected, it is advisable to check it with full power applied, particularly if it includes components such as capacitors, relays or transformers which might be liable to break down in the event of some fault or miscalculation.

Measurement of radiation pattern

In the case of a two-element beam the relative phase of the element currents determines the directions of nulls and this in turn fixes the gain and all the other details of the directional pattern, except that the depth of the nulls is determined by the ratio of the currents as explained in Chapter 5. If the currents are equal the nulls are complete, ie the signal in or received from these directions is zero. The *direction* of a null can therefore be used for setting the *phase* and (in principle at least) its *depth* can be used as an indication of the *current ratio*.

In principle, observations of the radiation pattern require either a transmitter or a receiver located far enough away for its distance and direction to be regarded as the same for all elements of the antenna system under test. Field strength tends to be proportional to distance squared for horizontal antennas at a low height above flat ground, so that with two elements spaced $\lambda/8$ and adjusted to give a null in a particular direction, a field-strength meter at a distance of λ as in Fig 18.2 would indicate a minimum signal level $1 - (7/8)^2$ of the signal from the front element alone.

This would be interpreted as a front/back ratio of only about 16dB instead of infinity but, even though the null is incomplete, tuning for a minimum or maximum in the appropriate direction should be sufficient to ensure correct phasing. On the other hand, halving the distance could reduce the depth of null sufficiently to make adjustment difficult, and too small a separation could also result in confusion due to near-field effects (p7) or mutual coupling between the antenna (A) of the field-strength meter and the antenna being tested (B).

It is important in these circumstances to resist any temptation to adjust the coupling between antenna elements so as to obtain a null on the meter since this will reduce the null depth on *distant* signals to 16dB. The correct criterion is twofold, namely (a) null in the right direction and (b) element currents equal. With more elements the situation is more complicated, and in general the larger the beam, the more separation is needed, though even with three elements it is possible in practice to make do with a separation of about 1λ if this cannot be increased.

Next we have to consider the effect of a possible third antenna C, probably located on top of the only mast available. Attenuation between antennas A and B is likely to be much greater than that between C and either A or B so that the signal reflected from C may exceed the direct signal. In an extreme case a maximum instead of a minimum may occur at A when B is pointing at C. Intermediate situations are more common, the presence of C making it impossible to obtain results that make sense. If C is a beam with a good front/back ratio it might be thought sufficient to point it in the opposite direction, but this if anything makes matters worse by bringing a *reflector* element closer to B! As explained in Chapter 5, *the properties of a beam are defined with respect to voltages at its feeder terminals and have no relation to its behaviour as a reflector of incoming signals.*

The situation becomes worse if A and B are moved further apart, and reflections from telephone or power wires then also become more important, so that even in the absence of C there may be an optimum separation distance. Often the problem can be resolved by ensuring that either B or C is end-on to the other, but if *both* are end-on this may increase the coupling if there is a considerable height difference. The best arrangement may be to use C as the test antenna.

The difficulty of making accurate pattern measurements at low height is one of many good reasons for using resonant feeders wired back to the shack from each element. Even where this is not desirable as a permanent feature, temporary lines can be very useful for the initial tune-up of a new antenna.

One incident is recalled in which a quad antenna gave very poor performance, having been constructed from handbook data according to which the reflector had been made 5% larger than the driven element. After reducing the size nearly to that of the driven element, tuning was carried out by means of a temporary open-wire stub (about $\lambda/2$), extending to near ground level. The operation was satisfactorily concluded by removal of an exact half-wavelength and it is possible that some other quads might benefit from the same procedure. The need for this (or otherwise) can be readily assessed by observing null directions (if any) and referring to Figs 5.5 or 5.6.

In general, when elements are correctly coupled, as tends to be the case with quads, the reflector should be self-resonant towards the LF end of the band. Referring to Fig 5.3, this tends to ensure that on tuning up through the band the operating point remains within the desired limits A–B. From inspection of this and other curves in Chapter 5 it will be seen that any errors in tuning a reflector need to be on the low side since tuning high leads into a region of low R with rapidly increasing SWR, inferior directivity, and eventually transition to operation as (in most cases) a rather inefficient director.

The experimental set-up illustrated in Fig 18.2 has been found satisfactory for these and other similar measurements, since it results in direct observation of the effects of adjustments as they are made, thereby simplifying and speeding up the process. The use of a field-strength indicator rather than the oscillator alternative has the advantage that the test device is broadband, whereas changing the frequency of an oscillator involves either a much more complicated device or the risk of straining the patience of neighbours whose co-operation may have been invoked. Even so, circumstances permitting, the use of an oscillator is to be preferred, not only for the reason given earlier but because of possible contamination of field-strength readings by other strong signals.

In view of the problems outlined above, however, it is essential in either case to check the end-product on actual signals; this can be difficult with a rotary beam due to the time required for beam rotation, but if the beam is instantaneously reversible the necessary checks of front-to-back ratio can be quickly and easily made on a number of stations from both directions. This can be done aurally, either on weak signals or with use of an RF gain control so that the AGC is not operative. On the other hand, use of signals for the initial tune-up process is difficult unless a stable signal can be arranged in conjunction with a portable receiver or suitable extension leads.

It is essential to provide the test receiver or oscillator with an efficient antenna having the same polarisation as the antenna under test, the usual 'tin box' type of field-strength meter with a short rod antenna being completely useless for this purpose. It is arguable that tests should be made for cross-polarisation due, for example, to feeder radiation, and it may

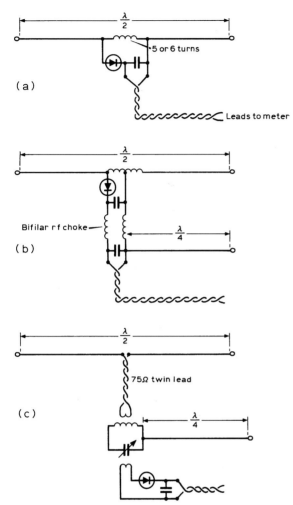

Fig 18.11. (a) Basic field-strength meter circuit. To reduce the risk that a vertically polarised component in the signal may modify the meter reading, the lead length plus that of the antenna should not be resonant. (b) Use of RF chokes to reduce pick-up on the leads. The λ/4 wire provides a much smaller impedance to ground than the RF chokes which are ineffective if the lead length is such that a high RF voltage can exist at the end of it. (c) Improved but less convenient arrangement using a tuned receiver: this usually eliminates pick-up of extraneous signals

be instructive to recall some experiments with rather large loop elements which produced a normal radiation pattern when tested as described above, but a mass of inconsistent observations (sometimes amounting to beam reversal) on actual signals. This was traced to a strong vertical component which had been overlooked in the basic design.

Design of a field-strength measuring device needs careful attention and it must be properly calibrated in terms of relative power or voltage. Preferably, germanium diodes such as the OA79 should be used in view of the sharp 'knee' in the characteristics of silicon diodes. Calibration against a power meter or oscilloscope is a simple matter, and it is usually

adequate to regard the meter as square law below and linear above a certain signal level.

For calibration the meter should be wired back to the shack and its readings plotted against antenna current, voltage or relative power, preferably using an oscilloscope with the RF applied directly to its plates since this can be relied on to provide a linear indication of voltage applied to the antenna.

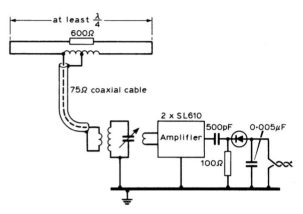

Fig 18.12. Broadband test antenna with tuned receiver and amplifier provides increased range and reduction of lead pick-up. As illustrated there is an amplifier gain of 40dB and (for the shortest length) an antenna loss of 14dB relative to a λ/2 dipole; the loss is almost independent of proximity to other objects, making this arrangement particularly suitable for a portable instrument used for the investigation of environmental effects

Fig 18.11(a) shows a very simple arrangement which has been used successfully, but RF pick-up on the meter leads can be a problem and it is essential to make sure that this does not reach the detector. RF chokes are not always sufficient and additional precautions include the use of a balun and an artificial ground as in Fig 18.11(b). A tuned circuit as in Fig 18.11(c) provides additional sensitivity as well as improved isolation of the meter leads, and some selectivity against strong signals which can cause interference when operating over long ranges and at low power levels. If more sensitivity is needed, eg to work with lower levels of transmitter power, a one- or two-stage amplifier may be used, in which case the additional selectivity is essential, though the antenna itself can then be broad-band as in Fig 18.12. Otherwise multiband dipoles may be used.

If enough space is available it is an advantage to use two meters so that relative field strengths can be observed in both directions simultaneously, and in appropriate cases meters may be permanently wired back to the shack for continuous monitoring of performance. It might be thought that antenna gain could be directly measured by substitution, observing first the signal strength from a dipole and then substituting the beam, but the ground-wave signal is greatly dependent on the reflected wave. However, the beam illuminates less of the Fresnel zone of the test antenna, and there is no guarantee that the reflections will be comparable even if there are no power lines or other objects to distort the picture [7].

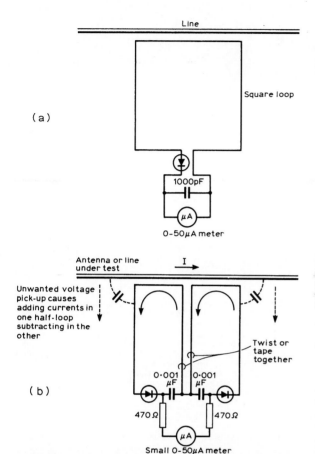

(a)

Line

Square loop

1000pF

μA

0-50μA meter

(b)

Antenna or line under test

I →

Unwanted voltage pick-up causes adding currents in one half-loop subtracting in the other

0·001 μF   0·001 μF

Twist or tape together

470 Ω   470 Ω

μA

Small 0-50μA meter

Fig 18.13. (a) Simple current probe. (b) Modification to reduce capacitive coupling effects; note tendency for magnetic and capacitive couplings to add in one half-loop and subtract in the other. Component values are not critical

The current probe and its uses

Fig 18.13(a) shows this in its simplest form, coupled to a wire carrying an RF current. Part of the field surrounding the antenna wire links with the probe as shown so that an induced voltage given by the usual formula, $V = j\omega MI$, is applied to the diode detector and meter, which should be calibrated as just described for the field-strength meter.

In the absence of other access to the transmitter output, a spare plug and socket joined by a small loop of, say, 1in (2.5cm) diameter may be arranged for insertion in the output lead or adjacent to the SWR meter, and this will also allow connection to an oscilloscope. The probe or other device to be calibrated is coupled into the small loop to obtain a full-scale reading and the power level reduced in steps. In use, one holds the loop close to the wire or some suitable distance from it, depending on the sensitivity required. Usually a rough estimate of current is sufficient and, having settled on a distance such as 0.5in (13mm) as judged by eye, the reproducibility of readings has proved adequate for the author's own purposes

RF current probe with balanced loop as recommended for rough estimates of relative current in different parts of an antenna system. Devices such as this are essential for the experimenter whose resources of time or money are limited

though a number of readers have felt the need for something better. The point should perhaps be made that at low levels rectifiers operate in a square-law mode causing differences to be exaggerated, but the desirability of a more precise instrument is recognised and Fig 18.14 shows a probe devised by G4FM which gives accurately repeatable readings [8]. Unfortunately, without further elaboration this fails the test of being able to cater for a wide range of conductor sizes, including the need to check for currents on the outer of coaxial cables.

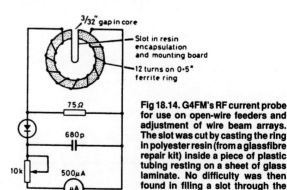

3/32" gap in core

Slot in resin encapsulation and mounting board

12 turns on 0·5" ferrite ring

75 Ω

680p

10k   500μA

μA

Fig 18.14. G4FM's RF current probe for use on open-wire feeders and adjustment of wire beam arrays. The slot was cut by casting the ring in polyester resin (from a glassfibre repair kit) inside a piece of plastic tubing resting on a sheet of glass laminate. No difficulty was then found in filing a slot through the resin and core

Fig 18.15 is an alternative devised to overcome this problem and avoid the need for cutting slots in a ferrite ring. It also retains the voltage-balancing feature of Fig 18.13(b), the need for this being confirmed by a test in which short-circuiting the

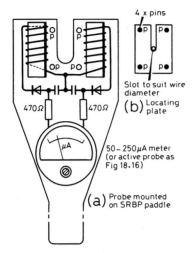

Fig 18.15. Voltage-cancelling probe based on Fig 18.13(b) but with accurate locators. p = holes for locating pins; coils are wound on ferrite rods and the gap between cores should be as small as possible, depending on maximum conductor size. Coils to be wound in opposite directions relative to the conductor

output of one of the diodes created a false impression of severe imbalance though the 600Ω line in question was in fact well balanced.

The probe, like the GDO, is an indispensable instrument for the experimenter but suffers from one drawback: the need to radiate considerable power in order to make reliable measurements. At 14MHz and above, 2 to 5W has usually been found adequate but more may be needed when looking

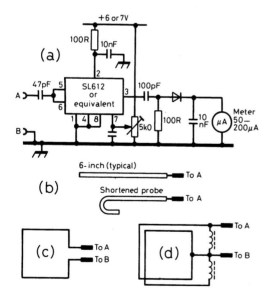

Fig 18.16. Probe and amplifier kit. (a) Amplifier circuit. (b) Capacitive probe. (c) Unbalanced inductive probe. (d) Two-turn inductive probe, balanced to reduce contamination of current readings by capacitive coupling

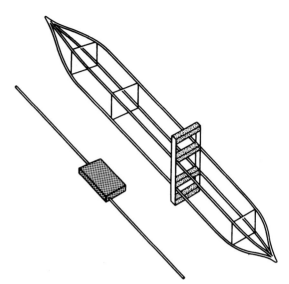

Fig 18.17. Radio receiver or active probe and a Villard cage. When the receiving device is in the cage, there is no connection between them. For end-on illumination, energy guided by and travelling down the cage is backscattered from the downstream end; because of symmetry, this travelling wave should have little effect on the whip and radio inside the cage. Waves having a polarisation aligned with the long dimension of the cage, and incident from the broadside direction, penetrate into the cage because of the incompleteness of the shielding. With the cage horizontal, the whip plus radio responds to horizontal polarisation; vertical polarisation is rejected. (SRI Technical Note)

for currents on the outer of coaxial feeder, trying to be sure that an indoor aerial is not inducing currents in the mains wiring, locating accurately the position of nulls in a high-Q resonant feeder system, and when working at lower frequencies. Apart from this, even 2W can produce big signals at long distances. In order to minimise this problem it is a simple matter to construct broadband amplifiers using IC devices such as the SL610 (or the SL612 which has the advantages of lower current consumption, higher gain and less risk of instability, offset by a fairly rapid drop-off in gain above about 20MHz) or their in-line equivalents. A 'kit' approach is suggested along the lines of Fig 18.16, based on two amplifiers which may be used separately or in cascade, a capacitive probe responsive to line voltages (this can be shortened by bending back on itself), one or more loop probes of different shapes and sizes, and one or more tuned circuits which, because of interference from other strong signals, are likely to be needed if using more than one stage of amplification. Apart from their main functions most of the kit components will be found to have other uses 'around the shack'.

Another device [9] which may be found useful in conjunction with the amplified probe is the 'Villard Cage': Fig 18.17. Devised by Mike Villard, W6QYT, for SW broadcast reception in a cluttered environment, it uses partial screening to discriminate in favour of signals having a polarisation aligned with the long dimension of the cage and arriving from the broadside direction. This results in sharp nulls which can be used for determining signal arrival angles in elevation as well as azimuth, and discriminating against reflections from electric wiring or any of the large metal objects, plumbing etc, to be found indoors. It can be used also for distinguishing between radiation off the back of a beam, radiation reflected via some other antenna, and radiation from feeders. The price for this includes a loss of some 20dB in sensitivity, though this is recoverable by parallel-resonating the whip at the inputs of the amplifier.

The device operates by screening out E-fields, including reflections from the human body and near-fields of adjacent conductors, while letting the H-fields through. The pointed ends minimise energy that would otherwise travel down the sides of the cage and reduce null depth through penetration of the imperfect screening. For our present purpose the probe rods are connected to the input of an amplifier (Fig 18.16), the meter and batteries being also enclosed in the cage, and the latter must not be penetrated by any other conductors (such as headphone leads). An external carrying handle is advisable.

The combination of probe, battery and meter constitutes an 'active asymmetrical dipole'. Nulls can be obtained from either end of the cage subject to accurate adjustment of elevation and azimuth, so that in the case of an elevated source any directional ambiguity can be resolved.

A particularly useful role for this device is the initial identification of problems such as feeder imbalance or current on the outer of coaxial cables, since an excellent bearing on a transmitting antenna becomes much less so if one wanders too close to a feedline which happens to be radiating! This is a common cause of TVI, noise and (due to RF in the shack) transmitter instability as discussed on p52–56.

Sometimes, for example when making observations on an open-wire line having a high SWR, readings may be affected by capacitance to ground via the user, a typical symptom of this being dependence of the reading on which way round the probe is held; this effect is minimised by the balanced diode circuit shown in Fig 18.13(b) and as a further measure the meter should be as small as possible. A long insulated handle may also help. Sometimes a voltage probe is used but this is not recommended for several reasons: (a) its dependence on capacitance to ground via the user, which is unpredictable and variable; (b) current is often the main, and for evaluation of losses the only, interest; (c) often there is no need to make observations except near current points, whereas when using a voltage probe one is forced to operate in the close proximity of voltage points. In this case the presence of one's body can seriously upset tuning and even introduce losses, thus invalidating the observations.

Use of the probe for observing current ratios and tracing feeder imbalance has already been described (p269). Further examples of its use include:

1. A dipole, Fig 18.18, is fed with a long 600Ω line. To improve bandwidth or because of losses (eg if the dipole is short or the line very long) it is desired to match the line by connection of a stub. Walking along the line, a point P is located where the current is almost zero; this can be

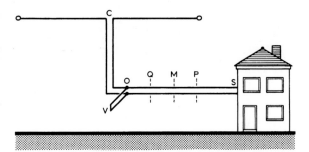

Fig 18.18. Use of probe to determine correct position and length of matching stub for a dipole fed with 600Ω line. In the absence of the stub, Q is a point of maximum current; by adjusting OV while maintaining the length COV constant, unity SWR is obtained in the line OS. The length COV is correct if the current in it is the same each side of O

done most accurately by finding adjacent points giving small but definite and equal deflections, the current minimum being taken as exactly half-way between them.

This position may be marked and a point Q of maximum current found by measuring a distance of $\lambda/4$, typically 16ft (4.9m) in either direction for 14MHz. Choosing a point O at about 3 or 4ft (1m) from Q, a stub OV = OQ is connected. Checking the current either side of O moving towards V and C, it should be equal; if not, O must be moved slightly but without altering OV. The reactance of the dipole plus OC is now equal and opposite to that of the stub OV so the impedance at O must be resistive. If this is 600Ω the probe will indicate that the line is matched, ie the current will be the same everywhere along the line OS.

If there is still a mismatch a minimum or maximum will be found at a point M about 16ft (4.9m) from O. The current ratio I_M/I_O or its reciprocal is equal to the SWR and the impedance at O is given by $(I_M/I_O) Z$, where Z for this example is 600Ω. As a second (and final) approximation, the length OV should be multiplied by $\sqrt{(I_a/I_M)}$ but without altering the length COV since this establishes the essential resonant condition. In other words, if OV has to be shortened by 1ft then O must be moved 1ft nearer to Q.

The system is now matched, and it will be seen that access to the line has enabled the SWR to be determined using only the current probe. Although an SWR/power meter could be devised for 600Ω line it is generally more useful to have such an instrument in the low-impedance line from the transmitter to the tuning unit or balun.

In principle, open-ended stubs can be used for matching, in which case one would have a stub of length ($\lambda/4$ – OV) at a point nearer to the transmitter by the amount $2 \times$ OV. Use of open-ended stubs should, however, be avoided if possible since they are more difficult to use and, unless the symmetry is perfect not only in regard to the line itself but also its relation to surrounding objects, line imbalance will result. Such effects should be readily detectable by means of the probe and, provided the position of P differs between the two wires by not more than a foot or so, this is more or less acceptable.

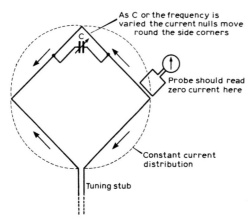

Fig 18.19. Use of probe for adjustment of bi-square element. A 14MHz quad loop uses a linear resonator to open-circuit the top end at 28MHz; if C is correctly set current minima appear at the corners, but move away in one direction or the other as the frequency is varied. They are located precisely by finding points of just-detectable current and bisecting the distance between them. The length of tuning stub for 28MHz may be any odd multiple of λ/4

2. Fig 18.19 shows a 14MHz quad loop with a linear resonator to open-circuit the top end at 28MHz and turn it into a bi-square. To tune it correctly the loop is spread out horizontally at a height of 5ft (1.5m) and C is tuned for maximum current in the resonator. Points of minimum current are located by the same method as P in the previous example and should occur at the side corners. This is achieved for the midband frequency by fine adjustment of C and, to determine the useful bandwidth, frequencies are found for which the null positions shift some 3 or 4ft (1m) either way. With an open-circuit in place of the resonator, the tuning is some five or six times less critical and a fairly narrow bandwidth (about 0.5MHz) is the price paid for this method of multibanding.

3. Fig 18.20 shows those portions of the antenna which are relevant to operation on 21MHz in the case of the three-band array using linear resonators which is described on p202. It is desired to know the efficiency.

Figures marked against each portion of the beam are relative *average* currents as estimated using the probe. The dimensions are marked in half-wavelengths as it is required to use resistance values extrapolated from Fig 3.10 which has been plotted on this basis. The figures in brackets after the currents are the average diameter of conductor followed by the ohms per half-wavelength; this assumes the use of aluminium alloy with a resistivity 2.6 times that of copper, so that its RF resistance is √2.6, ie 1.6 times that of copper. The current distribution in the driven element comprises roughly the centre portions of two half-wavelengths, and it is convenient to choose the current scale and power level so that '1.0' represents an average current of 1A in the outer portions of the element. Hoping to arrive at such a low figure for the loss that small errors are not important, no attempt is made in this

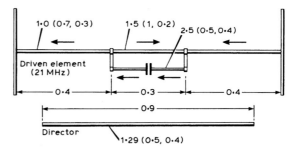

Fig 18.20. Use of probe to determine RF losses in a complex system. Loss resistances and radiation resistance are calculated from the dimensions and *relative* currents are observed with the probe; this allows estimation of the ratio of power lost to power radiated. Dimensions are marked in half-wavelengths and all important currents are indicated, followed by figures in brackets indicating the conductor diameters and, derived from these, the RF resistances

example to establish the *exact* current distribution or differentiate between average and RMS values. Similarly no correction has been made for the greater sensitivity of the probe when coupled to conductors of smaller diameter, though this can be determined and allowance made if necessary.

For the specified currents the losses add up as follows:

Outer portions of driven element: 0.25Ω (0.25W)
Inner portion of driven element: 0.05Ω (0.11W)
Path via capacitor: 0.10Ω (0.625W)
Parasitic element: 0.34Ω (0.56W)

Hence total loss = 1.54W

To determine the efficiency we need to know the power radiated. For a single element the effective length = 2 × 0.7 (ie 1.4) times λ/2, so with unity gain the current would be 0.7 times, and the radiation resistance therefore twice, that of a λ/2 dipole. Assuming the condition of maximum nominal front/back ratio, the fields from the two elements are in quadrature for the wanted direction, ie they are at right-angles.

The gain for the two elements, assuming no change in the radiation resistance, would be √2 times in field strength or 3dB: the gain would, however, be 4.2dB for λ/2 elements and in this case there is also a small amount of collinear gain. Assuming a gain of 4.8dB (ie three times in power) the radiation resistance is divided by 3/2, and one thus arrives at 73 × 2 × 2/3 or about 96Ω, corresponding to a radiated power of 96W and an efficiency of 98.5%. It follows that in this case the total loss (inclusive of that due to multibanding) is only 0.065dB. Proceeding in a similar manner, loss figures of about 0.3dB and 0.2dB have been obtained for 28 and 14MHz respectively.

RF bridges, their uses and how to manage without them

The value of SWR bridges has already been stressed and most users will agree with the view that they are indispensable if one is working with coaxial lines. It is true that other devices such as an admittance bridge can be used to measure the quality of matching, but at considerable cost in convenience, and the important advantage of continuous indication is lost. What the SWR bridge does *not* do, at least not directly, is tell what to do about the SWR in the event that it needs improving. This is where an admittance or impedance bridge can help in the event that one has direct access to the antenna or a feeder of known electrical length. In this latter case, a bridge measurement plus a quick reference to the Smith chart produces the actual value of antenna impedance, which can then in theory be adjusted to the correct value.

Noise bridges [4] use a wideband noise source as the signal and a receiver as the detector. In their original form they are suitable for the measurement of resistance only; for this the feeder length must be a whole number of quarter-wavelengths and the antenna itself exactly resonant. In the event of a general-coverage receiver being available, a noise bridge may be used to discover the resonant frequency of an antenna plus its feeder system, though this will be meaningless if the combined resonance occurs at a frequency for which parasitic elements are significantly detuned. In the event that an in-band balance is obtained and the electrical length of the feeder is known, the feedpoint impedance of the antenna may be deduced. From this, in the case of a monoband antenna, one can by use of the Smith chart deduce the value of components for correcting the matching, though if the antenna is multiband these are unlikely to be compatible with correct operation on the other bands. In any case the extra components should be unnecessary if adequate provision has been made for the adjustment of whatever matching system is in use, an operation which usually has to be carried out by trial and error.

It should be noted, and needs to be emphasised, that the impedance measurement is *not* a measurement of radiation resistance (except in the case of a simple series feed at a current point such as is commonly employed with quad antennas and single dipoles) since matching components other than baluns usually involve an 'unknown' impedance transformation.

On the other hand, knowledge of the current loop resistance R could be valuable in the case of a two-element beam since, in conjunction with knowledge of phase angle and element spacing, it provides a direct indication of gain which takes into account any losses in the antenna. Thus the current relative to that in a free-space dipole is given by $\sqrt{(73/R)}$ and, provided the nulls are deep enough, the currents in the elements can be assumed equal. An 'equivalent dipole' current and hence the gain is found by completing the triangle as on p77, the phase angle being obtained from the null directions by using Fig 5.7. Any feeder loss must be allowed for separately.

If the antenna is not resonant in-band this situation can be corrected by the use of a capacitor or inductor as described in Chapter 4 (p71), and use of a calibrated capacitor in this way allows a noise or other resistance-measuring bridge [5] to be used for impedance measurements. A capacitive mismatch can be converted into an inductive one by inserting an extra

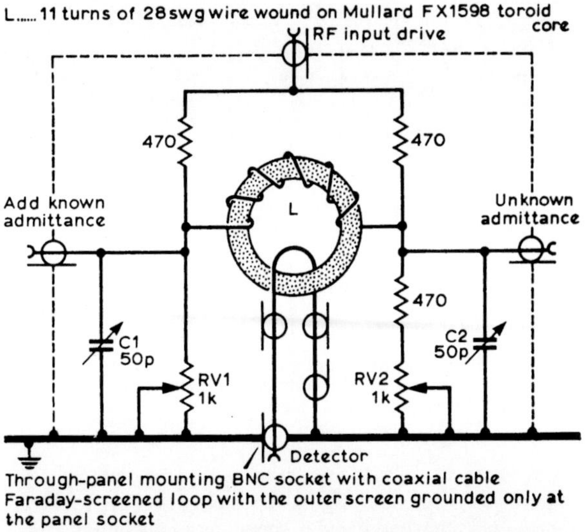

Fig 18.21. Admittance bridge. C1 is set to mid-capacitance and RV1 to full resistance, RV2 and C2 then being adjusted for minimum signal in the detector; this balances the "bridge strays". Applying the unknown admittance, the bridge is then re-balanced using RV1, C1 and if necessary additional external admittances. For measurement of inductance the unknown is shunted by a variable capacitor which is used for obtaining balance. The reactance (ie 1/admittance) of the added capacitor is then measured separately, being equal numerically to the required inductive reactance

$\lambda/4$ length of feeder, thus obviating the need for a variable inductor.

In contrast to the noise bridge in its original resistance-only measuring form, an admittance or impedance bridge has a wide range of uses including measurement of capacitors, eg for use in linear resonators or delta matches. Many bridges have been described, some being more difficult to use than others or requiring special components such as differential capacitors which may be difficult to obtain.

Fig 18.21 shows an admittance bridge designed by G3MYT which avoids these limitations [6], and Fig 18.22 illustrates one method of use. It should be possible to substitute a GDO for the RF input drive, and the detector plus amplifier illustrated in Fig 18.16 would appear to be suitable unless a convenient receiver is available. G3MYT pointed out that the bridge can be calibrated and a feeling for its use obtained by measuring various known combinations of R, C and L, the measurement of inductance being achieved by treating it as a 'negative capacitance' in which case

$$L = \frac{2.54 \times 10^4}{f^2 C}$$

where C is in picofarads, L in microhenrys and f in megahertz. Calibrated and used in this way, it is irrelevant whether the bridge is described as 'admittance' or 'impedance', and for application to feeder measurements it produces answers directly in the form of a parallel, not series, combination of R and C, conversion from one to the other being achieved if

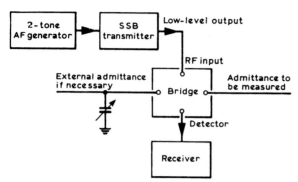

Fig 18.22. Block diagram showing method of use. The RF source and receiver are set to the desired frequency and the bridge adjusted for minimum received signal

necessary by use of the Smith chart as explained below. The importance is stressed of good screening, keeping leads as short as possible, and Faraday screening of the output loop, which means in practice that it should consist of a short length of coaxial cable with its outer screen grounded only at the socket on the panel.

In the case of an open-wire line, points of minimum current are readily identified with the probe so that, knowing the feeder length and having used the probe also to measure the SWR as already described, the Smith chart (Fig 18.24) can be used to obtain impedance at the antenna terminals and hence, for example, discover whether the antenna needs to be longer or shorter.

If there is no bridge available, a similar measurement may be carried out with coaxial line by inserting at least four short lengths of cable totalling $\lambda/2$ plus a simple diode voltmeter such as the one shown in Fig 18.23. Working at a low power level in order not to damage the rectifier, the relative voltage for each of the junctions and the position of the voltage minimum may be obtained by interpolation from the two lowest readings. The position of the minimum may be determined to any desired degree of precision by substituting a section consisting of even shorter lengths, but care must be taken in making the joins to expose as little as possible of the cable. Provided the electrical length of the feeder is known,

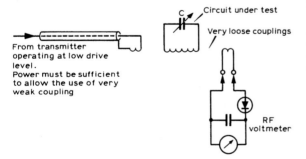

Fig 18.23. Measurement of Q. The source and the detector must be coupled very loosely to avoid degradation of the circuit under test

antenna impedance can be obtained using the Smith chart as in the previous example.

Measurement of Q

It may be necessary to measure the Q of an inductor or tuned circuit, or check for example that a capacitor used in an antenna has not become lossy due to moisture. Readers constructing their own antennas will probably have avoided the use of traps but, if the performance of a commercial beam is suspected, deterioration of traps is the most likely cause and in this case also a Q measurement is required. The recommended method is shown in Fig 18.23; a low-power signal is coupled very loosely into the tuned circuit under test and an equally loose output coupling is taken to an RF voltage probe. Loose coupling is essential to avoid loading of the tuned circuit which may degrade the Q, and to make sure it is loose enough each coupling should be varied in turn, rechecking the Q. If there is any change the coupling is not loose enough. The probe may be calibrated in the same way as the current probe described earlier and the transmitter frequency varied to obtain the '3dB down' points. The Q is given by the bandwidth, ie the separation between the 3dB points, divided into the frequency. For testing an inductance, C may be a variable capacitor, preferably with ceramic insulation. For testing a capacitor a high-Q inductor is needed; this can usually consist of a short length of open-wire line using the heaviest gauge copper wire available. Its inductance is selected to tune with the capacitor to the correct frequency, some distortion of the line being possible for fine tuning.

The voltage probe has other uses, for example checking the balance of a transformer – but take care not to burn out the diode!

Feeder loss measurement

One method has been described on p269. An easier method makes use of an SWR meter, but requires reasonable accuracy at high values of SWR. The feeder is connected to the transmitter via the meter and its far end is short-circuited or open-circuited; despite absence of the antenna the SWR will remain quite low if the feeder loss is large but go 'off scale' if the feeder loss is negligible. For intermediate SWR values Fig 4.10 can be used to read off the feeder loss.

Routine testing for feeder deterioration is possible in the event that power can be applied to the system at some frequency for which it is not designed, preferably a higher frequency where the losses will be greater. The SWR should be large initially but will decrease if the feeder deteriorates, allowing this to be readily detected.

Appendix – The Smith chart and why it is useful

Suppose using the SWR meter we obtain rather a high reading, let us say for example 2.5, and are not feeling too happy with this; we therefore want to know what is wrong

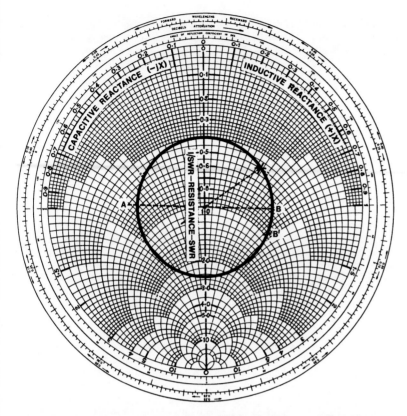

Fig 18.24. Smith chart, showing its use for finding the cause and cure for a high value of SWR. A measured impedance (point X) is plotted on the chart and its circle drawn in. By moving along the transmission line for the appropriate distance the impedance at the antenna end is given by a point such as A or its reciprocal B. By moving back slightly B moves round to the point B' on the R = 1.0 circle and a perfect match is obtainable, subject to tuning out the reactance 0.95Z₀ with the appropriate parallel capacitor

which will be discussed later. The point where the circle crosses the SWR scale indicates the SWR in the line and a set of concentric circles can be drawn representing various values of SWR. The chart owes its somewhat fearsome appearance mainly to professional users who like having a lot of lines drawn in; this means that answers can be read off to better than one place of decimals which does not usually help much but looks more impressive. Before being too critical of this version, however, the reader should count his blessings – most of them look a lot worse.

Copies of the chart may be obtained from various suppliers, and will be found to differ slightly from Fig 18.24. The author has deleted scales which the average amateur does not need and may find slightly confusing, and the resistance scale has also been used as the SWR scale which is what it is anyway. References to susceptance and conductance have also been deleted since these may confuse some readers and are merely reactance and resistance turned upside down, a useful trick which the chart is rather good at. This does not mean they have to be given new names but a lot of people think it helps and you may agree with them.

Using the chart

We must now return to the plight of the operator whose measurement of a SWR of 2.5 has caused him to appeal to the chart for help and who may by now be getting impatient. To simplify the example it will be assumed that the line has a characteristic impedance (Z_0) of 100Ω, in which case the scale markings can be read as 'hundreds of ohms' and the measured impedance ought to be a point such as $50 + 43j$ lying on the 2.5 SWR circle. If after checking the measurements it still fails to do so, one may need a new SWR bridge, a new impedance bridge or both but agreement is unlikely to be exact – it will probably be necessary to cheat slightly by coaxing the impedance measurement onto the nearest point on the circle.

The next step, and this is 'what the chart is all about', is to discover the impedance at the antenna end of the line by moving along the line the correct number of wavelengths as indicated by the scale round the outside of the chart. Each time round the circle is a distance of $\lambda/2$ and if, for example, the line length is 1.2λ we have to make 2.4 circuits of the chart 'towards the load'. This brings us to the point A which is an impedance of $(67 - 70j)\Omega$, and means that by connecting an inductance of $+j70\Omega$ in series we would be left with a resistive impedance of two-thirds the line impedance, ie an SWR of

with the antenna. By using an impedance bridge or one of the various tricks described in this chapter it should be possible to discover the impedance 'seen' by the transmitter, and before erecting the antenna the reader will have remembered of course to measure the electrical length of the feeder by coupling it into a GDO. You didn't? Sorry, but it is 'back to square one'; given this information a mere glance at the Smith chart would have revealed exactly what was wrong and what to do about it!

What it is

As explained in Chapter 4 (which should be consulted if the reader is looking for insight rather than an instruction book) the chart is simply a sheet of graph paper specially designed for the plotting of reactance against resistance. As one moves along a mismatched transmission line both of these quantities vary, and the unique feature of the Smith chart is the 'cooking' of the scales in such a way that, provided there is no attenuation in the line, *all the points lie on the same circle.*

The reader should now turn to Fig 18.24 which shows the chart, a point (marked X) with its circle, and two dotted lines

1.5. This might be acceptable but the example also tells us that a much better match can be obtained by changing to a feeder impedance of 75Ω, which has the further merit of being nearly a standard value.

There is still the possibility that we can do even better by using a shunt inductance as explained below, but first the reader must be introduced to another important virtue of the chart, namely the fact that with the scale markings arranged as they are so that '1.0' comes in the centre of the chart, it can be used for *any* value of line impedance Z_0. For this purpose an impedance must be divided by Z_0 before entering it on the chart, and the final answer must be multiplied by Z_0 to get it "back into ohms', as explained on p60. This is known as 'normalisation' and, following from the fact that the reciprocal of one is also one, it has the further virtue of allowing the same scales to be used for conductance/susceptance as for resistance/reactance which is its reciprocal.

Words like 'normalisation' have a deterrent effect but the reader has just been taken through this process quite painlessly (it is hoped) by leaving him free to think that the omission of a couple of noughts from the scale figures was due to laziness on the part of the chart designer. Reverting to more popular values of line impedance, one must of course be prepared to face up to such added difficulties as dividing by 50 instead of 100.

Series to parallel conversion

Thus far, the chart enables us to find the impedance at *any* point along a line of *any* impedance if we know what is happening at any other given point in the line. It will also be recalled from Chapter 4 that impedance inversion takes place along a λ/4 line so that a normalised impedance Z at one end appears like $1/Z$ at the other. So far we have in effect been putting $Z = R_s + jX_s$ but we know also that for the equivalent parallel circuit

$$\frac{1}{Z} = \frac{1}{R_p} + \frac{1}{jX_p}$$

because this is the way one 'adds' impedances in parallel. $1/R_p$ and $1/X_p$ are by definition the conductance and susceptance.

Let us therefore refer back to the impedance $R_s + jX_s = (67 - 70j)Ω$ which has just been obtained from the chart. In its normalised form this was $0.67 - 0.7j$ and to invert it all that is necessary is to go half-way round the circle. This pushes point A across to B at the opposite side of the circle where it may be read off as $0.73 + 0.76j$, the first of these terms being $1/R_p$ and the second one $1/jX_p$ which means that $X_p = -1/0.76$. This, after de-normalising, turns into a capacitive reactance of 132Ω and can be removed by connecting 132Ω of inductive reactance across the line, leaving only the conductance 0.73 which corresponds to an SWR of $1/0.73 = 1.37$. This is slightly better than the previous result.

Note in passing that

$$\frac{1}{jX_p} = -j\frac{1}{X_p}$$

is defined as the *susceptance* so that a positive reactance X_p becomes a negative susceptance ($1/X_p$) and vice versa. Notice also, however, that the problem was solved without using the 'susceptance' concept, but if a bridge was used for the initial measurement it may well have been designed to measure admittance (ie conductance plus susceptance) rather than impedance, and anyway if one is going to make a lot of use of the chart it is not a bad idea to get used to thinking 'both ways up'.

A further look at the chart shows how by taking a little more trouble a perfect match can be obtained. By moving back a distance of only 0.03λ towards the transmitter, B moves round to B' which is on the $R = 1.0$ circle; there is a susceptance of 1.05 but this can be tuned out with a parallel reactance of $100/1.05 = 95Ω$, leaving a perfect match in the remainder of the feeder.

The chart has a lot more tricks up its sleeve, but these are the basic ones which are most likely to result in the SWR meter contenting itself with the left-hand half of its scale. However, if the reader wants to get on really friendly terms with the chart and learn a few more of its tricks, he will be well advised to persevere with the more detailed explanations in Chapter 4.

For the chart to acquire its proper status among the test equipment in the shack, it may be mounted on a piece of board or stiff card with a rotating cursor made from a strip of perspex having scale markings corresponding to values of SWR from, say, 1 to 10. An alternative is to inscribe a set of SWR circles directly on the chart using coloured ink. The chart may be modified to line up with Fig 18.24 with the aid of typing correction paint and a pair of scissors, but there is no need for this once the user is master of the situation and no longer concerned by appearances.

References

[1] *The Radio Amateur's Handbook,* 53rd edn, ARRL, 1976, p520.
[2] *Radio Communication Handbook,* Vol 2, 5th edn, RSGB, 1977, p18.16.
[3] *Radio Communication Handbook,* Vol 2, 5th edn, RSGB, 1977, p18.22–23.
[4] *Radio Communication Handbook,* Vol 2, 5th edn, RSGB, 1977, p18.23–34.
[5] *Radio Communication Handbook,* Vol 2, 5th edn, RSGB, 1977, p18.10.
[6] 'A simple RF admittance bridge', G Garside, G3MYT/ VE3, *Radio Communication* January 1978.
[7] 'Quads versus Yagis', W Overbeck, N6NB, *Ham Radio* May 1979.
[8] 'Technical Topics', *Radio Communication* November 1984, p962.
[9] 'Partially shielded wideband active dipole receiving antenna for ground-or sky-wave interference reduction and direction estimation in cluttered environments', O G Villard, Technical Note 18R, SRI International, 333 Ravenswood Avenue, Menlo Park, CA 94025, July 1990.

Chapter 19

Antenna construction and erection

As readers will be quick to agree, amateur radio is many different hobbies, and 'playing around with antennas' can be one of the most absorbing. Using antennas for communication is another and, although these interests are often combined, the differences are liable to be reflected in attitudes to antenna construction.

In the author's case, a persistent urge to try out new ideas and resolve technical questions has often left little time for attention to mechanical details. In any case, for the average experimenter, precise details of antenna construction are likely to be of little value since, whatever advice is given, the constructor will quite rightly want to make the best use of his own particular skills and experience, as well as available materials and facilities. This applies particularly in the case of an experimenter who, after being in the game a long time, will certainly have acquired a large pile of surplus materials; he may moreover have only just recovered from being told the latest price of copper wire, and to insist that any he uses has got to be hard-drawn would certainly provoke a relapse. Properly tensioned, soft copper wire should last a long time and, if much pull is needed and breakage likely to result in serious embarrassment, the wire can be 'festooned' onto polythene cord which is very strong and relatively inexpensive.

The situation is of course different if new wire has to be purchased, particularly if it is intended to use a long span with a coaxial feeder hanging down from its centre. After many years of experimenting on a limited budget the author has acquired not merely a large junk-pile but much experience of improvisations, short cuts and economies – false and otherwise. The story is one of many failures but some successes and, while favouring in principle a professional approach to constructional matters, the fascination of amateur radio for the author lies largely in what can be achieved with limited resources and this chapter is biased accordingly.

It must, however, be confessed that constructional requirements for an 'experimental' antenna usually do little to ensure its survival in severe weather conditions, and the possession of at least one 'permanent' antenna can have its attractions for even the most ardent experimenter. In seeking to cater for both sets of requirements, constructional details to be found in earlier chapters which relate to some specific types of antenna are supplemented by the fruits of the author's own experience as well as ideas from other sources, but those with 'big' ambitions will need also to consult references [13], [14] and probably [12]. On the other hand, it is hoped to encourage would-be experimenters by providing an antidote to the

"It must, however, be confessed that constructional requirements for an "experimental' antenna usually do little to ensure its survival in severe weather conditions . . ."

Table 19.1. Leakage resistance of various insulators

Insulator	Resistance ($\Omega \times 10^{-4}$)	Loss (miniature beam) (dB)	Loss (wire dipole) (dB)
Polythene cord 1mm diameter, 6in (15cm) length, dry	700	0.06	
Ditto, wet	430	0.09	
Strip 6in by 1in (15cm by 2.5cm) cut from plastic piping, dry	38	1.0	0.08
Ditto, wet	13	2.5	
Wire ends sandwiched between pair of dry bricks	2.6		1.4
Bit of wet string (proverbial!), 6in (15cm)	0.3		5

'counsels of perfection' which (with a strong admixture of fallacy) constitute much of the advice currently available. In acting on such information the reader will hardly need reminding that safety considerations must at all times be paramount, and unfortunately attention must be drawn to some which appear hitherto to have been overlooked.

Constructional details of specific types of antenna will be found in the relevant chapters.

Insulation

The possibility of greatly reducing the weight of antennas, particularly beams, by judicious bracing with thin polythene cord or nylon line (p198) has not received the attention it deserves, possibly due to the traditional view that antennas (except for self-supported and correspondingly heavy elements) need insulators. In fact, if the principles of good insulator design are followed through to their ultimate conclusion, one is likely to end up with a length of nylon fishing line; this is readily available up to at least 120lb breaking strain, well in excess of the recommended tension for commonly used wire gauges (see Table 11.2).

The need for insulation varies enormously between different antennas. Thus an efficient miniature beam with a radiation resistance of 5Ω and fed with 400W will have between 4 and 5kV between each end of each element and ground compared with about 1.2kV for a $\lambda/2$ dipole, and losses in, say, an adjacent piece of wet bamboo will be about 16 times greater. The wet bamboo also has a considerable detuning effect and, except possibly in the case of full-sized quad antennas at points of maximum current, an antenna wire should never be attached directly to untreated bamboo.

The author has found recommended treatments singularly ineffective. Polyurethane varnish was messy, time-consuming and flaked off, whereas glassfibre-wrapped bamboo (from a commercial source) was found to be very brittle and had a short life. The easiest method consists of wrapping with ordinary *black* plastic insulating tape and has now been used extensively over a period of several years with no mechanical

failures. It has been reckoned unwise to rely on the electrical adequacy of this treatment in view of past experiences, but a recent accidental 'entanglement' has had no adverse wetweather consequences. It is nevertheless advised that short lengths of nylon fishing line should be used as insulators at the corners of loops; alternatively, insulated extensions can be contrived, for example, with the help of plastic tubing which, if not of sufficient quality in itself, can be used to form sockets for ceramic or nylon rods.

Some experiments at 28MHz with various material including low-cost insulating substances have yielded the values of leakage resistance shown in Table 19.1.

Transparent plastic tube salvaged from used ball-point pens is now widely used for insulators such as spacers for open-wire line.

Conductors and the joints between them

Soft copper stretches easily under tension. In one experiment a pull of 26lb (11.8kg) applied to 4ft (1.2m) of 19swg (1mm) wire produced a permanent extension of 2in (5cm), corresponding figures (estimated) for breaking strain and allowable working stress being 40lb (18.1kg) and 6lb (2.7kg) respectively. These weights can be assumed proportional to cross-sectional area and, as an alternative to try it and see, the suitability of a particular wire for a particular application can be calculated with the help of the windage formula on p301, noting also the example on p178. Permanent joins in copper wire must be soldered and given some protective coating such as Araldite, or insulating tape which is cheaper and does not demand careful cleaning of the joint. If the joint is required to take any mechanical strain it must start as a strong twisted joint capable of taking the full strain, the solder being used only to ensure electrical contact and not for mechanical strength.

In experimental work the use of plastic mains-connectors can be very convenient for temporary connections, but the screws rust very quickly unless protected by a liberal dollop of Vaseline (petroleum jelly) or some equivalent. Using insulating tape as well, lives of up to two years have been achieved, and this method has even been used successfully for making joins between copper and aluminium wire which pose an additional problem because of electrolytic action as discussed below. In general, however, inaccessible joins in antenna wires need to be treated with suspicion if they involve dissimilar metals or lack adequate waterproofing. However, such suspicions can usually be allayed in the case of loops by routine measurement of DC resistance. The DC continuity of a loop can also be exploited for de-icing or icing prevention by passing a current through it.

Resonant length of a wire may be affected by insulation or stranding, and a number of experimenters (including the author) have reported a lowering of the resonant frequency by some 3–5% in the case of typical plastic coverings.

In the case of tubing, structural as well as electrical considerations apply, and aluminium alloy is the only material likely to comply with both. Suggested tube sizes for

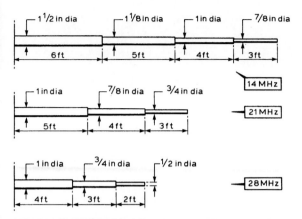

Fig 19.1. Suggested dimensions for one side of tapered Yagi elements for a three- or four-element beam. A single length of tubing extending each side of centre is advisable for the centre-piece of each element. Element lengths may be obtained from Figs 5.24 and 5.25. The boom may consist of 16–24ft (5–7m) of 3in (8cm) diameter tubing *(ARRL Antenna Book)*

conventional full-size beams are given in reference [1] and reproduced as Fig 19.1. Suggestions for a cord-braced design making optimum use of standard tubing lengths are given in Fig 19.2, though this is not yet tested and may have to be modified in the light of experience.

The requirements for telescopic construction are unrelated to those for minimising weight and windage so no attempt should be made to achieve a good fit; it is a simple matter to construct packing pieces from small strips of aluminium sheet, or tubing sawn in half. Some flexibility should be imparted to the end of the larger tube by making two saw cuts at right-angles, as long as possible, with a junior hacksaw. Hose clips may then be used over the slit ends to lock the tubes in position after final adjustment or, if the diameter is too small, a clip may be made by wrapping an aluminium strip round the join and drilling it so that it can be tightened with a nut and bolt or self-tapping screw.

Before assembly all parts should be smeared with Vaseline, any surplus wiped off, and the joint taped over. There is in general no need for driven elements to be weakened by splitting them in the centre if (eg as shown in Fig 12.1(b)) a balanced (delta or T-match) feed system is used, though one

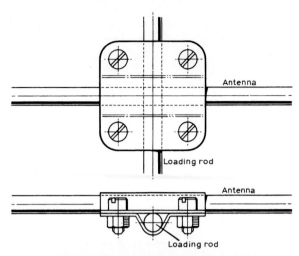

Fig 19.3. One method of joining lengths of tubing at right-angles, eg for end-loading. If one rod is of larger diameter the clamp must be modified accordingly. Clamps are made from squares of aluminium sheet crimped as shown. For weather protection parts should be smeared with petroleum jelly and the joint taped over. Typical dimensions are: end section of antenna 0.5in (13mm) diameter, loading rods 0.25in (6mm) diameter for lengths up to 6ft (1.8m)

of the suggested designs of compact beam (Fig 12.9) employs split parasitic elements and the centre insulator needs to be adequately reinforced. Vertical rods for end-loading when required may be attached as shown in Fig 19.3. The more usual cross arrangement uses slightly shorter rods but requires two of them so that the total weight tends to be increased to no advantage.

The method shown in Fig 19.4 may be used for the attachment of elements to a boom or the boom to a mast, and the figure also shows how a bearing can be contrived for a manually rotated beam. The collar should be fairly long and the screws staggered to ensure that the tubing is not appreciably weakened by the screw holes. With this construction it is easy to add a light mast extension, say 3–4ft (1m) of 5⁄8in (16mm) OD tubing, for supporting the radial ties of a light-weight beam. A short length of bamboo wrapped with insulating tape for weather protection has also been used successfully for the extension.

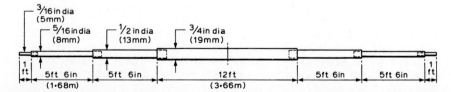

Fig 19.2. Suggested tubing dimensions for lightweight cord-braced beam for 14MHz, making best use of available sizes. It is suggested that thin-wire elements supported by the cords should be used for the higher frequencies, making full use of the available aperture to obtain extra gain plus increased radiation resistance and bandwidth. Dimensions shown should allow for full range of adjustment from reflector to director operation. The 3⁄16in (5mm) extensions are not likely to be required except (probably) for the reflector. The cord bracing should be attached to the end of the 5⁄16in (8mm) sections. Based on 12ft (3.7m) lengths of tubing, an overlap of 6in (15cm) has been assumed at each joint for the longest element. The boom may be made from 13ft (4m) of 1¼–1½in (32–38mm) tubing with telescopic extensions to give a total length of 16–17ft (4.9–5.2m)

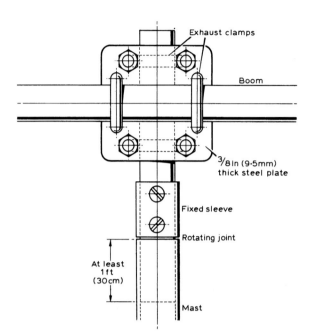

Fig 19.4. Method of securing boom to mast. Also shown is a simple form of rotating joint for a non-motorised system

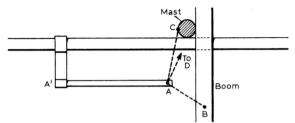

Fig 19.5. High-quality insulator contrived by use of three polythene cords as "guy wires'. AA′ is one half of a linear resonator and point A must be held rigid without introducing losses. This is achieved without the use of a solid insulator, the three cords from A (shown dotted) being anchored to a point B on the boom and points C and D on the mast, respectively above and below the boom

Packing pieces may be cut from short lengths of plastic piping to insulate elements from the boom. In the case of a reversible beam, rotation requires no more than a pair of polythene cords (eg 220lb (100kg) breaking strain) which should be attached to the boom and brought down to a convenient anchorage; the angle relative to the mast should be at least 45°, otherwise somewhat stronger cords may be advisable. About 120° of rotation is usually enough for a two- or three-element reversible beam but all-round rotation is usually possible with the use of additional anchorage points.

If a beam rotator is used it may be advisable to use self-tapping screws on the centre-line of the plate to prevent slippage. With conventional heavy-gauge elements (no cord ties), a better method of mounting is to attach the boom to a horizontal plate which is then bolted onto a pipe flange welded to a drive shaft, as recommended in reference [2].

A T-match or linear resonator may require the use of parallel lengths of tubing which can be mounted with straps as shown in Fig 19.5. A high quality of insulation is required in the centre of a linear resonator and this may be achieved at the same time as good mechanical rigidity by guying the ends of the rods in position as shown in the diagram.

Junctions between dissimilar metals, copper (or brass) and aluminium in particular, suffer from electrolytic corrosion, so there is a problem in achieving a low-resistance join between the feeder and the element. One method is to use tinned or plated soldering tags secured with self-tapping screws and shakeproof washers. Copper wires should be soldered to the tags and the joint can then be assembled using Vaseline and tape as described above. Polythene cord should be attached a

few inches from the joint and used to take any strain so that there is no pull on the latter. It is important also to ensure that flexing (if any) is within allowable limits, and in some cases it may be advisable to use a flexible insert such as a short length of outer conductor from a coaxial cable.

Electrolytic corrosion occurs because all metals are characterised by a particular value of electric potential which may be positive or negative. The difference of potential means that, in the case of dissimilar metals separated by a thin film of moisture, electrolytic action takes place, resulting in chemical changes or in other words corrosion. The greater the difference in potential, the worse the corrosion, metals of interest for the construction of antennas (ranged in order of potential from positive through negative) being aluminium, iron, solder, brass, and copper. In general, a soldered joint should give no trouble so that the use of well-tinned soldering tags is a first step in attaching a feeder to an aluminium element.

Beyond that, the main essential is to prevent the ingress of moisture. This is a problem which concerns not only joints between conductors but most of the components used in antenna systems and particularly coaxial feeder, which can be a source of gradual deterioration in antennas and (even if detected) replacement may be a difficult (and will certainly be an expensive) task. Apart from this, baluns must be sealed against moisture without preventing the escape of heat, inductors (with some exceptions in the event that turns are well spaced), capacitors (unless supplied as a sealed package), relays (if unsealed), switches and motors all require waterproofing. Where applicable components may be housed in plastic food boxes with the edges sealed by tape. The problem of coaxial cable is best resolved by using open-wire feeder wherever possible, though the question of which type of feeder is most likely to radiate remains controversial, with arguments apparently biased by ignorance of the success rate achieved by antenna currents in their efforts to flow on the outer of coaxial cable.

Detailed advice on waterproofing will be found in reference [15] to which the author is indebted for the following information supplementing his own standard practice of keeping on hand plenty of black vinyl tape. This can be used for most tasks (short of a professional job) with everlasting qualities; black is important because other colours deteriorate due to the effect of sunlight, and also to minimise visual impact, though a small quantity of red (which maximises visual impact) is also needed for wrapping round the handles of tools to aid recovery from long grass, bushes etc.

To quote the reference:

"Self-amalgamating tape comes in the form of a roll of what looks like thick insulating tape insofar as you peel off the backing strip and then proceed to wrap the tape around whatever it is you want to waterproof, overlapping each winding by about 50% of its width to ensure a good seal and keeping a bit of 'stretch' on the tape as wind so that it goes on under tension. It's best to start from the thinner end of the job, so to speak – meaning that if you want to waterproof, say, an in-line connector joining two pieces of coax, start the tape on or other piece of the cable, take it over the connector and on to the other piece. Having said that, if the job allows it's also a good move to make the joint what a professional would call 'half-lapped' – meaning that when you reach the thickest part of the job (such as the connector), cut the tape and then start again from the other piece of cable, overwinding the second tape run on to the first so that the connector is completely covered. This will ensure that there are no 'voids' in the join in which water could condense. The aim of the game is to get the self-amalgamating in intimate contact with whatever it is you're trying to waterproof.

What happens then is a little miracle of industrial chemistry. In a short time the separate layers of tape which you've wound on start to fuse together, so that ultimately the connector or whatever is completely covered with what amounts to a custom-made fully waterproof 'boot'. Provided that the physical construction of whatever it is you're waterproofing allows you to wind self-amalgamating tape on to it, it's far and away the best stuff for the job. There is one slight snag, though. Self-amalgamating tape is actually a plastic substance called polyisobutylene, which is one of a class of thermoplastics that doesn't like the ultraviolet content of sunlight much – so it tends to go a bit brittle and crack after a year or two. No problem at all – all you need to do is to wrap it with a layer of ordinary PVC insulating tape. If you feel like doing a really gold-plated mil-spec job, you can give the final result a couple of coats of clear polyurethane varnish.

If you do these things, you can rest assured that water doesn't have even a faint chance of getting into the cable and messing things up. At my last-QTH-but-one there were about fifteen connectors treated in the manner described above, and all of them were as good as new after just over eight years of service when the time came take all the antennas down prior to moving house. Actually, it's when you come to dismantle connections made in this way that the only real problem crops up. Self-amalgamating tape that's done it's stuff is amazingly tough, and nothing short of a Stanley knife with a new blade will make any impression on it. So when you decide to move house and take down the antennas, allow a little time for dismantling . . .

All in all, it's a very good move to keep a couple of rolls of self-amalgamating tape and ditto of the ordinary insulating tape in the shack. What happens, though, if we want to waterproof something like the connector block on the bottom of a rotator – or the driven element and balun connections on, say, a Cushcraft 144MHz antenna, which are all done with nuts and bolts? You probably can't get self-amalgamating tape to do the business here because it's physically impracticable to get it in or around the job. What you need here is a 'sealant' – and nowadays that usually implies something which comes out of a tube and which either (a) sets by chemical reaction of some sort into a waterproof non-conductive semi-solid which is rather 'rubbery' in nature or (b) something like silicone grease which

doesn't set – it just seals and protects. Of this latter type, the most common is Dow Corning MS4, which comes in what looks like a giant-sized toothpaste tube. MS4 is just the job for all sorts of filling and coating applications with a view to excluding moisture. Like most silicones it has high dielectric strength – 21.7kV/mm, to be precise – so it's quite happy in high-voltage applications. Actually, it's also incredibly handy for lubricating things like grommets or cables which need to be squeezed through confined spaces."

The reference also mentions two types of chemical sealant, one of which liberates acetic acid and "needs to be avoided like the plague", the other being of the acrylic variety, non-corrosive and safe for use on delicate connectors.

The author is unable to endorse the 'potting' of baluns for use with experimental antennas as this slows down the rate of escape of heat and can lead to destruction under fault conditions, or if one is tempted to use the antenna on a frequency for which it was not intended. Even with an SWR of 20 one may be able to put an S9 signal into VK, but not for long if the balun is encapsulated in Araldite. On the other hand, when almost exactly this situation arose (but without the Araldite) following damage to the main antenna (by the 1987 hurricane) the contact was able to continue until the shack had to be evacuated because of smoke. This was eventually traced to an overheated balun, although this thereafter appeared to be electrically undamaged!

Baluns constructed by the recommended method of binding straight wires tightly together with vinyl tape (in order to minimise leakage reactance as described on p56) and installed on a 'temporary' basis with no other weather protection have continued in use for months afterwards, apparently unaffected by rain, and off-hand there seems no reason to suppose that sealing the ends with acrylic would not suffice for a more permanent installation.

Open-wire line

Open-wire line can be easily constructed at a small fraction of the cost of the more popular types of feeder and is a great deal more efficient. There is some substance in the complaint that it is less convenient to use, since it cannot be trailed along the ground or taped onto a metal mast, and should be protected against accidental contact. The author well recalls one occasion when the SWR momentarily shot up to infinity with an accompaniment of sparks as an errant cow dashed past the shack window with a farming neighbour in hot pursuit.

Subject to these constraints very considerable liberties can be taken without adverse effect; contrary to general belief, radiation from the line is usually negligible although, as with coaxial line, it can be provoked by failure to take adequate precautions. Almost any wire can be used provided it is not resistance wire and not made of iron or steel. These have a high RF resistance due to poor DC conductivity combined with high magnetic permeability (μ), RF resistance being proportional to $\sqrt{\mu}$. In one case an observed loss of about 6dB in 100yd (91m) of line was traced to surplus 'copper' wire which turned out to be not copper but copper-plated steel.

The usual labour-intensive instructions for the construction

"Open-wire line . . . should be protected against accidental contact"

of 600Ω line are best ignored, and for most purposes can be substituted by the rule that 'anything goes' as the following example (already referred to in Chapter 4) illustrates. For several years the author used a 150yd (137m) line between a shack in the house and another on the antenna farm; this was made from lots of odd lengths of wire, suitably paired and ranging from 22swg (0.7mm) to 14swg (2mm) with several sharp bends which are sources of loss. An overall loss of only 1.6dB was measured at 14MHz between 50Ω terminations using 4:1 baluns for transformation into and out of the line, an ATU, several TV-type plugs and sockets and an antenna change-over relay (not designed for RF) out of the junk-box. Lead-in arrangements at both ends consisted of thin flex pushed through holes in the window sill.

However, due to the high efficiency of open-wire lines, this could be a fire risk under fault conditions such as a short- or open-circuit at the antenna: this would cause a very large voltage to appear at the lead-in. There is, however, no need to resort to the traditional practice of drilling holes in glass window panes. A few inches of coaxial cable may be used for each lead-in wire, disregarding the outer conductor, or almost any bit of high-tension lead will serve. Insulators may be 2–6in (5–15cm) in length cut from plastic tubing; two holes may be drilled at the end of each, a U of stiff wire being pushed through the holes and used to bind the insulator onto the line: Fig 19.6.

For long straight runs of feeder in an accessible position, a spacing of 6in (15cm) is recommended with very few insulators, the desirable number being a matter for experience. The author has used runs of up to 100ft (30m) with none at all – but it is as well to have a few handy in case of a storm brewing or problems with birds! For reliable performance in all weathers it will probably be found on average that about 8–10 spacers are needed per 100ft (30m). Smaller spacings

and thin wire are recommended for shorter runs and wherever a feeder has to be run close to a mast, trees, or any 'lossy' objects. As well as reduced risk of line-imbalance, advantages include lower cost, reduced visual impact, and even easier construction. As an example, following a move to a new location, a pair of 120ft lines were constructed by running pairs of 21swg wires along the desired route, lengths of fishing line attached to trees and other supports being used to steer them past obstructions. 2in spacers attached at intervals of 3 to 4ft provided adequate separation, and the matched line loss, calculated with the help of Fig 3.11, came to only 0.2dB compared with a typical loss of 1dB for a coaxial feeder. Even with an SWR of 5, a value rarely exceeded, the loss would have been only 0.5dB.

If the number of spacers is kept low it can be estimated with the help of Fig 3.10 that the losses should not exceed 0.2dB for 300ft (91m) of 14swg wire. Even in the case of 28swg

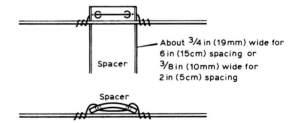

About 3/4 in (19mm) wide for 6 in (15cm) spacing or 3/8 in (10mm) wide for 2 in (5cm) spacing

Spacer

Spacer

Fig 19.6. Simple and inexpensive 600Ω line construction. Plastic piping of 2–3in (5–8cm) diameter is cut into short lengths and then sawn lengthwise into strips, a pair of small holes being drilled near each end of each strip. Spacing may be 2–6in (5–15cm), with insulation at intervals of some 12–15 times the line spacing. With wide spacing losses are reduced and construction is much quicker, but symmetry is more easily upset. Note that the spacers are slightly curved and this helps to prevent slippage

(0.3mm) the loss should not exceed 1dB, which is much less than the typical figure of 3dB for the same length of coaxial cable. Losses due to radiation from a balanced line are approximately equal to four times the power radiated from a doublet of length equal to the spacing [3], ie the power lost is given in watts per 'square ampere' (corresponding to 600W total radiated power) by $6316(D/\lambda)^2$ or 0.35W for a spacing of 6in (15cm) at 14MHz. This figure is independent of feeder length (unless very short) and represents a loss of considerably less than one thousandth of an S-unit!

Much larger amounts of radiation can be produced by out-of-balance currents, namely about 80W per square ampere [3] or a loss of 0.5dB for an out-of-balance current roughly equal to the matched line current; this is for a line height of $\lambda/4$, and increases with height but is almost independent of line length.

Unless beam rotation can be restricted to about 150° or less there are problems in getting a 600Ω line past the beam rotator without undue twisting or risk of contact between the line and the motor housing. The author's method is to use a short 300Ω insert at the rotator and, in addition, surround the motor with a jacket made from lengths of plastic pipe split down the middle; this ensures that the ribbon is kept well clear of the motor housing.

300Ω line

On one occasion an experimental antenna with a feedpoint impedance of 200Ω was fed with four half-wavelengths of 300Ω line. Using a 4:1 balun the SWR in a 50Ω line was 10. Next morning it was 3.0. After a lot of time had been wasted suspecting the antenna, the 300Ω line dried out and the SWR returned to 1.0, but rose again to 2 after running some 15ft (45m) of the line through a bucket of water. Prior to this, very erratic behaviour of an antenna had been traced (after weeks of wasted effort) to the use of the transparent plastic type of line which developed a loss of several decibels per 100ft (30m), though only when wet or still drying out. The fault appeared only after several months use and as a further indictment of the plastic it was noticed that one of the wires (the other being tinned) was suffering from severe corrosion.

Subsequent to these tests heavy-duty 300Ω slotted line has become available and samples from two different sources have been tested. Though three to four times better than the older line, there is a change of 5–6% in velocity factor between 'wet' and 'dry'; for one wavelength of feeder terminated in a 50Ω load (ie operating at an SWR of 6), this means that after setting the SWR down to unity by means of an ATU at the transmitter it rises to about 6 whilst the line is getting wet or drying out. With this result as a starting point, the Smith chart can be used to derive figures for other lengths and SWR values with a reasonable chance of arriving at acceptable compromises in the case of, say, an SDL array with short feeders. In the case of matched lines there is of course no problem. One suggestion, for which the author is indebted to PA0UHF, is to keep the line dry by enclosing it in a length of hosepipe.

For 450Ω line of similar construction the change in velocity factor (v) was halved, the actual values of v being 0.80 and 0.87 for 300 and 450Ω line respectively, decreasing when wet.

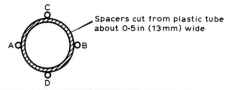

Fig 19.7. Construction of 300Ω line. Spacers are circular rings cut from plastic piping. A and B, likewise C and D, are connected in parallel at each end of the line

Air-dielectric 300 and 450Ω line (v = 0.95), though used elsewhere for TV, is not available in the UK up to the time of writing though, as we have seen, the construction of higher-impedance lines presents few problems. One way to construct 300Ω line requires rigid points for its attachment, separated by a straight run; the wire is stretched between them as tightly as possible, and enough 0.4in spacers inserted to keep them apart, intervals of about 15in being suitable. In most cases it is possible to combine one or more such straight runs with relatively short lengths of commercial line.

With an estimated loss in a half-wavelength of the open wire line of only 0.7dB at an SWR of 30 it would have been difficult to find a better way of feeding the Miniclaw (p216), but for one oversight which proved highly instructive. At first all went well, but after a short time an antenna fault developed and the feeder, being easy to twist and thus cause a short-circuit, was the obvious suspect until careful inspection revealed no sign of any such fault.

The antenna was lowered for inspection (a major task) but given a clean bill of health, and the matter remained a mystery until after dark when a glance out of the shack window disclosed a small but brilliant 'fireball'. This was traced to a plastic spacer (of which a small number had been used due to running out of ceramic ones), close to a point of maximum RF voltage on the feeder. This fault occurred because (a) the plastic was of poor quality (cut from piping) and (b) as related on p214, the antenna was being used in a way not originally intended, thereby subjecting the insulator to exceptional stress. However, this points clearly to a fire hazard since a short-circuit at the antenna would result in a far larger value of SWR, and the 'fireball' could equally well have occurred at the lead-in, indoors, or conceivably in a roof space. It could be inferred from this that the need for good constructional practices is greater, not less, in the case of indoor antennas, and the case for using coaxial cable rather than twin feeder for antennas in roof spaces is reinforced.

High-quality open-wire line with a typical impedance of 300Ω may be constructed using the four-wire principle: Fig 19.7. This can be considered as a pair of separate 600Ω lines in parallel, symmetry between them being such that the coupling is balanced out.

Coaxial cable

Resistance loss, calculated for the inner conductor on the basis of Fig 3.11, accounts for about half the attenuation of new coaxial cable. The remainder is resistance loss in the outer conductor, additional resistance loss due to proximity effect arising from the close spacing between conductors, and dielectric losses in the insulating material. Radiation loss is virtually zero, provided no current flows on the outside of the cable. With most of the older types of cable there is a considerable increase in resistance with age as a result of corrosion caused by chemicals used in the manufacture, and with cables of any age serious deterioration can result if joints are not adequately protected against moisture. A blackened inner conductor means that the cable is useless but any sign of discolouration or corrosion should be regarded with suspicion. Losses may be measured by methods described in Chapter 18.

For protection against moisture the author has been successful with ordinary plastic insulating tape, though care is needed to ensure the joint is thoroughly covered, leaving no cracks. Using short plastic-covered extension leads it is possible to tape over the end connections, but the best method is to bring these into a waterproof box which also houses the balun.

Coaxial cable is sometimes used for the construction of resonators but not recommended for high-Q applications; typically at 21MHz 50Ω cable has a loss of 0.09dB per quarter-wavelength which translates into a loss resistance of about 1Ω. Dividing this by two to allow for the sinusoidal current distribution in a resonant line gives a Q of 50/0.5 or 100 only. This contrasts with a Q of 800 in the case of a similar calculation for 600Ω line using heavy-gauge copper (12swg or 2.6mm). On the other hand, small-value capacitors with substantial voltage and current ratings are often required for use in antennas, particularly for multiband applications including traps and many of the arrangements described in these pages. It is often difficult or expensive to obtain the required values and the idea of making them up from short lengths of feeder is attractive. For this application resistance loss can be disregarded but there remains the question of how much of the total loss is due to the dielectric.

Having obtained a calculated copper loss of only about half the total, the author was at first inclined to reject this idea out of hand, but Q measurements on some capacitors of about 10pF made from coaxial line yielded figures around 300–400 which is good enough for most purposes including linear resonators, though if the loss in the capacitor is added to all the other losses, it further strengthens the case against traps. In view of the relatively low dielectric loss it is evident that more importance must be attached to the copper loss, much of this being accounted for by the braiding.

Inductors and capacitors

Inductors should be single layer and, if the turns are 'self-supporting' and spaced by several times the wire diameter,

should not require any further weather protection. In some cases loading inductors have been wound directly onto glassfibre with no adverse effects on comparative signal reports, though this is thought to have been partly responsible for wet-weather changes which often required some readjustment of the ATU.

With widely spaced turns, the RF resistance of an inductor is only slightly greater than the value obtained by estimating the total length of wire (in wavelengths) and consulting Fig 3.11, but at close spacings allowance must be made for 'proximity effect', reckoning that the resistance is roughly doubled when the gap between turns is about 0.6 times the wire diameter. Increased resistance is offset by greater inductance, and in consequence Q is not critically dependent on shape or frequency, though it is a maximum (16) for a length/diameter ratio of about 0.5, and roughly proportional to the square-root of coil diameter if inductance and shape are maintained constant. One problem still to be addressed concerns possible adverse effects on performance from water droplets lodged between turns in the event of windings being unprotected, but in many (probably most) cases it should be possible to space turns sufficiently to avoid the need for protection.

Small capacitors can be constructed from short lengths of twin feeder (subject to verification that 'wet/dry' variations are acceptable), though voltage breakdown has been experienced with low-impedance line and any exposed ends need to be well separated; coaxial cable is in general a better choice for this purpose, subject to adequate weather protection. Silvered-mica capacitors, which can be used in series or parallel, are probably the best choice for larger values, though some ceramics are suitable; others have a high power factor and tests should be made before using capacitors of unknown origin in sensitive positions.

Amateur needs in this respect are not well catered for, and this must be held accountable for suggestions based on the use of double-sided printed-circuit board; seizing on this idea with eager anticipation, the author measured Q's in the region of 20–30 compared with 160–200 for the same inductors tuned by air-dielectric capacitors or lengths of coaxial cable. Glassfibre was no better than the cheaper material although, in common with many other materials highly unsuitable as dielectric for high-Q capacitors, when cut into narrow strips it makes excellent spacers for 600Ω lines and appears also to be suitable for coil formers.

RF resistance of different types of conductor

Reference was made above to the likelihood of considerable losses if RF current is allowed to flow through magnetic materials. When steel masts or towers are energised as low-frequency antennas, the losses may be reduced to an acceptable level by virtue of the large surface area, particularly as the radiation resistance is likely to be quite high, but the need to avoid using magnetic wire is demonstrated by the following Q measurements on some λ/4 open-wire stubs at 14MHz.

19swg (1mm) enamelled copper	220
1/044 (1mm) tinned copper, plastic insulated	210
Plastic-covered iron wire, comparable gauge	17.5

Despite considerable corrosion and several soldered joints, a Q of 420 was measured for 14swg (2mm) bare copper compared with a theoretical Q of 660. Bare stranded wire, of comparable diameter and also corroded by use, yielded in contrast a Q of only 302.

Masts

An inexpensive mast for a dipole, inverted-V or vertical beam such as Fig 13.8(b) can be contrived by tying a light bamboo extension to a ladder, apex heights up to 40ft (12m) or more being achievable in this way. It is advisable to tie the foot of the ladder to a strong post which serves to prevent it slipping during erection and helps to support the ladder subsequently, one or two sets of guys being also required. It is a reasonable assumption that planning permission will not be required for this, particularly if it is moved around occasionally and falls down from time to time, thereby creating an impression of impermanence! It is likely in any case to be 'experimental' in the first instance, though some tact and forethought may be required; it should not be possible for example for its fall to demolish a greenhouse next door. The fears of neighbours that they may be afflicted with a permanent eyesore can probably be allayed by giving some thought to construction and positioning.

At the other end of the scale it would, putting it mildly, be unwise to embark on a major investment such as a 60ft (18m) tower without first making sure of the planning permission which is almost certain to be required. Somewhere in between these extremes is a 'grey area' where there are no clear legal precedents though, subject to maintenance of good neighbourly relations, there is a fair chance that common sense will prevail. It is clearly of prime importance to aim for minimum visual impact, and in general the supporting structure is likely to be more of a problem than the beam itself, though lighter beams can be supported by thinner masts. Poles attached to chimneys and similar to those used for supporting television antennas stand a reasonable chance of acceptance.

Planning requirements have been partly covered on pp247, 313; beyond this it can only be suggested that in cases of doubt an approach should be made to the local planning authority to ascertain whether they consider that planning permission is required for the proposed structure. In cases of difficulty RSGB members should get in touch with the RSGB which may be able to help.

Assuming visual impact to be related to the required surface area, a mast constructed of metal tubing would appear to have the edge over wooden masts and these are available from commercial sources. Home-constructed masts, both wood and metal, nevertheless exist in considerable numbers and almost as many different shapes and sizes [4], indicating a bias towards using whatever materials happen to be available. Inevitably, in the absence of professional expertise such masts tend to be overdesigned, other ones being short lived! Of the many published designs for wooden masts, arrangements somewhat similar to Fig 19.8(a) are featured in several sources and, apart from their basic simplicity, lend themselves to a number of useful adaptations such as telescopic or tiltover use.

The mast is constructed from three standard 20ft (6m) lengths of 4in by 2in (10 by 5cm) timber bolted together, the lower post being a 6ft (1.8m) length of oak or other hardwood, the lower third of its length being set in concrete. Fig 19.8(b) shows it in course of erection with the help of a small winch and a second much shorter post which can be temporary or permanent. The doubled rope and extra pulley provides a 2:1 mechanical advantage and halves the tension in the rope. This arrangement has been found particularly convenient for work on experimental antennas, a rest being provided so that when lowered the top of the mast is at a convenient height for assembling the antenna.

Alternatively, using an extra length of wood as a lever, the tiltover arrangement shown in Fig 19.8(c) may be used; if desired this can be counterbalanced so that the beam sails up at the touch of a finger.

A frequent complication is entanglement of the beam with guys holding up the lower part of the mast and, though this can be overcome by careful planning, the author found that in his case (a) was generally more convenient. This depends, however, on a lot of factors, including the space available and the existence of intervening tree branches etc. Fig 19.8(d) shows a telescopic arrangement which has also been used; two sets of cords, one each side, are desirable since there is a tendency to jam if the pull is one-sided. Methods (b) and (d) can be combined. In the case of (c) and (d) it is desirable to have ladder access to the top of the lower section for insertion of a final bolt.

A short length of metal tubing may be fixed to the top of the mast by U-bolts or clamps to support a rotary beam. In the case of a manually rotated compact or miniature beam such as Figs 12.9, 12.10 or 12.12, the height can be extended about 10ft (3m) by this means, assuming tubing of the order of 1½in (38mm) OD and 1/8in (3mm) wall thickness plus an additional set of guys. A 15ft (4.5m) bamboo extension carrying a spreader for the support of a three-band inverted-V beam, Fig 12.2(a), has also been used successfully. There are too many unknowns for the survival rate of such light extensions to be predictable under severe storm conditions and experience may dictate design changes; in line with the 'bias' indicated earlier, the emphasis here is on low cost, minimising the risk of serious damage in the event of failure, and easy repair.

There are a number of favourable as well as adverse circumstances which may further influence the choice of mast type. Masts can often be supported against the wall of a house, and access to a flat roof, even if it is only the roof of a garage, can be extremely helpful. For example, a pair of ladder sections can be set at right-angles, secured to the wall of a garage or bungalow, and used as a 'mini-tower' or lower section of a telescopic mast as shown in Fig 19.9.

The author was perhaps particularly fortunate in being able

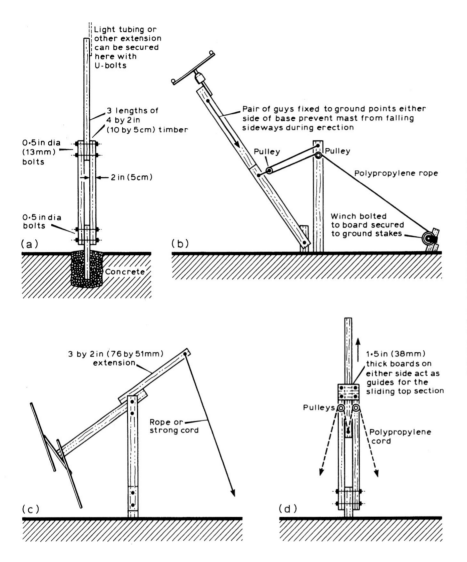

Fig 19.8. (a) Simple mast construction from three 20ft (6m) lengths of 4 by 2in (10 by 5cm) timber and a ground post. Overlaps should be at least 30in (75cm). (b) Method of erection using auxiliary mast, winch and elementary block and tackle. Washing-line pulleys are suitable. The winch must be securely anchored. (c) Tiltover modification allows easy erection provided the beam does not get entangled with guy ropes, trees, hedges etc. (d) Telescopic version greatly reduces strain on mast, winch etc during erection and may allow the use of a longer mast extension. To reduce tendency to jam, the cords and pulleys should be duplicated on the other side of the mast

to acquire a pair of identical 14ft aluminium ladder sections and a 5m length of 18swg 5cm diameter alloy tubing. With short extensions to give mast heights of about 30ft and taking advantage of easy access from the roof, this has been used to support a wide variety of experimental antennas of sizes up to a three-element Claw which, alas, served mainly to confirm the merits of sticking to two elements! The extension, complete with antenna, was found extremely light and easy to handle even at what some might consider an advanced age!

In extreme contrast to this, the author's main antenna (see photo p220) was required to be erected in a small space hemmed in by bushes and trees which ruled out the use of tilting or luffing such as Fig 19.11(b) or (c). In this case the lower mast section consisted of a 'pedestal' formed from four 20ft lengths of 4in by 2in timber sunk 3ft into concrete foundations. This structure, which was well braced and

guyed, initially supported a steel scaffold pole which was winched up inside it, a 3ft length of drainpipe set in the concrete allowing the pole to be lowered 3ft into the ground for easier access (by ladder) to its top. Later, replacement of steel by aluminium allowed a block and tackle made from two washing-line pulleys to be substituted for the winch. Later still, by means of lower-end extensions, this became a more or less conventional three-section telescopic mast surrounded by a largely redundant wooden structure.

In retrospect, the reasoning was not entirely sound, but some useful conclusion can be drawn; in working with telescopic masts having a beam on top of them there are potential hazards and it is essential for the lower section to be completely secure before starting to raise the next section. It must be possible to operate safely at the top of this lower section, eg by standing on a roof or secured to a ladder,

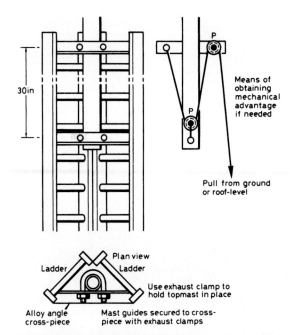

Fig 19.9. Mini-tower formed from two ladder sections. Reinforce with cross pieces as necessary (alloy angle)

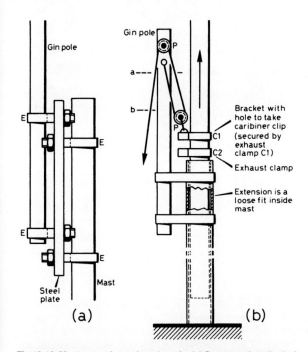

Fig 19.10. Mast extension using gin-pole. (a) Suggested method of attaching gin-pole to mast (ladder rest can be attached to steel plate). At least 3ft overlap is advised. (b) Method of extension. Start with both clamps tight. Raise through the distance ab. Drop C2 to lower position and lock. Drop C1 and repeat until mast is fully extended

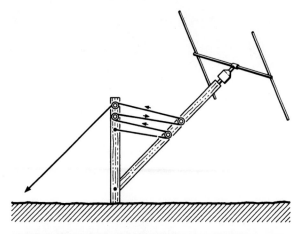

Fig 19.11. Block-and-tackle using washing-line pulleys to give 4:1 mechanical advantage for beam erection

without risk of falling off or being hit on the head in the event of slippage of the mast section carrying the beam. With a sufficiently light mast and beam, erection may be very easy; otherwise it has been found advisable to work with at least two exhaust clamps, extending the mast a small amount at a time and tightening first one and then the other. Using a gin-pole, as in Fig 19.10, all the hauling can be carried out from ground level, though the ladder must be climbed to manipulate the clamps. Nevertheless, the possibility of fully ground-based telescopic operation is a 'plus' safety feature of the earlier construction, the 'mini-tower', and Fig 19.8(d); each of these examples had the further important advantage that extension required only a single operation instead of several stages determined by the extent of the gin-pole.

A further hazard with telescopic masts, unless they can in an emergency be lowered whilst fully extended, is failure to telescope as a result of one section, being a tight fit in a lower one, becoming slightly bent. With reasonable overlap there is no need for a tight fit although, if there is felt to be too much freedom of movement, packing-pieces consisting (for example) of strips of aluminium bent over at the top end may be dropped into the gap before tightening the clamp. There is one final hazard to be mentioned: the possibility (through miscalculation) of over-extension, causing the top section (complete with beam) to leave its socket and crash to the ground. This can be prevented by, for example, marking out the correct height along a guy rope and securing it at the base of the mast.

Mast erection

In the case of fixed inverted-V or cubical quad antennas at apex heights up to 50ft (15m) the doubled rope method shown in Fig 19.8(b) was found adequate by itself without the winch, though it needed an assistant to take up rope slack with one turn round a firm post as the mast was raised.

If a stronger pull is required without going to the expense

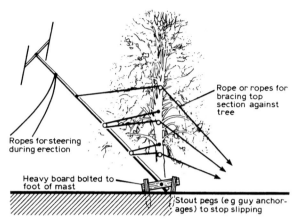

Fig 19.12. Method which has been used successfully for erecting a lightweight beam above a tree top. Pulleys and ropes are fixed as high as possible and if necessary at intervals on the tree trunk. It is useful to have a winch and at least one helper. Additional ropes may be used as required, with each tree presenting a different set of problems

Erection of 40ft (12m) mast by the gin-pole method (top) and attachment of ladder to base of mast (bottom)

of acquiring a winch, more pulleys may be used, as in Fig 19.11 which provides a 4:1 mechanical gain. This proved more than adequate for single-handed erection of the beam in Fig 12.10 (with rotator) at a height of 30ft (9.1m), the block and tackle being secured at the 20ft (6m) level. It will be seen that the length of rope increases in proportion to the mechanical advantage, but the tension and therefore the required cross-sectional area is reduced *pro rata* so that cost need not be greatly increased in order to obtain extra 'lift'. Using polypropylene rope and washing-line pulleys, it is, however, not possible to get below about 600lb (272kg) breaking strain because the rope gets jammed between the pulley and its housing.

In some cases it is possible to press a tree into service as part of the mast system using two or more doubled ropes and pulleys as in Fig 19.12. Possibilities include using the lower part of a thick tree trunk in lieu of the lower post in Fig 19.8 with normal sets of guys for the upper sections of the mast, but guys cannot be used if the mast is attached to parts of the tree which sway in the wind. Structural requirements vary over a wide range depending on the tree and how easy it is to climb. Hopefully the mast will merge into the tree and attract relatively little attention.

A simple method of raising a mast single-handed is illustrated in the photographs taken from reference [5] and shows a 40ft (12m) mast in course of erection; to quote the reference "the whole arrangement is perfectly stable and under complete control at all times. It took 45min (entirely unaided) to assemble and lay out the mast (four 10ft (3m) poles) and guys, and 15min to raise it and make the final adjustments." Two guys should be attached to anchorages on a line at right-angles to the mast as shown in the upper photograph so that they stay just taut or with a small amount of slack as the mast goes up; this prevents it falling sideways". This method is advised also with the other methods of erection, but if there

is only room for one guy (eg because of tree branches) it is not difficult to impart a bias to the proceedings, so that the mast tries to overbalance in one direction but is prevented by a single guy pulling the opposite way. A wooden mast may be protected with creosote but this makes painting impossible in the event of deciding that a different colour would provide a better match to the environment.

Guy wires

Advice against the use of rope, though still frequently given, is valid only in respect of old-fashioned hemp rope (which is liable to rot, and stretches when wet) and ignores both the major advances in synthetic materials and the shortcomings of the main alternative, stranded galvanised wire which rusts badly after a few years' use. Polypropylene, to quote the earlier reference [5], "is an excellent general-purpose rope equally suitable for use as guys or halyards at a price which will give years of reliable service at little cost". Terylene, which is slightly better, is twice as expensive but may be more suitable "in those parts of the world which enjoy more than their fair share of sunshine".

Polythene, much the cheapest material, is excellent for halyards and suitable for light-duty guys but stretches badly if subjected to more than a small fraction of the breaking strain; the author is puzzled by references to difficulty in tying knots in it, having tied very large numbers and found it much easier to handle than ordinary string or rope. The slippery nature of the surface has the advantage that knots are relatively easy to untie (provided they are first relieved of any tension), and this helps to make it an ideal material for many uses around the 'antenna farm'.

Nylon, with up to 10% stretch available, is ideal for halyards but expensive.

The adequacy of polypropylene for guying any of the masts described in this chapter is confirmed by the author's experience over many years, but for towers it is essential to be guided in this (as in other respects) by the advice of the manufacturer.

Nylon fishing line

Recommendations based on the use of monofilament nylon fishing line for supporting antennas have appeared in several earlier chapters, based on satisfactory personal experience and its obvious relevance for the elimination or reduction of visual impact.

Following advice that it is adversely affected by ultraviolet light, tests were made on two samples thought to have been in use for about two or three years and the breaking strain was found to have been halved, though at half of 75lb, this was still well in excess of the allowable stress in 'invisible' wires. The allowable 'stretch' was slightly reduced, the available amount for accommodating tree movement being about 6%.

An important feature of this line is its exceptionally slippery quality which allows almost anything to be used as a pulley, such as a pair of brass cup-hooks which, with a line passed over them and attached to a weight, have sufficed for automatic closure of the shack door. Despite constant use over a 10-year period there is no sign of wear, and on the strength of this a line was pushed up over a high tree branch using a long but very lightweight pole and a small weight; one end was secured near the base of the tree, the other to one end of a wire antenna attached to another tree about 115ft (35m) away. Accurate details have not been recorded, but this arrangement was dismantled after a period of at least two years which included severe storms. There were some antenna changes which included conversion of an 80m antenna into an 'end-fed single wire' as described on p46, but on average the length of wire would have roughly equalled that of the nylon, thus allowing about 5ft of relative tree movement.

A branch is of very uncertain quality as a 'pulley', anything resembling a sharp edge being instantly fatal, and most types of insulator make much better ones; it would have been a

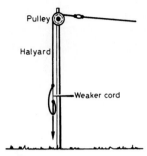

Fig 19.13. Mechanical fuse

simple matter to have hauled one up to the same branch using a cord with a slip knot, and other useful devices include a counterweight (p178), or a mechanical fuse: Fig 19.13. It may be possible to achieve greater height by enlisting the services of a professional tree-climber (look up 'tree surgeon' in the 'yellow pages'), in which case a spare pulley and cord should be provided if it can be fixed in a usable position.

Typical recommendations for guy anchorages include lengths of 2in (5cm) OD galvanised pipe and 2in by 2in angle iron, which should be driven into the ground for at least 2ft (0.6m) at right-angles to the angle of pull, though this distance should be increased in the case of sandy soil, large masts, large beams or the use of pipe. For securing the guys, those in a hurry can use any type of knot provided it tightens under tension, but for a permanent installation readers will find it to their advantage to consult the above references for a more professional approach.

If possible, guys should be at an angle of 45° to the mast, but the angle can be halved if there is no alternative; however, this doubles the tension required and also results in a strong downward pull which may cause the mast to buckle. To minimise this effect, guys should be left slightly loose but not so slack that it needs more than very slight movement of the mast to tighten them. In general two sets of three guys (at 120° intervals) are recommended for heights up to 30–35ft (9–10m) and three up to 40–45ft (12–14m).

Windage

It is necessary to be able to calculate the wind load presented by an antenna to be sure that the safe head load of a supporting structure is not exceeded. Manufacturers of towers and masts should be able to specify a safe head load for the maximum wind speed likely to be experienced in the reader's locality, as given [17] by Fig 19.14. Catalogue information normally relates to a specific wind speed and unfortunately there is no simple way of relating it to a different speed since, as will be evident from Fig 19.15, the mast and the head load are not subject to the same combination of forces. Subject, however, to due safety precautions, suitability for the anticipated head load could be checked by attaching a long cord to the top of the structure and applying the correct tension. It should be noted, however that severe icing can create an additional hazard, and also that some materials (including aluminium

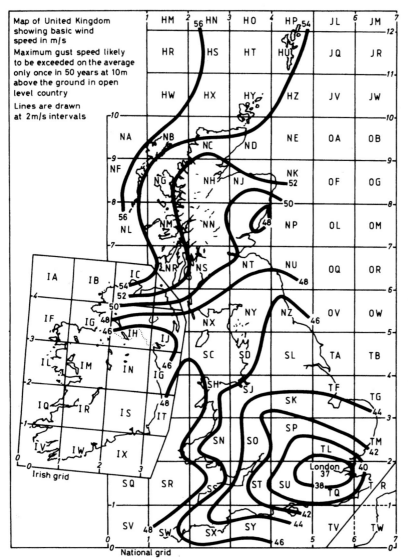

Fig 19.14. Basic wind speed map for the UK reproduced from CP3 Chap 5 Part 2. Based on information provided by the Meteorological Office and reproduced with the permission of the Controller of HMSO

constant depending on type of surface and aspect ratio, being typically 400 for round and 250 for flat surfaces [4, 6, 7]. Some easement as regards wind loading will result from the bending of elements which absorbs some of the wind pressure, though this is difficult to take into account and should perhaps be regarded merely as an addition to the factor of safety.

Wind loading on the mast takes two forms: axial and bending. The axial load arises from the top weight and the vertical component of the tensions in the guys. In itself it is not usually a problem, but the amount of bending stress is a complicated function of both types of loading and of the initial tension in the guys. Loading by snow and ice can result in greatly increased windage and to take care of this it has been suggested [4] that guys should have a breaking strain of six times the expected working load.

Wind pressure on a number of different types of antenna is listed in Table 19.2, assuming elements to be oriented at right-angles to the wind direction.

The pressures in the table are applied to the top of the mast as shown in Fig 19.15, resulting in a tension T in the guy which can be resolved into equivalent horizontal and vertical pulls, $T \sin \theta$ and $T \cos \theta$ respectively. The tangent of θ is d/h, so that θ (and therefore $\sin \theta$ and $\cos \theta$) may be readily obtained from tables or a pocket calculator. If, in the absence of the guy, the top of the mast is free to move, then T_H must exactly balance the wind pressure P so that $T = P/\sin \theta$, that is, unless the mast buckles under the downward force T_V as illustrated by the dotted lines, a tendency which may be corrected by additional guys. The tension T will be increased by wind pressure on the top section of the mast and a rough allowance for this can be made [4] by calculating the windage for the top one-third and adding it to P. This becomes the top third of the top half only, assuming the centre of the mast to be held rigid by guy wires at this point. This calculation indicates the strength required for the top guy ropes, the design of the mast itself being rather more complicated, as indicated above.

Values quoted for k differ slightly, depending on the source, but those for wind velocity vary widely with geographical area. Figures on imported American antennas refer to an EIA specification based on wind speeds of 80mph

alloy, of which there are several grades) can eventually be weakened by fatigue.

Further safety notes will be found in the next chapter but it will be all too evident that antenna construction and erection is not without its hazards, and observance of recommended safety performance needs to be supplemented by developing a keen sense of anticipation.

The wind-load rating can be obtained from the manufacturer and compared with the estimated wind load for the antenna using the formula:

$$\text{Wind pressure in lb/sq ft} = V^2/k$$

where V is the wind velocity in miles per hour and k is a

Table 19.2. Wind loading on various antennas

Antenna	Load at velocity 80mph (pressure 26lb/sq ft)	
	(lb)	(newtons)
Miniature beam as Fig 12.12, 21MHz with element diameter 1in (25mm), loading rods ½in (13mm)	28	124.5
Modified VK2ABQ, Fig 12.9	32	142.3
Three-band beam, cord braced, Figs 12.1 and 19.2	70	311.4
Monoband three-element Yagi based on Fig 19.1 (14MHz)	144	640.5
Typical three-element three-band trapped beam [4]	85	378.1
14MHz quad [4]	170	756.2
14MHz quad, arms 1in (25mm) diam (average) [6]	190	845.2

(129km/h) which is also in accord with standard building practice on the UK [4], and corresponds to a pressure of 26lb/sq ft (1250N/m²) for flat surfaces of large aspect ratio such as a mast or 16lb/sq ft (770N/m²) in the case of cylindrical surfaces, the area in the case of a cylindrical structure being reckoned as length multiplied by diameter. On the other hand, wind speeds in excess of 100mph (160km/h) are featured from time to time in news bulletins, and antennas at 50ft (15m) will experience higher wind speeds than buildings of average height. Putting $V = 100$mph brings the pressure up to 40lb/sq ft (1900N/m²) for flat surfaces. An accepted figure for areas liable to experience winds of hurricane force is 50lb/sq ft (2400N/m²) [6] but it should be safe to assume 25–30lb/sq ft (1200–1400N/m²) for sheltered areas in the UK.

Antenna supports resembling most of those featured in this chapter have been used successfully by the author over periods of several years, mostly for mast heights of 30–35ft

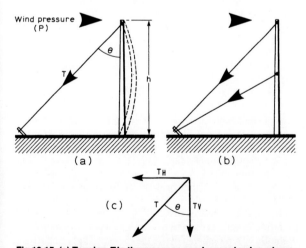

Fig 19.15. (a) Tension *T* in the guy rope can be resolved as shown at (c) into equivalent horizontal and vertical forces, T_H which is equal and opposite to the wind pressure *P*, and the downward force T_V which causes the mast to buckle as shown dotted. Additional guys as shown at (b) can be used to correct the buckling tendency

with a maximum of 40ft. Though ideal for experimental work and generally suitable for small beams or wire antennas at a sufficient height for 'good average' DX performance, many readers will be more ambitious and, after study of reference [12] and the acquisition of a tower, their next concern will be to ensure the permanence not merely of the tower but whatever is put on top of it.

The mechanical design of Yagi antennas has been the subject of a recent detailed study [13] aimed at ensuring survival even in extreme conditions; this includes computer-optimisation of design and its transformation into hardware, including ambitious monobanders designed for survival in 120mph winds as well as more modest structures. Few of us in the UK are able to erect very large structures, nor do we often experience the sort of winds which afflict locations such as Fig 10.1 or its Californian equivalent which seemingly inspired the above reference. Less fortunately, there are few such locations either! Points of general interest [13] include advice to use internal telescopic tubing for 'inner end' reinforcement of beam, boom, and mast sections, guying of booms in vertical and horizontal planes to improve wind survival, and moment compensation for the elimination of wind-induced torque on the mast.

Advice on foundations for masts and guy anchorages will be found in reference [14]. Other valuable advice in this reference includes a method of relieving the strain on beam rotators when using an extension tube, and on the maintenance of towers and antennas.

Lightning protection

In order to achieve the most efficient radiation from an antenna, it should in general be erected in the clear and as high as possible. Its potential as a lightning hazard is thereby increased and serious consideration should be given to this problem, which unfortunately is one of considerable complexity, so that no one set of simple rules can be devised to suit all situations. Some understanding of the general principles involved and, incidentally, the weakness of many common practices is therefore desirable.

The object of lightning protection systems is achieved by providing a *safe* conducting path between ground and the atmosphere above the structure to be protected [8]. Radio antenna installations usually embody the main ingredients of a protective system, but may tend to increase the hazard instead of reducing it because of failure to meet certain minimum specifications for such systems. The majority of lightning strikes involve currents in the region of 2000A to 100,000A, with an absolute maximum in the region of 220,000A. These are of short duration, eg a rise time of a few microseconds and decay time of a millisecond or less, though a complete lightning discharge may comprise a sequence of such strokes following the same path and lasting up to one second or more. Despite the short duration, these currents cause intense heating if they pass through a bad joint in a metal conductor or poor insulators such as trees or brickwork where they may cause sudden generation of steam. In each of these cases the effect may be explosive, fires may be started, and there is danger to any individual near the path of the discharge.

The current can pass safely to ground only if the following conditions are satisfied.

1. The current path is of adequate conductivity and cross-section.
2. The earth resistance is low enough.
3. Other conductors in the vicinity of the lightning conductor are adequately isolated or bonded to it.
4. There are no people or animals in the vicinity of the earth termination, where large potential gradients exist at the ground surface during a lightning strike.

The most frequent cause of damage to equipment is not a direct strike but voltage or current induced in antennas and mains wiring by lightning strikes in the vicinity at distances up to several hundred yards. Static charges due to an accentuation of normal atmospheric stresses also come into this category. Protection against these effects may be obtained even with a high-resistance earth connection, but the presence of an HF antenna, despite adequate protection against static electricity, could in some cases increase the likelihood of a direct strike without providing the means for dissipating it.

Lightning danger varies enormously between different areas of the world and this must obviously enter into the assessment of what precautions should be taken. The BSI Code of Practice [9] puts forward a 'points system' for deciding whether a building needs protection, and the majority of private dwelling houses in the British Isles would appear to be exempt, though many of them might be put at risk by erection of an HF beam or ground-plane antenna on the roof. Many antennas mounted on towers or tall masts would also appear to be in need of protection; on the other hand, some can be designed so that they themselves act as efficient protective systems. Short of full lightning protection it is recommended [10] that television antennas etc should be protected against atmospheric electricity by earthing with a conductor of not less than 1.5mm² cross-section, the outer conductor of a coaxial cable being regarded as suitable. An HF transmitting antenna should obviously receive at least this degree of protection. Antennas and masts may be earthed for this purpose by connection to an existing system of earthed metal work, eg suitable water pipes, the point of connection being as high as possible in the system. In the case of VHF or UHF antennas parasitic elements need not be earthed, but this may be advisable with the much larger elements used for HF beams.

Whether or not full protection is provided, the earth resistance should be as low as possible. For full protection the BSI Code of Practice [9] recommends a value not exceeding 10Ω and conductor cross-sections of the order of 60mm², though opinions differ on the latter figure. The official standards of some countries run as low as 28mm² and values as low as 5mm² have been described as adequate, despite a small number of instances of damage to 60mm² conductors

[8]. An earth resistance as low as 10Ω is often difficult to achieve but in such cases an annual dose of a solution of rock salt can be very effective. Low earth resistances are sometimes obtained by laying conductors in trenches near the surface, but it seems reasonable to suppose that this might tend, for a given resistance, to create dangerous potential gradients over a much larger area in the event of a strike.

The bonding of other conductors to the lightning protective system can raise complex problems and, if it appears necessary, the references should be consulted. Isolation is the alternative, and for full protection requires separations of 1ft (30cm) per ohm of earth resistance, plus 1ft for every 15ft (4.5m) of structure height to allow for the inductive voltage drop in the down conductor; however, for a slight increase in risk these distances may be halved. A rough idea of the zone of protection of a lightning conductor system is obtained by imagining a cone with a 90° apex angle extending down from the top of the conductor. This may be extended by the efficient bonding to the conductor of, say, a 'plumber's delight' HF beam erected over the roof. However, most HF transmitting antennas lie wholly or partly outside the protected zone and, because of inadequate conductor sizes, are unsuitable for its extension. In such cases the feeder (eg outer of coaxial cable), metal masts and parasitic elements should be connected to the highest convenient point on the lightning conductor. If there is no lightning protection system they should be *earthed outside the building*.

In the case of an antenna mounted on a tower or tall metal mast, all components including parasitic elements should be adequately earthed and, unless a separate lightning conductor is fitted, the tower must be free from high-resistance joints (eg fully welded). Even if resistance is initially low, possibilities of corrosion following exposure to the weather must not be overlooked. Otherwise, if the lightning current is allowed to pass to earth via the tower, explosive disintegration and collapse could occur. The earth resistance must be as low as possible, and a single 3ft (1m) earth spike, as often suggested, though adequate for the discharge of static electricity, is insufficient for lightning protection. Balanced feeders cannot be directly earthed except via resonant stubs as illustrated in Fig 19.16.

The usual change-over switch for earthing an antenna (and, worse still, other 'executive' arrangements likely to require the handling of a feeder during a thunderstorm, such as removing it from the rig and plugging it into an earth connection) are not merely useless for lightning protection but could prove highly dangerous. Even in the event that an operator remembers to 'switch to earth' before the onset of a storm, "any idea that they provide safety is illusory" [8]. This is because the switch is not capable of carrying lightning currents, nor is the gap sufficient for providing the required isolation which needs to be several feet as already indicated. It should be remembered that in the event of a lightning strike, even if the earth resistance is as low as 10Ω, voltages as high as two million could be lying around in the shack!

The BSI Code of Practice recommends where possible a common earth electrode for lightning protection and *all other*

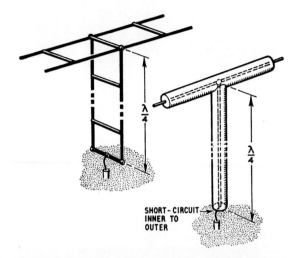

Fig 19.16. Quarter-wave lightning protection. The balanced line is approximately λ/4 in free space; the coaxial line is (λ/4)V where V is the velocity factor of the cable used for making the stub

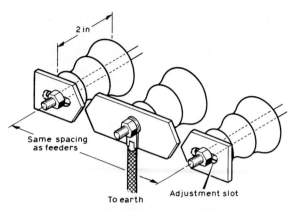

Fig 19.17. Simple lightning arrester for open-wire line using stand-off or feedthrough insulators and sections of ⅛ by ½in (3 by 13mm) brass or copper strip. It should be installed across the line at the point of entry to the station, the ground lead being of heavy-gauge conductor and as short and direct as possible. The gap should be just wide enough to prevent arcing during transmission *(ARRL Antenna Book)*

services, the lightning conductor being of course routed outside the building, and the installation must comply with regulations for the other services. It should be noted that an earth resistance of 10Ω is not low enough to provide in itself the fault protection required by wiring regulations and, if this is the best figure available, an earth-leakage trip will be fitted. Some older types are voltage-operated with a coil connected between true earth and the 'earth connection' of the wiring system. If an earthed coaxial feeder is plugged into a transmitter or receiver to which the usual three-pin plug is fitted, the trip coil will be wholly or partly short-circuited and a dangerous situation involving the whole of the house wiring could be created.

The earthing arrangements shown in Fig 19.16, though ideal for a monoband system, are inconvenient for multiband operation; simple earthing of the outer of coaxial cable will, at worst, only slightly increase the risk of damage to the cable and the use of a lightning arrester [11], as shown in Fig 19.17, is a reasonable compromise for open-wire lines.

References

[1] *The ARRL Antenna Book,* 13th edn, ARRL, 1974, p204.
[2] *The ARRL Antenna Book,* 12th edn, ARRL, 1970, p261.
[3] *Radio Engineers Handbook,* F E Terman, McGraw-Hill, 1943, pp193–194.
[4] 'Aerial masts and rotation systems', R Thornton, GM3PKV, and W H Allen, MBE, G2UJ, *Radio Communication* August/September 1972.
[5] 'Masts and rigging for amateurs – a professional approach', J M Gale, G3JMG, *Radio Communication* March 1970.
[6] *The ARRL Antenna Book,* 12th edn, ARRL, 1970, p277.
[7] *Antenna Theory and Design,* H P Williams, Vol 2, 2nd edn, Pitman, 1966.
[8] 'The protection of structures against lightning', J F Shipley, *Journal of the IEE,* Part I, December 1943.
[9] *The Protection of Structures Against Lightning,* British Standard Code of Practice, CP326, BSI, 1965.
[10] *The Reception of Sound and Television Broadcasting,* British Standard Code of Practice CP327.201, BSI, 1960.
[11] *The ARRL Antenna Book,* 13th edn, ARRL, 1974, p270.
[12] *Yagi Antenna Design,* J L Lawson, W2PV, ARRL, 1985.
[13] *Physical Design of Yagi Antennas,* Dave Leeson, W6QHS, ARRL, 1992.
[14] 'Wind loading', D J Reynolds, G3ZPF, *Radio Communication* April/May 1988.
[15] 'Waterproofing', 'In Practice', *Radio Communication* January 1989.
[16] *Radio Engineers Handbook,* F E Terman, McGraw-Hill, 1943.
[17] CP3, Chapter 5, Part 2, BSI.

Chapter 20

What kind of antenna?

The reader who has persevered with earlier chapters may by now have a fairly good idea as to the types of antenna best suited to his needs. Nevertheless, the factors to be taken into account are many and varied so that important aspects can be overlooked; the aim of this chapter is to provide some additional guidelines.

It is useful to start by asking two questions:

(a) What facilities are necessary to the full enjoyment of our hobby and what compromises are we prepared to make?
(b) How much is a decibel worth to us?

In dealing with the first question, the 'I want the lot' complex should, if possible, be avoided if only because the least important 20% is likely to be much more expensive than the remaining 80%. For this purpose, cost needs to be reckoned not only in cash but the effect that too big an antenna or the 'one antenna too many' may have on the tolerance of one's neighbours! Moreover, above a certain performance level the cost rises steeply with each additional decibel.

How much then *is* a decibel worth? In a contest it could be the difference between winning or losing, *or* between, say, the 12th and 14th place; in the first case it is clearly important, in the second case not very! One argument to be strongly rebutted is the frequent assertion that a decibel is unimportant *because one cannot measure it or hear the difference.* After possibly sacrificing several decibels in this way, the next step is probably to go out and purchase a linear amplifier, thus obtaining an advantage of 6dB at a cost of, say, £1000, or £160 for each 'worthless' decibel.

It may be suggested that decibels are perhaps not all of equal importance, and the author has indeed found that being without a 6dB linear is more of a handicap when working at the 100mW level than at the 100W level. Though based on much experience, this is little more than a vague personal impression and serves merely to confirm that within any small range, such as 6dB, all decibels can be regarded as equal. Communication in the amateur bands is usually restricted by interference rather than noise, so one might argue that little would be lost and much gained from a universally applied power limit of 30W. Nevertheless, as things are, we live in a competitive world and, taking a consensus of reasonable opinion, the cost of the linear is probably justified provided it does not escalate much further.

On this basis one would arrive at an 'economic cost' formula of 16p per milli-decibel from which it follows for example that, in the case of a typical small wire beam, the improvement in performance from increasing the wire diameter is far outweighed by the cost of the extra copper! Going on from this, it is easy enough to justify the cost of simple beams even without taking into account the reduction of interference which is probably more important, but the extra costs of a full-sized beam plus the tower which may be needed for it requires drastic revision of the formula; moreover, a small beam at 50ft (15m) should be at least as good as and probably less unpopular than a large one at 40ft (12m).

The value of a step in performance such as 6dB can be readily assessed by waiting for interference to occur and then switching in or out a linear amplifier or attenuator, or arranging for this to be done at the other end, whichever is appropriate. One rarely has long to wait for the opportunity and the result is likely to be convincing! In the absence of interference, however, the situation is very different since propagation is usually either good or non-existent. It is rarely marginal enough for communication to be seriously affected by a step which is small compared with the difference between the weakest useful signal and the strongest likely signal, typically of the order of 30dB. In practice, though 20W may well result in a lengthy DX contact 'Q5 all the way', the proportion of such contacts is increased and the number of repetitions or serious frustrations greatly reduced with a power level of 200W.

Another basis for assessment is suggested by the author's experience during the early years of the BERU Contest when a ratio of 1.6 was deduced for the increase in number of contacts corresponding to the 6dB power difference between the Senior and Junior contests, or roughly an increase in the number of contacts of 8% per decibel. As a statistical exercise the above examples may be open to criticism, but until a more up-to-date figure is available the author sticks to his view that the decibels wasted, for example, in traps add up to a poor bargain.

Some readers confronted with a bewildering choice of antennas and much conflicting advice may well be feeling 'out of their depth' despite the assurances given earlier (pp1–3). It may be worth restating at this stage that there are very few *essentially different* types of HF antenna which are both sound in concept and small enough to be of direct interest to the average amateur.

There are single elements, pairs of equal-current elements, and incursions by means of additional elements into a region of rapidly diminishing returns in pursuit of the elusive extra decibel or so. Horizontal antennas have their vertical counterparts, and within each category there are many different ways (eg loop or dipole elements) of achieving, for a given frequency, an identical result. There are alternative methods for meeting such practical needs as frequency mobility and minimising interference on as nearly as possible a real-time basis.

There are also circumstances which may enforce compromises, such as the acceptance of losses or a less-favourable radiation pattern in order to fit an antenna into a confined space or achieve additional height. Compromise is also demanded by typical methods of multibanding which introduce losses, cover only two or three bands and fail to exploit the additional aperture available by using the whole of a lowest-frequency radiator for the higher frequencies as well. 'Resonant' feeders (ie lines capable of operating efficiently at fairly high values of SWR) are free from these restrictions, especially if steps are taken to minimise the Z_0 of the antenna and equate it to that of the feeder as for Figs 20.2 or 12.25.

Overshadowing many of these options, especially in the case of vertical antennas, is the necessity of preventing feeder radiation; this is a problem which 'comes in different sizes' depending on the friendliness of the environment, since 10% of power radiated from the feeder is a loss of only 0.4dB in terms of the wanted signal but that implies a reduction of only 10dB in noise pick-up or TVI compared with the 20dB or more which may be needed.

A careful reading of Chapter 10 is recommended in view of the many different environmental factors which can arise. This will alert the reader to some popular fallacies, but particular note should also be taken of Chapter 11 (p188) in view of persistent claims that one type of antenna is better than another 'because it lowers the angle of radiation'; inspection of vertical radiation patterns appears to support such claims, but only because they are two-dimensional whereas antennas have three dimensions. It is important to remember (p114) that low-angle field strengths are always proportional to the free-space gain multiplied by a ground-reflection factor, which for a given height is the same for all antennas of like polarisation apart from a possible correction to allow for the variation of radiation resistance with height; this is small in the case of close-spaced beams.

The choice of an antenna and that of a mast for supporting it may be closely linked. This topic is addressed in reference [5] which needs to be consulted for detailed advice on mast foundations as well as guy anchorages suitable for large masts. Chapter 19 also includes basic data and formulae for an assessment of wind loading. However, reference [14] of the last chapter should be consulted for further guidelines, including detailed information about the strength of materials and structures together with methods of reinforcement.

The interest of amateur radio can often be enhanced by specialisation and this reacts favourably on antenna specifications. For those not yet sure of what they want, a simple beam based on Fig 12.2 or 12.20 is a good starting point, and for the lower frequencies inverted-V dipoles will provide good coverage to ranges within and somewhat beyond the 14MHz skip distance. At this stage, unless an eventual mast height of at least 40ft (12m) is contemplated, it will be useful to carry out comparative checks of vertical and horizontal polarisation, preferably using a vertical beam such as in Fig 13.8(b). The vertical antenna for this test must not be a ground-plane type and must be well clear of tree trunks or wet wood for most of its length. For a taste of DX at the lower frequencies an HF beam with its feeders can be excited as a vertical antenna working against a short counterpoise (p44).

Since the best choice of antenna system depends on personal priorities as well as the means at hand, there cannot be two cases alike. An earlier idea of trying to anticipate reader's problems and come up with ready-made answers has therefore been discarded; instead a number of scenarios have been devised for their merit as vehicles for discussion of the topics judged to be most important.

Much of this discussion has been simplified by the implicit assumption of flat sites without obstructions, but it should first be emphasised in line with Chapters 10, p160, and 16, p256, that those with sloping ground at their disposal are specially fortunate since for the down-slope direction outstanding DX performance can be achieved with very simple antennas such as inverted-V dipoles at heights of only a few metres. Moreover, this performance, good though it is, can be greatly enhanced by the use of fixed arrays which, because only low heights are required (with no rotation) can be very simple, inexpensive, and easily erected. It is a pity that such a valuable asset tends all too often to be wasted in whole or part through failure to realise that the antenna (which must be horizontally polarised) needs to be mounted down on the slope and not at the top of it.

The ideal antenna system (A)

The first example is an attempt to 'provide everything' inclusive of the best possible performance on all bands; it is further supposed there are no planning restrictions or financial constraints but as concessions to reality the following assumptions have been made:

(a) Height limited to 100ft (30m), with only one mast (or tower) of this height; though achieved infrequently in the UK, this is not unusual in some countries.

(b) Some space restriction, to the extent that large rhombic arrays are ruled out.

(c) Maximum length for tubular beam elements and booms not to exceed 45ft (13.7m) and 30ft (9.1m) respectively.

Presented with a 100ft (30m) mast or tower, the author's first instinct would be to fetch a saw and cut it in half, partly from 'fear of monsters' but also in the belief that a two-mast system offers important practical advantages. This will be treated in

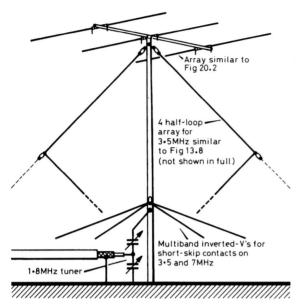

Fig 20.1. "Ideal" system based on 100ft (30m) mast which acts as a λ/4 top-loaded vertical antenna for 1.8MHz and supports four vertically polarised half-loops which operate as a two-element Yagi for 3.5MHz. The rotary beam on top of the mast uses three 42ft elements for coverage of all bands from 7–28MHz; these operate as collinear pairs at the higher frequencies. A low-height multiband dipole is included for short-skip working

due course as case (B) but it is instructive first to consider what might be done with the mast if still intact. The choices in this case are relatively simple and lead to an arrangement such as that shown in Fig 20.1. Here the mast is tuned as a λ/4 vertical antenna for 1.8MHz (p137) and used as support for a vertically polarised 3.5MHz array on the lines of Fig 13.8(b), thereby achieving a gain of about 6dB. An inverted-V dipole for 3.5 and possibly 1.8MHz is attached at about the 30ft (9.1m) level to provide coverage of short and medium ranges for which the vertical array is less suitable because of insufficient high-angle radiation.

Finding a suitable beam to put on top of the mast could present difficulty, since coverage of all bands from 7 to 28MHz, including 10, 18 and 24MHz, *and making full use on all bands of the available aperture,* is implicit in the terms of the scenario.

There is nothing available 'off the shelf' at the time of writing, though the log-periodic antenna would come fairly close to meeting the specification if 7MHz is deleted and the 'aperture' requirement relaxed, particularly in the case of the higher frequencies.

The solution offered consists of three dipole elements, each 42ft long and centre-fed with open-wire feeder, as illustrated in Fig 20.2 which is based on Chapter 12, p217, the outer pair of elements only being used on the two lower-frequency bands. To ensure peak performance on 7MHz, matching components are switched into position by relays or solenoid-operated DIY switches.

Values of SWR as given in Table 12.3 include a fairly high figure on 10MHz and, in the event of EMC problems resulting from this, additional relays may be needed; otherwise the specification should be fully met and there are no new or unproven techniques involved, though it might be unwise without some additional matching provision to extend feeder lengths much beyond what is needed for reaching to the top of the 100ft mast. Better, perhaps, to cut the mast in half and proceed at once to option (B)!

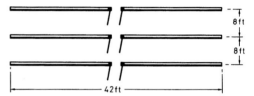

Fig 20.2. "Ideal" array. Three identical elements are used, with an average conductor diameter of 2cm. To exploit fully the "constant-Z₀" principle (p126), feeders should be 20swg, spaced 6in. Alternatively the development of switch boxes to allow feeding with coaxial cable would be technically feasible: see Fig 20.3. Frequency coverage: 7–29MHz. Series inductance matching at feedpoint (or matching stubs) to be switched into circuit on 7 and possibly 10MHz

The best solution, however, might be to use remote tuning with each element individually resonated on each band as required, eg as illustrated in Fig 20.3 which includes suitable component values. Subject to some switching of balun ratios, the centre element could then in principle be fed with coaxial cable which would need to be switched across to one of the outer elements for the two lowest-frequency bands; it is necessary, however, to retain the outer pair of open-wire lines in order to preserve the important features of deep-nulling and beam reversal. Unfortunately, unless and until suitable component kits become available, this can be no more than a suggestion for experimenters with time and mechanical ingenuity at their disposal.

An undesirable aspect of the above proposals is the need to split the elements at the feedpoint, where low-loss, low-capacitance insulation is essential due to high RF voltages at some frequencies, even if full use is made of the constant-Z₀ principle. A possible alternative is to use linear resonators (p134) with switched or servo-tuned capacitors, but this would mean scrapping the 7MHz option and also awaits the development of new components.

For operation on two or three bands, the use of stacked monoband Yagis is common practice and at least one commercial design of tribander is believed to have achieved near-monoband performance by the use of linear resonators in lieu of conventional traps. These may well be preferred options, though they fail to take advantage of the extra gain possible on 28MHz with multiband elements using centre-tuning or resonant feeders.

Apart from these options, specialisation holds a lot of attractions and, assuming the ability to support five or six elements, a monoband Yagi can be designed to a performance

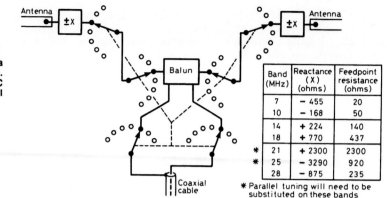

Fig 20.3. Switch box for feeding "ideal' antenna with coaxial cable. One position only shown. Can probably be simplified by substituting LC transformers for baluns. The balun ratio will also need to be switched

Band (MHz)	Reactance (X) (ohms)	Feedpoint resistance (ohms)
7	− 455	20
10	− 168	50
14	+ 224	140
18	+ 770	437
✱ 21	+ 2300	2300
✱ 25	− 3290	920
28	− 875	235

✱ Parallel tuning will need to be substituted on these bands

standard significantly beyond anything likely to be achievable in practice with multiband antennas. The art of Yagi design, unless restricted to simple examples like those on earlier pages, requires a book to itself, as also does the physical design of Yagis and similar structures; fortunately both exist [4, 5] and references to them have already been featured in Chapters 5, 12 and 19.

If searching for a simpler multiband system, one option is to accept lower gain at the higher frequencies (since most of the elements are out of use) by using a log-periodic array. A design which covers 13–30MHz has been described by P D Rhodes, K4EWG; this uses 12 elements, ranging in length from 38ft (11.6m) to 12ft (3.7m), the boom length being 26.5ft (8.1m) and the gain roughly equal to that of a three-element Yagi [1].

Using the procedure indicated on p243, this design could be extended to include 10.1MHz by adding three elements with a maximum length of 50ft (15.2m) and extending the boom length to 41ft (12.5m), though it might be a better compromise to retain the smaller antenna and surround it with VK2ABQ-type arrays for 7 and 10MHz.

As described, the log-periodic antenna has a total weight of 116lb (52.6kg) and a wind load area of 10.7sq ft (0.99m²) which has to be reckoned (p301) as a possible horizontal force of some 300lb (136kg) acting on the top of the tower.

These figures, together with a high 'visual impact factor', would probably rule out such an array for most locations in the UK regardless of the height of mast, but an alternative form of construction is suggested in Fig 20.4. Only three relatively thin tubing elements are used, the structure being cord braced and thin wire employed for the remainder. Mixing different gauges of conductor in this way tends to complicate the design because of differences in Z_a, but some degree of compensation can be effected by using pairs of wires in parallel as shown. It will also be necessary to compensate for the inward pull of the side cords by bending over the ends of the elements. Though yet to be tried and clearly not for the inexperienced, this could provide a possible means of achieving the benefits of a log-periodic array without the increased weight and windage of conventional designs.

As there could be problems due to the capacitive coupling between the bent-over ends, gaps of at least 2 or 3ft between the wire ends are probably desirable.

The ideal antenna system (B)

The two-mast system can follow similar lines to Fig 20.1, everything being duplicated except that 1.8 becomes 3.5MHz. For 3.5MHz a top-loaded λ/2 wire element may be suspended between the poles and this is also used as a monopole for 1.8MHz, some gain probably being obtainable on both bands for directions aligned with the towers by tuning these as parasitic elements. The lower height increases the likelihood that on 7MHz vertical polarisation will be superior, in which case the multiband beam can be simplified by deletion of the 7MHz requirement and the use of remote switching becomes much easier.

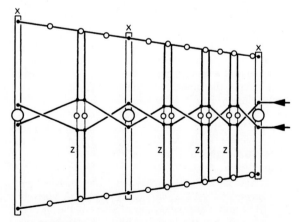

O ..... Insulator

X ..... Tubing elements insulated in centre providing mechanical support for the additional (interleaved) wire elements

Z ..... Thin wire elements using double wires to minimize impedance discontinuities

Fig 20.4. Suggestion for lightweight log-periodic antenna. Structure is basically that of a cord-braced three-element array with additional elements formed from pairs of thin wires

It will be noticed that the relatively commonplace 'single tower' situation differs from (B) mainly as regards the lack of duplication, and calls for little by way of additional comment except that the need often arises to switch quickly between two different directions, eg for participation in a multi-way contact or the assessment of band conditions. At such times the availability of a second antenna, even if only a ground-plane, can be extremely useful.

Provision is assumed for driving the two sets of arrays in phase (p222), thus giving the option of a gain boost in one direction or instantaneous switching between any two directions. The breakeven height is likely to be at least 55ft (17m) for horizontal and vertical polarisation at 7MHz, so that for a mast height of 55ft there would be a height loss for low angles of 5dB compared with the previous example (A), this being offset by 3dB of gain from phasing plus 2dB from the additional elements. Between 55 and 70ft (21m) the extra height gain is nil in the vertical case and about 2dB in the horizontal case.

It is possible (as explained in Chapter 13) to use both 7MHz arrays as monopoles for 3.5MHz, in which case the 3dB gain from phasing should at least equal any loss incurred in going from dipoles to monopoles and at all of the higher frequencies the theoretical gain should be fully realisable. Consequently, broadly speaking, nothing has been lost by going from one 100ft (30m) to two 70ft (21m) masts; on the other hand, use of two antennas provides a worthwhile improvement in directivity. A possibly more important bonus lies in having the option of being able to switch instantly between *any* two directions including their reciprocals.

High-angle coverage for the lower frequencies requires inverted-V dipoles as for system A.

Making the best of limited resources

We descend next from the lofty heights inhabited by big antennas to what, for most of us, is the real world where towers are a figment of the imagination. Looking around for other possible antenna supports there may be one or more trees around, and probably a chimney with a TV antenna already attached to it. With reasonable luck it should be possible to contrive at least one other support suitable for an SDL or VK2ABQ array. Mast kits are readily available and a number of well-tested homebrew mast and mini-tower ideas suitable for heights in the region of 20 to 40ft will be found in Chapter 19.

Recommended beams for mast-mounting include the ul-tra-lightweight Fig 12.20, the slightly more 'up-market' Fig 12.22(b) which is tolerant of longer feeders, or the top of the range, Fig 12.25, which is slightly heavier and mechanically more complicated but electrically the simplest. For one- or two-band operation the VK2ABQ is suitable and there are other options. A full-sized quad as described below is ideal for mounting in a tree which is easy to climb but, if outside help (electrically unskilled) has to be enlisted, the only beam that can be recommended consists of a pair of elements

similar to Fig 12.17(b). This type of element is well adapted also for pushing up into trees from below or from the top of a ladder. Vertical antennas can also be used in trees, though (as related on pp169), large amounts of absorption can occur in directions 'through the trunk'.

For 7MHz DX, beams along the lines of Fig 13.14 are likely to be the easiest solution, though arrays such as Figs 13.8–13.13 should be a better option if it is possible to arrange a lightweight mast extension giving a total height of some 50ft; a wire size of 22 or 24swg should be electrically adequate, though mechanical reliability may be less easy to achieve. Good results have also been obtained with a larger version (see p210) of the 14MHz tree-mounted SDL and this can be expected to do better in a poor location.

In line with arguments presented in earlier chapters it should be possible to equal or improve on the performance of most of the beams in current use by means of pairs of equal-current elements which can be relatively small and light, can be tuned (with certain reservations) to any waveband, and provide other incidental advantages. If at least two reversible beams can be erected, there may be no need for beam rotation unless it is desired to exploit possibilities of phasing for obtaining up to 3dB of extra gain. In the case of fixed beams even lighter structures may be feasible for heights up to 30 or 40ft. The estimated gain, about 4.5dB after allowing for losses in the elements (18 or 20swg copper), is only half an 'official' S-unit down on that of a four-element monoband Yagi on a 0.5λ boom at the same height (see p104 and associated references) for which a tower with its attendant problems and hazards (p311) would be essential.

For operation on 7, 3.5, and possibly 1.8MHz, the higher-frequency antennas can be pressed into service as vertical antennas by joining feeders in parallel, ground connections being provided in the form of short radials with a common loading coil (p324).

Assuming reversibility and a suitably placed shack, most of these arrays could be rotated from the operating position by means of two polythene cord lines.

For high-angle coverage on 3.5/7MHz, an end-fed long wire with its end folded over is probably the simplest device, although if wires can be carried over the house a 3.5/7MHz inverted-V dipole supported by the TV pole would be ideal, and might even have some useful DX potential as well. It is important to make sure such wires do not upset the HF arrays, any interaction being readily curable by detuning the long wire or inverted-V.

Some of these ideas have been assembled in Fig 20.5.

Tree-mounted quad

In this example no assumptions are made beyond the exist-ence of a large climbable tree in the garden. The advantages of loops for antennas mounted in trees and some of the problems of erection have been discussed in Chapters 11 and 12.

Preferred options include an 8–10ft (2.4–3m) spreader mounted as high as possible in the tree, and if possible at the

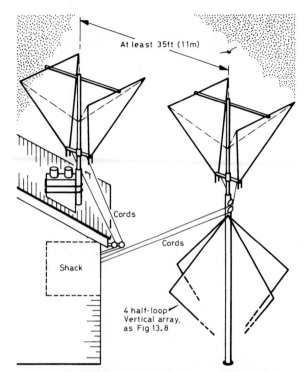

Fig 20.5. High-performance all-band system for small garden using a pair of 30–40ft (9–12m) supports spaced at least 35ft (11m) to accommodate a phased pair of simple arrays for 14–28MHz. The half-loop vertical array can be used to form a pair of monopole arrays for 7MHz or, with series tuning, as a top-loaded monopole for lower frequencies

top of a short pole secured to the tree and projecting above it. The top corners of two 17ft (5.2m) square loops such as those shown in Fig 7.3 or 11.13(d) or (e) may either be attached to the spreader before erection or hauled up afterwards using cords running through slip knots, which perform the role of pulleys at lower cost! Unless convenient branches exist, a second spreader is attached to the tree about 23ft (7m) below the top one and used to support the lower corners of the loops. The side corners may be supported by spider arms fixed to the tree trunk or branches. Open-wire feeders about 34ft (10.3m) long drop down to a four-pole beam-reversing relay, so that the lower ends are connected either to a reflector tuning stub or through a balun into a 50Ω feeder.

There is a slight difference in the length of open-wire feedline required for 14 and 21MHz which can be compensated by high-capacitance resonant circuits tuned to about 18MHz (p124), but for the driven element, unless one is particularly keen on keeping the SWR down to a low value, this is usually not necessary. For the reflector, changing from 14 to 21MHz requires either a change of about 18in (46cm) in the length of stub or an intermediate position for the short, which may be replaced by high-capacitance circuits tuned to 18MHz. A larger or smaller capacitor will be required if the tuning does not coincide for the two bands.

At 18MHz the overall electrical length of the system is quite close to 1.25λ and matching could be effected by series capacitance but it would be simpler (and in view of the limited bandwidth probably acceptable) to disconnect the stub and rely on an ATU in the shack. With this in mind, it may be decided to accept the nuisance of having to alter the position of the short whenever the band is changed. At 24MHz the electrical length is 1.75λ so again there should be little change in tuning, but considerable pattern break-up can be expected and there may not be much (if any) gain in the normal direction. At 28MHz there is virtually no response in the normal direction, although a single loop is an efficient low-gain radiator for the 45° directions.

A single 14MHz loop of this type has been used *with no retuning* on both 28 and 7MHz, good DX signal reports being obtained on 7MHz and DX worked on SSB with a small fraction of a watt on 28MHz. For 3.5MHz the loops may be used separately or in parallel (both alternatives should be tried) as λ/4 radiators working against a counterpoise or two-radial ground plane. Operation as a beam should be possible at 10MHz, since in this case the restricted bandwidth is unimportant, though there could be some losses.

There remains the possibility of adding a linear resonator as in Fig 11.13(e) to convert the quad into a 'bi-square', giving high gain at 28MHz over a bandwidth of about 0.3MHz. In this case an alternative feeder system and reflector short-circuits must be provided as explained in Chapter 11, the feedpoint being moved 8ft (2.4m) from the one used for all the other bands and a 4:1 balun employed. A better arrangement is to add, for 28MHz only, a third bi-square element in the centre; this should be the driven element, the other two being switched to act as directors or reflectors. This simplifies band changing and improves performance on 28MHz. The third element should also be usable at 24MHz, and it allows the spacing of the other two elements to be increased for better efficiency on 10MHz and a better front/back ratio on 14MHz.

As described so far, provision has been made for only one direction and its reciprocal. In principle, a second beam at right-angles can be mounted a few feet lower in the same tree, the beam not in use being open-circuited or otherwise disabled. This has been achieved successfully *for one band,* but for multiband operation difficulties can be expected owing to the fact that the elements can be resonant in a vertical mode not affected by the position of a feeder short. This mode can be shifted by lengthening the feeder and, given a particular interest in one or two bands, the problem would certainly be soluble but once again there is a complicated situation. Hopefully it will be possible instead to contrive a second antenna for coverage of other directions.

Making the most of even more limited resources

This ground has been largely covered in Chapter 15 and the discussion of the indoor environment in Chapter 10. Unless some kind of mast is available, it will not be possible to achieve a rotary beam though, in the case of some versions of the SDL array, an effective height of 10–15ft in excess of the mast height means that extremely useful performance can be achieved with a pole height of only 10ft. There is no truth in statements that beams do not work at low height, though below about λ/6 ground losses will (for example) decrease the current in a reflector and require an increase of coupling which will then be excessive in the event of height being subsequently increased.

For fixed arrays, possibilities include spider's web arrays and SDL or inverted-V arrays suspended from the boom of a large TV or FM receiving aerial (p247). As a last (and perhaps in some cases, first) resort, a vertical beam along the lines of Figs 13.8, 13.13 or 13.20 should usually be feasible.

A horizontal wire or large delta loop may be a useful option for other frequencies or directions, and the use of 18 or 20swg copper or alloy wire supported by nylon fishing line (75lb breaking strain) is suggested; the line is an ideal insulator, capable of a large amount of 'stretch' for accommodating tree movement (p299) and slides easily over smooth surfaces so that (for example) an ordinary insulator can be used as a pulley. If necessary 'invisibility' can be achieved by using 24–26swg wire held up by a lighter grade of nylon line. This recommendation must be qualified to the extent that as yet there is little recorded experience of this type of antenna, though the author had such an arrangement in 'unbroken' use for about a year which included the storm (1990) to which reference has already been made. It would probably be unwise to hang feeders from the centre of a wire supported in this way but for monoband operation the new methods (p47) of end-feeding (single-wire or coaxial cable) are suitable; in many cases the delta-loop configuration (horizontal or vertical) is preferable and at 3.5MHz an efficiency of about 65% can be expected from a 0.6λ loop using 20swg copper wire.

Though relatively expensive, small vertical loops (pp258–262) are efficient, require less space than other antennas, and are another important option, although their size advantage is partly offset by the high Q which makes them less tolerant of 'lossy objects' in their vicinity. Since 'small spaces 'come in various shapes and sizes, Chapter 17 features (in addition to loops) a number of dipole arrangements designed to fill them as effectively as possible.

It is unfortunately true that the smaller the space, the more likely it is to be close to local noise sources. A small transmitting antenna may be particularly vulnerable in this respect so that it is worth considering the possibility of a separate antenna for reception.

In the case of a transmitting beam, reasonable efficiency can be maintained down to a size of about 10ft square (Fig 12.14) at 14MHz and *pro rata*; below this, losses and operating difficulties escalate rapidly. Even at 10ft a price has been paid in the form of added weight, complexity, and restriction to monoband operation. The 'Miniclaw', p217, is only slightly larger but multiband and therefore more attractive (though still rather 'heavy'), and a further increase of only 50% in span brings one to the right-angled SDL, Fig 7.6, which is considered to be one of the 'best buy' options.

Indoor antennas

In some cases there is no alternative to an indoor antenna or the conditions attaching to an outdoor antenna may be so restrictive that there is a difficult choice, needing to be resolved by experiment. Most of what has been said above about antennas for small spaces is equally applicable in this case but, in addition, it is particularly important to avoid injecting RF into the mains wiring or picking up mains-borne noise during reception.

Measures to these ends (which are essentially the same) are described on p172. It is important to keep the radiation resistance (R) as high as possible but, subject to the use of end-loading, there is no need to exceed a length of about λ/3 and it may be necessary to settle for less if this causes the antenna to couple more tightly into the mains wiring. In general it is probably advisable to use coaxial feeder since, even if perfectly balanced, twin feeder will couple into adjacent wiring unless spaced from it by a distance large compared with its own spacing. There is also the point that it is easier to test for zero current on the outer of the coaxial cable than for accurate line balance.

For multiband operation, resonant feeders may increase the risk of coupling into the mains but band-switching of a centrally-located tuning unit should be relatively easy to implement indoors.

The W8JK appears to be widely favoured for indoor beam antennas, but it is impossible to conceive of a worse choice. As explained on p100, it has for its size the lowest possible value of radiation resistance, only a quarter that of a pair of elements phased for maximum F/B ratio, and even in the clear this tends to be exceeded by the losses except with oversized elements, the opposite of what one is likely to have in a roof space. There could even be a serious fire hazard, as illustrated by the incident related on p293.

Beams providing useful gain on 14MHz are achievable in some roof spaces, 28MHz being of course a much easier proposition. The use of separate receiving antennas (as discussed in Chapter 9) would be useful in many cases, particularly in the form of superdirective arrays which could provide an exciting new field for the experimenter.

Improving the existing station

Many readers will have already solved their antenna problems to the extent of possessing, say, a 35–40ft (11–12m) mast surmounted by a three-element trapped beam, this being the type of antenna which appears to be most in demand from commercial suppliers. It should be possible to obtain better performance (including reversibility, deep-nulling and coverage of the 10, 18 and 24MHz bands) by removing the traps and converting the elements into small delta loops as suggested on p210. The mast and beam can also be used as a λ/4 top-loaded vertical for 3.5MHz or as a λ/2 vertical for 7MHz on the lines of Fig 7.18, but it would be worth trying a vertical beam for 14MHz which could be used to provide (a) at least one extra switched direction, (b) in some cases quieter reception due to less short-skip interference and cosmic noise, and (c) operation as a monopole array for 7MHz.

Compared with the 'ideal station case (B)', performance will be down about 8dB in all, or two average S-units at 14MHz, due to the lower height (about 5dB) and loss of the 3dB of extra gain provided by the phased pair of case B. Compared with the original trapped beam, up to 0.5 S-unit advantage can be expected at 14MHz and at least one S-unit at 28MHz, though the main benefit from the exercise has been to widen the choice of operating frequencies.

Sloping ground

This case has been largely covered elsewhere (pp165–167) but some additional options suggest themselves; the example which follows is based on an actual case where the ground slope was 20° and the garden comprised largely of about half-an-acre (0.2ha) of woodland. With fixed collinear arrays a height of only $\lambda/4$ provided near-optimum performance in the down-slope direction. In this case it would have been possible to achieve a pair of log-periodic arrays stacked side by side at a height of 15–20ft (4.5–6m) to give a low-angle gain of nearly 10dB over the entire band from 10–30MHz for the down-slope direction. Space could still have been found for a two- or three-element Yagi for 7MHz, though not for extending the log-periodic arrays to include 7MHz.

A two-element beam was used at 40ft (12m) for coverage of directions other than down the slope, and this cleared the top of the hill by about 30ft (9m) to provide 'average' short-path (up-slope) communication with Australia, despite a performance differential of at least two S-units for the two directions. For coverage of all bands from 7–28MHz there are many alternatives to log-periodic antennas, and fixed wire beams based on Fig 20.2 should be suitable for the down-slope directions.

Safety aspects

This is a particularly important aspect of the decision-making process. Towers, for whatever reason, do not have an unblemished survival record, and there must obviously be no danger to people or animals or of collapse onto neighbouring property. In particular, there must be no chance of any tower, metal mast, or antenna wire coming into contact with a power line either during erection or subsequently.

Most towers in use in the UK are of the tilt-over and crank-up variety but these can be dangerous in inexperienced hands [3], and there may not be enough space to allow for tilting, particularly with the antenna in place. One alternative is to use a crank-up tower with two or more sections nesting down to a height of about 20ft which can be reached by ladder for attachment of the antenna; however, sections can jam and create a dangerous situation.

The most usual variety of tower elsewhere than in the UK [3] consists of equal sections which have to be added one at a time and finally climbed to the top for attachment of the antenna, a terrifying prospect compounded by the supposition

that helpers can escape from tools dropping on their heads by merely standing clear of the tower base; pliers dropped from the author's usual ladder height of a mere 20ft invariably ricochet on the way down before disappearing permanently, and an unblemished safety record must be attributed entirely to the absence of helpers.

Hazards for helpers

Advice favouring crank-up towers on safety grounds has appeared in more than one publication but, being based on the assumption of lowering when not in use, is oblivious alike of human nature, the risks of the mechanism jamming, and the hazards of trailing guy ropes. That said, in view of the assumed ladder access to the junction there would appear to be no insuperable problem in the case of towers limited to two sections and designed with an adequate factor of safety.

In contrast, light structures such as the SDL or VK2ABQ arrays are usually able to collapse without damage to anything else and thus tend to act as mechanical fuses so that wind-loading disappears from the masthead before the mast itself is endangered! Nevertheless, despite some instances of mechanical failure, the survival record of SDL arrays (including the Claw) over a period of several years, which included the hurricanes of October 1987 and January 1990, has been very encouraging.

Since the author was first licensed in 1928, with an enduring interest in antennas, an enormous number of different supports were used before arriving at the concept of a 'secure pedestal', sufficiently strong (or, in most cases, overdesigned!) to inspire complete confidence. This then serves as the means for erecting and usually reinforcing a taller mast, either by acting as a gin pole (Fig 19.8(b)), the fulcrum for a 'tilt-over' arrangement as shown at Fig 19.8(c), or the lower section of a telescopic mast as in Figs 19.8(d), 19.9 and 19.10. This approach, though supported by the author's long experience under more-or-less typical circumstances, rests on personal judgement which needs to be reinforced by windage calculations (p299) and good practice in the matter of mast foundations, guys, and guy anchorages [6]. Designs could also be tested by the application of known loads, using if necessary a winch or block-and-tackle. See Chapter 19, p301, for guidelines in respect of lightning protection.

Antennas with adverse features

(a) *The 'ZL Special' and sundry other driven or parasitic two-element arrays.* As the reader will have appreciated from Chapter 5, efficient operation of a two-element close-spaced beam depends on achieving the correct phase and amplitude balance. This is critically dependent on the mutual coupling without which there could be no gain, whereas most of the phasing methods described in the literature rest on the implied assumption of no mutual coupling. Such systems are unlikely to provide much gain, 3dB being quoted in reference [2] as a typical figure for the ZL Special, although this can be expected to do reasonably well in respect of front/back ratio (p92). The probability of efficient operation, though dependent on a number of coincidences, is nevertheless high enough to account for two cases known to the author of outstanding performance, which could, however, have been sought with much better chances of success by other methods.

(b) *Use of traps.* As explained in Chapter 7, the use of traps for achieving operation on several bands usually results in unnecessary losses and there tend to be better ways of achieving the same objective, though subject to the use of improved design procedures (p131) and restriction to two bands this argument loses much of its force.

(c) *Antennas which are 'high risk' in respect of feeder radiation.* These include the standard ground plane (p42), end-fed arrangements other than those fed against a counterpoise or using a balancing stub (p47), and any antenna fed with coaxial cable and without balun. Note, however, that the term 'high risk' is intended to be taken literally and implies also a chance that no ill effects will follow from omission of the balun.

(d) *Various forms of X beams.* These were analysed in detail in Chapter 5, and it may be recalled that when points of high current are brought together at the centre of an X the adjacent sections of conductor contribute relatively little to the radiation and therefore radiation resistance is decreased. Moreover, along the lines of the X the front/back ratio is unity and there is also a strong component of radiation in what would be the endwise directions of a normal antenna (p95).

(e) *Antennas with large built-in losses.* This includes the Windom (p45) unless the feeder length is short, short

elements with long resonant feeders, antennas with large loading inductances (unless there is no alternative, as may be the case for mobile operation) and the W8JK, though in this case, assuming heavy-gauge full-size elements erected well in the clear, the main drawbacks are the narrow bandwidth and lack of front/back ratio.

(f) *The quad antenna.* Despite the popularity of the quad, its use as a rotary beam is strongly deprecated for reasons which can be summed up by quoting remarks made to the author during the writing of this book. For much of the time he was using a fixed (reversible) quad and many of the stations contacted, after commenting on the excellence of this type of antenna, added that they used to have one themselves but it blew down. This in some cases has reduced them to using an inferior type of antenna such as a typical commercial trapped beam.

Rotary beams, moreover, fail to exploit the real virtues of the quad which have been put to good use earlier in this chapter and in Chapters 7, 11 and 12. In some cases the greater height of the top portions of the loops may place them clear of obstructions, thereby improving performance, and another favourable feature in comparison with conventional Yagi arrays is easier adjustment, though in this respect resonant feeder systems score heavily by virtue of the fact that all adjustments can be made in the shack.

(g) *Slopers.* These have some useful features but are likely to be somewhat inferior as DX antennas to the 'bent dipole' arrays such as those featured in Chapter 13, p247.

Will it work?

The antennas described in these pages range from simple systems, well suited to the beginner, to challenges for the ingenious and experienced, and, whereas some systems have benefited from the experience of numerous users over many years, others with perhaps equal prospects are still at the beginning of this process. If a design is new and not yet widely tested, it would be unwise to attempt it without the ability to carry out tests such as those described in Chapter 18, plus the possibility of returning the antenna to ground level for further adjustment if necessary after testing at full height.

On the other hand, it might be expected that the data available in various textbooks for such well-established antennas as the quad would be reliable; yet frequently it turns out that reflector lengths are too long and other instances of the unreliability of data are reported from time to time. The reasons for this are largely wrapped in mystery, and those purchasing commercial antennas are perhaps even worse off since they enjoy no immunity and the remedies are less likely to be under their own control. This will be best appreciated by home constructors who, after years of coping successfully with their own mistakes and misfortunes, are suddenly confronted with a faulty PCB in a commercial transceiver!

It is believed that the best answers to this problem are provided by antennas which can be tuned or at least subjected to a fine-tuning process from the shack or some other point at ground level. This includes most of the vertical antennas recommended in these pages and arrangements based on resonant feeders or using motor-operated tuning devices in or close to the antenna.

What of the future?

The availability of the WARC bands is having an increasing impact on operating habits and antenna development. Already, log-periodic antennas account for a lot of S9+ signals from Australia where big antennas are a relatively common feature of the landscape, though ground planes and G5RV antennas still seem to predominate elsewhere. The efficiency of spectrum utilisation is not enhanced by radiating energy in unwanted directions or by lack of front-to back ratio, so that as these narrow bands fill up, the effective use of them can be expected to diminish unless the merits of using resonant feeders for the multibanding of beams attracts more attention or some new and even better system emerges.

Remote tuning of antennas, in one form or another, has just been cited as a solution of adjustment problems but it is also the key to efficient multiband operation. This applies not only to resonant feeder sustems as discussed earlier but the matching of elements directly into lines of any impedance, a process which likewise requres the Z_0 of the antenna to be reduced to the lowest possible value.

At least one very successful antenna is known to have been constructed on this basis, though the future will depend mainly on the willingness or otherwise of manufacturers to produce suitable hardware. Possibilities include switches driven by impulse motors, and the development at an economic price of servo-controlled capacitors for remote tuning of beam elements would also open up new doors for the experimenter. Assuming linear resonators, a range of 8–50pF would allow operation on any band from 14 to 28MHz, including rapid beam reversal subject to suitable programming. For two or three bands the same objective should, however, be achievable using fixed capacitors switched by relays, and on present form this seems more probable. Relays 'designed for the job' of RF switching are likely to be heavy and expensive but reference has been made (Chapter 7) to small light-relays which appear to be suitable, and it should be noted that it is not necessary to switch power since safety interlocks can be devised to prevent operation while RF power is applied.

Possibly the most important area for new development will be that of short active antennas for reception which, operating in conjunction with single-element antennas, could lead to greatly improved rejection of unwanted stations. This could follow from commercial developments already under way.

The antenna and the planners

Regulations governing the erection of antennas vary enormously from country to country, though for large erections such as those considered at the beginning of this chapter they are almost certain to be inescapable. On the other hand, for some lesser structures the position could well be rather obscure, as indicated by the following guidelines for the UK which were kindly supplied to the author by Bob Price, G4BSO:

"Basically, in town & country planning we have to consider whether the combined structure of antenna and support is such that its erection is a 'building operation'. Unfortunately 'building' has a very wide definition as 'any structure or erection', but we have some judicial interpretation which limits this definition as otherwise every piece of wire or cord may be a 'building'. The judicial interpretation appears to indicate that there must be something sufficiently substantial or permanent in nature to affect the physical character of the house and garden. (For the purpose of this book it is assumed that all antennas will be associated with a dwelling-house, otherwise some different considerations will apply).

By letter (1969) to the RSGB, the Minister of Housing & Local Government agreed that an antenna system similar to a domestic TV or FM broadcast antenna does not require planning permission because it does not materially affect the external appearance of the building. Put another way, it is expected to be found on most houses and is part of the general residential scene. It is doubtful whether we are entitled to use this pronouncement where UHF broadcast antennas are in use but the amateur antenna is more like the Band I type. This is just an example of the multitude of uncertainties with which we are faced. Nevertheless the 'local type' of TV antenna would always be a useful support for a wire antenna attached to a tree at the other end. One cannot imagine any planning authority seriously suggesting that a long wire tied to the chimney at one end and a tree at the other requires planning permission. It cannot be a 'building' even within the very wide definition indicated above.

Another Court decision on the definition of 'building' is that the subject must be built of constructed things of substantial size. It is thought that a trap or balun in a long wire or wire dipole could in no way be described as 'of substantial size'.

It should be explained that there are vast areas of uncertainty simply because antennas have not been the subject of many Court decisions, presumably because no amateur feels that it is worth spending a considerable sum in pursuing an appeal through the Courts. The Planning Appeal Decisions of the Department of the Environment are of great interest and afford some guidance, but they do not set binding precedents in the same way as do Appeal Court Decisions on points of law.

Whether in any given circumstance planning permission is required is a point of law; whether when planning permission is necessary it ought to be granted on the merits of the application is not a point of law."

Amateurs who feel that they may be operating in one of these "areas of uncertainty" would be well advised to cultivate good relations with neighbours, above all avoiding EMC problems and planning their antenna systems with a view to minimum visual impact; try to avoid the skyline or erecting anything which looks very unusual. From Chapter 11 onwards this has been featured as one of the important characteristics of antenna systems and towers with a log-periodic antenna or four-element quad on top of them get few marks under this heading.

Bob Price comments further that in his experience "more people run into planning problems as a result of TVI than for any other reason. This is because when the Post Office gives the amateur a 'clean bill of health', the neighbours search frantically for some other means of getting the station closed down."

He points out also that many "houses and flats now have covenants imposed on them by their deeds or tenancies which absolutely prohibit the fixing of antennas of any kind to the structure of the building or in the garden. Where such covenants exist we can do little about them beyond checking that they are legally enforceable. The amateur in such circumstances will have to be satisfied with an indoor antenna or put up something which is virtually invisible."

Invisible antennas are the subject of Chapter 15 and we returned to this topic with further planning guidelines in Chapter 19, p295.

References

[1] *The ARRL Antenna Book,* 13th edn, ARRL, 1974, p160.
[2] *The ARRL Antenna Book*, 12th edn, ARRL, 1970, p214.
[3] *ARRL Antenna Book*, 15th edn, ARRL, 1988, p22-7.
[4] *Yagi Antenna Design*, J L Lawson, W2PV, ARRL, 1986.
[5] *The Physical Design of Yagi Antennas*, Dave Leeson, W6QHS, ARRL, 1992.
[6] 'Wind loading', D J Reynolds, G3ZPF, *Radio Communication* April/May 1988.

Index